The Voucher Worth

£1

***May** be redeemed in accordance with the conditions overleaf at any of the establishments whose gazetteer entry shows the symbol ⓥ.*

The Voucher Worth

£1

***May** be redeemed in accordance with the conditions overleaf at any of the establishments whose gazetteer entry shows the symbol ⓥ.*

The Voucher Worth

£1

***May** be redeemed in accordance with the conditions overleaf at any of the establishments whose gazetteer entry shows the symbol ⓥ.*

The Voucher Worth

£1

***May** be redeemed in accordance with the conditions overleaf at any of the establishments whose gazetteer entry shows the symbol ⓥ.*

The Voucher Worth

£1

***May** be redeemed in accordance with the conditions overleaf at any of the establishments whose gazetteer entry shows the symbol ⓥ.*

The Voucher Worth

£1

***May** be redeemed in accordance with the conditions overleaf at any of the establishments whose gazetteer entry shows the symbol ⓥ.*

Conditions

A copy of AA Guesthouses, Farmhouses and Inns in Britain 1988 must be produced with this voucher.
Only one voucher per person or party accepted.
Not redeemable for cash. No change given.
The voucher will not be valid after 31st December, 1988.
Use of the voucher is restricted to when payment is made before leaving the premises.
The voucher will only be accepted against accommodation at full tariff rates.

Conditions

A copy of AA Guesthouses, Farmhouses and Inns in Britain 1988 must be produced with this voucher.
Only one voucher per person or party accepted.
Not redeemable for cash. No change given.
The voucher will not be valid after 31st December, 1988.
Use of the voucher is restricted to when payment is made before leaving the premises.
The voucher will only be accepted against accommodation at full tariff rates.

Conditions

A copy of AA Guesthouses, Farmhouses and Inns in Britain 1988 must be produced with this voucher.
Only one voucher per person or party accepted.
Not redeemable for cash. No change given.
The voucher will not be valid after 31st December, 1988.
Use of the voucher is restricted to when payment is made before leaving the premises.
The voucher will only be accepted against accommodation at full tariff rates.

Conditions

A copy of AA Guesthouses, Farmhouses and Inns in Britain 1988 must be produced with this voucher.
Only one voucher per person or party accepted.
Not redeemable for cash. No change given.
The voucher will not be valid after 31st December, 1988.
Use of the voucher is restricted to when payment is made before leaving the premises.
The voucher will only be accepted against accommodation at full tariff rates.

Conditions

A copy of AA Guesthouses, Farmhouses and Inns in Britain 1988 must be produced with this voucher.
Only one voucher per person or party accepted.
Not redeemable for cash. No change given.
The voucher will not be valid after 31st December, 1988.
Use of the voucher is restricted to when payment is made before leaving the premises.
The voucher will only be accepted against accommodation at full tariff rates.

Conditions

A copy of AA Guesthouses, Farmhouses and Inns in Britain 1988 must be produced with this voucher.
Only one voucher per person or party accepted.
Not redeemable for cash. No change given.
The voucher will not be valid after 31st December, 1988.
Use of the voucher is restricted to when payment is made before leaving the premises.
The voucher will only be accepted against accommodation at full tariff rates.

GRANADA SERVICE AREAS AND LODGES

Caring for the traveller - accommodation, food and fuel

High standard of accommodation at budget prices

Wholesome food freshly prepared and served

Petrol and diesel at competitive prices

Variety and value

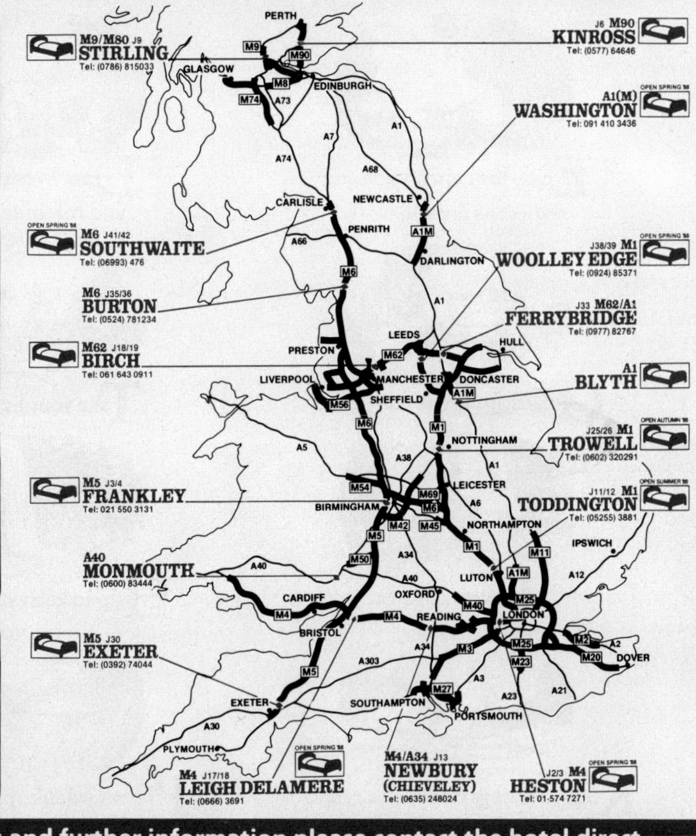

For bookings and further information please contact the hotel direct, or ring Sally Burton on Toddington (05255) 3881 during normal office hours

GRANADA Lodge HOTELS

This voucher is worth £2.00 off the cost of a double or family room at any Granada Lodge Hotel.

Only one voucher accepted per room.
Valid until 31st March 1989.
Not redeemable for cash.

CASHIER AAG

GRANADA Lodge HOTELS

This voucher is worth £2.00 off the cost of a double or family room at any Granada Lodge Hotel.

Only one voucher accepted per room.
Valid until 31st March 1989.
Not redeemable for cash.

CASHIER AAG

GRANADA MOTORWAY RESTAURANTS

30p

This voucher is worth 30p off the cost of food and beverages at any Granada Motorway Service Area

Only one voucher per person accepted per transaction. Valid until 31st March 1989.
Not redeemable for cash. No change given.

CASHIER AAG

GRANADA MOTORWAY RESTAURANTS

30p

This voucher is worth 30p off the cost of food and beverages at any Granada Motorway Service Area

Only one voucher per person accepted per transaction. Valid until 31st March 1989.
Not redeemable for cash. No change given.

CASHIER AAG

Follow the Country Code

Enjoy the countryside and respect its life and work.

Leave livestock, crops and machinery alone.

Guard against all risk of fire.

Take your litter home.

Fasten all gates.

Help to keep all water clean.

Keep your dogs under close control.

Protect wildlife, plants and trees.

Keep to public paths across farmland.

Take special care on country roads.

Use gates and stiles to cross fences, hedges and walls.

Make no unnecessary noise.

AA

GUESTHOUSES, FARMHOUSES & INNS IN BRITAIN 1988

Editor: Jackie Rathband
Art Editor: Glyn Barlow
Designer: Liz Baldin
Illustrations: Alan Roe
Research Co-ordinator: David Hancock
Black and white feature: Researched and written by Myrrhine Raikes

Gazetteer compiled by the Automobile Association Researchers in co-operation with the Accommodation Inspectorate of the Automobile Association.

Maps: prepared by the Cartographic Services Department of the Automobile Association

Cover Picture: Grey Friars Lodge, Cumbria (E A Bowness)

Head of Advertisement Sales: Christopher Heard
Tel (0256) 20123 (ext 22020)
Advertisement Production: Karen Weeks
Tel (0256) 20123 (ext 23525)
Advertisement Sales Representatives:
London, East Anglia, East Midlands, Central, Southern and South East England: Edward May
Tel (0256) 20123 (ext 23524) or (0256) 467568
South West, West, West Midlands: Bryan Thompson
Tel (0272) 393296
Wales, North of England, Scotland: Arthur Williams
Tel (0222) 20267

Typeset, printed and bound in Great Britain by William Clowes Limited, Beccles and London.

Colour produced by J B Shears & Sons Ltd, Basingstoke, Hampshire and typeset by Kempshott Phototypesetting Services Ltd, Basingstoke, Hampshire.

Every effort is made to ensure accuracy, but the publishers do not hold themselves responsible for any consequences that may arise from errors or omissions. Whilst the contents are believed correct at the time of going to press, changes may have occurred since that time or will occur during the currency of this book. The up to date position may be checked through AA regional offices.

Published by the Automobile Association, Fanum House, Basingstoke, Hampshire RG21 2EA.

ISBN 0 86145 6327
AA Reference: 50937

CONTENTS

GLENORLEIGH HOTEL

Cleveland Road, TORQUAY, DEVON. Tel: (0803) 22135

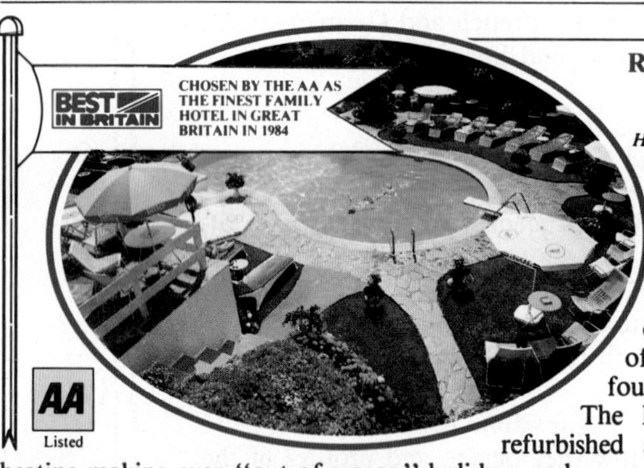

BEST IN BRITAIN
CHOSEN BY THE AA AS THE FINEST FAMILY HOTEL IN GREAT BRITAIN IN 1984
AA
Listed

Residential Licence

Heated pool and patio

Winners of Torbay in Bloom for 1981, 1982, 1983, 1984, 1985, 1986, 1987

The Glenorleigh Hotel is a friendly hotel and the proprietors Michael and Maureen Rhodes pride themselves on maintaining their high standards of good home cooking and provide a four course dinner in the evening.

The Hotel itself has been completely refurbished and decorated, with full central heating making even "out of season" holidays a pleasure. The cosy bar lounge is ideal for a relaxing evening where a wide range of wines, spirits and beers are available. Enjoy music from the Hammond Organ and live professional entertainment two evenings a week.

All bedrooms are equipped and furnished to the highest standards, in keeping with a first class hotel. Most have private shower and toilet so a selection of single, double, twin-bedded and family rooms are available with these facilities. Children are most welcome at reduced rates. (Radio/intercom and baby listening in all rooms).

Tea making facilities in every room.

Access to all rooms at all times with guests having their own keys.

The Glenorleigh's secluded garden faces South and has won many prestigious awards, the "Garden News Special Award" for the Best Hotel Garden in Great Britain; Best Floral Container (pictured below) and Torbay in Bloom (winners for five consecutive years).

Terry Underhill and the television film crew spent an enjoyable day filming for the series "Gardens for All" which was screened in January 1986.

An outstanding feature of the garden is the beautiful heated swimming pool with Spanish-style sun patio, sun beds, sun shades, tables and chairs (pictured). Apart from the pool there is a solarium and a games room with pool table, darts and video games.

Stay at the Glenorleigh Hotel and you may rest assured that every care and attention will be made to ensure you have a happy and memorable holiday.

Fire Certificate Awarded. Private Parking

AA Recommended 1986
AA Selected 1987

TERMS FROM £75 WEEKLY

Stamps please for coloured brochure

FARMHOUSE OF THE YEAR

• NATIONAL WINNER 1987/8 •

Frog Street Farm

BEERCROCOMBE, SOMERSET

In quiet rural surroundings, this attractive stone and beamed farmhouse surrounded by over 100 acres of farmland, has a secluded garden with a swimming pool for summer use and a trout stream running through the meadows. The overall winner of our Farmhouse of the Year Award for 1987/88, is Frog Street Farm at Beercrocombe, a building full of character and history.

Dating back to the 15th century, its name is derived from a corruption of the Anglo-Saxon for 'meeting place' which is a very appropriate name for this outstanding farmhouse. The house has been tastefully restored, but still retains the original features, such as exposed beams, inglenook fireplaces and fine Jacobean panelling dating back to James I.

•NATIONAL WINNER 1987/8•

Mrs Cole, who runs the business, is very hospitable and very welcoming to her guests, and soon puts them at their ease. When guests arrive, although there are tea and coffee making facilities in the bedrooms, after helping them with their luggage and showing them to their rooms, Mrs Cole makes up a tea tray and serves it in the lounge, a thoughtful gesture when you've been travelling for a long time.

The lounge on the ground floor is welcoming with Jacobean wood panelling, wooden ceiling beams and an inglenook fireplace with woodburning stove. The colour television is here but for those guests who prefer to be away from the distractions of television, a small reading room is available for them to relax in.

Accommodation is in three bedrooms, one with bath, and one with shower. The decoration is most attractive and in a cottagey style. The furnishings are of a high standard.

Mrs Cole is well known in the area for her farmhouse food, which is meticulously prepared using produce either from the farm, or locally grown. Although no choice is offered she takes the trouble to find out the likes and dislikes of her guests and the menu is then set accordingly. This is possible because the maximum number of guests staying here is six.

A wide choice of starters is offered to guests to choose from. A typical meal could consist of ½ ogen melon, roast beef, yorkshire pudding, carrots, cauliflower and new potatoes. For pudding, chocolate mousse followed by cheese and biscuits. All the meals are taken in the attractive dining room with its exposed beams and inglenook fireplace. After dinner, coffee is served in the lounge and the Cole family chat to their guests. Breakfast is cooked to order and if you do not want to have a full cooked breakfast, there is always a choice of cereals and fruit juices.

Mrs Cole says that they treat their guests as friends and this is certainly the impression you receive after staying here. The whole family goes out of its way to make sure that guests have every comfort and thoroughly enjoy their holiday here. An excellent example of the food, hospitality and service that you expect to find when staying in a farmhouse, and a deserving winner of our Farmhouse of the Year Award. Guests will enjoy their stay here.

Full details of facilities and prices will be found in the gazetteer entry under Beercrocombe.

• WINNER FOR NORTH •

Whashton Springs Farm

RICHMOND, NORTH YORKSHIRE

Situated in the heart of Herriot country, this delightful farm is set high in the hills just to the north of the historic town of Richmond.

The stone-built farmhouse is a most attractive Georgian building, featuring two huge and quite unusual semi-circular bay windows. It is home to the Turnbull family who are all involved in the running of this busy working farm or looking after its guests.

In the house there are three bedrooms, one with a four poster bed and private facilities. These three rooms are spacious, have excellent decor, furnishings, carpets and fabrics. However, there are a further six bedrooms in the delightfully converted stable courtyard. These too have private facilities and are really charming with their pine and rustic style decor and furnishings, pretty fabrics, and quality carpets.

The dining room is nicely furnished too, with its polished floor and individual table settings. After dinner, coffee is taken in the cosy sitting room with its huge fire and comfortable seating.

Dinner here is a splendid affair with a choice of starter and sweet and a delightfully cooked and well presented farmhouse dinner. Mr Turnbull waits at table and always enjoys conversing with his guests. The Yorkshire farmhouse breakfast here is excellent too.

There is a lovely family atmosphere about Whashton Springs and, coupled with its fine hospitality, excellent food and comfortable well-furnished accommodation, make it an obvious choice for our Farmhouse of the Year Award for Northern England. We had no hesitation in making it Farmhouse of the Year for the North of England.

Full details of facilities and prices can be found in the gazetteer entry under Richmond.

• WINNER FOR MIDLANDS •

Lower Doddenhill Farm

NEWNHAM BRIDGE, HEREFORD AND WORCESTER

This 17th-century farmhouse with its wealth of exposed timbers and exquisite views, stands proudly overlooking the lovely Teme valley in an idyllic country setting.

A busy working farm, it is home to the Adams family where the emphasis is quite definitely on individual attention and comfort for their guests. The farmhouse has a wealth of character with its low beamed ceilings, uneven floors, pretty country cottage decor and lovely antique furniture. Combined with a really homely atmosphere, it makes both a delightful and memorable house to stay in.

There are three lovely guest bedrooms here all on the first floor, one having an en suite shower.

There is also a fine lounge with its huge fireplace, where guests can sit and relax and where the whole family will join you over coffee in the evening.

Joan Adams cooks local produce with a very confident hand using traditional farmhouse dishes in the grand British style. A considerable appetite is required to tackle one of Joan's excellent English breakfasts. Even at meal times she still finds time to chat to her guests.

This is truly a worthy winner of our Midlands Farmhouse of the Year Award. The Adams work very hard to ensure guests enjoy individual attention, delightful food, amid fine accommodation.

Full details of facilities and prices will be found in the gazetteer entry under Newnham Bridge.

•WINNER FOR SOUTH EAST•

Little Hemingfold Farm

BATTLE, SUSSEX

Just 2½ miles from the historic site of the famous Battle of Hastings in 1066, you find this lovely part 17th-century farmhouse in a secluded setting with over forty acres of grounds.

Owned by Mr and Mrs Benton, the interior of the house is as attractive as the outside. Full of character with sloping ceilings. The bedrooms are most attractive and decorated in soft shades with lots of stripped pine fixtures and fittings. All of the bedrooms have en-suite bathrooms, and colour TV is provided plus the usual tea and coffee making facilities.

Meals are cosy and informal, served at two or three large tables, set with pretty crockery and well presented. A nice touch is place cards with people's names on. The order for your first course is taken while you relax in either the comfortable lounge or bar so that when you sit down at the table, your starter is ready and waiting for you. The starters range from home-made soups, prawns in garlic, or avocado vinaigrette. The main course is set but there is always an alternative offered for those who are vegetarian. Desserts are delightful, apple crumble, strawberries and cream, usually home produced Jersey cream. Two glasses of wine are included in the price of dinner. Coffee is served in the lounge. Tennis and fishing are two sports that guests can enjoy when staying here.

A most relaxing place to spend a holiday in a farmhouse full of character and very efficiently run by Mrs Benton and her helpful and friendly staff.

Full details of facilities and prices can be found in the gazetteer entry under Battle.

• WINNER FOR WALES •

Tyn Rhos Farm

LLANDDEINIOLEN, GWYNEDD

Quietly situated in the hamlet of Seion, surrounded by the magnificence of Snowdonia and overlooking the Anglesey countryside is Ty'n-Rhos, our Farmhouse of the Year for Wales. Lynda and Nigel Kettle bought the farmhouse in 1972. It was originally a dairy farm but in 1986, they sold off most of the herd, just retaining a few cows to provide milk, cream, yoghurt and cheese.

Although Nigel comes from a farming background – his grandfather was in farming – before coming to Ty'n-Rhos he worked as a traffic administrator and his wife was a nurse.

The farmhouse has been recently extended and now has nine bedrooms. The bedrooms are spacious and well decorated. All of them have en suite bathrooms.

The dining room is very attractive and cosy with a Victorian fireplace and separate tables. Mr Kettle serves at the tables, while his wife cooks the meals. Mrs Kettle prides herself on her cooking, serving all home made fare. The vegetables and fruit are either from their own garden or locally produced and the meat is home-produced as well. A residential licence is held by the owners, and guests can choose from a selection of moderately priced wines.

Although there is no choice, an alternative is always available. Guests having finished their meals can retire to the comfortable lounge where coffee and mints are served. They are welcome to wander round the farm and there are usually young calves and pigs among the livestock that can be seen.

Mr and Mrs Kettle are excellent hosts, guests are made very welcome and enjoy their stay here.

Full details of facilities and prices can be found in the gazetteer entry under Llanddeiniolen.

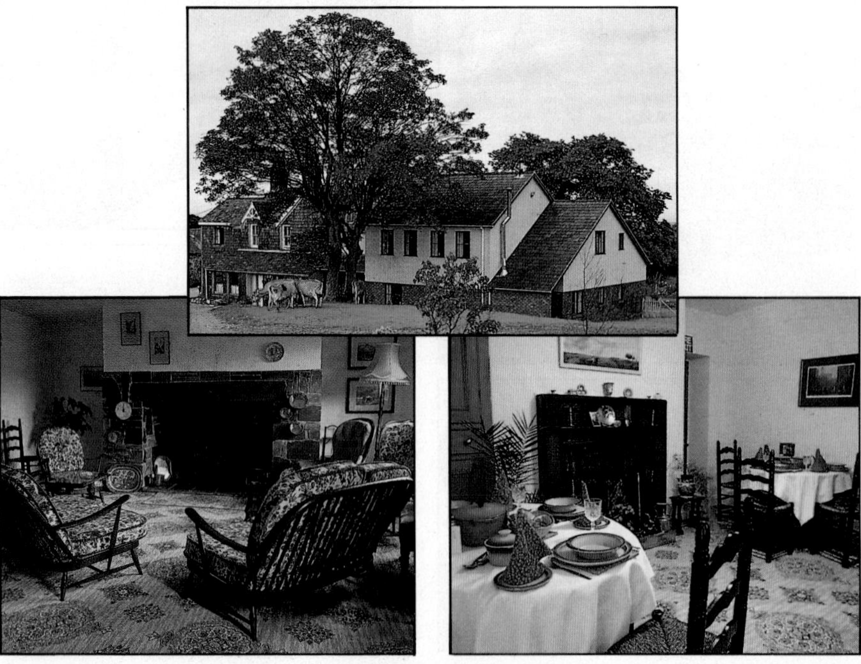

• WINNER FOR SCOTLAND •

Gall Farm

BORELAND, DUMFRIES AND GALLOWAY

Gall Farm stands on a private road high above the village church, with wonderful views of green hills and pasture. This is very much a family farm; it has been in the Maxwell family for generations. Mr Maxwell, its present owner was born here. A working farm with sheep and cattle, specialising in an unusual breed of sheep called Rouge de l'Ouest.

The accommodation side of the farm has been developed over the last sixteen years. Mrs Maxwell and her daughter run the house in a friendly but unobtrusive manner, ensuring guests have every comfort and feel relaxed and at home during their stay here.

The bedrooms are spacious, well furnished and all of them have lovely views overlooking the surrounding countryside. There is a comfortable and roomy residents lounge with colour TV.

Breakfasts are substantial with generous portions. Dinner offers a choice of starters, excellent home made soups among them, and the main course is meat, vegetables etc. Puddings may be home made pies, apple, rhubarb etc or wicked concoctions of chocolate, plus if you still feel peckish, cheese and biscuits. Although the main course is set, Mrs Maxwell will also cater for special diets if people so wish. Finally, around 9 o'clock tea, biscuits and shortbread are served as a light snack in the lounge. Guests will never go to bed hungry here.

Off the regular tourist track, but well worth the detour, guests will be given a warm welcome, stay in comfortable accommodation and enjoy home cooking at its best.

Full details of facilities and prices will be found in the gazetteer entry under Boreland.

Seaside Guesthouses

It is hard to imagine a time when the British did not head for the seaside every summer, and yet for centuries people took little interest in their own coastlines. However, in the middle of the 18th century, the claim that sea water taken as a drink or bathed in was good for the health persuaded the rich to leave their inland spas and make for the coast. A fashion that was further spurred on by Royal patronage.

In the early days the seaside resort was often no more than a small cluster of villas in some fishing village built to entice the rich to winter-holiday in a health-giving area. Later, with the advent of the railway, the seaside gradually became accessible to the masses eager to escape from their industrial surroundings and find amusement. For holiday-makers like these, the normal annual practice was to take 'lodgings', which were usually in private houses – in smarter terraces for the more genteel and in smaller, back street cottages for the working class visitors. Such lodgings might have included full service with the provision of every meal, they might have been a suite of rooms with facilities for the family's own servants, or most commonly, a suite of rooms in which the food was provided by the family and cooked by the proprietor.

The normal practice of a middle class family on holiday in the late 1800s was for the lady to go shopping each morning to buy bread, meat and vegetables. These provisions would be delivered to the lodgings in time for the proprietor to prepare a meal for when the family returned from the beach or spa. By doing this, the family believed that they were protecting themselves against possible over-charging by their landlady and that they would receive home from home food cooked, hopefully, in the manner to which they were accustomed.

This sounded fine in theory, but in practice the landladies, especially those in the less salubrious areas, often syphoned off a considerable amount of their guests' food in the direction of their own families. This, together with their questionable

culinary skills and cleanliness and the often unsatisfactory sleeping arrangements, makes it clear that early holidays were more often something to be endured rather than enjoyed. But, as the few hotels and commercial eating establishments that existed at that time were beyond the pockets of all but the very rich, and the age of the motor car had not yet arrived, most working and middle class holidaymakers, once booked into their lodgings, had little choice but to stay.

But, the tide was soon to turn in the favour of holidaymakers. The development of the railway network which allowed for the easy and cheap distribution of foodstuffs throughout the country prompted the rapid growth of commercial eating establishments aimed at the mass market.

By the 1900s, as more and more inviting tea shops and English-style cafes arrived on the scene and the upper classes (following the example of their peers) started to take their holidays on the Continent, landladies began to realise that they would have to work hard to improve standards if they were going to retain their clients. Soon the number of lodgings where the proprietors cooked their guests' own food started to diminish in favour of establishments which offered bed and breakfast or full board in houses which boasted loudly that they had separate dining tables. Competition was bringing about the necessary improvement in accommodation standards.

The AA has been involved in the business of inspecting hotels since 1908 and appointed its first unclassified hotel in 1913. Since then, in response to the growing demand from members for reliable information about good, but reasonably priced, accommodation, the Association has continued to watch, encourage and play an important part in bringing about the dramatic improvements that have taken place in guesthouse standards.

Today's guesthouses are a far cry from the endurance-testing lodgings available at the turn of the century, and provide an increasing array of luxuries (including en-suite bathrooms, colour televisions, tea and coffee making facilities etc) that holiday-makers might expect to find only in classified hotels. The number of AA approved guesthouses has now reached 2458 and the Association's Guide to Guesthouses, Farmhouses and Inns in Great Britain has become the best selling of all their annual guides. Last year the Association introduced a new Quality Award which it gave to 130 guesthouses felt to be superior to the rest.

ABOUT THE OWNERS

Just as guesthouses today are a far cry from those early lodgings, so too the landladies that run them have changed beyond recognition. Today, the landlady has become something of an institution – occasionally laughed about, but more often loved – a person to whom the same families return, and entrust their holidays, year after year.

Everyone has a picture postcard image of the seaside landlady, but what sort of person is it that really goes into, and often stays, in the guesthouse business for many decades? We have talked to five landladies and landlords (one for each of the AA's five regions) who have totalled between them nearly 150 years as guesthouse owners, to discover what led them into this type of work and what changes they have noticed in the business over the years.

May & James Strachan

GLENBURNIE HOTEL OBAN

May and James Strachan have run the Glenburnie Hotel on Oban's Esplanade for the last 19 years.

'It was a funny set of circumstances that led us into buying the Glenburnie Hotel' explained May. 'The previous owners had only just moved in, when the lady, who was pregnant, fell down the stairs and injured herself and we were called upon to step in and help. This gave us our first taste of guesthouse life. Soon after that the Glenburnie came back onto the market and although James said at first that there was 'no way we were going to buy the place', we did buy it and we've been there ever since'.

Although the Strachans found the first years tough and took a little while to adjust to being tied from Easter to September, it was their guests that made it all worthwhile. May continued 'I'd say 99% of the people who stay with us are really nice and this is what makes the work so rewarding. The same people come back to us year after year and from all over the world. We've got three generations of one American family visiting us at different times each year. 'Things have changed

since we took over here – we don't get as many families with children as we used to and people certainly expect much more in the way of facilities today. But it's a good way of life and one that we wouldn't change. There must be something in it, because our son, who's getting married this year, is also going into the guesthouse business'.

Ann Wansker

ARANDORA STAR BLACKPOOL

Ann Wansker has been involved with the Arandora Star guesthouse, which is situated on Blackpool's seafront, for the last 39 years. 'Originally my aunt and uncle took on the place just after the war' explained Ann 'but the business didn't suit them so they did a swap with my parents who were running a grocery store in Stoke on Trent. When my parents retired, my husband, Geoffrey, and I took over and now my son is hoping to join us too.

'You have to like this business to stay in it', Ann continued, because it really does take up every minute of your time – there's no private life. My husband used to work in a gents' outfitters, but he gave it up to work here and we really like working together.'

The Wanskers have noticed a big change in the guesthouse business over the years, as Ann explained 'In the early days people wanted full board and always booked for one or two whole weeks. They'd never have thought of only staying for a couple of nights or coming for a weekend break.

People are also far more difficult to please these days. At one time anything went and whatever you did was accepted, but now people go abroad and they expect so much more. We've had central heating in our guesthouse for about 25 years – which was really unusual in the early days – in fact we used to put a sign in the window advertising the fact. Now, of course, all guesthouses have central heating.

By the time we get to the end of October I sometimes think that if I see any more people I shall scream,' admitted Ann, but after a couple of week's rest I'm wishing they were all back again'.

Tony & Norma South

CRAWFORD HOTEL SKEGNESS

Tony South first became interested in the guesthouse business when he was working as a builder and joiner carrying out alterations to other people's hotels and guesthouses.

'One day, the guesthouse that I'd just finished working on – The Crawford Hotel, on the seafront at Skegness – came on the market' said Tony 'and although everyone told me I was daft to spend out all that money, I decided to go ahead and buy the place anyway. One day my wife Norma was living in a bungalow and cooking for four people, and the next day she was living in a 20 bedroomed guesthouse and cooking for 54'.

The Souths spent the Christmas before they took over the Crawford Hotel helping the previous owners, which really helped them to learn the ropes. 'Of course, it wasn't easy to begin with' went on Tony

'and I know Norma found it hard cooking such large amounts of food for such large numbers of people. You see, at that time there was none of this keep fit lark and people expected to be given three good meals a day.

'Yes, things have changed in the 16 years we have been here. In those first years, if we weren't booked up by January 1st we knew there was something wrong, but now booking is spread throughout the whole of the season. And today everyone expects really good facilities too – en suite bathrooms and so on – so we've had to spend a lot of money on the place.

'We've had a good time here, especially with the pensioners that come and stay, they make our work very worthwhile – they're always so grateful for everything we do'.

Norma South also speaks enthusiastically about their 16 years at the Crawford Hotel 'We've had a lot of happy years and a good life here. Of course, by the end of the season we're tired, but after a week's rest we're wanting our guests back again'.

Eric & Elsa Norris

STIRLING HOUSE HOTEL EASTBOURNE

Eric and Elsa Norris who own and run the Stirling House Hotel, which is just two minutes walk from the sea at Eastbourne, came into the guesthouse business after spending 26 years in catering.

'After I came out of the navy I first went to work in a J. Lyons cornerhouse' explained Eric. 'Then we decided to buy our own little cafe in which we served food and drink all day long. Later we expanded our business by opening a wine bar in Welwyn Garden City and a grill bar as well. Eventually, though, we decided to sell all these leasehold properties and buy a freehold guesthouse instead'.

Eric and Elsa considered many different resorts but eventually decided to look for a guesthouse to buy in Eastbourne. 'After quite a search we found the Stirling House Hotel' continued Eric 'and we've been there ever since – it suits us down to the ground. My family have always been in hotels, so I suppose it must be in my blood.

'Yes, it's hard work running a guesthouse – but it's a good life and there's plenty of job satisfaction – especially when we're inundated with plants and flowers and grateful thanks by people who have enjoyed their stay with us. We like to laugh, joke and socialise with our guests – making people happy makes us happy too. People may frown on hard work these days, but at the end of each week we certainly feel that our efforts have been very worthwhile.

Vicky Mason

SUNRISE
ST. IVES

Mrs Vicky Mason, who was the AA's Landlady of the year in 1977, has owned and run 'Sunrise' at St Ives in Cornwall for 36 years. She has been involved with the hotel industry for nearly half a century.

Although she is now 85 years old and is greatly helped by her daughter she still works in the hotel each day and takes particular pride in cooking and especially in the 80 – 100 scones that she bakes daily for her son who runs the nearby coffee gardens.

'I started off working as an agent for an assurance company' explained Vicky 'but there was too much walking involved. So, when I saw an advertisement to work as a book-keeper/receptionist in a nearby inn I thought it looked just the job for me. So I applied for the job and got it'. After that Vicky worked her way up in different hotels in different parts of the country until, eventually, she became manager of a hotel in St Ives. From there it was a natural progression for her to become the owner of a guesthouse. In 1951 she bought Sunrise.

'Even after all these years I still love meeting people and looking after them' said Vicky. 'We give our guests a warm welcome and comfortable rooms and we also like to think we serve the best breakfast in town. The way I look at it is that people entrust their holidays to us, so we like to take good care of them.

People don't believe that I'm 85 years old and they often ask me how I manage to keep so young and active. I tell them its keeping on working and being interested in my guesthouse that keeps me young – that's the secret.'

USING THE GUIDE

This guidebook is for those travellers who are looking for the personal attention, comfortable accommodation and warm reception that are now more likely to be found in a good guesthouse, small hotel, farmhouse or inn than in many more expensive, but impersonal hotels. We list over 3,000 of these establishments all over Britain, and at each of them you can be assured that you will get good value for money, and that standards will be acceptable, because AA Inspectors visit each place regularly and we update our information every year.

Selected: In the gazetteer we highlight the very best of the establishments using the heading 'Selected' and enclosing the whole of the entry in a box. These places have been chosen by our inspectors as offering standards of cooking, accommodation and hospitality that are well above the normal requirements for an AA listing. In all, only about 163 establishments have been awarded the distinction this year. The colour supplement in the guide this year, is on farmhouses, all offering that extra special something that makes them the inspectors choice. Turn to page 17 for our feature on seaside guesthouses, how they first came into being, what they're like now and profiles on the people who run them today.

— WHAT IS A GUESTHOUSE? —

The term 'guesthouse' can lead to some confusion, particularly when many include the word 'hotel' in their name. For our purposes we include small and private hotels in this category when they lack some of the requirements for our star classification system. This is not to say that they are inferior to hotels – just that they are different – and many offer a very high standard of accommodation. It is not unusual to be offered en suite bathrooms, for instance, or to find a colour television in your room. It is true that some guesthouses will only offer a set meal in the evening, but many provide a varied and interesting menu and a standard of service which one would expect of a good restaurant. At the other end of the scale, some guesthouses offer bed and breakfast only, and it would also be wise to check if there are any restrictions to your access to the house, particularly late in the morning and during the afternoon.

We do have certain basic requirements which establishments must meet if they are to be listed in the guide, although, as we have said, many will exceed these. Usually they must offer at least six bedrooms and there should be a general bathroom and toilet for every six bedrooms which do not have private facilities. Fully licensed premises are now considered for inclusion, although many have a residential or restaurant licence only. We also stipulate that parking facilities, if not on the premises, should be within a reasonable distance.

Guesthouses in the London section of the book are treated differently. They are actually all small hotels and so their entries are not accompanied by the **GH** symbol used throughout the rest of the book. Of course, London prices tend to be higher than those in the provinces, but those that we list provide cost-conscious accommodation, although bed and breakfast only is normally provided. To allow for all eventualities, we have also included a few which provide a full meal service and the charges for these will naturally be higher.

— STAYING AT A FARMHOUSE —

Farmhouse accommodation has a special quality and is particularly noted for being inexpensive and cosy with a high standard of good home cooking. Those listed in our book are generally working farms and some farmers are happy to allow visitors to look around the farm or even to help feed the animals. However, we must stress that the modern farm is a potentially dangerous place, with all the machinery and chemicals involved, and visitors must be prepared to take great care, particularly if they bring children. Never leave children unsupervised around the farm. Some of the guest accommodation, on the other hand, is run as a separate concern from the farm on which it stands and visitors are discouraged from venturing beyond the house and garden. In some cases the land has been sold off, and although the gazetteer entry states the acreage and the type of farming carried out, it is advisable to check when booking to make sure that your requirements are met. To qualify for inclusion in the book, farms must have a minimum of two letting bedrooms, preferably fitted with washbasins, together with a bathroom with hot and cold running water and an inside toilet. As with the guesthouses, standards will vary considerably and are often far above what one would expect. Some of our farmhouses are grand ex-manor houses, furnished with antiques and offering a stylish way of life, and again some will have a residential or restaurant licence. All of the farmhouses are listed under town or village names, but obviously many will be some distance from other habitation. Proprietors will, of course, give directions when you book, and we publish a six figure map reference against the gazetteer entry which can be used in conjunction with Ordnance Survey maps.

INNS

We all know what we can expect to find in a traditional inn – a cosy bar, convivial atmosphere, good beer and pub food. Nevertheless, we have a few criteria which must be met here too. There must be a minimum of three and ideally a maximum of fifteen letting bedrooms, each having washbasins with hot and cold running water. Most bedrooms should be served by a bathroom and toilet on the same floor and although a residents' lounge is not essential, there must be a suitable breakfast room.

Breakfast is a must, of course, but the inn should also serve at least light meals during licensing hours. Our inn category may also include a number of small, fully licensed hotels and the character of the properties will vary according to whether they are pretty country inns or larger establishments in towns.

COMMON TO ALL

Whatever the type of establishment, there are certain requirements common to all, including a well-maintained exterior; clean and hygienic kitchens; good standards of furnishing; friendly and courteous service; access to the premises at reasonable times; the use of a telephone; full English breakfast; an adequately heated sitting room when half-board is provided (except inns – see above); bedrooms equipped with comfortable beds, a wardrobe, a bedside cabinet, a washbasin with soap, towel, mirror and shaver socket and at least a carpet beside the bed; there should be an extra charge for the use of baths or lavatories, and heating should be unmetered.

NB Where an establishment shows the central heating symbol, it does not necessarily mean that it will be available all year round. Some places only use the central heating in winter, and then only at their own discretion.

BOOKING

Book as early as possible, particularly if accommodation is required during a holiday period (beginning of June – end September, plus public holidays and, in some parts of Scotland, during the skiing season).

Although it is possible for chance callers to find a night's accommodation, it is by no means a certainty, especially at peak holiday times and in the popular areas, so to be certain of obtaining the accommodation you require, it is always advisable to book as far in advance as possible. Some establishments will also require a deposit on booking.

We have tried to provide as much information as possible about the establishments in our gazetteer, but if you should require further information before deciding to book, you should write to the establishment concerned. Do remember to enclose a stamped addressed envelope, or an international reply paid coupon if writing from overseas, and please quote this publication in any enquiry.

CANCELLATION

If you later find that you must cancel your visit, let the proprietor know at once because if the room you booked cannot be re-let, you may be held legally responsible for partial payment. Whether it is a matter of losing your deposit, or of being liable for compensation, you should seriously consider taking out cancellation insurance, such as AA Travelsure.

It is regretted that the AA cannot at the present time undertake to make any reservations.

COMPLAINTS

Members who have any cause for complaint are urged to do so promptly on the spot. This should provide an opportunity for the proprietor to correct matters. If a personal approach fails, members should inform the AA regional office.

FIRE PRECAUTIONS

Many of the establishments listed in the guide are subject to the requirements of the Fire Precautions Act of 1971.

As far as we can discover every establishment in this book has applied for, and not been refused a fire certificate. The Fire Precautions Act does not apply to the Channel Islands, or the Isle of Man, which exercise their own rules regarding fire precautions for hotels.

FOOD AND DRINK

In some parts of Britain, particularly in Scotland, *high tea* (i.e. a savoury dish followed by bread and butter, scones, cakes etc) is sometimes served instead of dinner which may, however, be available on request. The last time at which high tea or dinner may be ordered on weekdays is shown, but this may be varied at weekends.

On Sundays, many establishments serve the main meal at midday and provide only a cold supper in the evening.

If you intend to take dinner at the establishment, note that sometimes the meal must be ordered in advance of the actual meal time. In some cases this may be at breakfast time, or even at dinner on the previous evening. If you have booked for dinner, bed and breakfast terms, you may find that the tariff includes a set menu, but you can usually order from the à la carte menu, where one exists, and pay a supplement if you so desire.

LICENCES

The gazetteer entry will show whether or not the establishment is licensed to serve alcoholic drinks. Most places in the guesthouse category do not hold a full licence, but all inns do. Licensed premises are not obliged to remain open throughout the permitted hours and they may do so only when they expect reasonable trade. Note that in establishments which have registered clubs, club membership does not come into effect, nor can a drink be bought, until 48 hours after joining. For further information AA leaflet HR192 'The Law about Licensing Hours and Children/Young Persons on Licensed Premises' is available to members on request from AA offices.

THE MONEY-OFF VOUCHER SCHEME

In the front of this book you will find six £1 vouchers which can be redeemed against your bill for accommodation at any of the establishments which show the Ⓥ symbol in the gazetteer. If you use all of the vouchers, you will in effect, be saving the cost of this book. This year for the first time Granada vouchers to the value of £4.60 are also included. For more details about their conditions of use, see page 3.

PAYMENT

Most proprietors will only accept cheques in payment of accounts if notice is given and some form of identification (preferably a cheque card) is produced. If a hotel accepts credit or charge cards, this is shown in its gazetteer entry (see page 28 for details).

PRICES

It should be noted that terms quoted throughout this publication are per person and should include rates for minimum double occupancy and maximum single occupancy where appropriate.

The Hotel Industry voluntary Code of Booking Practice was revised in 1986, and the AA encourages its use in appropriate establishments. Its prime object is to ensure that the customer is clear about the precise services and facilities he is buying, and what price he will have to pay, before he commits himself to a contractually binding agreement. If the price has not been previously confirmed in writing, the guest should be handed a card at the time of registration, stipulating the total obligatory charge.

The Tourism (Sleeping Accommodation Price Display) Order 1977 compels hotels, motels, guesthouses, farmhouses, inns and self-catering accommodation with 4 or more letting bedrooms to display in entrance halls the minimum and maximum prices charged for each category of room. This order complements the voluntary Code of Booking Practice.

The tariffs quoted in the gazetteer of this book may be affected in the coming year by inflation, variations in the rate of VAT and many other factors. You should always ascertain the current prices before making a booking. Those given in this book have been provided by proprietors in good faith and must be accepted as indications rather than firm quotations.

In some cases, proprietors have been unable to provide us with their 1988 charges, but to give you a rough guide we publish the 1987 price, prefixed with an asterisk (✱). It is, also a good idea to ascertain exactly what is included in the price. Weekly terms can vary according to what meals may be included in the price. The text indicates whether weekly price includes bed and breakfast, breakfast and evening meal. It is possible, that at the height of the season, some establishments will offer accommodation only on a weekly basis – often Saturday to Saturday – and this too is indicated in the gazetteer. We cannot indicate whether or not you are able to book mid-week, so if this is your intention, do check when making your reservation.

Where information about 1988 prices is not given, you are requested to make enquiries direct.

VAT is payable, in the United Kingdom and in the Isle of Man, on both basic prices and any service. VAT does not apply in the Channel Islands. With this exception, prices quoted in this guide are inclusive of VAT (and service where applicable).

INTRODUCING THE GAZETTEER

This gazetteer is listed alphabetically under place name throughout England, Scotland and Wales, the Isle of Man and the Channel Islands. Establishments on islands are listed under the appropriate island heading.

The example of a gazetteer entry see opposite page, is to help you find your way through the entries. All the abbreviations and symbols are explained on the inside covers of the book. 'Using the Guide' on pages 23–26 gives further information.

INTRODUCING THE GAZETTEER

SAMPLE ENTRIES The entries are fictitious

LOOE
Cornwall
Map **2** SX25 — 1

|→-|**GH Ram Hotel** High Rd — 2
☎(05036) 4321 Plan 9 — 3, 4

Etr–Oct — 5

12hc (2⇨ 4fl) (Annexe 2fl) (1fb) CTV in 6 bedrooms ⅟ in 3 bedrooms Ⓡ — 6

B&b £7–£8 Bdi £12–£13 W Bdi £85–£105 LDO 5pm — 8

Lic 𝍶 CTV 9P ⌂ — 7

Credit cards 1 3 — 9

FH Mr & Mrs J Smith **Homestead** (*SXO75149*) ☎(05036) 3421 — 10

4hc ✈ ✱ B&b £7–£8 W B&b £85 𝍶 CTV 2P nc 7yrs 20 acres arable sheep

INN White Horse Brewery St — 2
☎(05036) 2341 — 3

rs Jan — 5

12hc (2⇨ 5fl) (2fb) CTV in 8 bedrooms ✈ Ⓡ B&b £12–£14 Bdi £20–£25 W Bdi £120–£150 Lunch 95p–£5 Dinner 8pm £5–10 & alc — 6, 8

Lift 𝍶 CTV P ⛟ — 7

Credit cards 1 2 3 5 Ⓥ — 9

1 **Town Names** listed in gazetteer in strict alphabetical order including London. This is followed by the county or region. This is the administrative county, or region, and not necessarily part of the correct postal address. Towns on islands (not connected to the mainland by a bridge) are listed under the island name. With Scottish regions or islands, the old county name follows in italics. The **map reference**, which follows denotes first, the map page number. Then follow grid reference; read 1st figure across 2nd figure vertically within the appropriate square.

2 |→-| This symbol indicates that the establishment expects to provide bed and breakfast for under £9 per person per night during 1988, but remember that circumstances can change during the currency of the guide.

3 **Establishment name,** address and telephone number. When establishments' names are shown in *italics* the particulars have not been confirmed by the proprietor. Guesthouses are identified with **'GH'**, Farmhouses with **'FH'** and Inns with **'INN'** – this is also the order in which they are listed beneath the town headings. Some establishments in the gazetteer belong to: Guestaccom Consortium, Claremont House, Second House, Hove, E. Sussex BN3 2LL. The **telephone exchange** quoted is that of the town heading. Where not, the name of the exchange is given after the ☎ symbol and before the dialling code and number. In some areas, numbers are likely to be changed during the currency of this book. In case of difficulty check with the operator.

4 **Town Plan.** Where a town plan exists, we locate each establishment on the plan using numbers. The plan will appear as close to the relevant towns as possible within the gazetteer. See key to town plan symbols.

5 **Opening details.** Unless otherwise stated, the establishments are open all year, but where dates are shown they are inclusive: eg Apr–Oct indicates that the establishment is open from the beginning of April to the end of October. Although some places are open all year, they may offer a restricted service during the less busy months, and we indicate this in the gazetteer by using the 'rs' abbreviation. This may mean that there is a reduction in meals served and/or accommodation available and, if you see this within the gazetteer, you should telephone in advance to find out the nature of the restriction.

6 Accommodation details. The first figure shows the number of letting bedrooms. Where rooms have *en suite* bath or shower and WC, the number precedes the appropriate symbol.

Annexe — bedrooms available in an annexe are shown, this indicates that their standard is acceptable. Facilities may not be the same as in the main building however, and it is advisable to check the nature of the accommodation and the tariff before making a reservation.

⅟ — number of bedrooms for non-smokers

fb — family bedrooms.

CTV — Colour or black and white television available in lounge. This may also mean televisions permanently in bedrooms or available on request from the management. Check when making reservations.

🐕 — no dogs allowed into bedrooms. Some establishments may restrict the size of dogs permitted and the rooms into which they may be taken. Establishments which do not normally accept dogs may accept guide dogs. Generally dogs are not allowed in the dining room. Check when booking the conditions under which pets are accepted.

Prices — prices given have been provided by the proprietor in good faith and are indications rather than firm quotations. Check current prices before booking. See also page 26.

7 Facilities. For key to symbols see inside front cover.

🚌 — No coaches. This information is published in good faith from information supplied by the establishments concerned. Inns, however have well-defined legal obligations towards travellers and it is for the customer to take up with the proprietor or the local licensing authority.

nc — establishments listed accommodate children of all ages unless a minimum age is given (eg nc4), but they may not necessarily be able to provide special facilities, nc by itself indicates 'no children'. For very young children, check before booking about such provisions as cots and high chairs and any reductions made.

🏠 — establishments with special facilities for children, which will include baby sitting service or baby intercom system, playroom or playground, laundry facilities, drying and ironing facilities, cots, high chairs and special meals. Some establishments offer free accommodation to children provided they share the parent's room.

♿ — disabled people accommodated. Information has been supplied by the proprietor and it is advisable to check before booking. Further details for disabled people will be found in AA *Travellers' Guide for the Disabled* available from AA offices, free to members, £2.95 to non-members. Intending guests with any form of disability should notify proprietors so that arrangements can be made to minimise difficulties, particularly in the event of an emergency.

8 Prices. Bed & breakfast per person per night for full explanation see page 26

9 Payment details

1 — Access/Euro/Master card accepted (but check current position when booking)

2 — American Express

3 — Barclaycard/Visa

5 — Diners

Ⓥ — Establishment accepts AA Money-Off Vouchers as detailed on first page of book.

10 Ordnance Survey Map Reference. This is shown for farmhouse entries only. As they are often in remote areas, we provide a six-figure map reference which can be used with Ordnance Survey maps.

KEY TO TOWN PLANS

Recommended Route

Other Routes

Restricted Roads

✝ Churches

i Tourist Information Centre

AA AA Centre

P Car Parking

❻ Guesthouse, inn, etc.

4 ½m Distance to guesthouses etc from edge of plan

ASHFORD 16m Mileage to town from edge of plan

Gazetteer

Abberley — Aberdeen

ABBERLEY
Hereford & Worcester
Map **7** SO76

FH Mrs S Neath ***Church*** *(SO753678)*
☎Great Witley (029921) 316
Apr–Oct

An early Victorian farmhouse in the peaceful village of Abberley. Off A443 on B4202, in ¼m turn right into village.

2hc (1fb) ✗

TV 5P 2 300acres arable beef

ABBOTS BROMLEY
Staffordshire
Map **7** SK02

FH Mr & Mrs W R Aitkenhead **Fishers Pit** *(SK098244)* ☎Burton-on-Trent (0283) 840204

Early Victorian two-storey brick-built farmhouse, 1m from village on B5234.

5hc (2fb) CTV in all bedrooms Ⓡ B&b£10–£12 Bdi£15–£17 WBdifr£95 LDO4pm

CTV 6P nc3yrs 63 acres mixed

FH Mrs M K Hollins **Marsh** *(SK069261)*
☎Burton-on-Trent (0283) 840323

Closed Xmas

Large two-storey, cement-rendered farmhouse set in open countryside 1m from village.

2hc (1fb) Ⓡ in 2 bedrooms B&b£8.50–£9.50 Bdi£12.50–£13.50 WBdifr£84 LDO5pm

CTV 6P 87acres mixed

ABERAERON
Dyfed
See **Pennant**

ABERDARE
Mid Glamorgan
Map **3** SO00

GH Cae-Coed Private Hotel Craig St, off Monk St ☎(0685) 871190

A neat but modestly appointed guesthouse.

6hc (2fb) TV in 2 bedrooms CTV in 1 bedroom ✱B&b£9 Bdi£12.50 WBdifr£80 LDOam

Lic CTV

Ⓥ

ABERDEEN
Grampian *Aberdeenshire*
Map **15** NJ90

GH Alelanro 272 Holburn St ☎(0224) 575601

Neat and homely house with limited lounge facilities.

6hc (2fb) CTV in all bedrooms Ⓡ B&b£9–£10

GH Broomfield Private Hotel 15 Balmoral Pl ☎(0224) 588758

A well-maintained and extended house situated in a residential area of the City.

9hc (1fb) Ⓡ ✱B&b£12–£13 Bdi£18–£19 WBdifr£126 LDO5pm

CTV 10P

GH La Casa 385 Great Western Rd
☎(0224) 313063

A well maintained house with pleasant bedrooms.

12hc (2 10) (2fb) CTV in all bedrooms Ⓡ ✱B&b£16–£22 Bdi£23–£29 W£161–£203 LDO6.30pm

Lic 10P

REMEMBER

Prices quoted in the gazetteer are minimum double room occupancy to maximum single room occupancy **per person.**

Selected

GH Cedars Private Hotel 339 Great Western Rd ☎(0224) 583225

This immaculately maintained private hotel is run to a high standard by Mr and Mrs McBeath who are friendly and dedicated hosts. Although varying in size, all bedrooms are modern, well equipped and thoughtfully arranged. Guests will enjoy the attractive, comfortable public rooms.

13hc (2 2) (4fb) CTV in all bedrooms Ⓡ ✱B&b£20–£25 WB&bfr£121

CTV 13P

Credit card 2

GH Klibreck 410 Great Western Rd
☎(0224) 316115
Closed Xmas & New Year

Homely, well-appointed guesthouse with some ground-floor bedrooms.

6hc (1fb) ✗ Ⓡ B&b£10.50–£12 Bdi£15.50–£17 LDO3pm

CTV 3P

Ⓥ

GH Mannofield Hotel 447 Great Western Rd ☎(0224) 315888

10hc (3fb) CTV in 6 bedrooms ✗ Ⓡ ✱B&b£17.25–£19.55 Bdi£24.15–£26.45 WBdifr£166.90 LDO7.45pm

Lic CTV 12P

GH Open Hearth 349 Holburn St
☎(0224) 596888

Neat, cheerfully decorated guesthouse with modern bedrooms.

12hc (1fb) in 6 bedrooms CTV in all bedrooms Ⓡ ✱B&b£12.65–£13.80

CTV 6P

GH Strathboyne 26 Abergeldie Ter
☎(0224) 593400

A compact house with homely atmosphere.

6hc (2fb) Ⓡ B&b£10–£11 Bdi£15–£16 WBdi£100–£108

CTV

GH Tower Hotel 36 Fonthill Rd ☎(0224) 584050
Closed Xmas & New Year
Spacious, traditionally furnished hotel with a pleasant dining room. Caters for business clientele.
9hc (1⇌) (2fb) ✱B&b£15 Bdi£21.50
Lic 卌 CTV 8P

ABERDOVEY
Gwynedd
Map **6** SN69

GH Bodfor Sea Front ☎(065472) 475
Closed Jan–Feb rs Nov–Dec
16hc (1⇌ 10ƒl) (3fb) CTV in all bedrooms Ⓡ B&b£13.50–£18 Bdi£19–£26 WBdi£125–£155 LDO8.15pm
Lic 卌 CTV ⚐
Credit cards ① ③ Ⓥ

GH Brodawel Tywyn Rd ☎(065472) 347
May–Sep
This tastefully furnished Edwardian house is situated in an excellent position overlooking Aberdovey Golf Course, one mile from the town centre.
6hc (2ƒl) (2fb) CTV in 2 bedrooms ✈ Ⓡ B&b£11
CTV 7P

GH Cartref ☎(065472) 273
Family-run guesthouse near beach and recreation area.
7hc (1⇌ 2ƒl) (2fb) CTV in 2 bedrooms Ⓡ in 2 bedrooms B&b£10–£13 Bdi£15–£18 WBdi£105–£125 LDO5pm
卌 CTV 8P
Ⓥ

ABEREDW
Powys
Map **3** SO04

FH Mrs M M Evans **Danycoed** (SO079476) ☎Erwood (09823) 298
Etr–Oct
Stone-built, two-storey farmhouse. Pleasant situation on edge of River Wye.
3rm (2hc) ✈ ✱B&b£8–£9.50 Bdi£11–£12.50 WBdifr£80 LDO5.30pm
P 239acres sheep mixed

ABERFELDY
Tayside *Perthshire*
Map **14** NN84

GH Balnearn Private Hotel Crieff Rd ☎(0887) 20431
Large house with modern bedroom wing.
13hc (2fb) TV in 1 bedroom Ⓡ B&b£11.50–£12.05 Bdi£18.40–£19.55 WBdi£128.80–£136.85 LDO6.30pm
CTV 15P 2🚗 ♿

⊢**GH Caber-Feidh** 56 Dunkeld St ☎(0887) 20342
Very well-appointed little guesthouse above town-centre shops. Many attractive features.
6hc (2fb) Ⓡ B&b£8–£8.50 Bdi£14 WBdi£95 LDO8.45pm
卌 CTV 5P

Selected

GH Guinach House Urlar Road ☎(0887) 20251
15 Mar–Oct
A delightful guesthouse set in 3 acres of grounds and gardens with views over the town and Strath Appin. The country house atmosphere is reflected in the warmth and attention shown to guests by the owners who go out of their way to make everyone's stay a memorable one. The charming bedrooms are tastefully furnished to a high standard, as are the public rooms. The food features many traditional Scottish dishes.
7hc (1⇌ 1ƒl) CTV in all bedrooms Ⓡ B&b£18–£20 Bdi£29.50–£31.50 WBdi£199.50–£210 LDO8.30pm
Lic 卌 8P 1🚗 nc8yrs

GH Nessbank Crieff Rd ☎(0887) 20214
Apr–Oct
A very comfortable little hotel with high standards throughout.
6hc (1fb) ⚟ in all bedrooms ✈ Ⓡ B&b£11 Bdi£17.50 WBdi£110 LDO6pm
Lic CTV 6P 2🚗
Ⓥ

ABERGAVENNY
Gwent
Map **3** SO21

GH Belchamps 1 Holywell Rd ☎(0873) 3204
Small, personally-run guesthouse with cosy bedrooms and comfortable lounge and dining room. Near to both town and river.
5hc (2fb) ✈ Ⓡ ✱B&b£10–£12 Bdi£15.50–£18 WBdi£103–£120 LDO10am
卌 CTV 5P nc3yrs
Ⓥ

GH Llanwenarth House Govilon ☎Gilwern (0873) 830289
Closed Feb
Partly 16th-century, country house property in rural surroundings. Charm and elegance are keynotes of drawing- and dining-rooms; bedrooms are spacious.
5hc (3⇌ 2ƒl) (1fb) CTV in all bedrooms Ⓡ B&b£19.50–£23.50 Bdi£34–£39 WBdi£238–£273 LDO8pm
Lic 卌 5P nc5yrs
Ⓥ

FH Mrs D Miles **Great Lwynfranc** *(S0327193)* Llanvihangel Crucorney. (Off A465 3mN) ☎Crucorney (0873) 890418
Mar–Nov
Near Abergavenny, a farmhouse of character with views over the Brecon Beacons. Bedrooms bright and airy; lounge and dining rooms elegantly furnished. Perfect for a tranquil holiday.
3hc (1fb) Ⓡ B&b£9.50–£10 WB&bfr£65
卌 CTV 10P ⌂ 154acres mixed
Ⓥ

FH Mrs J Nicholls **Newcourt** *(SO317165)* Mardy ☎(0873) 2300

Closed 1wk Xmas

16th-century, stone-built farmhouse with views of Sugar Loaf Mountain.

3hc ⊠ in all bedrooms TV in 1 bedroom CTV in 2 bedrooms 🚫 Ⓡ B&b£10–£12.50 Bdi£12.50–£19.50 WB&b£70

🍽 CTV 10P nc6yrs 160acres arable beef dairy

ⓥ

ABERHOSAN
Powys
Map **6** SN89

FH Mrs A Lewis **Bacheiddon** *(SN825980)* ☎Machynlleth (0654) 2229
May–Oct

From the windows there are lovely views of the surrounding mountains and countryside. Off unclassified road linking Machynlleth and Dyliffe/Staylittle (B4518).

3⋔ 🚫 B&bfr£11 Bdifr£15 WBdifr£105

CTV P 830acres sheep mixed

ABERPORTH
Dyfed
Map **2** SN25

GH Ffynonwen Country ☎(0239) 810312

Rural guesthouse full of character.

11hc (6⇌) (2fb) ✱B&b£12–£14 Bdi£18–£20 WB&b£75.60–£78.20

Lic 🍽 30P

ⓥ

ABERSOCH
Gwynedd
Map **6** SH32

GH Llysfor ☎(075881) 2248
Etr–Oct

Detached Victorian house near beach and shops.

8hc (1⇌) (2fb) Ⓡ B&b£11 Bdi£16 WBdi£112 LDOam

Lic CTV 12P

ⓥ

ABERYSTWYTH
Dyfed
Map **6** SN58

See plan on page 32

GH Glyn-Garth South Rd ☎(0970) 615050 Plan **1** *A2*
Closed 1 wk Xmas (rs Oct–Etr)

Victorian, double fronted, mid-terrace property adjacent to beach, harbour and castle, ¼m from the shops.

10hc (4⇌ 2⋔) (3fb) CTV in all bedrooms Ⓡ ✱B&b£11–£17 Bdi£18–£24 WBdifr£115 LDO4.30pm

Lic 🍽 CTV 🚫P nc7yrs

ⓥ

GH Llety-Gwyn Llanbadarn Fawr (1mE A44) ☎(0970) 3965 Plan **2** *D2*

8hc (4⋔) Annexe: 6hc (1⇌ 3⋔) (4fb) CTV in 11 bedrooms TV in 3 bedrooms Ⓡ ✱B&b£12–£16 Bdi £19–£23.50 LDO5pm

Lic 🍽 CTV 55P snooker

Credit card ⊡

GH Plas Antaron Pen Parcau ☎(0970) 611550
Plan **3** *B1*

A comfortable guesthouse situated about 1½m from the town centre and sea front.

11hc (6⋔) (1fb) CTV in 6 bedrooms Ⓡ B&b£9.50–£13.50 Bdi£14–£18 WBdi£98–£105 LDO6pm

Lic 🍽 CTV 40P

See advertisement on page 32

⟼**GH Shangri La** 36 Portland St Ⓡ ☎(0970) 617659 Plan **4** *B3*

Closed Xmas

Single-fronted, mid-terrace Victorian building adjacent to shops and ¼ mile from beach.

6hc (3fb) TV in all bedrooms Ⓡ B&b£9 WB&b£72

🍽 CTV 🚫P

Aberystwyth

1	Glyn-Garth	**4**	Shangri-La
2	Llety-Gwyn	**5**	Windsor Private Hotel
3	Plas Antaron		

GH Windsor Private Hotel 41 Queens Rd ☎(0970) 612134 Plan **5** *B4*

Victorian mid-terrace house in residential area adjacent to shops and beaches.

9hc (1fb) in 2 bedrooms TV in 6 bedrooms CTV in 3 bedrooms Ⓡ B&b£9–£11.50 Bdi£13.50–£16 WBdi£85–£95 LDO5pm

Lic CTV

Ⓥ

ABINGTON
Strathclyde *Lanarkshire*
Map **11** NS92

FH Mrs M Hodge **Craighead** *(NS914236)* ☎Crawford (08642) 356
May–Oct

Large farm building in courtyard design. Set amid rolling hills on the banks of the River Duneaton. Main buildings date from 1780. Off unclassified Crawfordjohn Road. 1m N of A74/A73 junc.

3rm (1fb) B&b£8.50–£9 Bdi£13–£13.50 WBdifr£91 LDO5pm

CTV 6P 4 600acres mixed

Ⓥ

FH Mr D Wilson **Crawfordjohn Mill** *(NS897242)* Crawfordjohn ☎Crawfordjohn (08644) 248
May–Sep

Two-storey, brown-brick farmhouse. Situated off the A74 1m SE of Crawfordjohn on an unclassified road.

2rm B&b£8.50 Bdi£12 WBdifr£80 LDO5pm

CTV 2P 180acres mixed

FH Mrs M E Hamilton **Kirkton** *(NS933210)* ☎Crawford (08642) 376
Jun–Sep

Stone-built farmhouse dating from 17th century and set amongst rolling hills overlooking the River Clyde. Situated 120 yds off A74, 2m S of Abington.

3rm B&b£8

CTV 3P nc4yrs 750acres beef sheep

Visit your local AA centre

Selected

FH Mrs J Hyslop **Netherton** *(NS908254)* (on unclass road joining A74 & A73) ☎Crawford (08642) 321

The location of this former shooting Lodge seems far from the madding crowd but it is, in fact, just ½m from the A74. It is meticulously maintained with spacious attractive bedrooms and comfortable public rooms. Dinner is served houseparty style and Mrs Hysford's Cordon Bleu cooking is to be commended, as are her hearty breakfasts. Excellent value for money.

3hc (1fb) in all bedrooms B&b£9–£10 Bdi£14–£15 WB&bfr£60 LDO5pm

CTV 3P 3000acres beef sheep

Ⓥ

ACASTER MALBIS
North Yorkshire
Map **8** SE54

INN Ship ☎York (0904) 703888

18th-century riverside inn retaining many original features. Separate restaurant and good range of bar meals.

5hc (2fb) CTV in all bedrooms Ⓡ B&b£11–£13 Bdi£16–£18 WBdifr£102 Bar lunch £1.45–£5.50 Dinner 9.30pm£5&alc

90P

Credit cards 1 3 Ⓥ

See advertisement under York

ACHARACLE
Highland *Argyllshire*
Map **13** NM66

FH Mrs M Macaulay **Dalilea House** *(NM735693)* ☎Salen (096785) 253
Etr–6 Oct

A splendid turreted house with surrounding grounds giving excellent views over farmland hills and Loch Shiel. A blend of ancient and modern.

6hc (1fb) Ⓡ *B&b£11–£13 Bdi£19–£21 WBdifr£120 LDO7pm

8P 13000acres beef sheep fish

Ⓥ

AINSTABLE
Cumbria
Map **12** NY54

FH Miss K Pollock **Basco Dyke Head** *(NY529450)* Basco Dyke ☎Croglin (076886) 254
Mar–Dec

A cheery welcome awaits the visitor to this quaint 18th century farmhouse. Good traditional accommodation furnished with many antiques.

3hc (2fb) Ⓡ B&b£7.50–£11.50 Bdi£12.50–£17.50 WBdifr£85.50 LDO6pm

CTV 4P 2 216acres arable dairy

AISLABY
North Yorkshire
Map **8** NZ80

FH Mrs B A Howard **Cote Bank** *(NZ827070)* ☎Whitby (0947) 85314
Closed Xmas

A quiet farmhouse in a pleasant valley, near Whitby.

3rm (2hc) (2fb) in all bedrooms. Ⓡ in 2 bedrooms B&b£10 Bdi£17 WBdifr£119 LDO4pm

CTV 3P 300acres dairy mixed

Ⓥ

Credit Cards

1 Access/Euro/Mastercard
2 American Express
3 Barclaycard/Visa
5 Diners

Selected

FH Mrs J F Roberts **Intake** *(NZ841082)* ☎Whitby (0947) 810817

Friendly and enthusiastic proprietors welcome guests to this most charming farmhouse. Situated in an elevated position there are beautiful views of the Esk Valley. The spacious house offers both comfort and luxury throughout, from the elegant lounge to the attractive dining room. Here guests can enjoy superb home-cooked meals seated around a large table. The bedrooms are all large and comfortably furnished.

3hc (1fb) ⅌ in all bedrooms B&b£10–£10.50 Bdi£16–£16.50 LDO6.30pm

Lic CTV 10P nc5yrs 16acres mixed

ALDEBURGH
Suffolk
Map **5** TM45

GH Cotmandene 6 Park Ln ☎(072885) 3775

A double-fronted Victorian house, modernised but retaining its original character. Fresh home cooking.

6hc (2fb) TV in all bedrooms ✱ Ⓡ B&b£14–£16 Bdi£19–£26 WBdifr£120 LDO7.30pm

Lic 🍽 CTV ₱

Credit cards 1 3

ALDERMINSTER
Warwickshire
Map **4** SP24

FH Mr & Mrs V Miller **Alderminster** *(SP219492)* ☎(078987) 296
Apr–Oct

A Georgian farmhouse in lovely countryside, convenient to Stratford.

2hc (1fl) (1fb) ✱ Ⓡ B&b£12–£14 Bdi£22–£28 WBdifr£154 LDO previous evening

🍽 CTV 4P 1🚗 nc7yrs 250acres arable sheep

ALDERSHOT
Hampshire
Map **4** SU85

GH *Cedar Court Hotel* Eggars Hill ☎(0252) 20931
Closed 24 Dec–1 Jan

Well-maintained private house, offering helpful and efficient service. TV and private facilities in most of the modern bedrooms. Comfortable lounge and separate breakfast room.

8hc (3fl) Annexe: 4hc (1⇌ 3fl) (2fb) CTV in 8 bedrooms LDO3pm

Lic 🍽 CTV 14P

ALDWARK
Derbyshire
Map **8** SK25

FH J N Lomas **Lydgate** *(SK228577)* ☎Carsington (062985) 250

Peace and comfort are assured in this delightful 17th-century stone farmhouse.

3rm (1fb) ⅌ in 2 bedrooms ✱ Ⓡ B&b£8.50–£10 Bdi£14.50–£16 WBdi£100–£112 LDO2pm

🍽 CTV 5P 300acres mixed

Ⓥ

ALFRISTON
East Sussex
Map **5** TQ50

FH Mrs D Y Savage **Pleasant Rise** *(TQ516027)* ☎(0323) 870545
Closed Xmas week

Very attractive farm with large, bright and clean accommodation, delightfully appointed. Badminton, cricket nets and extensive tennis facilities. Adjacent to B2108 Seaford road.

4hc (1fl) (1fb) Ⓡ B&b£11–£12.50

🍽 CTV 8P nc9yrs 🎾(hard) 100acres mixed

Ⓥ

ALKMONTON
Derbyshire
Map **7** SK13

FH Mr A Harris ***Dairy House*** *(SK198367)* ☎Great Cubley (033523) 359

16th-century brick farmhouse, comfortably modernised yet retaining character. Nature Reserve.

7hc (2fb) ✱ Ⓡ LDO8pm

Lic 🍽 CTV 8P 🏠 82acres dairy

ALLENDALE
Northumberland
Map **12** NY85

Selected

FH Mr & Mrs Fairless **Bishopfield** *(NY826565)* (1m W) ☎(043483) 248
Mar–Dec

This impressive 18th-century farmhouse is tastefully furnished with charm and elegance and the atmosphere is relaxed and informal. Dinners are a highlight of a stay at Bishopfield and Kathy Fairless' baked ham and home-made soups are a popular feature on the generous four-course menu. There are two comfortable lounges and a full-size snooker room. Additional attractions include a well-established garden, a small nature reserve and trout fishing.

8 ⇌ fl (lfb) CTV in all bedrooms B&b£17 Bdi£25 WBdi£175 LDO7pm

Lic 🍽 20P ♩ snooker 48acres mixed

Credit cards 1 5 Ⓥ

See advertisement on page 35

ALNMOUTH
Northumberland
Map **12** NU21

GH Blue Dolphin
11 Riverside Rd ☎(0665) 830893

A comfortable, spacious Victorian house set in a peaceful location overlooking the estuary and the sea.

5hc (2⇌ 3fl) (1fb) CTV in all bedrooms Ⓡ ✱B&b£12.50–£15

Lic 5P

See advertisement on page 35

GH Marine House Private Hotel 1 Marine Dr ☎Alnwick (0665) 830349 Feb–Nov

Friendly staff and home-cooking ensure a comfortable stay at this pleasant house overlooking the bay.

8hc (2fl) (4fb) B&b£15–£16 Bdi£19–£22.50 WBdi£133–£150

Lic CTV 12P

ALNWICK

Northumberland
Map **12** NU11

GH Aln House South Rd ☎(0665) 602265

Friendly, comfortable guesthouse serving home-cooked food.

8hc (2⇌ 1fl) (3fb) ® B&b£10–£12 WB&b£65–£80

Lic CTV 8P

GH Aydon House South Rd ☎(0665) 602218

A comfortable house, with good bedrooms, on main road.

10hc (4fb) CTV in all bedrooms B&b£9–11 Bdi£16–£18 WBdifr£100 LDO5pm

Lic 12P

GH Bondgate House Hotel Bondgate Without ☎(0665) 602025

Friendly, personally-run, town-centre house with quaint, comfortable rooms.

8hc (1fl) (3fb) CTV in all bedrooms ® B&b£10–£15 Bdi£16–£18.50 WBdifr£107.50 LDO4.30pm

Lic 8P

⊢⊣**GH Hope Rise** The Dunterns ☏(0665) 602930

In quiet residential area, house offers comfortable accommodation and a friendly atmosphere.

7hc (2fb) ✗ Ⓡ B&b£8.50–£9 WB&b£58–£60

CTV 12P nc5yrs

FH Mrs A Davison **Alndyke** *(NU208124)* ☏(0665) 602193
May–Oct

Comfortable house offering good home-cooking.

3hc (1fb) ⅄ in all bedrooms ✗ Ⓡ B&b£11–£12 Bdi£17–£18 WBdifr£112 LDOnoon

CTV 5P nc5yrs 320acres arable beef dairy sheep mixed

ALSTON
Cumbria
Map **12** NY74

⊢⊣**FH** Mrs P M Dent **Middle Bayles** *(NY706451)* ☏(0498) 81383
Closed Xmas & New Year

Charming old-world hill farm overlooking South Tyne Valley. Attractive accommodation.

2hc (1fb) Ⓡ B&b£8.50 Bdi£13 WBdi£82 LDO4pm

CTV 2P 300acres beef sheep

Ⓥ

ALTRINCHAM
Gt Manchester
Map **7** SJ78

GH Bollin Hotel 58 Manchester Rd ☏061-928 2390

Well-furnished small hotel on A56 near town centre.

10hc (2fb) Ⓡ B&b£16.10–£26.15 WB&bfr£112.70

CTV 10P

ALYTH
Tayside *Perthshire*
Map **15** NO25

INN Losset Losset Rd ☏(08283) 2393

Recently converted, and modernised, this small country town inn dates from 1730. Low-beamed ceilings and polished wood furniture help retain period character. Though small, the bedrooms are modern in decor, furnishings and facilities. Friendly owners ensure a warm welcome and the food is freshly prepared and well-presented.

3⫶ CTV in all bedrooms ✗ Ⓡ B&b£13–£15 Bdi£16–£21 WBdifr£125 L£2.65–£6 & alc Dinner 9pm £3–£7 & alc

Ⓥ

AMBLESIDE
Cumbria
Map **7** NY30

GH Chapel House Hotel Kirkstone Rd ☏(05394) 33143
Closed Jan & Feb

Former 16th-century cottages retaining old-world atmosphere. Very good food.

9hc (3⫶) (1fb) ✗ Bdi£18–£22 WBdi£122–£132 LDO6.45pm

Lic P

GH Compston House Hotel Compston Rd ☏(05394) 32305

Family run hotel, overlooking park and fells.

10hc (2fb) CTV in all bedrooms ✗ Ⓡ B&b£9.95–£11.95 Bdi£15.50–£17.50 WBdifr£117.50 LDO5pm

Lic P nc5yrs

GH Gables Private Hotel Church Walk, Compston Rd ☏(05394) 33272
Mar–Oct rs Jan & Feb

Tudor-style house in central position overlooking the bowling green and tennis courts.

15hc (3⇌ 2⋔) (4fb) Ⓡ B&bfr£11.50 Bdifr£17.50 WBdifr£119

Lic ꟻ CTV 10P

Ⓥ

GH Gale Crescent Hotel Lower Gale ☎(05394) 32284

Peaceful, hill-top house with fine lakeland views.

8hc (1⇌ 1⋔) (2fb) ✈ Ⓡ B&b£11.50–£14 Bdi£18–£20.50 WBdifr£126 LDO5pm

Lic CTV 10P

Selected

GH Grey Friar Lodge Country House Hotel Brathay (1m W off A593) ☎(05394) 33158
Mar–Oct

A charming slate built house surrounded by attractive gardens with superb views of the Langdale Valley. Excellent food and service is offered here including five-course evening meals and wholesome breakfasts. Guests will enjoy the comfortable lounges and attractive dining rooms as well as the tastefully furnished and decorated bedrooms.

8hc (4⇌ 3⋔) (1fb) CTV in all bedrooms Ⓡ Bdi£26–£29.50 WBdi£160–£190 LDO7.30pm

Lic ꟻ 12P nc12yrs

Ⓥ

See advertisement on page 38

GH Hillsdale Hotel Church St ☎(05394) 33174

A homely, terraced town-centre guesthouse.

8hc (1⇌) (1fb) ✈ Ⓡ ✱B&b£10–£13 Bdi£16–£19 WBdi£105–£126 LDO4pm

Lic ꟻ CTV ₱

Ⓥ

GH Horseshoe Rothay Rd ☎(05394) 32000
Closed 6 Jan–Feb

Town centre guesthouse overlooking park. Recently extended to offer en-suite bedrooms. Traditional or wholefood breakfast is available.

Ambleside

12hc (5⋔) (3fb) CTV in all bedrooms Ⓡ ✱B&bfr£12 Bdifr£18.50 WBdifr£125 LDO5pm

Lic ꟻ 15P

Ⓥ

See advertisement on page 38

GH Lattendale Hotel Compston Rd ☎(05394) 32368

A friendly family run hotel situated in the town centre serving a variety of traditional home cooking. The attractive lounge features a real fire.

7hc (2⇌) (3fb) CTV in all bedrooms ✱B&b£10–£15 Bdi£17–£22.50 WBdi£115–£144 LDO7.15pm

Lic ꟻ CTV ₱

Credit cards 1 3 Ⓥ

GH *Melrose* Church St ☎(05394) 32500

An attractive slate-built house with feature marble fireplaces and basement dining room.

6hc (2⋔) (3fb) TV in 3 bedrooms Ⓡ

ꟻ CTV ₱

See advertisement on page 38

GH *Romney Hotel* Waterhead ☎(05394) 32219
Etr–Oct

A tranquil country house atmosphere prevails and the resident proprietors give service in keeping.

19hc (1⇌ 1⋔) (5fb) LDO7pm

Lic CTV 20P 3🚗 ⌂

Credit card 3

GH Rothay Garth Hotel Rothay Rd ☎(05394) 32217

Hotel offers very relaxing atmosphere and comfortable accommodation.

15hc (4⇌ 8⋔) (3fb) ⍻ in 4 bedrooms CTV in all bedrooms Ⓡ ✱B&b£15–£27 Bdi£24–£35 WBdi£145–£225 LDO7.30pm

Lic ꟻ CTV 17P ⌂

Credit cards 1 2 3 5

Ⓥ

See advertisement on page 38

Selected

GH Rydal Lodge Hotel (2m NW A590) ☎(05394) 33208
Closed 7 Jan–4 Feb

A charming guesthouse which dates from the early 1600s with attractive gardens leading down to the River Rothay. The drawing room on the first floor is very comfortable and the cosy TV room on the ground floor has a log fire. Excellent five-course dinners are served in the pretty dining room overlooking the gardens.

8hc (1fb) ✱B&b£13–£14.50 Bdi£19.85–£21 WBdi£133–£140 LDO7pm

Lic CTV 12P ♪

Credit cards 1 3 5

Ⓥ

See advertisement on page 39

GH Rysdale Hotel Kelsick Rd ☎(05394) 32140
Closed 21 Dec–10 Jan

House with pretty window boxes and a well-appointed dining room.

9hc (1⋔) (4fb) TV in 3 bedrooms CTV in 6 bedrooms ✈ Ⓡ B&b£11.50–£11.95 Bdi£17.30–£17.75 WBdifr£120 LDO5.30pm

Lic ꟻ 2P

Ⓥ

GH Smallwood Hotel Compston Rd ☎(05394) 32330
Mar–Oct

Spacious detached house close to town centre. Pleasant, comfortable accommodation with attractive lounge and pretty dining room where tasty home-cooked meals are served.

13hc (1⇌ 1⋔) (4fb) Ⓡ B&b£11–£13.50 Bdi£17.50–£20 WBdi£112.50–£129 LDO5pm

ꟻ CTV 10P nc3yrs

See advertisement on page 39

GH Thrang House Compston Rd
☎(05394) 32112
Mar–Dec

A slate-built house serving good, hearty breakfasts.

6hc (2fl) ✗ Ⓡ B&b£10–£14 Bdi£16–£20 WBdifr£110 LDO6pm

🌡 CTV 5P nc10yrs

Ⓥ

See advertisement on page 40

ANCASTER
Lincolnshire
Map **8** SK94

Ambleside — Andoversford

⊢⊣**FH** Mrs F R Mival **Woodlands** West Willoughby (*SK966437*) (1½m W on A153)
☎(0400) 30340
Etr–Sep

This delightful 19th-century stone built farmhouse situated in the rolling Lincolnshire countryside offers comfortable accommodation as well as wholesome home-cooked food.

3rm (1fb) B&bfr£8.50 Bdifr£12.50

CTV 3P 🏠 12acres mixed

ANDOVERSFORD
Gloucestershire
Map **4** SP01

GH Old Cold Comfort Dowdeswell (1m W A436) ☎Cheltenham (0242) 820349

Small, attractive 17th-century hotel which serves good English food.

8hc (1⇌ 1fl) CTV in all bedrooms ✗ Ⓡ B&b£14.50–£16.50 Bdi£21.50–£23.50 WBdifr£138 LDO8pm

Lic 🌡 12P 1🚗

Credit cards 1 3

ANNAN
Dumfries & Galloway *Dumfriesshire*
Map **11** NY16

GH *Ravenswood Private Hotel* St Johns Rd ☎(04612) 2158
Sandstone villa dating from 1880 standing in residential street close to town centre.
8hc (2fb) ✖ LDO8.30pm
Lic 🍽 CTV 𝙿

APPLEBY-IN-WESTMORLAND
Cumbria
Map **12** NY62

GH Bongate House Bongate ☎(07683) 51245
Closed Xmas
Detached house in attractive garden offering high standard of accommodation.
7hc (1⇄ 3⊪) (3fb) ® B&b£11–£13 Bdi£16.50–£18.50 WBdi£99–£111 LDO6pm
Lic 🍽 CTV 8P 2🚗
ⓥ

GH Howgill House ☎(0930) 51574
Etr–Oct
Spacious, detached house situated in an attractive garden ½m south of the town centre.
6hc (3fb) ✖ ® ✱B&bfr£8 WB&bfr£48
CTV 6P

⊢⊣**FH** Mrs M Wood **Gale House** *(NY695206)* ☎(07683) 51380
Etr–Sep
Farmhouse standing in small garden surrounding open fields. Traditional farmhouse furnishings. Facilities nearby include fishing, golf and bathing.
2rm (1fb) ✖ ® B&b£8.50–£9 WB&bfr£59.50
3P nc5yrs 165acres dairy
ⓥ

ARBROATH
Tayside *Angus*
Map **12** NO64

⊢⊣**GH Kingsley** 29 Market Gate ☎(0241) 73933
Small and friendly family-run guesthouse close to harbour.
14hc (8fb) B&b£9–£10 Bdi£12.50–£13.50 WBdifr£80 LDO7.30pm.
Lic 🍽 CTV 4P snooker solarium
ⓥ

ARDBRECKNISH
Strathclyde *Argyllshire*
Map **10** NN02

FH Mrs H F Hodge **Rockhill** *(NN072219)* ☎Kilchrenan (08663) 218
Etr–Sep
Loch-shore farm. Trout and perch fishing (free), and at the farm's private loch by arrangement.
6hc (3fb) CTV in all bedrooms ® B&b£15–£22 Bdi£22–£29 WBdi£132–£174 LDO7pm
Lic 8P nc7yrs ⸙ 166acres sheep horses
Credit card ①
ⓥ

See advertisement under Dalmally

ARDEN
Strathclyde *Dunbartonshire*
Map **10** NS38

⊢⊣**FH** Mrs R Keith **Mid Ross** *(NS359859)* ☎(038985) 655
Apr–Oct
Farmhouse pleasantly located close to Loch Lomond 3m N of Balloch off A82.
3hc (1fb) ✖ B&b£8–£10 WB&b£50–£60
🍽 CTV 10P 40acres arable beef sheep mixed
ⓥ

ARDERSIER
Highland *Inverness-shire*
Map **14** NH85

⊢⊣**FH** Mrs L E MacBean **Milton-of-Gollanfield** *(NH809534)* ☎(0667) 62207
Apr–Oct

Stone farmhouse set on north side of A96 5m W of Nairn, 9m E of Inverness.

3hc (1fb) ✗ B&b£8–£12

CTV P 360acres arable

ARDFERN
Strathclyde *Argyllshire*
Map **10** NM80

FH Mrs M C Peterson **Traighmhor** *(NM800039)* ☎Barbreck (08525) 228
Closed Nov

Modern loch-side bungalow with three small working crafts nearby, one of which has a mini equestrian centre.

3rm ✗ B&b£10 Bdi£15 LDO6.30pm

CTV 6P 56acres mixed

ARDGAY
Highland *Sutherland*
Map **14** NH58

⊢⊣**GH Croit Mairi** Kincardine Hill ☎(08632) 504
Closed 2 wks early Nov

Comfortable modern-style house in secluded location with pleasant views.

6hc (1fb) Ⓡ B&b£9–£11 Bdi£14.50–£16 LDO6.45pm (later by arrangement)

Lic 𝍖 CTV 10P nc4yrs

Credit cards 1 2 3 5

ARDROSSAN
Strathclyde *Ayrshire*
Map **10** NS24

⊢⊣**GH Ellwood House** 6 Arran Pl ☎(0294) 61130

Bright and cheerful guesthouse close to sandy beach.

8hc (1fb) Ⓡ B&b£8 WB&bfr£56

CTV P̸

Ⓥ

ARINAGOUR
Coll (Island of) Strathclyde *Argyllshire*
See **COLL (Island of)**

ARMATHWAITE
Cumbria
Map **12** NY54

INN Fox & Pheasant ☎(06992) 400

7hc (3⇌ 1⫪) CTV in 4 bedrooms Ⓡ in 5 bedrooms B&b£15–£17 Bdi£22 Bar lunch £2.10–£6.50 Dinner 9pm £9.25

50P 1🚘 ⌡

Ⓥ

ARRAN, ISLE OF
Strathclyde *Buteshire*
Map **10**

CORRIE
Map **10** NS04

GH Blackrock House ☎(077081) 282
Closed Dec

Stone house dating from 1930 with modernised interior and good sea views.

9rm (8hc) (3fb) Ⓡ in 5 bedrooms B&b£10 Bdi£15.50 WBdifr£105 LDO5pm

𝍖 CTV 8P

LAMLASH
Map **10** NS03

GH Glenisle Hotel ☎(07706) 258
Closed mid Oct–mid Nov

Victorian house with extensions standing on main road in small village, with sea views. 9-hole putting green

15hc (3⇌ 4⫪) (6fb) CTV in 12 bedrooms ✗ Ⓡ in 14 bedrooms B&b £13.50–£17.50 Bdi£19–£23 WB&b£94.50–£122.50 LDO9pm

Lic 10P

Credit card 3 Ⓥ

GH *Marine House Hotel* ☎(07706) 298
Mar–Oct

Converted and modernised coastguard building in own grounds of ¾-acre with views over to Holy Island.

18hc (6⫪) (6fb)

CTV 16P

LOCHRANZA
Map **10** NR95

GH *Kincardine Lodge* ☎ (077083) 267
Apr–Oct

Converted house dating from 1910, standing in own grounds overlooking the bay and castle.

6hc (4fb)

CTV 6P

SANNOX
Map **10** NS04

⊢⊣**GH Cliffdene** ☎Corrie (077081) 224
Closed Oct & Nov

Stone house built in 1900 on main road overlooking beach and sea.

5hc (3fb) ✗ B&b£8.75 Bdi£12.25 WBdifr£85.75 LDO6.30pm

CTV 5P

ARRETON
Isle of Wight
See **Wight, Isle of**

ARUNDEL
West Sussex
Map **4** TQ00

GH Arden 4 Queens Ln ☎(0903) 882544
Closed 10 Dec–10 Jan

Small house with friendly, homely atmosphere.

8hc (2⫪) (1fb) CTV in all bedrooms ✗ Ⓡ B&b£12–£14 WB&b£70–£84

𝍖 4P

Ⓥ

GH *Bridge House* 18 Queen St ☎(0903) 882142
Closed Xmas wk

Well-maintained with good homely atmosphere in attractive situation overlooking river and facing the castle.

11hc (4⫪) (6fb) CTV in 7 bedrooms Ⓡ

𝍖 CTV 9P 4🚘

Credit cards 1 3

INN Swan Hotel High St ☎(0903) 882314

Georgian-style inn, overlooking the River Arun.

11hc (8⇌ 3⫪) CTV in all bedrooms ✗ Ⓡ B&b£19–£23 Bdi£27.50–£41.50 WBdi£173.50–£257.50 Lunch £8.50alc Dinner £8.50&alc LDO9.30pm

𝍖 P̸ 🚘

Credit cards 1 2 3 5 Ⓥ

ASCOT
Berkshire
Map **4** SU96

GH Highclere House Kings Rd, Sunninghill ☎(0990) 25220
rs 24 Dec–2 Jan

Well-appointed and recently refurbished property run by friendly young proprietor.

11hc (7⫪) (2fb) CTV in all bedrooms Ⓡ B&b£20–£41 Bdi£25–£45 WBdifr£235 LDO9pm

Lic 𝍖 CTV 10P 2🚘 ⌂

Credit cards 1 3 Ⓥ

ASHBURTON
Devon
Map **3** SX77

GH Gages Mill Buckfastleigh Rd ☎(0364) 52391
Mar–Nov

Carefully restored 600-year-old mill in one acre of well-kept garden surrounded by beautiful countryside.

8hc (1⇌ 3⫪) (1fb) ✗ Ⓡ ✱B&b£10.50–£13.50 Bdi£17–£20 WBdi£112–£122.50 LDO3pm

Lic CTV 10P nc5yrs

FH Mrs Young **Bremridge** *(SX785701)* Woodland (2mE unclass towards Denbury) ☎(0364) 52426
Closed Dec

3hc (3fb) B&b£10–£12 Bdi£14.50–£16.50 WBdi£78–£95 LDO6pm

𝍖 CTV 6P ⌂ 8acres mixed

Ⓥ

ASHFORD
Kent
Map **5** TR04

GH Croft Hotel Canterbury Rd, Kennington ☎(0233) 22140
Comfortable simple accommodation with more modern annexe.
15hc (2⇌ 7⋔) Annexe: 13hc (8⇌ 5⋔) (3fb) CTV in all bedrooms Ⓡ B&b£16–£31 Bdi£25–£40 LDO8pm
Lic ♨ CTV 30P
Credit card [1]

GH Downsview Private Hotel Willesborough Rd, Kennington ☎(0233) 21953
16hc (2⇌ 9⋔) (2fb) CTV in all bedrooms Ⓡ B&b£16–£22 Bdi£19.50–£28.30 WBdifr£134 LDO8.30pm
Lic ♨ CTV 20P
Credit cards [1] [2] [3] [5] Ⓥ

INN George High St ☎(0233) 25512
Closed Xmas Day
Small, olde-worlde inn with cosy well-decorated bedrooms.
14hc (1⇌ 1⋔) (2fb) CTV in all bedrooms ✗ Ⓡ B&b£18.50–£27.50 Lunch£3–£8&alc Dinner 10pm (10.45pm wknds) £3–£8&alc
♨ CTV 5P 8🚘
Credit cards [1] [2] [3] [5]

ASHPRINGTON
Devon
Map **3** SX85

FH Mrs T C Grimshaw ***Sharpham Barton*** *(SX814583)* ☎Harbertonford (080423) 278
Modern farmhouse in 11 acres with well-appointed bedrooms.
3rm (2hc 1⋔) TV in all bedrooms LDOday prior
♨ TV 3P ≏heated 🎾grass ∪ 11acres mixed non-working

ASHTON-UNDER-LYNE
Greater Manchester
Map **7** SJ99

GH Welbeck House Hotel 324 Katherine St ☎061–344 0751
A modern, well furnished, town-centre hotel, privately owned and run.
7⇌ ⋔ (2fb) CTV in all bedrooms Ⓡ B&b£28 Bdi£33 LDO8pm
Lic ♨ CTV 12P
Credit cards [1] [2] [3] [5]

ASHURST
Hampshire
Map **4** SU31

GH Barn 112 Lyndhurst Rd ☎(042129) 2531
Etr–Sep
Attractive detached house offering comfortable bedrooms.
6hc ✗ B&b£9.50–£10
♨ CTV 8P 1🚘(charge)
Ⓥ
See advertisement under Southampton

ASHWELL
Hertfordshire
Map **4** TL23

INN *Three Tuns Hotel* 6 High St ☎(046274) 2387
Country inn with pleasant individually-furnished bedrooms.
7hc Annexe: 5hc (1⇌ 1⋔) (1fb) CTV in all bedrooms Ⓡ LDO10.30pm
♨ 25P solarium
Credit cards [1] [2] [5]

ASKRIGG
North Yorkshire
Map **8** SD99

Selected

GH Winville Hotel ☎Wensleydale (0969) 50515
Apr–Oct
Situated on a typical Dales village main street Winville offers a warm welcome and the friendly resident proprietors ensure guests are comfortable and relaxed during their stay. The bedrooms are attractive and offer private facilities, CTV and hot beverage trays. Barbara Phelon serves freshly cooked dishes of high quality.
6⇌ ⋔ (3fb) CTV in all bedrooms ✗ Ⓡ B&b£14.95–£21.50 Bdi£21.90–£29.25 WBdifr£150 LDO7.30pm
Lic ♨ 12P 2🚘 nc10yrs
Credit cards [1] [2] [3] [5] Ⓥ

ASTBURY
Cheshire
Map **7** SJ86

INN Egerton Arms Hotel ☎Congleton (02602) 73946
Village inn with pleasant bedrooms and popular restaurant.
7hc CTV in all bedrooms Ⓡ B&b£15–£19 Bdi£20–£24 WBdifr£140 Lunch£4.60 Dinner9.30pm£8.95&alc
♨ CTV 100P ⛟ ⌂
Credit cards [3] [5]

ASTON
Staffordshire
Map **7** SJ74

FH Mrs N Y Bourne **Larksfield Country Accommodation** *(SJ747415)* Larksfield, Stoniford Ln (off A525 ¾ E of Woore) ☎Pipegate (063081) 7069
5rm (4hc) (2⋔) (2fb) CTV in 2 bedrooms TV in 3 bedrooms Ⓡ B&b£12–£14
♨ CTV 8P ✓ clay pigeon shooting 30acres arable

ATHERSTONE
Warwickshire
Map **4** SP39

Selected

GH Chapel House Friars Gate ☎(0827) 718949
Closed Xmas
A most charming and hospitable 18th-century house with walled garden and swimming pool. Pleasantly furnished bedrooms and lounge have a comfortable, welcoming atmosphere. A good set menu is served in the elegant dining room during the week, and on Fridays and Saturdays is open to non-residents also, with a well-chosen a la carte menu that is deservedly popular in the locality.
11hc (8⋔) CTV in all bedrooms ✗ ✱B&b£16.50–£25 Bdi£24–£32.50 LDO7pm
Lic ♨ 10P
Credit card [1] [3] [5] Ⓥ

ATTLEBOROUGH
Norfolk
Map **5** TM09

INN Griffin Hotel Church St ☎(0953) 452149
A friendly inn, recently renovated, offering good fare.
8hc CTV in 2 bedrooms TV in 6 bedrooms ✗ Ⓡ ✱B&b£16–£18 Lunch£3.50alc Dinner9pm £8.50alc
♨ 20P

AUCHTERMUCHTY
Fife
Map **11** NO21

FH Mrs I Steven Ardchoille **Woodmill** *(NO248096)* ☎(0337) 28414
This smartly-appointed farmhouse is close to the village of Dunshalt. All bedrooms are well-equipped.
3hc (2⋔) (1fb) CTV in all bedrooms ✗ Ⓡ B&b£15–£18 Bdi£27.50–£30
♨ CTV 8P ∪ 460acres arable mixed
Ⓥ

AUDLEY
Staffordshire
Map **7** SJ75

FH Mrs E.E. Oulton ***Domvilles*** *(SJ776516)* Barthomley Rd ☎Stoke-on-Trent (0782) 720378

Large farmhouse overlooking Cheshire Plain. Dairy farm with pigs, geese and tropical birds, situated close to Junct. 16 of M6 .

3rm (1fl) (1fb) CTV in 1 bedroom ✕ LDO6pm

Lic CTV 5P ⌂ snooker 120acres dairy mixed

See advertisement under Stoke-on-Trent

AUSTWICK
North Yorkshire
Map **7** SD76

FH Mrs M Hird ***Rawlinshaw*** *(SD781673)* ☎Settle (07292) 3214
Etr–Sep

200-year-old farmhouse with attractive views to the front of the house.

2hc (2fb) ✕ Ⓡ

🁢 CTV P U 206acres dairy sheep

AVETON GIFFORD
Devon
Map **3** SX64

⊢**FH** Mrs G M Balkwill **Court Barton** *(SX695477)* ☎Kingsbridge (0548) 550312
Closed Xmas

7hc (2fb) ✕ B&b£8–£10.50 WB&b£56–£70

🁢 CTV 10P ⇌ ↙ 300acres arable

Ⓥ

Audley — Ayr

AVIEMORE
Highland *Inverness-shire*
Map **14** NH81

GH *Corrour House* Inverdruie ☎(0479) 810220
Closed Nov

Stone-built house standing in tree-studded grounds ½m E of Aviemore on B970.

11rm (9hc) (5fb) Ⓡ LDO6.30pm

Lic CTV 12P ⌂

Credit card ③

See advertisement on page 44

GH Craiglea Grampian Rd ☎(0479) 810210

Detached stone-house with garden and childrens play area.

11hc (1fl) (4fb) B&b£10.50–£11.50 WB&b£68–£75

CTV 12P sauna bath

Ⓥ

Visit your local AA centre

GH *Ravenscraig* ☎(0479) 810278

Detached house on main road at north end of Aviemore, with annexe to the side.

6hc (1fl) Annexe: 6fl (3fb)

🁢 CTV 12P ⌂

AXBRIDGE
Somerset
Map **3** ST45

⊢**FH** Mr L F Dimmock **Manor** *(ST420549)* Cross ☎(0934) 732577
Closed Xmas

At junction of A38 and A371 roads.

7rm (2hc) (2fb) Ⓡ B&bfr£9 Bdifr£14 WBdifr£95 LDO5pm

CTV 10P U 250acres beef sheep horses

Ⓥ

See advertisement on page 44

AYR
Strathclyde *Ayrshire*
Map **10** NS32

GH Arrandale Hotel 2–4 Cassilis St ☎(0292) 289959
rs Winter

A friendly, family run commercial and tourist hotel situated close to the sea front and town centre amenities.

13hc (1fl) (6fb) CTV in 4 bedrooms ✕ B&b£10–£16 Bdi£15–£21 WBdi£95

Lic CTV ⊘P

Ⓥ

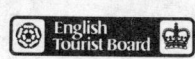

GH Clifton Hotel 19 Miller Rd ☎(0292) 264521

Detached sandstone house with rear gardens situated in residential area.

12⫿ (2fb) CTV in all bedrooms ✗ Ⓡ B&b £17–£19 Bdi£24–£26 WBdi£144–£156

Lic CTV 12P

Credit cards 1 2 3

GH Parkhouse 1A Ballantine Dr ☎(0292) 264151

Situated in a quiet residential area to the south of the town centre.

7hc (2fb) TV in all bedrooms ✗ Ⓡ ✱B&b£10

Lic CTV

Ⓥ

GH *Windsor Hotel* 6 Alloway Pl ☎(0292) 264689

rs Nov

Victorian stone house on main road near seafront.

10hc (3fb) LDO4.30pm

CTV

FH Mr & Mrs A Stevenson **Trees** *(NS386186)* ☎Joppa (0292) 570270

Closed Xmas & New Year

White farmhouse offering good quality accommodation at modest prices.

3hc (1fb) ✗ B&b£10–£12 Bdi£16–£18 WBdifr£108

CTV 5P 75acres grazing

Ⓥ

AYTON, GREAT
North Yorkshire
Map **8** NZ51

INN Royal Oak Hotel High Green ☎(0642) 722361

5hc (1⇌) CTV in all bedrooms Ⓡ ✱B&b£20 Lunchfr£5.25&alc Dinner9.15pmfr£10.25&alc

Credit cards 1 3 Ⓥ

BABELL
Clwyd
Map **7** SJ17

FH Mrs M L Williams **Bryn Glas** *(SJ155737)* ☎Caerwys (0352) 720493

Feb–Nov

Comfortable modern farmhouse situated in a quiet, rural area near Mold.

2hc (1fb) TV in all bedrooms ✗ Ⓡ B&b£8.50–£9.50 WB&bfr£59

CTV 2P 1 40acres beef sheep mixed horses

Ⓥ

BADACHRO
Highland *Ross and Cromarty*
Map **13** NG77

GH Harbour View ☎(044583) 213

rs Xmas

4⫿ (2fb) CTV in all bedrooms Ⓡ ✱B&bfr£9.50 Bdifr£14.50 WBdifr£100 LDO7pm

7P

BAKEWELL
Derbyshire
Map **8** SK26

GH Cliffe House Hotel Monsal Head ☎Great Longstone (062987) 376

Pleasant house at the head of Monsal Dale.

7hc (2fb) ✗ Ⓡ B&b£10.25–£13.50 Bdi£16.50–£19.75 WBdifr£106 LDO10am

Lic CTV 14P

Ⓥ

Selected

GH Merlin House Country Hotel
Ashford Ln, Monsal Head ☎Great Longstone (062987) 475
Closed Xmas & New Year rs Nov–Feb
Well tended lawns, shrubs and trees provide attractive surroundings for this quiet retreat in the Peak District. The immaculately kept and well proportioned rooms include an attractive dining room with adjoining coffee lounge, a pretty sun lounge and a small bar. Mr and Mrs Berisford are tireless in their efforts to ensure that their guests have an enjoyable stay.
7hc (1⇌ 1fl) ✈ Ⓡ B&b£15–£17 Bdi£23.50–£26 WBdifr£159 LDOnoon
Lic 📺 CTV 8P nc8yrs

BALA
Gwynedd
Map **6** SH93

GH Frondderw ☎(0678) 520301
Closed Xmas & New Year
Large Georgian house with lawned gardens set high above village, overlooking lake.
8hc (1⇌ 1fl) (3fb) ✈ Ⓡ B&b£9.50–£12.50 Bdi£15.50–£18.50 WBdi£97.50–£118 LDO5pm
Lic 📺 CTV 10P
Ⓥ
See advertisement on page 46

GH Plas Teg Tegid St ☎(0678) 520268
Semi-detached late nineteenth century house, set back from the road with garden in front.
6hc (6fb) Ⓡ ✱B&b£9.75 Bdi£15.75 WBdi£95 LDO5pm
Lic CTV 12P
Ⓥ
See advertisement on page 46

FH Mrs E Jones **Eirianfa** *(SH967394)* Sarnau (4m N on A494) ☎Llandderfel (06783) 389
Mar–Oct
This modernised farmhouse overlooks the Berwyn Mountains. Free trout fishing is available in the farm's private lake.
3hc (1fb) ✈ Ⓡ B&b£8.50–£9 Bdi£13–£14 WBdifr£85 LDO7pm
📺 CTV 3P 🎣 150acres mixed
Ⓥ

FH Mr D Davies ***Tytandderwen*** *(SH944345)* ☎(0678) 520273
Etr–Oct
Two-storey, manor house style, farmhouse in open country. Stone-built and modernised in parts. Borders on the River Dee.
3rm (2hc)
📺 CTV 3P 🎣 40acres mixed

BALDOCK
Hertfordshire
Map **4** TL23

GH Butterfield House Hotel Hitchin St ☎(0462) 892701
Small private hotel with spacious bedrooms and Victorian-style conservatory.
13⇌ (1fb) CTV in all bedrooms ✈ Ⓡ B&b£20–£30 Bdi£28–£38 LDO8.45pm
Lic 📺 14P
Credit cards 1 2 3

BALLACHULISH
Highland *Argyllshire*
Map **14** NN05

GH Lyn-Leven White St ☎(08552) 392
Closed Xmas
Comfortable and well-appointed modern bungalow, situated close to A82 overlooking Loch Leven.
8hc (7fl) (1fb) CTV in all bedrooms Ⓡ ✱B&b£9–£14 Bdi£15–£20 WBdi£105–£140 LDO8pm
Lic 📺 12P

BALLATER
Grampian *Aberdeenshire*
Map **15** NO39

Selected

GH Moorside Braemar Rd (Guestaccom) ☎(0338) 55492
Mar–Oct

An enthusiastic welcome is assured by the hospitable owners of this small hotel, Mr & Mrs Hewit. The attractive bedrooms are bright and well-equipped and the public rooms, though compact are very comfortable.

8hc (3🛁 5🚿) (3fb) Ⓡ B&bfr£12 Bdifr£20 WBdifr£122 LDO7pm

Lic 🍽 CTV 10P

GH Morvada ☎(0338) 55501
27 Apr–7 Oct

A neat, well-maintained house set back from the main street.

7hc (4🚿) CTV in all bedrooms Ⓡ B&bfr£10 Bdifr£16 WBdifr£124 LDO6pm

Lic 🍽 7P

Ⓥ

GH Netherley 2 Netherley Place ☎(0338) 55792
Mar–Nov rs Dec–Feb

A neat guesthouse offering cosy accommodation. Bedrooms in the main building are spacious while those in the extension are more compact.

9hc (1🛁) (1fb) TV in 1 bedroom B&b£9.50–£11.50 Bdi£16–£18 WBdifr£108 LDO6pm

CTV 🅿̸

Ⓥ

BALLAUGH
Isle of Man
See **Man, Isle of**

BALMACLELLAN
Dumfries & Galloway *Kirkcudbrightshire*
Map **11** NX67

⊢⊣**FH** Mr & Mrs A Shaw **High Park** *(NX644765)* ☎New Galloway (06442) 298
Apr–Oct

Neat roadside farmhouse with pleasant bedrooms.

3hc (1fb) Ⓡ B&b£7.50–£8 Bdi£11–£12 WBdifr£75 LDO6pm

🍽 CTV 3P 171acres beef dairy sheep mixed

Ⓥ

BALMAHA
Central *Stirlingshire*
Map **10** NS49

GH Arrochoile ☎(036087) 231
Apr–Oct

Attractive white-painted house, set back from the main road and looking west across Loch Lomond.

6hc (1🚿) (1fb) 🐕̸ ✱B&b£9 WB&b£63

🍽 CTV 12P

Ⓥ

BAMPTON
Devon
Map **3** SS92

GH Bridge House Hotel Luke St ☎(0398) 31298

Character hotel, approximately 250 years old with local hunting, fishing and walking.

7hc (3🛁 1🚿) (2fb) CTV available in bedrooms 🐕̸ Ⓡ B&b£12.50–£14.50 Bdi£19.50–£21.50 WBdi£110–£130 LDO10pm

Lic 🍽 CTV 🅿̸

Credit cards 1 3 Ⓥ

Selected

FH Mrs R A Fleming ***Holwell*** *(SS966233)* ☎(0398) 31452
Closed Xmas

Devonshire longhouse with friendly atmosphere offering traditional home-produced country fare.

3hc ✗LDO2pm

CTV 8P nc 25acres mixed

FH Mrs R Cole **Hukeley** *(SS972237)* ☎(0398) 31267
Etr–Oct

16th-century farmhouse, on edge of Exmoor with fine old beams. Rooms are comfortable and well-decorated.

2hc ✗ Ⓡ B&bfr£9 Bdifr£14 WBdifr£98 LDO4pm

CTV 4P 120acres arable beef sheep mixed

BAMPTON
Oxfordshire
Map **4** SP30

FH Mrs J Rouse **Morar** *(SP312026)* Weald St (½m SW off A4095) ☎Bampton Castle (0993) 850162 Telex 83343 ref Morar
Closed 21–27 Dec

Small modern farmhouse with comfortable rooms and pleasant garden.

3hc ⅄ in all bedrooms ✗ Ⓡ B&b£10–£15 Bdi£20–£25 WBdifr£140 LDOnoon

CTV 4P nc6yrs 450acres arable beef dairy mixed

Ⓥ

BANAVIE
Highland *Inverness-shire*
Map **14** NN17

FH Mrs A C MacDonald **Burnside** *(NN138805)* Muirshearlich ☎Corpach (03977) 275
Apr–Sep

Small, stone-built farmhouse with open views over Caledonian Canal, Loch and north face of Ben Nevis 3m NE off B8004.

3hc B&b£8–£8.50 Bdi£11.50–£12 WBdifr£75 LDO4.30pm

CTV 3P 69acres mixed

Ⓥ

BANBURY
Oxfordshire
Map **4** SP44

Selected

GH Mill House North Newington (3m W off B4035) ☎Wroxton St Mary (029573) 212
Closed 21 Dec–3 Jan

Picturesque, part 16th-century Mill-house on edge of Cotswolds, with comfortable well-appointed bedrooms.

5hc (2⇌ 3fl) CTV in all bedrooms Ⓡ B&b£18–£22 Bdi£30–£34 WBdi£189–£215 LDOnoon

Lic 9P

Credit card 1 3 5 Ⓥ

GH Tredis 15 Broughton Rd ☎(0295) 4632

Small, cosy and welcoming guesthouse.

6hc (1fb) ⅄ in 2 bedrooms CTV in all bedrooms Ⓡ B&b£10–£12 LDO1.30pm

3P

BANFF
Grampian *Banffshire*
Map **15** NJ66

GH Carmelite House Hotel Low St ☎(02612) 2152

This former town house of historic interest is now a private hotel. It is set back from the main street in this attractive conservation area. →

7hc (4fb) B&b£9.90–£10.90 Bdi£15.15–£16.65 WBdifr£99 LDO7.45pm

Lic CTV 6P

Credit cards 1 3 V

GH *Ellerslie* 45 Low St ☎(02612) 5888

Nicely decorated, well-appointed guesthouse occupying 1st floor and above in terraced row on main shopping street.

6hc (1fb) ✗ R LDO5pm

Lic CTV ₱

INN Tolbooth Hotel 1 Strait Path ☎(02612) 5034

Closed New Years Day rs 2wks Xmas/New Year

Completely renovated in 1986 to provide modern, attractive bedroom. Meals are modestly priced.

4hc (2fb) CTV in 2 bedrooms TV in 2 bedrooms ✱ B&b£9–£10 Bdi£12–£15 WBdifr£80 Lunch£2–£3.50 Dinner7pm£3–£5

₱

BANTHAM
Devon
Map **3** SX64

INN Sloop ☎Kingsbridge (0548) 560489

Comfortable, friendly inn which dates back to the 16th century when it was owned by John Widdon – a famous local smuggler. Situated close to the beach, most of its well-equipped bedrooms have sea or river views.

5hc (4⇌) (2fb) CTV in all bedrooms R B&b£15–£16 Bdi£22–£25 WBdi£144–£168 Lunch£5.50–£8&alc Dinner10pm £5.50–£8&alc

35P

BARHAM
Kent
Map **5** TR25

INN *Old Coach House* A2 Trunk Rd ☎Canterbury (0227) 831218

10hc (4fb) CTV in all bedrooms LDO10pm

60P snooker

Credit cards 1 2 3 5

Banff — Barnstaple

BARKESTONE-LE-VALE
Leicestershire
Map **8** SK73

FH Mrs S H Smart **The Paddocks** *(SK781351)* ☎Bottesford (0949) 42208

Closed Xmas

North of village off 'The Green'.

2hc Annexe: 3hc (2fb) CTV in 2 bedrooms TV in 3 bedrooms ✗ R B&b£9.50–£10.50 WB&bfr£65

CTV 10P (heated) 150acres sheep

V

BARMOUTH
Gwynedd
Map **6** SH61

GH Cranbourne Hotel 9 Marine Pde ☎(0341) 280202

Feb–Nov

10hc (1⇌ 6fl) (6fb) CTV in all bedrooms ✗(ex guide dogs) R ✱B&b£14.50–£18 Bdi£21.50–£22.95 WBdifr£129

Lic CTV 4P

Credit card 1 V

GH Lawrenny Lodge ☎(0341) 280466

Detached Edwardian house on outskirts of town ¼m from shops and beach.

10hc (1⇌ 3fl) (4fb) R B&b£11.40–£16.50 Bdi£16.90–£22 WBdifr£115 LDO9.30pm

Lic CTV 15P

Credit cards 1 3 V

REMEMBER

Prices quoted in the gazetteer are minimum double room occupancy to maximum single room occupancy **per person.**

GH Morwendon Llanaber ☎(0341) 280566

Mar–Nov

Detached Victorian house overlooking Cardigan Bay, located 1m N A496.

6hc (3fl) (3fb) CTV in all bedrooms ✗ R B&b£9–£12 Bdi£14.25–£17.25 WBdi£95–£115 (W only Jul & Aug) LDO5pm

Lic CTV 7P

GH Plas Llwyd Llanaber Rd ☎(0341) 281043

Apr–Sep

A comfortable, well appointed hotel overlooking Cardigan Bay, 1m north of the town.

6hc ✗ ✱B&bfr£8.50 Bdifr£12.50 LDO7pm

CTV 8P nc5yrs

INN Crown Hotel Church St ☎(0341) 280326

This family-run hotel has been recently modernised to provide comfortable bedrooms and an attractive lounge, complete with log fire.

9hc (2fl) CTV in all bedrooms R B&b£14–£17 WB&b£80–£90 Lunch£3.80–£12&alc Dinner9.30pm£4–£12

Credit cards 1 3 V

BARNSTAPLE
Devon
Map **2** SS53

GH Cresta 26 Sticklepath Hill ☎(0271) 74022

Closed Xmas

Detached house on main Barnstaple to Bideford road, 1 mile from Barnstaple town centre.

5hc (1fl) Annexe: 1⇌ (1fb) CTV in all bedrooms ✗ R B&b£10–£15 WBdi£70–£84

CTV 6P

V

GH Yeo Dale Hotel Pilton Bridge ☎(0271) 42954

Family run hotel dating back to the 16th century overlooking Pilton Park and river.

10hc (3fb) ® B&b£12.50 Bdi£18 WBdifr£126 LDO5pm

Lic 🍴 CTV

Ⓥ

FH Mrs G Hannington ***Fair Oak*** *(SS530348)* Ashford ☎(0271) 73698
May–Oct

Modern farmhouse in rural position overlooking Taw Estuary.

4rm (3hc) (3fb) ✗ ® LDO3pm

🍴 CTV 6P ⌂ 89acres beef sheep mixed

FH Mrs J Stanbury **Halmpstone Manor** *(SS595285)* Bishops Tawton. (2m SE Bishop's Tawton off unclass) ☎Swimbridge (0271) 830321

Excellent home cooking at handsome, stone-built farm. Rooms tastefully decorated and furnished.

4rm (2hc) (1fl) (2fb) ✗ B&b£12.50–£15 Bdi£20.50–£23 WBdi£143.50–£161 LDO9pm

Lic CTV 15P ⌂ 235 acres dairy

Credit cards 1 3 Ⓥ

⊢FH Mr & Mrs J Dallyn **Rowden Barton** *(SS538306)* Roundswell (2m SW B3232) ☎(0271) 44365

Modern farmhouse with glorious views. Friendly atmosphere.

2rm ✗ ® in 1 bedroom B&b£8 Bdi£12.50 WBdifr£80

🍴 CTV P ⌂ 100 acres beef sheep

BARRY
South Glamorgan
Map **3** ST16

GH *Maytree* 9 The Parade ☎(0446) 734075
Closed 2 wks Xmas

Victorian seafront house with lounge for residents at the front.

15hc (2fl) (2fb)

Lic 🍴 CTV 3P

BARTON-ON-SEA
Hampshire
Map **4** SZ29

Barnstaple — Bath

GH *Cliff House Hotel* Marine Drive West ☎New Milton (0425) 619333
Mar–Oct

Clifftop hotel with panoramic views, offering nicely-appointed bedrooms, spacious sun lounge and family-run restaurant.

10hc (3fl) CTV in 3 bedrooms LDO7pm

Lic 🍴 CTV 20P

Credit cards 1 2 3 5

GH Old Coastguard Private Hotel 53 Marine Drive East ☎New Milton (0425) 612987

7hc (5fl) ® ✱B&b£14–£17.50 Bdi£20–£23.50 WBdi£125–£150 LDO5pm

Lic 🍴 CTV 10P nc12yrs

BASINGSTOKE
Hampshire
See **Sherfield-on-Loddon**

BASSENTHWAITE
Cumbria
Map **11** NY23

GH *Link House Hotel* ☎Bassenthwaite Lake (059681) 291
mid Mar–4 Nov

A Victorian house, comfortably converted to offer well-appointed bedrooms and cosy lounges.

7hc (6fl) (1fb) CTV in 6 bedrooms TV in 1 bedroom ✗ ® LDO5pm

Lic 🍴 6P nc7yrs

GH *Ravenstone Hotel* ☎Bassenthwaite Lake (059681) 240
Mar–Oct

Charming country house, built in 1865 of local slate. Distant views of Bassenthwaite Lake; Spacious accommodation.

12hc (3⇌) ® LDO6pm

Lic 🍴 CTV 15P snooker

See advertisement under Keswick

⊢FH Mrs A M Trafford **Bassenthwaite Hall (East)** *(NY231322)* ☎Bassenthwaite Lake (059681) 393
Nov–Feb rs Dec & Jan

Fully modernised 17th-century farmhouse in picturesque village close to quiet stream.

2hc (1fb) B&b£7–£12 WB&b£49–£80

🍴 CTV 6P nc 2yrs 200acres beef sheep poultry

⊢FH Mrs D Mattinson **Bassenthwaite Hall (West)** *(NY228323)* ☎Bassenthwaite Lake (059681) 279
May–Oct

Traditional farmhouse in village centre with good mountain views.

3hc (1fb) ✗ B&b£8.50–£10 Bdi£13–£15

CTV 4P 135acres beef sheep

BATH
Avon
Map **3** ST76
See also **Keynsham** and **Timsbury**
See plan on pages 50–51

GH Arden Hotel 73 Great Pulteney St ☎(0225) 66601 Plan **1** *E4*
Closed mid Dec–1 Feb

12hc (1⇌ 3fl) (3fb) CTV in all bedrooms ✗ ® B&bfr£20

Lic 🍴 CTV

See advertisement on page 53

GH Arney 99 Wells Rd, Bathavon ☎(0225) 310020 Plan **2** *B1*

7hc (1fl) (3fb) B&b£11–£14 WB&b£77–£98

🍴 CTV 🅿

Ⓥ

GH Ashley Villa Hotel 26 Newbridge Rd ☎(0225) 21683 Plan **3** *A3*
Closed 2 wks Xmas

14hc (3⇌ 6fl) (3fb) CTV in all bedrooms ® B&b£15–£29 Bdi£22–£36 WBdi£132–£216 LDO9pm

Lic 🍴 CTV 10P ♿ ⛱ (heated) solarium gymnasium

Credit cards 1 3 Ⓥ

GH Astor House 14 Oldfield Rd☎(0225) 29134 Plan **4** *B1*
Apr–Oct

Bath-stone Victorian villa with friendly atmosphere, overlooking the city.

7hc ✕ Ⓡ ✱B&b£10–£12

₥ CTV 4P nc7yrs

GH Avon Hotel 9 Bathwick St ☎(0225) 446176 Plan **5** *E4*
Closed Xmas

Georgian end of terrace with well furnished bedrooms. Ample parking and close to shops and tourist sites.

20hc (17🚿) (11fb) 🚭 in 4 bedrooms CTV in all bedrooms Ⓡ B&b£13.50–£22

Lic ₥ CTV 20P 2🚗

Credit cards [1] [3] [5] Ⓥ

See advertisement on page 52

Bath

Selected

GH Brompton House Hotel St John's Rd ☎(0225) 20972 Plan **6** *D4*
Closed Xmas

Delightful Regency residence which was once the rectory to St Marys Church, adjacent. Set in secluded gardens it is within walking distance of the town centre. The house has recently been redecorated in keeping with its period and character while incorporating all modern amenities.

12hc (1⇌ 11🚿) (1fb) CTV in all bedrooms ✕ Ⓡ B&b£18.50–£19.50 WB&bfr£135

Lic ₥ 12P

Credit card [1]

See advertisement on page 53

GH Carfax Hotel Great Pulteney St ☎(0225) 62089 Plan **7** *D4*

35hc (23⇌ 7🚿) (3fb) 🚭 in 5 bedrooms CTV in all bedrooms ✕ Ⓡ B&b£15.75–£35 Bdi£21.25–£40.50 WBdifr£185.50 LDO7.50pm

Temperance lift ₥ 13P 4🚗

Credit cards [1] [2] [3] Ⓥ

GH Chesterfield Hotel 11 Great Pulteney St ☎(0225) 460953 Plan **8** *D4*
Closed 22 Dec–1 Jan

Terraced Georgian building in wide, elegant avenue. Close to tourist attractions and shops.

27hc (12⇌ 3🚿) (2fb) CTV in all bedrooms ✕ Ⓡ B&b£17–£26

Lic ₥ CTV 2P (charge) 6🚗(charge)

Credit cards [1] [2] [3] [5] Ⓥ

See advertisement on page 53

GH Dorset Villa 14 Newbridge Rd ☎(0225) 25975 Plan **10** *A3*
May–Oct

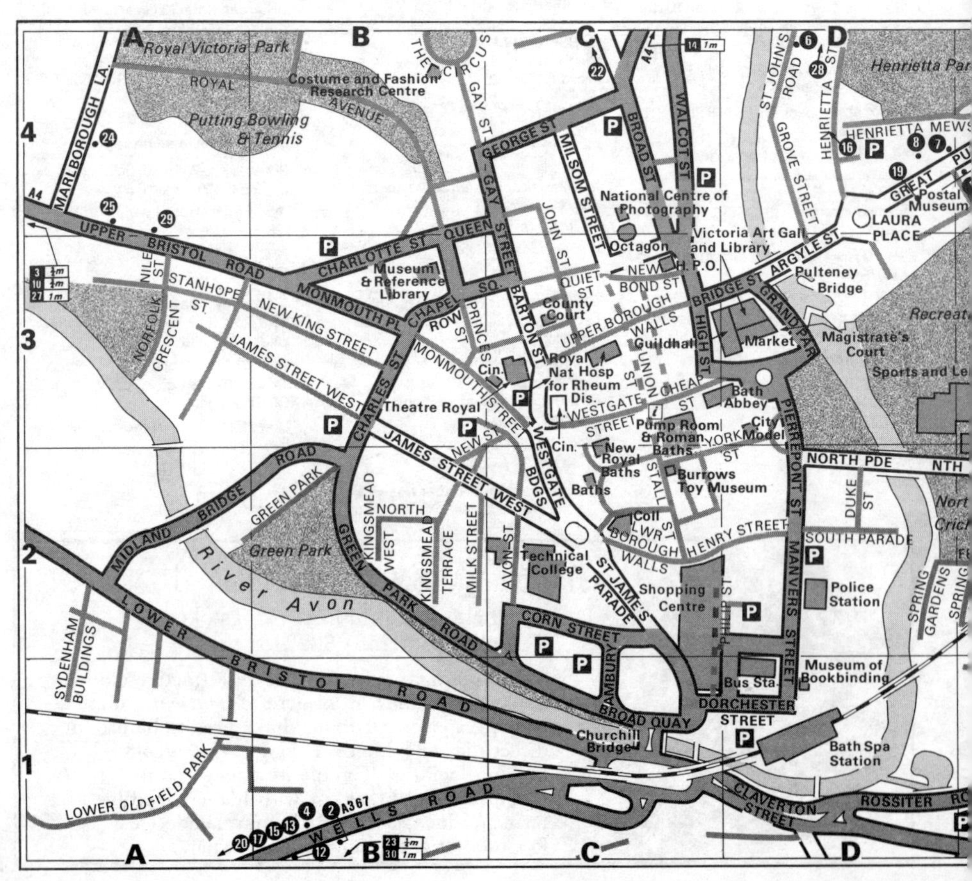

6hc ✖ ✱B&b£10
♨ CTV 6P

GH Eagle House Church St, Bathford (3m NE A363) (Guestaccom) ☎(0225) 859946 Not on plan
Closed 23–30 Dec

Listed Georgian house set in own grounds some 3½m from Bath. Spacious public rooms and well fitted bedrooms.

6hc (5⇌ 1⚟) (2fb) CTV in all bedrooms Ⓡ B&b£16–£25

Lic ♨ 8P

Selected

GH Edgar Hotel 64 Great Pulteney St ☎(0225) 20619 Plan **11** *E4*

Original Georgian town-house in historic city centre.

14⚟ (1fb) CTV in all bedrooms ✖ Ⓡ ✱B&b£19–£27

Lic ♨ CTV ⌀

See advertisement on page 53

Bath

⊢GH Escobeck Hotel 127 Wells Rd ☎(0225) 310143 Plan **12** *B1*

Closed 24–27 Dec

Situated on the main road out of the city (SP Exeter) this Bath-stone house is approached by steps and offers panoramic views across the Spa. Well-furnished accommodation and a friendly, informal atmosphere.

6hc TV in all bedrooms B&b£9–£10 Bdi£15–£16 WBdi£105–£125 LDO5pm

♨ ⌀

See advertisement on page 54

GH Fern Cottage 9 Northend, Batheaston (2½m NE off A4) ☎(0225) 858190 Not on plan

Bath-stone, Georgian cottage in quiet hamlet. Well converted and very comfortable.

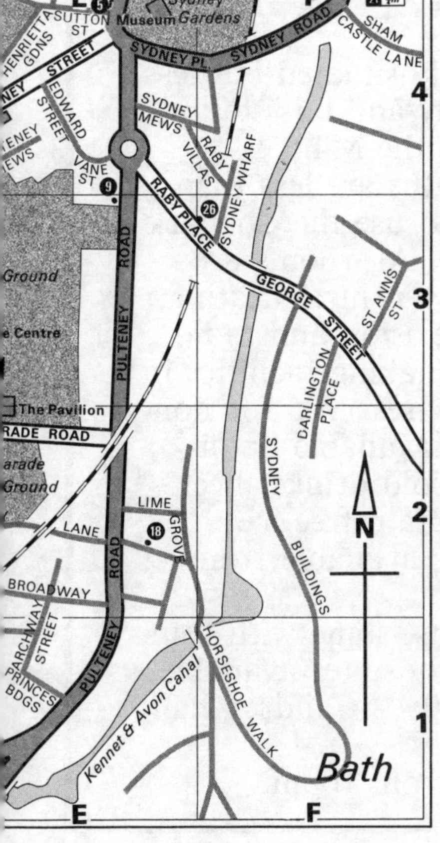

Bath

1 Arden Hotel
2 Arney
3 Ashley Villa Hotel
4 Astor House
5 Avon Hotel
6 Brompton House
7 Carfax Hotel
8 Chesterfield Hotel
9 County Hotel (*Inn*)
10 Dorset Villa
11 Edgar Hotel
12 Escobeck Hotel
13 Glenbeigh Hotel
14 Grove Lodge
15 Highways House
16 Kennard Hotel
17 Leighton House
18 Lynwood
19 Millers Hotel
20 Oldfields
21 Orchard House Hotel
22 Oxford Private Hotel
23 Paradise House Hotel
24 Parkside
25 Hotel St Clair
26 Somerset House
27 Tacoma
28 Villa Magdala Private Hotel
29 Waltons
30 Wentworth House Hotel

8hc (2⇌ 2⚟) CTV in all bedrooms Ⓡ B&b£15–£20 Bdi£21–£27 WBdi£147–£189 LDO6pm

Lic ♨ 8P nc7yrs

GH Glenbeigh Hotel 1 Upper Oldfield Park ☎(0225) 26336 Plan **13** *B1*
Closed Xmas wk

12hc (1⇌ 2⚟) (2fb) CTV in 3 bedrooms Ⓡ B&b£13–£18

Lic ♨ CTV 9P 3🚗

Ⓥ

GH Grove Lodge 11 Lambridge, London Rd ☎(0225) 310860 Plan **14** *C4*

8hc (2fb) CTV in all bedrooms ✖ (ex guide dogs) B&b£13.50 WB&bfr£85

Lic ⌀

Ⓥ

GH Highways House 143 Wells Rd ☎(0225) 21238 Plan **15** *B1*
Closed Xmas

7hc (1⇌ 6⚟) CTV in all bedrooms ✖ Ⓡ B&b£16–£22 WB&b£110–£150

♨ 8P nc5yrs

Ⓥ

GH Kennard Hotel 11 Henrietta St ☎(0225) 310472 Plan **16** *D4*
Closed Xmas

Pleasant Georgian house, close to city centre. Bedrooms compact, bright and fresh.

12hc (7⚟) (3fb) CTV in all bedrooms Ⓡ B&b£16–£20 WB&b£106–£133

♨ ⌀ nc3yrs

Credit cards [1] [3] Ⓥ

GH Leighton House 139 Wells Rd ☎(0225) 314769 Plan **17** *B1*
Closed Xmas

A comfortable, enthusiastically-run hotel with good degree of hospitality.

7hc (2⇌ 2⚟) (2fb) CTV in all bedrooms Ⓡ B&b£14–£31 WBdi£88–£195

♨ 7P

Credit cards [1] [3]

See advertisement on page 54

GH Lynwood 6 Pulteney Gdns ☎(0225) 26410 Plan **18** *E2*
Closed Xmas

14hc (3fb) CTV in all bedrooms ✖ Ⓡ B&b£13–£15

♨ 2P 1🚗 nc3yrs

Credit cards [1] [2] [3] [5]

GH Millers Hotel 69 Great Pulteney St ☎(0225) 65798 Plan **19** *E4*
Closed Xmas wk

Bright, agreeable Georgian terraced house in historic part of city centre.

14hc (5⇌ 1⚟) (3fb) CTV in 6 bedrooms ✖ (ex guide dogs) B&b£15–£28

Lic ♨ CTV ⌀

Ⓥ

GH Oldfields 102 Wells Rd ☎(0225) 317984 Plan **20** *A1*
Closed mid Dec–mid Jan

Detached house with garden promoting Victorian elegance and attentive service.

14hc (1⇌ 7⋔) CTV in all bedrooms ✗ Ⓡ ✱B&b£14–£28

ℳ 8P

Credit cards 1 3

Selected

GH Orchard House Hotel Warminster Rd (A36), Bathampton ☎(0225) 66115 Plan **21** *F4*

Modern and very comfortable small hotel, with welcoming atmosphere. Bedrooms offer plenty of space, and are very well equipped, with mini-bars and fridges, plus the usual tea- and coffee-making facilities. Small but satisfactory table d'hôte menu for dinner; attentive service.

14⇌⋔ (3fb) CTV in all bedrooms Ⓡ ✱B&b£20–£26 Bdi£28.50–£29.50 LDO7.45pm

Lic ℳ 16P sauna bath solarium

Credit cards 1 2 3 5 Ⓥ

GH Oxford Private Hotel 5 Oxford Row, Lansdown Rd ☎(0225) 314039 Plan **22** *C4*

9hc (3⋔) (1fb) ✗ Ⓡ B&b£11–£14

CTV P̸ nc 10yrs

Bath

GH Paradise House Hotel Holloway ☎(0225) 317723 Plan **23** *B1*
Closed 15 Dec–Jan

An elegant, comfortably appointed hotel in cul-de-sac overlooking the city. Splendid walled garden.

8hc (5⇌ 1⋔) (1fb) CTV in all bedrooms ✗ Ⓡ B&b£25–£40 WB&b£160

ℳ 3🚗 (charge)

Credit cards 1 3

GH Parkside 11 Marlborough Ln ☎(0225) 29444 Plan **24** *A4*

Closed Xmas wk

This spacious Bath-stone Edwardian House lies on the edge of Victoria park withn walking distance of the city centre. A quiet, genteel atmosphere prevails.

6hc (1fb) Ⓡ ✱B&b£12–£15 Bdi£18–£21 LDO5pm

ℳ CTV P̸

GH Hotel St Clair 1 Cresent Gdns, Upper Bristol Rd ☎(0225) 25543 Plan **25** *A3*

10hc (2⋔) (1fb) CTV in all bedrooms Ⓡ B&b£15–£20

Lic ℳ P̸ nc3yrs

Credit card 3

Selected

GH Somerset House 35 Bathwick Hill ☎(0225) 66451 Plan **26** *F3*
1st 2 wks Jan

A large restored Georgian house surrounded by well tended gardens situated in an excellent position overlooking the city. The well appointed bedrooms are all individually furnished and are each named after George III children. On the lower ground floor are two comfortable lounges, a new conservatory and a most atttractive dining room. A small menu is available although meals are prepared only from fresh local produce. This strictly non-smoking establishment is run by caring and attentive hosts who create a happy and relaxed atmosphere.

9hc (8⇌ 1⋔) (4fb) ⊬ in all bedrooms Ⓡ ✱Bdi£31 WBdifr£200 LDO6.30pm

Lic ℳ CTV 12P nc10yrs

Credit cards 1 2 3

GH Tacoma 159 Newbridge Hill ☎(0225) 310197 Plan **27** *A3*
Closed Xmas & New Year

8hc (2fb) ✗ Ⓡ B&b£9–£12

ℳ CTV 5P

Ⓥ

OLDFIELDS

ELEGANT & TRADITIONAL BED & BREAKFAST

Oldfields, a restored Victorian family house, overlooks Bath and surrounding hills. We offer a clean, comfortable and relaxed atmosphere (there's Mozart at breakfast), attentive service with free coffee and tea and biscuits. Each bedroom has colour TV and central heating, with en suite shower room and W.C. in eight rooms—all with Laura Ashley prevailing!

Parking in drive. Ten minutes walk to Roman Baths and Abbey.

102 Wells Road, Bath (at the corner of Upper Oldfield Park) Telephone 0225 317984

The Old Malt House Hotel

Radford, Timsbury, Nr Bath.
Telephone (0761) 70106

Situated in beautiful countryside, ideal for touring Bath, Wells, Mendip Hills, Bristol, Cheddar. Full licence, and restaurant. Well known for good food and hospitality. Built originally in 1835 now transformed into a comfortable hotel, all bedrooms have private facilities. Write or telephone for full details and brochure.

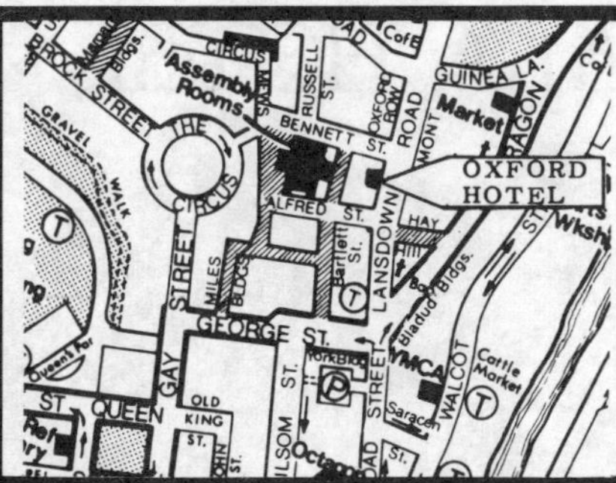

THE OXFORD HOTEL

5 Oxford Row, Lansdown Road, Bath
BA1 2QN Avon.
Telephone: Bath (STD 0225) 314039

An 18th Century House-Hotel in the City Centre (near the Assembly Rooms).

Proprietress: Diana Thomas

Tacoma Guest House

159 Newbridge Hill, Bath
Telephone: Bath (0225) 310197

Lovely old Victorian house situated on quiet main road (A431 to Bristol). Pleasant views. Large comfortable TV lounge. Central heating, H&C and tea and coffee making facilities in all bedrooms. Parking. Good bus service into city.

Bath — Beattock

GH Villa Magdala Private Hotel
Henrietta Rd ☎(0225) 66329 Plan **28** *D4*
Closed Jan

17hc (13⇌ 4fl) (3fb) CTV in all bedrooms ✈ ® B&b£21–£23

𝕸 13P 2🚗 nc6yrs

Credit card ③

GH Waltons 17 Crescent Gdns ☎(0225) 26528 Plan **29** *B3*

15hc (3fb) ✱B&b£11–£15 WB&b£77–£105

𝕸 CTV

GH Wentworth House Hotel
106 Bloomfield Rd ☎(0225) 339193
Plan **30** *B1*

20hc (6⇌ 7fl) (4fb) CTV in 13 bedrooms TV in 7 bedrooms ® B&b£12.50–£20.50 Bdi£20–£28.50 WBdi£120–£179 LDO5pm

Lic 𝕸 20P ⛵

Credit cards ① ③ ⑤ Ⓥ

INN County Hotel 18–19 Pulteney Rd ☎(0225) 25003. Plan **9** *E4*
Closed Xmas

23hc (1⇌ 11fl) (5fb) CTV in all bedrooms ® B&b£22.50–£35 WB&b£141.75–£220.50 Bar lunch £2alc Dinner 10pm £10alc

𝕸 CTV 60P

Credit card ③

BATTLE
East Sussex
Map **5** TQ71

Selected

FH Mrs A Benton **Little Hemingfold** *(TQ774149)* Telham (2½m SE on N side of A2100) ☎(04246) 4338

This charming farmhouse in the most rural of settings, is approached by an unmade road. The building is full of character with open hearths and low ceilings. The bedrooms in the farmhouse and adjacent outbuildings are comfortable and well-equipped. Mrs Benton prepares the meals which are taken family-style around large tables in the dining room. She provides excellent meals using freshly grown produce.

Winner for South-East of the 1987/8 AA Farmhouse of the Year Award.

12⇌ ⚟ in 3 bedrooms CTV in all bedrooms ® ✱B&b£18 Bdi£25–£36 WBdi£198–£240

Lic 𝕸 20P nc12yrs 🎾 (grass) ⚓ 40acres mixed

Credit cards ① ② ③ Ⓥ

BEAMINSTER
Dorset
Map **3** ST40

Selected

GH Hams Plot Bridport Rd ☎(0308) 862979
Apr–Sep

An elegant Regency country house with attractive bedrooms, majestic public areas and friendly service.

5hc (3⇌ 2fl) ✈ ® ✱B&b£15–£27 Bdi£27–£29 WB&b£94.50–£170.10 LDOnoon

Lic 𝕸 CTV 7P nc10yrs ⛵ 🎾 (hard)

BEATTOCK
Dumfries & Galloway *Dumfriesshire*
Map **11** NT00

FH Mr & Mrs Bell **Cogrie's** *(NY106974)* (3m S off A74) ☎Johnstone Bridge (05764) 320
Mar–Nov

Attractive and homely farmhouse in an attractive location just off the A74 Glasgow-Carlisle road.

4hc (3fb) ⚟ in all bedrooms ✈ ® ✱B&bfr£8 Bdifr£12.75 WB&bfr£52.50 LDO7.30pm

𝕸 CTV 6P 275acres dairy mixed

Ⓥ

Beauly — Beccles

BEAULY
Highland *Inverness-shire*
Map **14** NH54

GH *Chrialdon* Station Rd ☎ Inverness (0463) 782336
Mar–Dec
Detached house in own grounds on main road.
8hc (2fb) ✗ Ⓡ LDO7pm
Lic 🍽 CTV 15P

GH Heathmount Station Rd ☎(0463) 782411
Closed Dec & Jan
Comfortable, well-appointed accommodation situated on a main road, close to shops.
5hc (2fb) B&b£9–£10 Bdi£15–£16 WBdifr£100 LDO6pm
🍽 CTV 5P

FH Mrs M R Munro **Thornhill** *(NH531475)* ☎(0463) 782338
May–Oct
Attractive, well-appointed farm-house set back from main road near town.
3hc ✗✱B&b£9 Bdi£13–£14 WBdifr£90 LDO6.30pm
🍽 CTV 3P 3🚗 nc
100acres arable
Ⓥ

Selected

FH Mrs E Munro **Tomich House** *(NH531480)* (1m N A862) ☎(0463) 782225
Apr–Oct
Mrs Munro's superbly appointed Georgian farmhouse enjoys a peaceful location amid 6 acres of wooded grounds. The sitting room is tastefully furnished in period style with an interesting collection of paintings and prints lining the walls. The spacious bedrooms are comfortable and are decorated in attractive pastal shades.
3hc ✗ ✱B&b£10 WB&b£70
🍽 CTV P nc12yrs
600acres arable beef sheep mixed
Ⓥ

BEAUMARIS
Gwynedd
Map **6** SH67

GH Sea View 10 West End ☎(0248) 810384
Closed Xmas
Single-fronted Victorian house at water's edge adjacent to the shops.
6hc ✗ B&b£10–£12 Bdifr£18
CTV 5P nc10yrs

Selected

INN Liverpool Arms ☎(0248) 810362
Attractive coaching inn, recently modernised but retaining it's character.
10hc (8⇌ 2fl) CTV in all bedrooms ✗ Ⓡ B&bfr£24 Bar lunch fr£3 Dinner 9.30pm fr£8
🍽 8P 🚗 nc5yrs
Credit cards 1 3 5
See advertisement on page 58

BECCLES
Suffolk
Map **5** TM49

GH Riverview House Ballygate (Guestaccom) ☎(0502) 713519
Closed 21 Dec–4 Jan
12rm (10hc) (1fl) (2fb) CTV in all bedrooms Ⓡ B&b£12.50–£16.50 Bdi£19.50–£21.50 WB&b£80.50 LDO10am
🍽 CTV P

BEDALE
North Yorkshire
See Patrick Brompton

BEDDGELERT
Gwynedd
Map **6** SH54

GH Sygun Fawr Country House Hotel
☎(076686) 258

17th-century stone country house in own grounds ½m from village.

7hc (3⇌ 3fl) (1fb) Ⓡ B&b£16.50–£17.25 Bdi£24–£25.70 WBdifr£158 LDO7.30pm

Lic 🍽 CTV 30P

BEDFORD
Bedfordshire
Map **4** TL04

GH Clarendon House Hotel 25/27 Ampthill Rd ☎(0234) 66054
Closed 24–29 Dec

Attractive Edwardian house run by a young professional couple. Comfortable accommodation with good facilities.

17hc (13fl) (2fb) CTV in all bedrooms ✈ Ⓡ B&b£16–£26 Bdi£22.50–£32.50 WBdi£157.50–£227.50 LDO7.45pm

Lic 🍽 CTV 16P

Credit cards [1] [2] [3] [5]

Ⓥ

GH *Kimbolton Hotel* 78 Clapham Rd
☎(0234) 54854
Closed 25–31 Dec

Three storey Victorian house, family-run on traditional lines.

15hc (2⇌ 11fl) CTV in all bedrooms ✈ Ⓡ LDO8.30pm

Lic 🍽 CTV 15P nc3yrs

Credit card [3]

Beer
Beeston

BEER
Devon
Map **3** SY28

GH Abergrange Long Hill ☎Seaton (0297) 23072
An attractive Victorian house overlooking the town and sea, offering comfortable accommodation and pleasant service.
5hc (3fb) CTV in all bedrooms ⊁ in all bedrooms ✗ Ⓡ ✱B&bfr£12.50 Bdifr£19.45 LDO5pm
Lic 8P nc10yrs
Credit card ③

⊢GH Bay View Fore St ☎Seaton (0297) 20489
Etr–mid Oct
Property at end of village overlooking the beach and sea.
6hc (2fb) B&b£9–£10 WB&bfr£63
CTV P nc5yrs
Ⓥ

BEERCROCOMBE
Somerset
Map **3** ST32

Selected

FH Mrs V A Cole **Frog Street Farm** Frog St *(ST317197)* ☎Hatch Beauchamp (0823) 480430
Closed Xmas & New Year
Attractive stone and beamed farmhouse, dating back to the 15th century with exposed beams, inglenook fireplaces and fine Jacobean panelling. There is a secluded garden with a swimming pool and a trout stream. Mrs Cole ensures that her guests are made very welcome and prepares excellent dinners using produce from the farm, or local sources.
National Winner of the 1987/8 AA Farmhouse of the Year Award.
3hc (1⇌ 1fl) (1fb) ✗ Ⓡ B&b£12–£16 Bdi£22–£26 WBdi£126–£154 LDO2pm
CTV P nc11yrs ⩯(heated)
160acres dairy mixed Ⓥ

Selected

FH Mrs C M Mitchem **Whittles** *(ST324194)* ☎Hatch Beauchamp (0823) 480301
Mar–Oct rs 15 Jan–Feb
Superb accommodation in peaceful surroundings are assured at this friendly farmhouse.
4rm (3fl) CTV in all bedrooms ✗ Ⓡ B&b£14.50–£16 Bdi£23–£24.50 WBdifr£161 LDO9am
Lic 4P nc12yrs 200acres beef dairy
Ⓥ
See advertisement under Taunton

BEESTON
Nottinghamshire
Map **8** SK53

GH Brackley House Hotel 31 Elm Av ☎Nottingham (0602) 251787
Closed Xmas & New Year
13hc (3⇌ 7fl) (1fb) CTV in all bedrooms ✗ B&b£25–£30 Bdi£35–£45 LDO9.15pm
Lic CTV 15P 1⌂ nc10yrs ⩯heated pool table
Credit cards ① ② ③ Ⓥ

GH Fairhaven Private Hotel 19 Meadow Rd, ☎Nottingham (0602) 227509

Large house 3½m SW of Nottingham and close to Beeston Station. Simple but comfortable accommodation.

11hc (1fb) B&b£8.50–£15 Bdi£13–£19.50 WBdifr£102 LDO2pm

Lic CTV 12P

BELFORD
Northumberland
Map **12** NU13

INN Black Swan Market Sq ☎(06683) 266

Closed Xmas

Simple village inn with informal atmosphere. Situated in village centre on A1.

8hc (1 ⇌) (3fb) Ⓡ B&b£12.50–£15 WB&bfr£65 Bar lunch 50p–£5 LDO8.30pm

CTV 20P

Selected

INN Waren House Hotel Waren Mill ☎Bamburgh (06684) 211

Mar–Nov

A charming country house style inn offering luxurious accommodation. There are three suites, two with their own lounge and feature fires, the third suite having two comfortable bedrooms. All are well-appointed with many thoughtful extras. The proprietors, Karen and John Lamb are superb hosts and with the help of their staff give friendly and attentive service. Karen produces excellent value home cooked meals. Also available here are speciality weekends such as sporting, historical, fishing or shooting.

3⇌ (1fb) CTV in all bedrooms Ⓡ ✱B&bfr£27.50 Lunch £2.75alc Dinner 9pmfr£11.50 24P

Credit cards 1 3

BELL BUSK
North Yorkshire
Map **7** SD95

Beeston — Bethesda

GH Tudor ☎Airton (07293) 301

This friendly hospitable little guesthouse by the Settle–Carlisle line was once Bell Busk station.

6hc 1fl (1fb) Ⓡ B&b£9.50–£12 Bdi£16–£18.50 LDO7pm

Lic CTV P

BELSTONE
Devon
Map **2** SX69

INN Tors ☎Okehampton (0837) 840689

3hc (1fb) CTV in all bedrooms Ⓡ ✱B&b£10–£11 Bdi£14.50–£15.50 WBdifr£95 Bar lunch £1.40–£3.25&alc High tea fr£1.50 Dinner 9.30pm £3.10–£7&alc

CTV 10P

Ⓥ

Credit Cards

1 Access/Euro/Mastercard

2 American Express

3 Barclaycard/Visa

5 Diners

BELTON
Leicestershire
Map **4** SK80

FH Mrs S L Renner **Old Rectory** *(SK814008)* ☎(057286) 279

Lovely old house incorporating a rural museum, craft shop, a miniature farm and a children's play area.

4hc (1⇌) (3fb) CTV in all bedrooms Ⓡ B&b£10–£17 WB&bfr£70

lift CTV 6P 6 30acres beef pastural sheep

BEPTON (nr Midhurst)
West Sussex
Map **4** SU81

Selected

GH Park House Hotel ☎Midhurst (073081) 2880

Part-17th-century house with homely welcome and accommodation. Set in attractive lawns for croquet, putting and tennis.

9⇌fl Annexe: 2⇌fl CTV in all bedrooms Ⓡ B&b£31.62–£37.95 Bdi£40.25–£48.30 WBdi£275–£335 LDOnoon

Lic CTV 25P (heated) (grass)

See advertisement under Midhurst

BERKELEY
Gloucestershire
Map **3** ST69

FH Mrs B A Evans **Greenacres** *(ST713008)* Breadstone (2m E off A38) ☎Dursley (0453) 810348

Closed Dec–2 Jan

16th-century house with beams and inglenook fireplaces.

3hc (1⇌ 1fl) Ⓡ ✱B&b£10.50–£12.50 Bdi£16–£18 WBdi£108–£120 LDO6.30pm

CTV 10P 47acres horse breeding

BETHESDA
Gwynedd
Map **6** SH66

FH Mrs D Williams **Maes Caradog** *(SH635626)* Nant Ffrancon ☎(0248) 600266

Pleasant stone-farmhouse amidst mountain scenery.

2hc (1fb) B&b£8–£9.50 Bdi£12–£13.50 WBdifr£87.50 LDO6pm

CTV 12P 636acres sheep

Ⓥ

BETLEY
Staffordshire
Map **7** SJ74

⊢⊣**FH** Mrs S Berrisford **Alderley Green** *(SJ 775474)* Heighley Castle Lane ☎Crewe (0270) 820203

3rm (1hc1⋒) (1fb) ⊁in 2 bedrooms CTV in all bedrooms Ⓡ B&b£8–£12 Bdi£13–£16 WBdifr£90 LDO2pm

⚐ CTV 6P 3🚗 ⌂ ♪(grass) ♩ snooker 250acres dairy mixed

Ⓥ

BETTISCOMBE
Dorset
Map **3** ST30

GH Marshwood Manor ☎Bridport (0308) 68442

A 19th-century country manor house set in ten acres of well kept grounds with an outdoor swimming pool and mini golf course. The rooms are all elegantly decorated and home cooked food, using local produce is served in the dining room.

9hc (2⇌) Ⓡ ✱B&bfr£17 Bdifr£24 LDO7pm

Lic CTV 10P

See advertisement under Bridport

BETWS GARMON
Gwynedd
Map **6** SH55

⊢⊣**GH Bryn Gloch Farm** ☎Waunfawr (028685) 216

Converted farmhouse with glorious views, on edge of Snowdonia National Park.

4rm (3hc) (1fb) CTV in all bedrooms ⋈ B&b£8.50–£9 Bdi£13.50–£15 WBdifr£91 LDO9.30pm

Lic CTV 10P ♩

Ⓥ

BETWS-Y-COED
Gwynedd
Map **6** SH75

GH Glenwood ☎(06902) 508
Feb–Nov

Attractive house with good standard of accommodation, set back from main road.

6hc (3fb) ⋈ B&b£11.50–£12.50

⚐ CTV 12P nc4yrs

Ⓥ

⊢⊣**GH Hafan** ☎(06902) 233

Detached Victorian house in rural surroundings, near centre of village.

7hc (4⋒) (3fb) CTV in 6 bedrooms ⋈ Ⓡ B&b£8.50–£13.50 WB&bfr£59.50

Lic ⚐ CTV 7P

Ⓥ

GH Henllys (Old Court) Hotel ☎(06902) 534

Converted police station and cells, adjacent to village centre.

11hc (3⇌ 4⋒) CTV in all bedrooms Ⓡ ✱B&b£14.75–£19.75 Bdi£24.60–£29.60 WBdi£160–£196 LDO9pm

Lic ⚐ 12P nc4yrs

Ⓥ

GH Tyn-y-Celyn Llanwrst Rd ☎(06902) 202

This large comfortable guesthouse lies on the outskirts of Betws-y-Coed and enjoys fine views of mountain and valley.

8rm (6⋒) (3fb) CTV in all bedrooms Ⓡ ✱B&b£13–£18 Bdi£20–£25 WB&bfr£90

Lic ⚐ CTV P

Ⓥ

FH Mrs E Jones **Maes-y-Garnedd** *(SH816548)* Capel Garmon (3m E unclass off A470) ☎(06902) 428
Apr–Sep

A 19th century house on a working farm situated close to the town.

2rm (1⇌) (1fb) ⋈ ✱B&b£8.50–£9 Bdi£11.50–£12 WBdifr£80.50

CTV P ⌂ 153acres beef sheep mixed

Credit cards 1 3

BEXHILL-ON-SEA
East Sussex
Map **5** TQ70

GH *Chantry Close Hotel* 13 Hastings Rd ☎(0424) 222024
Mar–Oct

Mock-Tudor house in own grounds with comfortable, well-appointed bedrooms.

7hc (1⇌ 1⋒) (2fb) CTV 2 bedrooms ⋈ Ⓡ LDO5pm

⚐ CTV 6P nc3yrs

GH Dunselma Hotel 25 Marina ☎(0424) 212988

A clean, well kept house with comfortable bedrooms and lounge, situated close to the sea and shops.

11hc (2⇌) (1fb) CTV in 1 bedroom TV in 2 bedrooms Ⓡ ✱B&b£13–£17 Bdi£18–£22 WBdi£105–£115 LDO5pm

Lic CTV Ᵽ

BEYTON
Suffolk
Map **5** TL96

FH The Grange *(TL940632)* ☎(0359) 70184

The village lies about 5m E of Bury St Edmunds, signposted from A45. Grange Farmhouse is a smallholding selling its produce in the farm shop. Large rooms and a relaxing atmosphere attract tourists and businessmen alike. Mrs Nicholson makes full use of her own and local produce in her interesting home-cooked meals.

3hc (1fb) ⋈ B&b£11 Bdi£17 WBdi£119

⚐ CTV 30P 6acres horses

BICKINGTON (nr Ashburton)
Devon
Map **3** SX77

GH Privet Cottage ☎(062682) 319
May–Sep

Attractive, white-stone, cottage-style house in central position for touring south Devon.

5hc B&b£9.50–£10.50 Bdi£15.50–£16 WBdifr£90 LDO6.30pm

CTV 6P ⌂

FH Mr & Mrs Ross ***East Burne*** *(SX799711)* ☎(062682) 496
Closed Xmas & New Year

Isolated farmhouse of great charm with modern, fitted bedrooms.

3rm (2hc 1🚿) ✖ ® LDO24hrs notice

CTV 8P ⛆ (heated) 25acres mixed

BICKLEIGH (nr Tiverton)
Devon
Map **3** SS90

GH Bickleigh Cottage ☎(08845) 230
May–Sep rs Oct

10hc (2🛁 2🚿) ✖ ® ✱B&b£10.50–£15 Bdi£16.50–£21 LDO5pm

CTV 10P nc10yrs ♪

BIDEFORD
Devon
Map **2** SS42
See also **Eastleigh, Littleham & Westward Ho**

GH *Edelweiss* 2 Buttgarden St ☎(02372) 72676
rs Jan (B&b only)

Proprietor-run guesthouse with à la carte restaurant.

8hc (2fb)

Lic 🍽 CTV 🅿 nc5yrs

Credit cards ① ② ③ ⑤

GH Kumba Chudleigh Rd, East-the-Water ☎(02372) 71526

Comfortable, detached country-house, situated in private road overlooking the town and River Torridge.

9hc (1🚿) (5fb) ⚒ in 2 bedrooms B&b£11–£12 Bdi£16–£17 WBdi£95–£110 LDO2pm

Lic CTV 14P 2🚗 ⌂

Ⓥ

GH Mount Private Hotel Northdown Rd ☎(02372) 73748

Closed 2wks Xmas

Detached Georgian house standing in attractive walled garden with terrace at front.

6hc (1🛁 2🚿) (1fb) ✖ ✱B&b£14–£18 Bdi£19–£25.50 WBdifr£129 LDO2pm

Lic 🍽 CTV 5P

Bickington — Bingley

GH Pines at Eastleigh nr Bideford (3m E off A39 at East-the-Water) ☎Instow (0271) 860561
Apr–Oct

Delightful, friendly, Georgian house with large gardens and glorious views.

8hc (2fb) ✖ ® ✱B&b£12.50–£14 Bdi£20–£21 WBdifr£130 LDO5.30pm

Lic 🍽 CTV P nc4yrs

Credit cards ① ③ Ⓥ

GH Tadworthy House Hotel Tadworthy Rd, Northam (2m N off A386) ☎(02372) 74721

A 16th-century family-run hotel close to the sea and the Royal North Devon Golf Club.

6hc (1🚿) (2fb) CTV in 5 bedrooms TV in 1 bedroom ® ✱B&b£14.50–£16 Bdi£22–£23.50 WBdifr£155 LDO8.30pm

Lic 🍽 CTV 12P ⌂

Credit cards ① ③ Ⓥ

BIDFORD-ON-AVON
Warwickshire
Map **4** SP15

Selected

FH Mrs F G D Muscott **Bidford Grange** *(SD117517)* ☎(0789) 773376

This charming Cotswold-stone farmhouse is situated on the banks of the River Avon in 500 acres of rolling Warwickshire countryside. This is the place to stay if you like luxurious, comfortable accommodation and warm, attentive hospitality in beautiful surroundings.

3🛁 (1fb) CTV in all bedrooms ✖ ®
B&b£14–£22.50 Bdi£23.95–£33.45 WBdi£151–£176.95 LDO8.30pm

🍽 CTV 8P 6🚗 nc9yrs ⛆ ♪ sauna bath

500acres arable. Credit card ② Ⓥ

See advertisement on page 468

BIGBURY
Devon
Map **3** SX64

GH Bigbury Court Hotel ☎(0548) 810225

Set amid an unspoilt rural landscape, this 17th-century farmhouse welcomes families. Friendly service and good home cooking.

7hc (1🛁 5🚿) (3fb) ® B&b£13–£22 Bdi£20–£34 WBdi£140–£168 (Wkly only Jul–Aug) LDO8.30pm

Lic 🍽 CTV 12P ⌂

Credit card ③ Ⓥ

See advertisement under Kingsbridge

BILLINGSHURST
West Sussex
Map **4** TQ02

GH Newstead Hall Adversane ☎(040381) 3196

7🛁🚿 CTV in all bedrooms ® B&b£13.50–£22.50 Bdi£22.50–£37.50 WBdi£147 LDO10pm

Lic 🍽 CTV 18P

Credit cards ① ② ③ ⑤ Ⓥ

BINGLEY
West Yorkshire
Map **7** SE13

GH Hall Bank Private Hotel Beck Ln ☎Bradford (0274) 565296
Closed Xmas

Conversion of an old mill owner's house has provided large, comfortable rooms, plus conservatory, in lovely Aire valley setting.

8hc (3🛁 4🚿) Annexe: 2hc (1fb) CTV in all bedrooms ✖ ® B&b£16–£22 Bdi£22–£28 WBdi£165–£245 LDO7.30pm

🍽 CTV 20P nc2yrs

Ⓥ

⊢⊣**FH** Mr & Mrs G Warin **March Cote** *(SE103374)* Cottingley (2m S B6146) ☎Bradford (0274) 487433
Closed Xmas & New Year

Extended and modernised 17th-century farmhouse retaining many original features.

2rm (1fb) CTV in 1 bedroom TV in 1 bedroom ✗(ex guide dogs) Ⓡ B&b£9–£11 Bdi£15–£17 WBdifr£100

CTV P 🚗(charge) 230acres beef dairy mixed sheep

Ⓥ

BIRKENHEAD
Merseyside
Map **7** SJ38

GH Gronwen 11 Willowbank Rd, Devonshire Park ☎051-652 8306

Pleasantly furnished small guesthouse set in quiet residential area.

6hc (1fb) Ⓡ ✻B&b£10–£12 Bdi£15–£17 WBdifr£100 LDO7.30pm

CTV no P

BIRMINGHAM
West Midlands
Map **7** SP08

See plan on pages 64–65

GH Alexander 44 Bunbury Rd ☎021-475 4341 Plan **1**

12hc (2fb) B&b£12–£14 Bdi£16.50–£17 WBdifr£119 LDO6pm

Lic CTV 12P

GH Beech House Hotel 21 Gravelly Hill North, Erdington ☎021-373 0620 Plan **2**
Closed 2 wks Xmas

Friendly, personally run Tudor-style hotel set back from main road.

10hc (2⇌ 3fl) (1fb) CTV available in 2 bedrooms✻B&b£17–£23 Bdi£22–£28 WBdifr£154 LDOnoon

CTV 10P nc5yrs

Credit cards 1 3

GH Bridge House Hotel 49 Sherbourne Rd, Acocks Gn ☎021-706 5900 Plan **3**

Closed Xmas & New Year

9hc (14⇌ fl) CTV in all bedrooms ✗ Ⓡ B&b£14.25–£19.55 Bdi£20–£26 WBdi£140–£182 LDO8.30pm

Lic CTV 48P

Credit card 1

REMEMBER

Prices quoted in the gazetteer are minimum double room occupancy to maximum single room occupancy **per person.**

GH Cape Race Hotel 929 Chester Rd, Erdington ☎021-373 3085 Plan **4**

Spacious converted private house with large rear garden containing lawns and hard tennis court.

7hc (5fl) CTV in all bedrooms Ⓡ B&b£20.70–£24.15 Bdi£28–£32.20 WBdifr£196 LDO7pm

Lic CTV 15P ⇨(heated) ℛ(hard)

Ⓥ

GH Hagley Court Hotel 229 Hagley Rd, Edgbaston ☎021-454 6514 Plan **5**
Closed Xmas

28hc (21⇌ 5fl) (2fb) CTV in all bedrooms ✗ Ⓡ ✻B&b£16–£40 LDO9.30pm

Lic CTV 28P

Credit cards 1 2 3 5 Ⓥ

GH *Heath Lodge Hotel* Coleshill Rd, Marston Green ☎021-779 2218 Plan **6**

15hc (2fb) ✗ LDO9.30pm

Lic CTV 15P

Credit cards 1 3

GH *Hurstwood Hotel* 775–777 Chester Rd, Erdington ☎021-382 8212 Plan **7**

10fl (2fb) CTV in all bedrooms ✗ Ⓡ LDO9.15pm

Lic CTV 15P

Credit cards 1 2 3 5

See advertisement on page 66

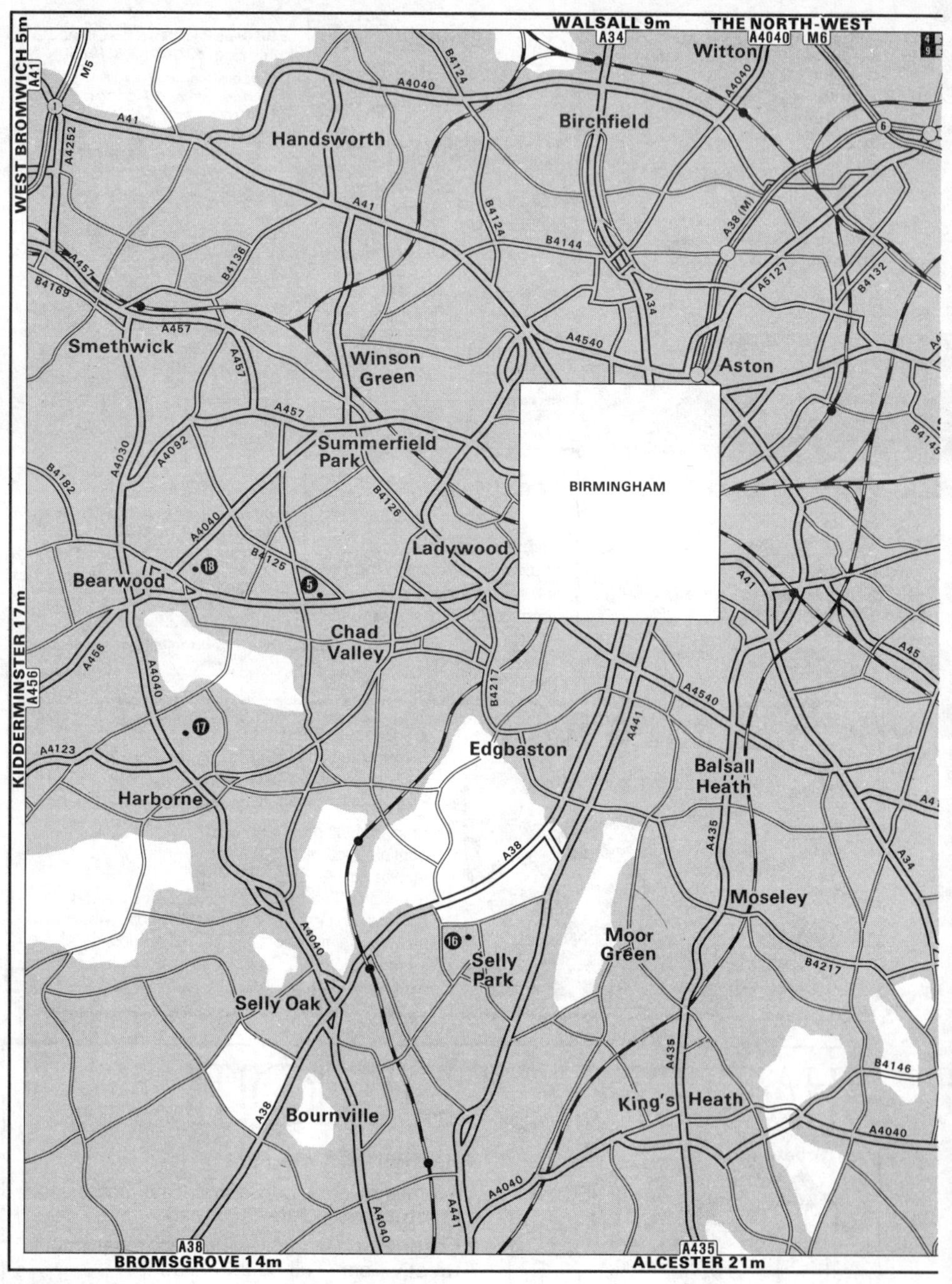

Birmingham & District

1 Alexander
2 Beech House Hotel
3 Bridge House Hotel
4 Cape Race Hotel
5 Hagley Court Hotel
6 Heath Lodge Hotel
7 Hurstwood Hotel
8 Kerry House Hotel
9 Linden Lodge Hotel
10 Lyndhurst Hotel

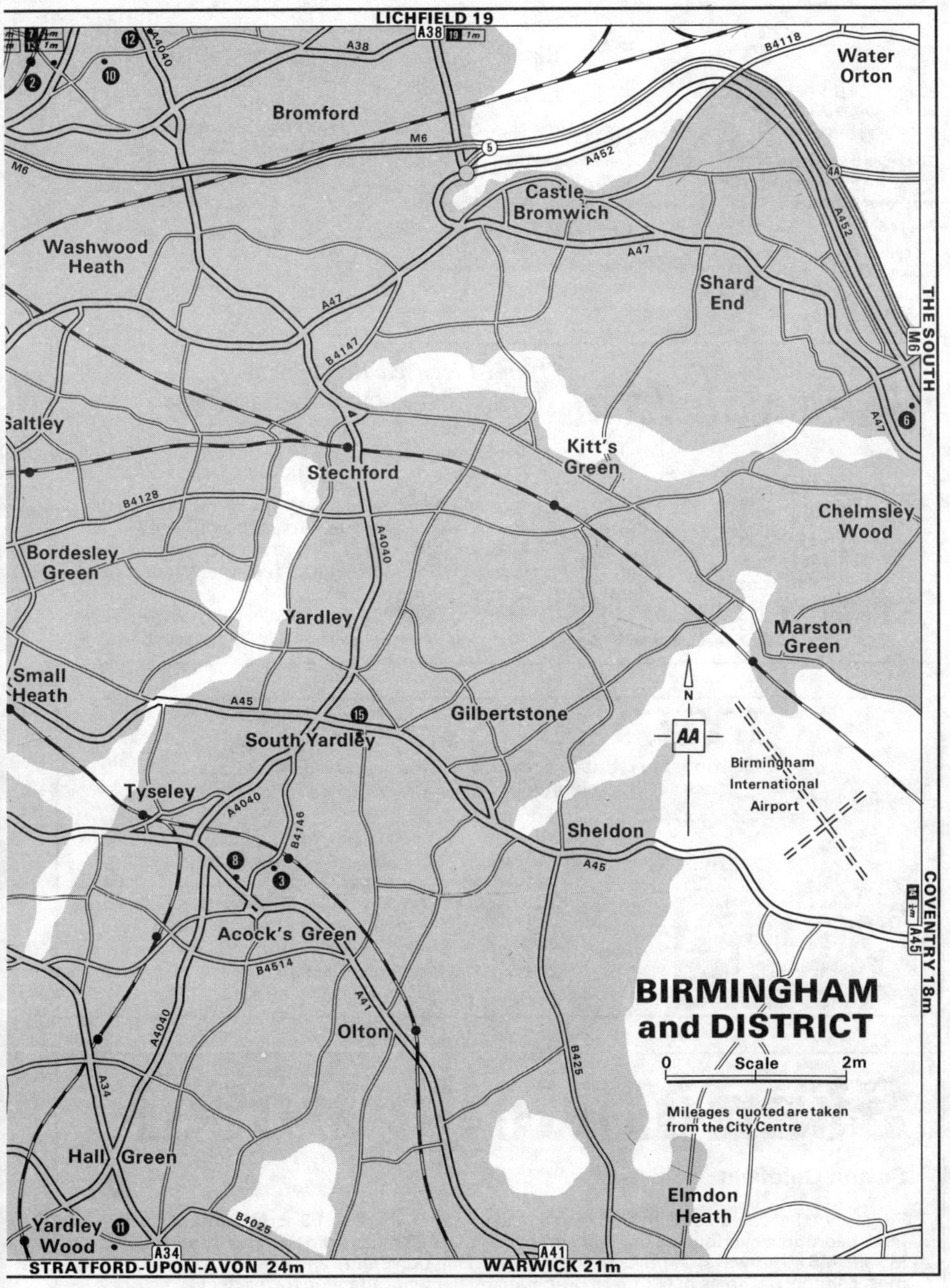

11 Robin Hood Lodge
12 Rollason Wood Hotel
13 Stanbridge Hotel
(*Listed under Sutton Coldfield*)

14 Tri-Star Hotel
15 Welcome House
16 Wentsbury Hotel

17 Wentworth Hotel
18 Westbourne Lodge
19 Willow Tree Hotel

GH Kerry House Hotel 946 Warwick Rd, Acocks Gn ☎021-707 0316 Plan **8**
Closed Xmas

25hc (6⥮) (2fb) CTV in all bedrooms B&b£18.40–£19.55 LDO6pm

Lic ₩ CTV 25P nc3yrs

GH Linden Lodge Hotel 79 Sutton Rd, Erdington ☎021-382 5992 Plan **9**

6hc (1fb) ✖ B&b£10 Bdi£12.50

₩ CTV 8P

GH *Lyndhurst Hotel* 135 Kingsbury Rd, Erdington ☎021-373 5695 Plan **10**

14hc (2⥮) (4fb) CTV in 8 bedrooms ✖

Birmingham

₩ CTV 15P

Credit cards 1 2 3 5

GH Robin Hood Lodge 142 Robin Hood Ln, Hall Green ☎021-778 5307 Plan **11**

Large detached house with front car park and small rear garden, offering well-equipped accommodation and friendly service.

7hc (1⇌) (1fb) CTV in all bedrooms Ⓡ ✱B&bfr£15 Bdifr£21.75 LDO8.30pm

Lic CTV 11P nc12yrs

Credit card 1

GH Rollason Wood Hotel 130 Wood End Rd, Erdington ☎021-373 1230 Plan **12**

35hc (1⇌ 10⥮) (4fb) CTV in 11 bedrooms Ⓡ B&b£12–£21 WB&bfr£67 LDO9pm

Lic ₩ CTV 35P

Credit cards 1 2 3 5

GH Tri-Star Hotel Coventry Rd, Elmdon ☎021-779 2233 Plan **14**

15hc (2⬚) (3fb) CTV in all bedrooms ✗ Ⓡ ❋B&b£20.70–£23 Bdi£27.30 WBdifr£191.10 LDO8pm

Lic 🍽 CTV 25P

Credit card ③

GH Welcome House 1641 Coventry Rd, Yardley ☎021-707 3232 Plan **15**
Closed 24–28 Dec

8hc (1⬚) (1fb) CTV in 2 bedrooms TV in 6 bedrooms ✗ B&b£12 WB&b£84

🍽 8P nc

GH Wentsbury Hotel 21 Serpentine Rd, Selly Park ☎021-472 1258 Plan **16**

Large detached house with garden in residential area close to city centre.

14hc (2fb) CTV in 8 bedrooms Ⓡ B&b£15–£18.50 Bdi£21–£24.50 WBdi£137–£158 LDO4pm

🍽 CTV 13P 1🚗

ⓥ

GH Wentworth Hotel 103 Wentworth Rd, Harborne ☎021-427 2839 Plan **17**
Closed Xmas wk

21hc (7⬚) (1fb) CTV in all bedrooms Ⓡ ❋B&b£15.50–£23 Bdi£22.50–£30 LDO9pm

Lic 🍽 CTV 14P 1🚗

GH Westbourne Lodge 27–29 Fountain Rd, Edgbaston ☎021-429 1003 Plan **18**
Closed Xmas wk

22hc (6⇌ 8⬚) (1fb) CTV in 18 bedrooms ✗ B&b£18.40–£27.60 Bdi£28.17–£37.37 WBdifr£178.82 LDO7pm

Lic 🍽 CTV 12P ♿

Credit cards ① ③

GH Willow Tree Hotel 759 Chester Rd, Erdington ☎021-373 6388 Plan **19**
rs Xmas

Small, comfortable hotel on the outskirts of the City. Large rear garden.

7hc (5⬚) (2fb) CTV in all bedrooms ✗ Ⓡ ❋B&b£16.10–£21.28 Bdi£19.50–£30 W£131–£205 ⱡ LDO8.30pm

Lic 🍽 CTV 7P

ⓥ

BISHOP'S CLEEVE
Gloucestershire
Map **3** SO92

GH Old Manor House 43 Station Rd ☎(024267) 4127

6hc (3fb) ✗ Ⓡ B&bfr£10.50

CTV 6P

BISHOP SUTTON
Avon
Map **3** ST55

⊢⊣**FH** Mrs R M Shellard **Overbrook** *(ST585607)* Stowey Bottom ☎Chew Magna (0272) 332648
Mar–Sep

Attractive, comfortable farmhouse with 3½acres of land. Trout fishing in Chew Valley Lake.

2hc ✗ B&b£9 Bdi£15 LDO11am

🍽 CTV 3P 1🚗

3½acres sheep

ⓥ

BISHOPSTON
West Glamorgan
Map **2** SS58

See also **Langland Bay** and **Mumbles**

Selected

GH *Winston Hotel* 11 Church Ln, Bishopston Valley ☎(044128) 2074
Closed 24–29 Dec

Well-equipped small hotel with good indoor heated-pool, sauna and solarium.

14rm (3hc 3⬚) Annexe: 5hc (4⇌ 1⬚) (2fb) CTV in 5 bedrooms Ⓡ

Lic 🍽 CTV 20P ⛆ (heated) snooker sauna bath

See advertisement under Swansea

BISHOP WILTON
Humberside
Map **8** SE75

INN *Fleece* ☎(07596) 251

Village inn on edge of Yorkshire Wold with good standard of rooms. Bar meals or à-la-carte menu for lunch and dinner.

4hc ✗ LDO9pm

🍽 CTV 20P ⌗ nc12yrs

BLACKPOOL
Lancashire
Map **7** SD33

See plan on page 68

GH *Arandora Star Private Hotel* 559 New South Prom ☎(0253) 41528 Plan **1** *A1*

Family-run seafront hotel.

18hc (3fb) LDO5pm

Lic 🍽 CTV 12P 8🚗 (charge)

Credit cards ③

See advertisement on page 69

GH Arosa Hotel 18–20 Empress Dr ☎(0253) 52555 Plan **2** *A5*
Apr–Nov & Xmas

Well-furnished modern hotel just off the Promenade.

20hc (2⇌ 10⬚) (6fb) CTV in all bedrooms Ⓡ B&b£12–£16 Bdi£15–£19 LDO4pm

Lic 🍽 CTV 7P

GH Ashcroft Private Hotel 42 King Edward Av ☎(0253) 51538 Plan **3** *A5*
Mar–Dec

Attractively-furnished hotel, just off the Queens Promenade.

11hc (3fb) CTV in 8 bedrooms Ⓡ B&b£9.50–£12.50 Bdi£11.50–£14.50 WBdifr£80.50LDO2.30pm

Lic 🍽 CTV 5P

ⓥ

See advertisement on page 69

GH Beaucliffe 22Holmfield Rd ☎(0253) 51663 Plan **4** *A5*

A friendly, well furnished hotel set on a quiet side road just off the North Promenade. →

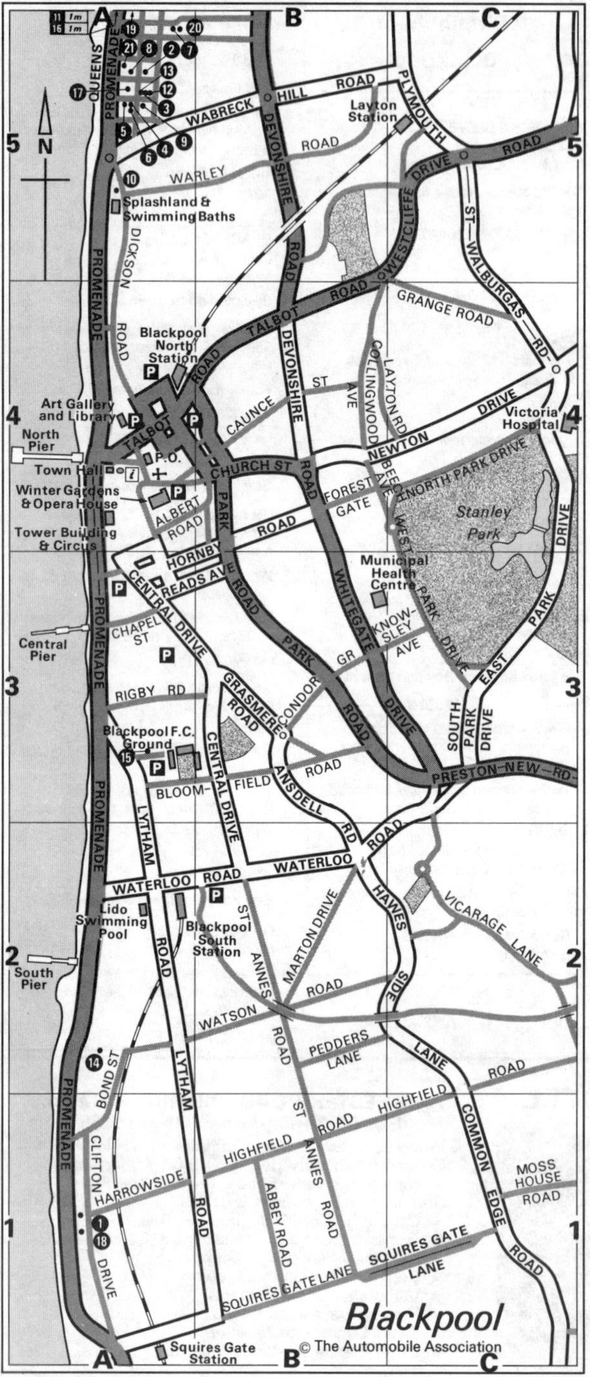

12hc (2fb) ✗ ® B&b£9.50–£10.50 Bdi£11–£13 WBdi£77–£91 LDO4.30pm

Lic 🍽 CTV 10P

Ⓥ

⊢⊣ **GH Berwick Private Hotel** 23 King Edward Av ☎(0253) 51496 Plan **5** *A5*
Closed 29 Dec–11 Jan

Set in a quiet side road, this is a modern, well-furnished hotel with friendly atmosphere.

8hc (1fb) ✗ ® B&b£8.50–£12 Bdi£10.50–£14.50 WBdifr£73.50 LDO3pm

Lic 🍽 CTV 4P nc3yrs

GH Brooklands Hotel 28–30 King Edward Av ☎(0253) 51479 Plan **6** *A5*

An attractive hotel set in a quiet side road off the North Promenade.

16hc (5⥮) (3fb) CTV in 5 bedrooms TV in 2 bedrooms ✗ ® ✱B&b£10.35–£17.50 Bdi£11.50–£18.60 WBdi£80.50 LDO5pm

Lic 🍽 CTV 5P

Ⓥ

GH Burlees Hotel 40 Knowle Av ☎(0253) 54535 Plan **7** *A5*
Closed Xmas

Pleasantly situated family-run hotel a short walk from the Promenade.

11hc (2fb) ✗ ® B&b£11–£12 Bdi£15–£16.50 WBdifr£100 LDO7pm

Lic 🍽 CTV 5P 1🚗 ⌂

Credit cards 1 3 Ⓥ

GH *Cliftonville Hotel* 14 Empress Dr, Northshore ☎(0253) 51052 Plan **8** *A5*
Apr–Nov & Xmas

A lift, and bedrooms with private facilities, are features of this private hotel near the sea front.

19⥮ (8fb) ✗ ® LDO5pm

Lic lift 🍽 CTV 5P solarium

Credit cards 1 3

Blackpool

1 Arandora Star Private Hotel
2 Arosa Hotel
3 Ashcroft Private Hotel
4 Beaucliffe
5 Berwick Private Hotel
6 Brooklands Hotel
7 Burlees Hotel
8 Cliftonville Hotel
9 Denely Private Hotel
10 Derwent Private Hotel
11 Garville
12 Hartshead Hotel
13 Lynstead Private Hotel
14 Lynwood
15 Motel Mimosa
16 New Heathcot Private Hotel
17 North Mount Private Hotel
18 Rewa
19 Sunnycliff
20 Sunray Private Hotel
21 Surrey House Hotel

Arandora Star Private Hotel

559 New South Promenade,
Blackpool, Lancs. FY4 1NF.
Tel. 0253 41528

Licensed to Residents.
FREE PARKING GARAGE.
Res Prop Mr & Mrs G Wansker

Offers you the finest position overlooking the beach and promenade. Bathing from hotel. Lounges with television. Hot and cold services in all rooms. All bedrooms fitted with divans and spring-interior beds. Bedhead lighting. Room keys. Shaving points and electric fires. Twin beds available if desired. Full central heating. Christmas festivities. Fire certificate obtained. Modern bathrooms and separate shower room available. Cocktail bar. Established 37 years ago. Finest English cuisine and personal service. Sun lounge. Week end and mid-week periods available if desired.

Ashcroft Private Hotel

42 King Edward Avenue, Blackpool NS, FY2 9TA
Telephone: (0253) 51538

A small friendly hotel offering personal service, high standards of comfort and good home cooking.

- ★ South facing position
- ★ All 11 bedrooms have tea/ coffee making facilities
- ★ Reductions for children
- ★ Well stocked licensed bar
- ★ Fully centrally heated
- ★ Full English breakfast
- ★ Parking available
- ★ 4 day Xmas party
- ★ Winter/Xmas shopping breaks

Situated off Queens Promenade, 2 minutes from sea and Gynn Gardens and within easy reach of all main attractions.

BEAUCLIFFE PRIVATE HOTEL

22 Holmfield Road, Blackpool FY2 9TB
Tel: Blackpool (0253) 51663

The Beaucliffe Licensed Hotel is a small family run hotel ideally situated near Gynn Gardens and approximately 100 yards from the Queens Promenade. Excellent cuisine, lounge with colour TV. Separate dining tables. Tea and coffee making facilities in all rooms. Car park.

Under the personal supervision of the resident owner: Mrs V A BIRD.
Open all year round.

BURLEES HOTEL

40 Knowle Avenue, Blackpool FY2 9TQ
Telephone: 0253 54535

Situated in a quiet residential area just off Queens Promenade & very close to North Shore Golf Club. "Burlees" is a small family hotel which offers a high standard of catering ensuring an excellent and varied cuisine. No parking restrictions, car park on the premises. Most bedrooms on 1st floor all with heating, tea/coffee facilities. Pleasant garden facing south where you may sit & relax. Licensed to residents. Personal attention at all times.
Mike & Linda Lawrence.

GH Denely Private Hotel 15 King Edward Av ☎(0253) 52757 Plan **9** *A5*

A delightful, small, privately-run hotel in a quiet side road on the north shore.

9hc (1fl) (2fb) ✱ Ⓡ B&b£9.50–£10 Bdi £11–£13 WBdifr£77 LDO3.30pm

📺 CTV 6P

GH Derwent Private Hotel 8 Gynn Av ☎(0253) 55194 Plan **10** *A5*
Mar–3 Nov

A friendly, well-furnished hotel occupying a middle terrace in a quiet road.

12hc (4fl) (2fb) Ⓡ ✻B&b£10.50–£13.25 Bdi£13.50–£15.50 LDO2pm

Blackpool

Lic 📺 CTV 4P nc3yrs

Ⓥ

⊢GH Garville 3 Beaufort Av, Bispham (2m N) ☎(0253) 51004 Plan **11** *A5*

Pleasant, family run guesthouse close to the seafront.

7hc (2⇌) (2fb) ⚡ in all bedrooms ✱ B&b£7.50–£8 Bdi£10–£10.50 WBdifr£67 LDO1pm

Lic 📺 CTV 5P

GH Hartshead Hotel 17 King Edward Av ☎(0253) 53133 Plan **12** *A5*

A well-run, friendly house with good furnishings. Set in a quiet side road just off the promenade.

9hc (1⇌ 1fl) (2fb) Ⓡ ✻B&b£9–£11 Bdi£10.50–£12.50 WBdifr£73.50 LDO5pm

Lic 📺 CTV 8P

Credit cards 1 3 Ⓥ

GH *Lynstead Private Hotel* 40 King Edward Av ☎(0253) 51050 Plan **13** *A5*
Closed first 2 wks Jan

The 'Tram Bar' is a unique feature of this modern hotel in a quiet road.

10hc (5fl) (4fb) ✱ Ⓡ LDO3pm

Lic lift 📺 CTV

GH Lynwood 38 Osbourne Rd ☎(0253) 44628 Plan **14** *A2*
Closed Xmas & New Year

A small and friendly hotel with good bedrooms situated in a side road close to Sandcastle Entertainment Centre and the Pleasure Beach.

8hc (1⇌ 5fl) (1fb) CTV available in bedrooms ✗ Ⓡ B&b£10–£12.50 Bdi£14–£16.50 WBdifr£98 LDOam

CTV

Ⓥ

GH Motel Mimosa 24A Lonsdale Rd ☎(0253) 41906 Plan **15** *A3*

Blackpool

Well-appointed, modern establishment with spacious bedrooms complete with television and en-suite facilities. Breakfast is served in guests' rooms.

15hc (6⇌ 9fl) (3fb) CTV in all bedrooms Ⓡ *B&b£11.95–£13.95 WB&bfr£69

Lic 13P 2

Credit cards 1 3

GH New Heathcot Private Hotel 270 Queens Prom ☎(0253) 595130 Plan **16** *A5*

A pleasant, small, family-run guesthouse on the North Shore overlooking the sea.

9hc (4fb) B&b£9–£10 Bdi£11.50–£12.50 WBdi£80.50–£87.50 LDO4pm

Lic CTV 6P

Ⓥ

GH North Mount Private Hotel 22 King Edward Av ☎(0253) 55937 Plan **17** *A5*

A charming, personally-run guesthouse on the north shore in peaceful surroundings. →

8hc (1fb) Ⓡ B&b£8.50–£10.50 Bdi£10.50–£13 WBdi£73.50–£91 LDO3.30pm

Lic 🍽 CTV 1P

⟼**GH Rewa Private Hotel** 561 New South Prom ☎(0253) 42463 Plan **18** *A1* rs Nov–Mar

18hc (1⇌ 2🚿) (2fb) ✖ Ⓡ B&b£9–£10 Bdi£11–£17 WBdi£77–£95 (W only Jul & Aug)

Lic 🍽 CTV 12P

Credit card ③ Ⓥ

GH Sunny Cliff 98 Queens Prom, Northshore ☎(0253) 51155 Plan **19***A5* Etr–Nov

Blackpool

Seaside hotel with modern frontage, family-owned and run.

12hc (4fb) Ⓡ B&b£9.50–£10 Bdi£11.75–£13 WBdifr£85.75 LDO5pm

Lic CTV 8P

Ⓥ

GH Sunray Private Hotel 42 Knowle Av, Queens Prom (Guestaccom) ☎(0253) 51937 Plan **20** *A5* Closed 15 Dec–5 Jan

Comfortable small hotel in quiet residential area, close to Queens Promenade and Blackpool's many attractions.

9hc (1⇌ 8🚿) (2fb) CTV in all bedrooms Ⓡ B&b£20–£32 Bdi£28–£45 WBdi£144–£182 LDO4pm

🍽 CTV 6P

Ⓥ

GH Surrey House Hotel 9 Northumberland Av ☎(0253) 51743 Plan **21** *A5* Apr–Oct rs Mar & early Nov

Excellent hospitality is offered at this small hotel in a quiet residential area.

11hc (2⇌ 7⌸) (2fb) ⚟ in 1 bedroom Ⓡ B&b£7.75–£11 Bdi£11.50–£14 WBdi£80–£98 LDO5pm

⌸ CTV 6P 1⌂(charge) nc3months

Ⓥ

BLACKWOOD
Gwent
Map **3** ST19

INN Plas Gordon Rd ☎(0495) 224674

Comfortable and popular family-run inn enjoying elevated location.

6hc (4⌸) (1fb) CTV in all bedrooms Ⓡ ✱B&b£12.50–£19 Bar lunch £2.85–£3.80 Dinner 9.45pm

Blackpool — Blairgowrie

⌸ 50P

Credit cards 1 3 5

BLAENAU FFESTINIOG
Gwynedd
Map **6** SH74

⊢⊣**GH Don** 147 High St ☎(0766) 830403

Three-storey stone Victorian house near centre of village.

6hc (3fb) ✱ B&b£9–£9.50 LDO7pm

Lic ⌸ CTV 2P 2⌂

Ⓥ

BLAIRGOWRIE
Tayside *Perthshire*
Map **11** NO14

GH Glenshieling Hatton Rd, Rattray ☎(0250) 4605

Victorian house set in its own grounds, in a secluded location. Although small, the bedrooms are bright and well-maintained. The residents' lounge has an adjoining sun lounge. A set three-course dinner provides quality rather than choice. The owners offer a friendly, cheerful service.

→

6hc (1⌂) (2fb) Ⓡ B&b£11–£12.50 Bdi£17–£18.50 WBdifr£116 LDO7pm

Lic 𝍖 CTV 16P

Ⓥ

GH Ivybank House Boat Brae, Rattray ☎(0250) 3056

A well-furnished, large, Victorian house standing in own grounds, with floodlit tennis court. Personally run.

6hc (2fb) CTV in all bedrooms Ⓡ B&b£10.50 Bdi£17 WBdifr£114 LDO6pm

𝍖 CTV 6P ⚲(hard)

Ⓥ

Selected

GH Rosebank House Balmoral Rd ☎(0250) 2912

Jan–Oct

A delightful Georgian house set in its own well-tended gardens and outside the town centre. The owner's careful attention to detail is apparent in the attractive bedrooms with their co-ordinated decor, soft furnishings and furniture. A cosy lounge offers a welcoming log fire on cooler evenings. Wholesome four-course dinners are served in the neatly-appointed dining room. Warm friendly atmosphere.

6hc (5⌂) (2fb) CTV in 2 bedrooms ✗ Ⓡ B&b£12.50–£13.50 Bdi£19.95–£20.95 WBdi£138 LDO6pm

Lic 𝍖 CTV 12P nc10yrs

Ⓥ

BLAWITH
Cumbria
Map **7** SD38

GH Water Yeat Country Water Yeat ☎Lowick Bridge (022985) 306

Closed 10 Jan–11 Feb

This charming farmhouse dates from the 17th century. Good food is the main attraction here, from unusual bar lunches to delicious afternoon teas. Guests should be well satisfied with the interesting four-course dinners.

6hc (2⌂) (1fb) ✗ Ⓡ ✱B&b£11.50–£14 Bdi£21.50–£23 WBdi£132.50–£148.50 LDO7.30pm

Lic 𝍖 CTV 10P nc5yrs

Ⓥ

BLORE
Staffordshire
Map **7** SK14

⊢⊣**FH** M A Griffin **Coldwall** *(SK144494)* Okeover ☎Thorpe Cloud (033529) 249

Etr–Oct

Stone-built farmhouse approximately 200 years old. Views of Dovedale. 4 miles NW of Ashbourne.

2hc (2fb) ✗ B&b£8–£9 Bdi£12–£13 LDO6pm

CTV 4P 250acres dairy sheep

Ⓥ

BLUE ANCHOR
Somerset
Map **3** ST04

⊢⊣**GH Camelot** ☎Dunster (0643) 821348

7hc (3fb) B&b£9 Bdi£11–£14 WBdifr£90 LDO8pm

Lic 𝍖 CTV 7P

Ⓥ

BOAT OF GARTEN
Highland *Inverness-shire*
Map **14** NH91

Selected

GH *Moorfield House Hotel* Deshar Rd ☎(047983) 646

Closed Nov

A warm welcome awaits visitors to Mell and Letty Sims' delightful 19th century guesthouse. This handsome pink-granite building stands in its own grounds in this pleasant Highland village. Nicely-appointed bedrooms are comfortable and well-maintained. The residents' lounge is designed for relaxation and it is a joy to eat in the charming dining room. Moorfield offers a friendly atmosphere and attentive service.

6hc (3⌂) (2fb) Ⓡ LDO6pm

Lic 𝍖 CTV 12P

BODEDERN
Gwynedd
Map **6** SH38

INN Crown Hotel ☎Valley (0407) 740734

Old country coaching inn with pleasant homely atmosphere, situated a few miles from holiday beaches and the Irish car ferry terminal.

5hc (2fb) CTV in 3 bedrooms TV in 2 bedrooms ✗ B&b£11.50–£13 LDO9.45pm

𝍖 50P

BODENHAM
Hereford & Worcester
Map **3** SO55

FH Mr & Mrs P J Edwards **Maund Court** (*SO561505*) ☎(056884) 282

Feb–Nov

Guests are given a warm welcome by Raymond and Pauline Edwards on arrival at this 100 acre farm. Well tended gardens and a swimming pool are available for guests.

3hc (1fb) ✱B&bfr£10.50 ✗ Ⓡ

CTV 4P nc10yrs ⛀(heated) 130acres mixed

BODLE STREET GREEN
East Sussex
Map **5** TQ61

FH Mr & Mrs R Gentry **Stud Farm** (*TQ163658*) ☎Herstmonceux (0323) 833201

Closed Xmas

A small, homely farmhouse in picturesque countryside.

3hc (1⌂) ✗ Ⓡ ✱B&b£10–£11 Bdifr£16 WBdifr£112

𝍖 CTV 3P

70 acres beef sheep

BODMIN
Cornwall
See **Roche**

BOGNOR REGIS
West Sussex
Map **4** SZ99

GH *Lansdowne Hotel* 55–57 West St ☎(0243) 865552

Modernised property incorporating cottage-style restaurant, set in a quiet residential area near the sea front.

8hc (5fb) ✱ LDO10pm

Lic CTV no babies

Credit cards 1 2 3 5

BOLLINGTON
Cheshire
Map **7** SJ97

INN ***Turners Arms*** 1 Ingersley Rd ☎(0625) 73864

A small, well-run village pub with a good range of food.

4hc (2fb) CTV in all bedrooms LDO9.30pm

2P

BOMERE HEATH
Shropshire
Map **7** SJ41

FH Mrs D M Cooke ***Grange*** *(SJ200484)* ☎(0939) 290234
Closed Xmas

Large house with attractive gardens and open rural views.

2hc (1fb) ✱ LDO3pm

CTV 4P 360acres arable dairy

BONDLEIGH (nr North Tawton)
Devon
Map **3** SS60

Bognor Regis — Bonsall

FH Mrs M C H Partridge **Cadditon** *(SS644050)* ☎North Tawton (083782) 450
Mar–Nov

Attractive, friendly farmhouse with old beams and fireplaces.

1¼m W unclassified road.

2hc (1fb) ✱ Ⓡ ✱B&b£8–£9 Bdi£13–£14 WBdi£84–£98

CTV P 147acres beef dairy

BO'NESS
Central *West Lothian*
Map **11** NS98

REMEMBER

Prices quoted in the gazetteer are minimum double room occupancy to maximum single room occupancy **per person.**

Selected

FH Mrs B Kirk **Kinglass** *(NT006803)* Borrowstoun Rd ☎(0506) 822861

The hospitality of Mrs Kirk and her staff make Kinglass Farm a popular haunt of tourist and businessman alike. An attractive sandstone building, it stands on the southern outskirts of town overlooking the Firth of Forth. Attractive bedrooms are equipped to a high standard and the public areas are smart and comfortable.

7rm (6hc) (1fb) TV in all bedrooms Ⓡ B&b£10 Bdi£16–£20 WBdifr£112 LDO5.30pm

Lic CTV 20P 120acres arable

Ⓥ

BONSALL
Derbyshire
Map **8** SK25

GH Sycamore 76 High St, Town Head ☎Wirksworth (062982) 3903
Mar–Dec

Stone-built former farmhouse dating from the early 18th century.

6hc (3fb) Ⓡ ✱B&b£11.50 Bdi£17.50 LDO6pm

Lic CTV 7P

See advertisement under Matlock

GH Town Head Farmhouse 70 High St
☎Wirksworth (0629) 523762
Apr–Oct

200-year old stone-built farmhouse with attached converted barns, located on edge of village.

6hc (1fb) Ⓡ B&b£11–£13.50 Bdi£18–£20.50 WBdifr£123 LDO5pm

Lic 🍽 CTV 8P nc10yrs

See advertisement under Matlock

BONTDDU
Gwynedd
Map **6** SH61

INN Halfway House Hotel ☎(034149) 635

Half timbered inn in centre of small village.

3hc (1⇌) Annexe: 1⇌ (1fb) Ⓡ B&b£10–£15 Bdi£19.75–£24.75 Bar lunch £3.50alc Dinner 9.15pm £9.75

🍽 CTV 12P 1🚗

BOOT
Cumbria
Map **7** NY10

GH Brook House ☎Eskdale (09403) 288
Closed Nov–28 Dec

Good home-cooking, with some dishes for vegetarians, in a spacious comfortable house.

6hc (2fl) (2fb) TV in all bedrooms B&b£11–£19 Bdi£18–£26 WBdi£120–£175 LDO8.30pm

Lic 🍽 CTV 14P

Ⓥ

BORELAND
Dumfries & Galloway *Dumfriesshire*
Map **11** NY19

GH Newton House ☎(05766) 269
Apr–Oct

Set back from the road alongside the village school, the accommodation is spacious and comfortable and guests are made welcome by the friendly proprietors.

3hc (1fl) (1fb) ✗ Ⓡ ✱B&bfr£11 Bdifr£16 LDO1pm CTV 3P

Bonsall — Boscastle

Selected

FH Mrs I Maxwell **Gall** *(NY172901)*
☎(05766) 229
Apr–Oct

An immaculate farmhouse overlooking surrounding rolling hills and pastureland. Mrs Maxwell and her daughter are most welcoming hosts and guests can expect a relaxing and peaceful stay. Homely, comfortable public areas and spacious, airy bedrooms are all tastefully appointed. Good home cooking is a feature.
Winner for Scotland of the 1987/8 AA Farmhouse of the Year Award.

3hc (1fb) ✗ Ⓡ B&b£10–£10.50 Bdi£15–£15.50 LDO5pm

🍽 CTV 4P 2🚗 🏠 1066acres beef sheep

Ⓥ

BOROUGHBRIDGE
North Yorkshire
Map **8** SE36

GH Farndale Horsefair ☎(09012) 3463
Closed 19 Dec–3 Jan

Restored Edwardian building with spacious attractive lounge and separate TV area.

13hc (2⇌ 2fl) (4fb) CTV in 4 bedrooms B&b£12–£17 Bdifr£12 LDO9pm

Lic 🍽 CTV 9P

BORROWDALE
Cumbria
Map **11** NY21

GH Greenbank Country ☎(059684) 215
Closed Dec

Delightful family-run country guesthouse with good home cooking.

10hc (8⇌ 2fl) (1fb) ✗ Ⓡ in 3 bedrooms Bdi£18.50–£24 WBdi£129.50–£154 LDO5pm

Lic 🍽 CTV 15P

Ⓥ

GH Langstrath Hotel ☎(059684) 239

Small, comfortable hotel with lots of character and peaceful setting.

13hc (2fl) (3fb) B&bfr£17.50 Bdifr£23 WBdifr£155 LDO3pm

Lic 🍽 20P

GH *Mary Mount Hotel* ☎(059684) 223
Telex no 64305
Feb–Nov

Magnificent views from the elegant dining room. Comfortable, well-appointed bedrooms.

7fl Annexe: 5⇌ CTV in all bedrooms ✗ Ⓡ

Lic 🍽 40P

BORTH
Dyfed
Map **6** SN68

GH Glanmor Princess St ☎(097081) 689
Mar–Oct

A sea-front hotel with comfortable accommodation, good food and warm hospitality. Opposite safe sandy beach.

7hc (2fl) (3fb) ✗ Ⓡ B&b£11.50 Bdi£17 WBdifr£119 LDO10pm

Lic CTV 6P 🏠

Credit cards 1 2 3 5

Ⓥ

BOSCASTLE
Cornwall
Map **2** SX09

GH St Christophers Country House Hotel High St ☎(08405) 412
Mar–Oct

Charming cottage-style guesthouse with comfortably-furnished accommodation. The happy, enthusiastic owners serve good home cooking at excellent value-for-money prices.

8hc (5fl) CTV in 1 bedroom Ⓡ B&b£12–£17.50 Bdi£19–£24.50 WBdi£123–£158 LDO9am

Lic 🍽 CTV nc12yrs

Ⓥ

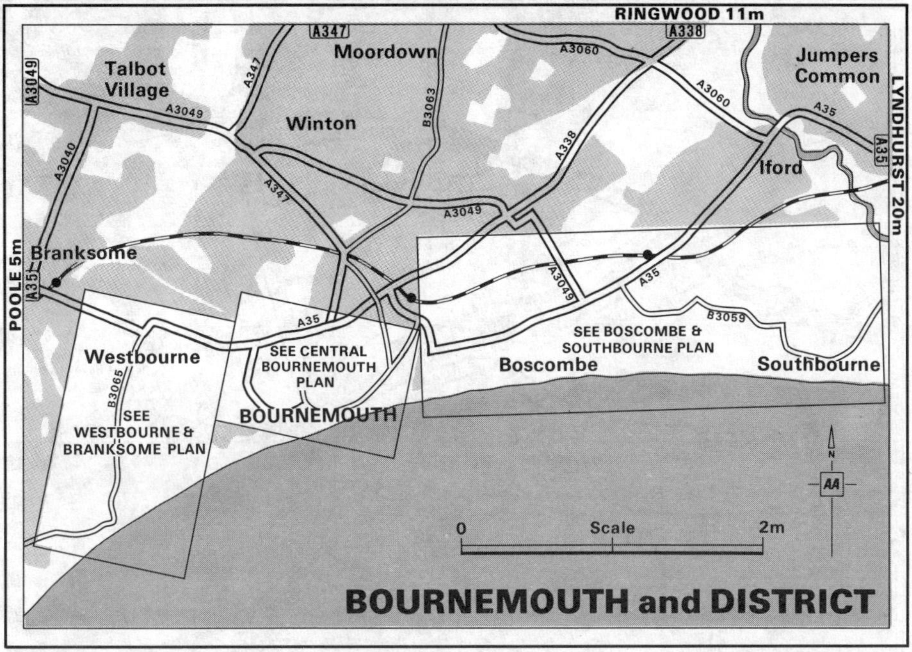

RINGWOOD 11m
A347
A338
Moordown
A3060
Jumpers Common
A3049
Talbot Village
A347
A3049
Winton
B3063
A3060
A35
LYNDHURST 20m
A3040
A338
A35
Iford
A347
A3049
POOLE 5m
Branksome
A35
A3049
A35
A35
B3059
SEE BOSCOMBE & SOUTHBOURNE PLAN
Westbourne
SEE CENTRAL BOURNEMOUTH PLAN
Boscombe
Southbourne
B3065
SEE WESTBOURNE & BRANKSOME PLAN
BOURNEMOUTH
N
AA
0 Scale 2m

BOURNEMOUTH and DISTRICT

BOSHAM
West Sussex
Map **4** SU80

GH White Barn Crede Ln (Guestaccom) ☎(0243) 573113
Closed Dec & Jan

5hc (1⇨ 2⋔) (1fb) ⊁ in all bedrooms ⋈ Ⓡ B&b£15–£16 Bdi£26 WBdifr£175

⋔ CTV 5P 2⊜ Ⓥ

BOURNEMOUTH AND BOSCOMBE
Dorset
Map **4** SZ09

See **Key Map** (p 77), **Central Plan** (pages 78–79), **Boscombe** and **Southbourne** Plan (pages 80–81) and **Westbourne** & **Branksome** Plan (page 85)

For additional guesthouses see **Poole** and **Christchurch**

GH Albemarle Private Hotel 123 West Hill Rd ☎(0202) 21351
Central plan **1** *A1*

Small, comfortable terraced hotel, near town centre, offering excellent food and hospitality.

12hc (3⋔) (3fb) CTV in all bedrooms (charge) Ⓡ B&b£11–£14 Bdi£15–£18 WBdi£86–£115 LDO5.30pm

Lic ⋔ CTV 2P

Credit cards [1] [3] Ⓥ

See advertisement on page 78

GH Alum Bay Hotel 19 Burnaby Rd, Alum Chine ☎(0202) 761034 Westbourne & Branksome plan **58** *B2*

Victorian house within a few minutes walk of Alum Chine and the beach.

12hc (6⋔) (4fb) CTV in 6 bedrooms Ⓡ B&b£12–£14.50 Bdi£17.25–£19.55 WBdi£103.50–£120.75 LDO6pm

Lic ⋔ CTV 8P

Credit cards [1] [3] Ⓥ

GH Alumcliff Hotel 121 Almhurst Rd ☎(0202) 764777 Westbourne & Branksome Plan **59** *B2*

17hc (2⇨ 8⋔) (4fb) CTV in all bedrooms Ⓡ B&b£16.50–£19.50 Bdi£21–£29.50 WBdifr£130.50 LDO6.30pm

Lic ⋔ 16P nc7yrs solarium

Credit cards [1] [2] [3] Ⓥ

See advertisement on page 79

GH *Alum Grange Hotel* 1 Burnaby Rd, Alum Chine ☎(0202) 761195 Westbourne & Branksome plan **60** *B2*

Within two minutes walking distance of the sea. →

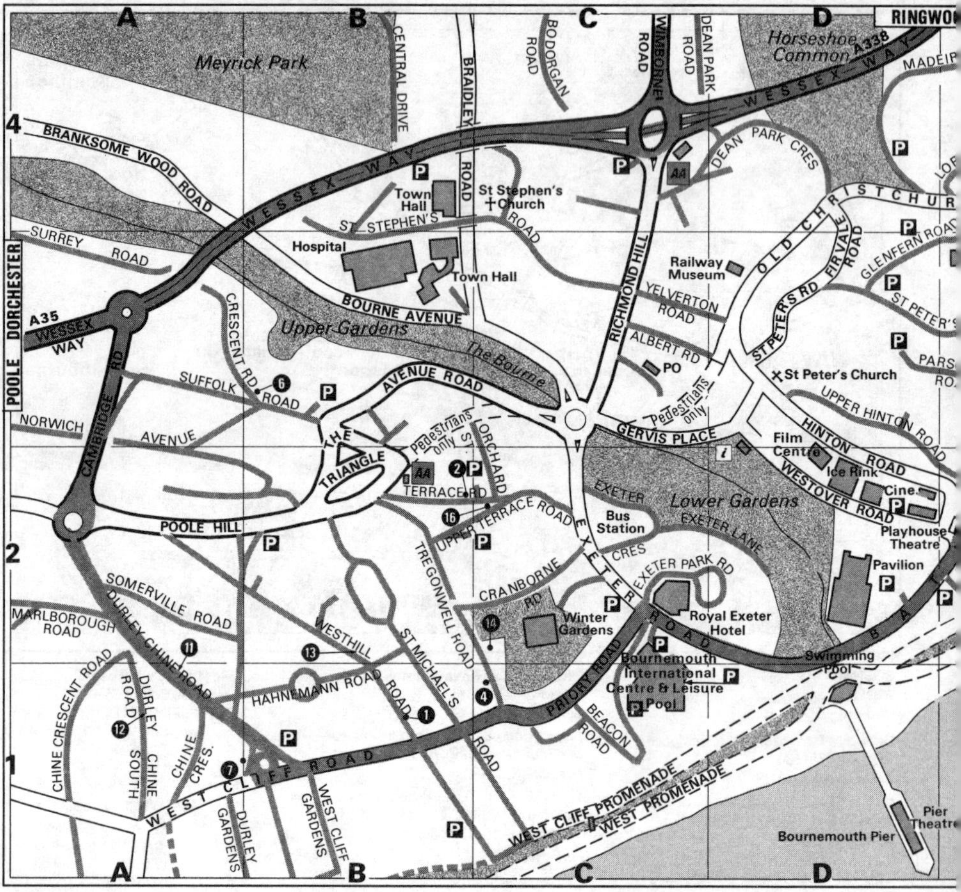

14hc (4⇆ 6⫚) (5fb) CTV in all bedrooms ✗ Ⓡ

Lic ⫪ 9P nc3yrs

GH Bay Tree Hotel 17 Burnaby Rd, Alum Chine ☎(0202) 763807 Westbourne & Branksome plan **62** *B2*

Etr–Dec

Adjacent to Alum Chine, a few minutes from beach.

12hc (2⫚) (4fb) ✗ Ⓡ B&b£9.50–£15.50 Bdi£13.50–£19.50 WBdifr£83 LDO4pm

Lic CTV 7P

⊢⊣ **GH Blinkbonnie Heights Hotel** 26 Clifton Rd, Southbourne ☎(0202) 426512 Boscombe & Southbourne plan **21** *F1*

11hc (1⇆) (3fb) ✗ Ⓡ B&b£8.50–£12.50 Bdi£12–£15 WBdi£84–£104

Lic ⫪ CTV 10P ♿

⊢⊣ **GH Blue Cedars Hotel** Portchester Pl ☎(0202) 26893 Boscombe & Southbourne plan **22** *A3*

rs Oct–Mar

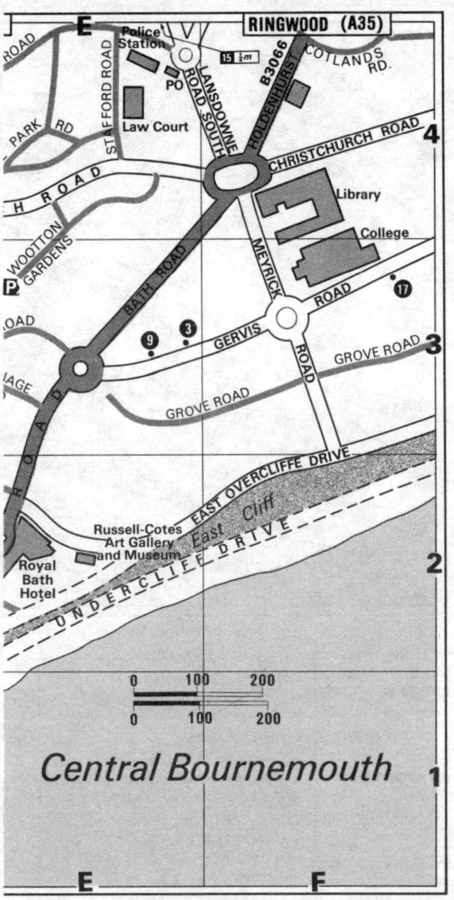

Central Bournemouth

1 Albemarle Private Hotel
2 Hotel Bristol
3 Bursledon Hotel
4 Carisbrooke Hotel
6 Crescent Grange Hotel
7 Croham Hurst Hotel
9 Gervis Court Hotel
11 Kensington Hotel
12 Langton Hall Hotel
13 Mae-Mar Private Hotel
14 Mount Stuart Hotel
15 Silver Trees Hotel
16 Terrace Garden Hotel
17 Tudor Grange Hotel

13hc (3fb) CTV in all bedrooms ✖ B&b£9–£12 Bdi£13.50–£16.50 WBdi£65–£84 (W only Jun & Aug) LDO6pm

Lic 🍽 9P

Ⓥ

GH *Borodale Hotel* 10 St Johns Rd, Boscombe ☎(0202) 35285 Boscombe & Southbourne plan **23** *B2*
Mar–Nov

Short distance from Boscombe pier with nearby shopping complex.

16hc (1⇌ 2fl) (6fb)

Lic 🍽 CTV 20P

⊢⊣**GH Braemar Private Hotel** 30 Glen Rd, Boscombe ☎(0202) 36054 Boscombe & Southbourne plan **24** *C2*
Mar–Oct

Simple accommodation is offered at this gabled hotel near Boscombe Pier.

11hc (1⇌ 2fl) (4fb) ✖ Ⓡ B&b£9–£12 Bdi£12–£15 WBdifr£75 (W only Jul–Aug) LDO6pm

Lic 🍽 CTV 6P

Ⓥ

GH Hotel Bristol Terrace Rd ☎(0202) 27007 Central plan **2** *B2*

Central popular hotel convenient to theatres.

28hc (4⇌) (6fb) B&b£13–£18 Bdi£19–£24 WBdi£100–£129

Lic lift 🍽 CTV 25P nc2yrs

Ⓥ

GH *Britannia Hotel* 40 Christchurch Rd ☎(0202) 26700 Boscombe & Southbourne plan **25** *A2*
Closed Xmas

On main Christchurch road into Bournemouth.

28hc ✖

🍽 CTV 30P nc3yrs

GH Bursledon Hotel 34 Gervis Rd ☎(0202) 24622 Central plan **3** *E3*

Central position on East Cliff within short walking distance of shops and theatres.

23hc (2⇌ 9fl) (4fb) CTV in 5 bedrooms TV in 1 bedroom B&b£12.65–£19.55 Bdi£16.10–£25.30 WBdifr£104.65 LDO6.30pm

Lic 🍽 CTV 20P 5🚗 nc3yrs

Credit card ③ Ⓥ

GH Carisbrooke Hotel 42 Tregonwell Rd ☎(0202) 290432 Central plan **4** *C1*
Mar–Dec

Modern family run hotel near the Winter Gardens.

24hc (5⇌ 10fl) (4fb) CTV in all bedrooms ✖ Ⓡ B&b£12–£18 Bdi£16–£21.50 WBdifr£95 LDO7pm →

Boscombe & Southborne

21 Blinkbonnie Heights Hotel
22 Blue Cedars Hotel
23 Borodale Hotel
24 Braemar Private Hotel
25 Britannia Hotel
26 Charles Taylor Hotel
27 Cintra
28 Clifton Court Hotel
29 Cransley Private Hotel
30 Crossroads Hotel
31 Derwent House
32 Farlow Private Hotel
33 Hawaiian Hotel
34 Highlin Private Hotel
35 Linwood House Hotel
36 Lynthwaite Hotel
37 Mayfield Private Hotel
38 Myrtle House Hotel
39 Naseby-Nye Hotel
40 Norland Private Hotel
41 Oak Hall Private Hotel
42 Pine Beach Hotel
43 St John's Lodge Hotel
46 Sea Shells
47 Sea View Court Hotel
48 Sherbourne Hotel
49 Hotel Sorrento
50 Stonecroft Hotel
51 Stratford Hotel
52 Valberg Hotel
53 Vine
54 Waldale
55 Weavers Hotel
56 Wood Lodge Hotel
57 Woodside Private Hotel

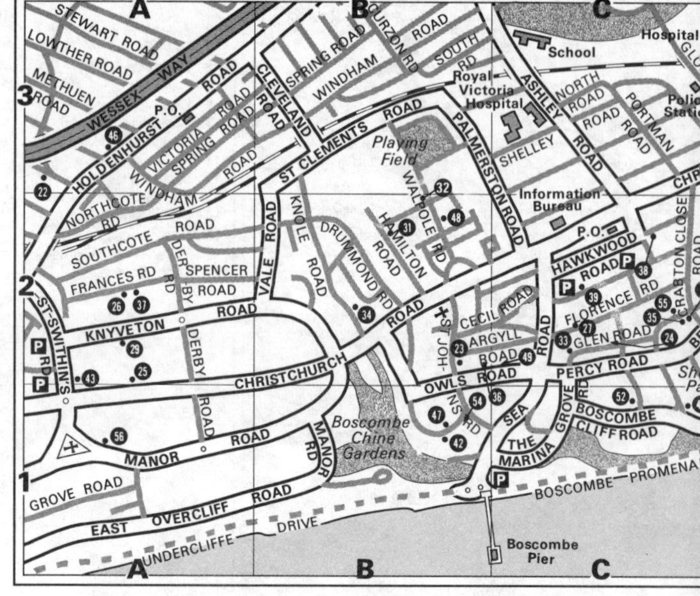

Lic CTV 19P

Credit cards 1 2 3 Ⓥ

⊢→**GH Charles Taylor Hotel** Knyveton Gdns, 40–44 Frances Rd ☎(0202) 22695 Boscombe & Southbourne plan **26** *A2*
Mar–Dec

Friendly, family-run private hotel with a convivial atmosphere. Set in a quiet yet convenient location overlooking gardens and bowling greens.

26hc (10⇌) (4fb) Ⓡ ✖ (ex guide dogs) B&b£8.50–£14.50 Bdi£11.50–£17.50 WBdi£70–£105 LDO6.30pm

Lic 𝌮 CTV 10P nc8yrs

Credit cards 1 3 Ⓥ

GH Chineside Private Hotel 15 Studland Rd, Alum Chine ☎(0202) 761206 Westbourne & Branksome plan **63** *B2*
Etr–Oct

Modern, well-appointed hotel near sea front.

12hc (3⋔) (3fb) CTV in all bedrooms ✖ (ex guide dogs) Ⓡ B&b£10.25–£19 Bdi£15.25–£24 WBdi£89–£132 LDO4pm

𝌮 CTV 12P nc

GH Cintra 10–12 Florence Rd, Boscombe ☎(0202) 36103 Boscombe & Southbourne plan **27** *C2*

Within walking distance of pier and shopping centre.

40hc (5⇌ 3⋔) (6fb) Ⓡ ✱B&b£10.50–£12.50 Bdi£12.50–£15 WBdifr£98 LDO6.30pm

Lic CTV 10P

Credit cards 2 3

Selected

GH Cliff House Hotel 113 Alumhurst Rd, Westbourne ☎(0202) 763003 Westbourne & Branksome plan **64** *B2*
Mar–Nov & Xmas

High standard of accommodation and some fine sea views are offered at this hotel adjacent to Alum Chine.

12hc (2⇌ 9⋔) (4fb) CTV in all bedrooms ✖ Ⓡ B&b£17.82 Bdi£25.87 WBdi£150–£188 LDO6.30pm

Lic lift 𝌮 12P nc7yrs snooker

GH Clifton Court Hotel 30 Clifton Rd ☎(0202) 427753 Boscombe & Southbourne plan **28** *F1*

Well-furnished guesthouse with modern extension.

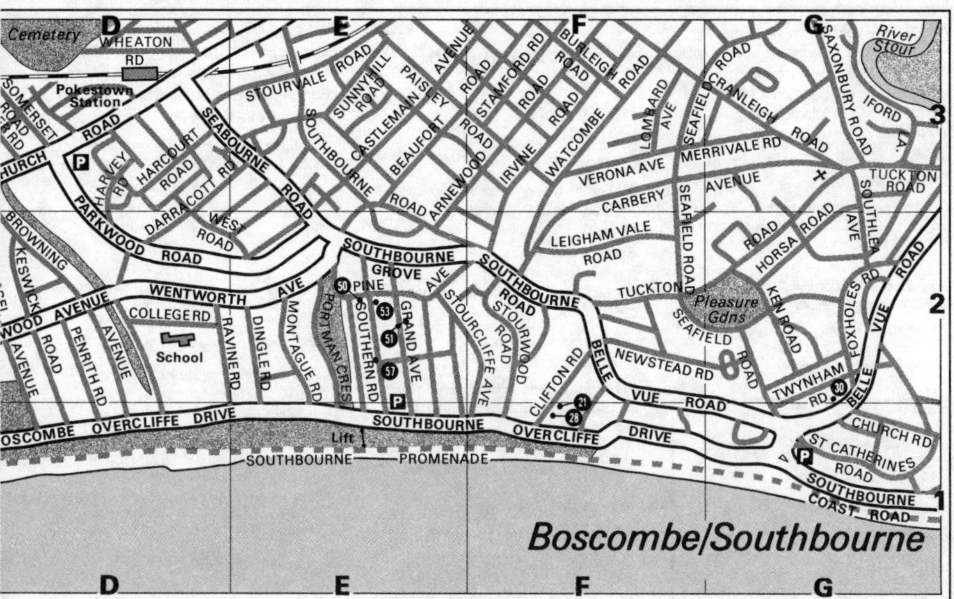

12hc (2⇨) (2fb) Ⓡ ✱B&b£9.50–£14 Bdi£13–£16 WBdi£79–£109 LDO10am

Lic 🍽 CTV 10P

Ⓥ

GH Cransley Private Hotel 11 Knyveton Rd, East Cliff ☎(0202) 290067 Boscombe & Southbourne plan **29** *A2*
Apr–Oct

12hc (5⇨ 5⋒) (2fb) CTV in 9 bedrooms TV in 1 bedroom Ⓡ B&b£9.20–£15 Bdi£14–£20 WBdi£75–£112

Lic CTV 10P

Credit cards 1 3 Ⓥ

GH *Crescent Grange Hotel*
6–8 Crescent Rd, The Triangle ☎(0202) 26959 Central plan **6** *B3*

Backing onto central gardens and convenient to shops and theatres.

19hc (16⇨ 3⋒) (2fb) CTV in all bedrooms Ⓡ LDO5pm

Lic 🍽 CTV 24P nc3yrs

Credit cards 1 3

GH *Croham Hurst Hotel* 9 Durley Rd, West Cliff ☎(0202) 22353 Central plan **7** *B1*
Etr–Nov

26hc (17⇨ 3⋒) (7fb) CTV in all bedrooms ✈ Ⓡ LDO6pm

Lic CTV 20P

See advertisement on page 82

⊢⊣**GH Crossroads Hotel** 88 Belle Vue Rd, Southbourne ☎(0202) 426307 Boscombe & Southbourne plan **30** *G2*

Pleasant, detached property near cliff-top at Southbourne. Comfortable, personally-run.

10hc (6⋒) (5fb) ✈ CTV in 5 bedrooms TV in 5 bedrooms Ⓡ B&b£8–£11 WB&bfr£55

Lic 🍽 CTV 15P nc5yrs

GH Derwent House 36 Hamilton Rd, Boscombe ☎(0202) 309102 Boscombe & Southbourne plan **31** *B2*

Detached property with Mansard roof, close to Boscombe shops.

9hc (4⋒) (3fb) CTV in all bedrooms Ⓡ B&b£10–£13 Bdi£13–£17 WBdi£82–£105 LDO5pm

Lic 🍽 CTV 10P

Credit cards 1 3 Ⓥ

GH Earlham Lodge 91 Alumhurst Rd, Alum Chine ☎(0202) 761943 Westbourne & Branksome plan **65** *B2*

Neat, modern house, a few minutes walk from Alum Chine and beach.

14hc (6⋒) (4fb) CTV in all bedrooms ✈ Ⓡ B&b£11.50–£14 Bdi£14.50–£18.50 WBdifr£95

Lic 🍽 CTV 6P

See advertisement on page 82

GH Egerton House Private Hotel 385 Holdenhurst Rd, Queens Park Not on plan ☎(0202) 34024

8hc (5fb) CTV in 7 bedrooms ✖ Ⓡ ✱B&b£10–£12 Bdi£14.50–£16 WBdifr£96.50

Lic ♛ CTV P

Credit cards 1 2 3

⊢GH Farlow Private Hotel Walpole Rd, Boscombe ☎(0202) 35865 Boscombe & Southbourne plan **32** *B2*
Apr–Oct

Well-maintained hotel with sound furnishings and personal service.

12hc (2fb) ✖ B&b£8.50–£10 Bdi£12.50–£14 WBdi£75–£90 LDO4pm

Credit Cards

1 Access/Euro/ Mastercard

2 American Express

3 Barclaycard/Visa

5 Diners

Bournemouth

CTV 12P nc4yrs

Credit card 1 Ⓥ

GH Gervis Court Hotel 38 Gervis Rd ☎(0202) 26871 Central plan **9** *E3*
Apr–Oct

Amidst pines on East Cliff.

16hc (4⇌ 3fl) (3fb) ✖ Ⓡ B&b£13.50–£15.50 Bdi£18.75–£20 WBdifr£91.50 LDO7.15pm

Lic CTV 17P ⌂

Credit card 3 Ⓥ

GH *Golden Sands Hotel* 83 Alumhurst Rd ☎(0202) 763832 Westbourne & Branksome plan **66** *B2*
Feb–Nov

Attractive guesthouse close to Alum Chine. Good standard of furnishings and very comfortable bedrooms.

9hc (5⇌ 4fl) (1fb) CTV in all bedrooms ✖ Ⓡ LDO6.30pm

Lic CTV 10P nc4yrs

GH Hawaiian Hotel 4 Glen Rd ☎(0202) 33234 Boscombe & Southbourne plan **33** *C2*
Mar–mid Oct

Nice, bright property near Boscombe Pier and shops.

12hc (4⇌ 3fl) (4fb) Ⓡ B&b£9.50–£12.50 Bdi£13–£16.25 WBdi£80–£104 LDO4pm

Lic ♛ CTV 8P nc4yrs Ⓥ

GH Highclere Hotel 15 Burnaby Rd, Alum Chine ☎(0202) 761350 Westbourne & Branksome plan **68** *B2*
Apr–Sep

Neat, well-maintained hotel with sea views. Easy walk to Alum Chine and beach.

9hc (4⇌ 5fl) (5fb) CTV in all bedrooms Ⓡ B&b£12.70–£13.90 Bdi£17.85–£19.62 WBdi£109.20–£123 LDO5pm

Lic ♛ CTV 7P ⌂ solarium Ⓥ

⊢**GH Highlin Private Hotel** 14 Knole Rd ☎(0202) 33758 Boscombe & Southbourne plan **34** *B2*

In a quiet area near Boscombe Chine.

10hc (1⇌) (5fb) Ⓡ B&b£8.50–£11 Bdi£11.50–£14 WBdifr£75

Lic ♛ CTV 7P 1🚘 Ⓥ

GH Holmcroft Hotel 5 Earle Rd, Alum Chine ☎(0202) 761289 Westbourne & Branksome plan **69** *B2*
Mar–Dec

Neat, well-maintained accommodation, close to Alum Chine woods and beach.

21hc (1⇌ 7⋒) (5fb) CTV in all bedrooms Ⓡ available in bedrooms B&b£10–£15 Bdi£17.50–£22.50 WBdi£110–£157.50 LDO6pm

Lic CTV 12P nc3yrs

Credit cards 1 2 3 Ⓥ

GH *Kensington Hotel* Durley Chine Rd, West Cliff ☎(0202) 27434 Central plan **11** *A1*
Etr–Oct

Detached hotel within walking distance of West Cliff. Attractive dining room with adjoining bar.

26hc (2⇌ 19⋒) (3fb) ✗ Ⓡ LDO7pm

Lic 𝍖 CTV 26P

GH Langton Hall Hotel 8 Durley Chine Rd, West Cliff ☎(0202) 25025 Central plan **12** *A1*
May–Oct rs Feb–Apr

35hc (12⇌ 13⋒) (4fb) CTV in all bedrooms ✗ Ⓡ ✱B&b£14–£18 Bdi£18–£26 WBdi£119–£135 LDO7pm

Lic Lift 𝍖 35P

Credit cards 1 2 3 Ⓥ

GH Linwood House Hotel 11 Wilfred Rd ☎(0202) 37818 Boscombe & Southbourne plan **35** *C2*
Mar–Oct

Attractively-decorated guesthouse in quiet road near beach and Boscombe town centre.

10hc (5⋒) (2fb) CTV in 3 bedrooms TV in 1 bedroom ✗ Ⓡ B&b£10–£13.50 Bdi£14–£17.50 WBdifr£75 (W only mid Jun–mid Sep)

Lic 𝍖 CTV 7P nc6yrs

GH Lynthwaite Hotel 10 Owls Rd, Boscombe ☎(0202) 38015 Boscombe & Southbourne plan **36** *B2*

Comfortable small hotel with good bedrooms, friendly atmosphere and easy parking.

14hc (6⇌ 1⋒) (3fb) CTV in 10 bedrooms ✗ Ⓡ ✱B&b£9.50–£16 Bdi£14.50–£21 WBdifr£90 LDO5pm

Lic CTV 17P

Credit card 3 Ⓥ

Bournemouth

GH Mae-Mar Private Hotel 91–93 West Hill Rd, West Cliff ☎(0202) 23167 Central plan **13** *B2*

In the heart of West Cliff hotel area.

30hc (11⋒) CTV in all bedrooms Ⓡ B&b£12–£14.50 Bdi£15–£18 WBdifr£85 LDO5pm

Lic lift 𝍖 CTV

Credit cards 1 3 Ⓥ

GH Mayfield Private Hotel 46 Frances Rd, Knyveton Gdns ☎(0202) 21839 Boscombe & Southbourne plan **37** *A2*
Closed Dec

Situated in quiet area with easy walk to beach.

8hc (2⋒) (1fb) Ⓡ ✱B&b£7.50–£9.50 Bdi£10.50–£12.50 WBdi£65–£85 (W only last wk Jul & 1st wk Aug) LDO9am

Lic 𝍖 CTV 5P nc7yrs

Ⓥ

GH Mount Stuart Hotel 31 Tregonwell Rd ☎(0202) 24639 Central plan **14** *C2*
Mar–Dec

Behind the Winter Gardens on West Cliff.

18hc (1⇌ 10⋒) (5fb) CTV in all bedrooms ✗ Ⓡ B&b£12–£18 Bdi£16–£21.50 WBdifr£95 LDO7pm

Lic 𝍖 CTV 17P

Credit cards 1 2 3

GH *Myrtle House Hotel* 41 Hawkwood Rd, Boscombe ☎(0202) 36579 Boscombe & Southbourne plan **38** *C2*

Short distance from Boscombe shops and pier.

10hc (1⇌ 2⋒) (5fb) ✗ LDO4pm

Lic 𝍖 CTV 8P

Credit card 1

Selected

GH *Naseby-Nye Hotel* Byron Rd, Boscombe ☎(0202) 34079 Boscombe & Southbourne plan **39** *C1*

Large detached house set in gardens close to cliff-top. Comfortable, well-appointed rooms.

13hc (3⇌) (4fb)

Lic 𝍖 CTV 12P nc5yrs

GH Newfield Private Hotel 29 Burnaby Rd, Alum Chine ☎(0202) 762724 Westbourne & Branksome plan **70** *B2*

Short distance from beach in Alum Chine area.

12hc (1⇌ 3⋒) (3fb) CTV in all bedrooms Ⓡ B&b£9.50–£16 Bdi£15–£22 WBdi£134

Lic 𝍖 CTV 4P

Ⓥ

GH Norland Private Hotel 6 Westby Rd, Boscombe ☎(0202) 36729 Boscombe & Southbourne plan **40** *C2*
Jan–Oct

Semi-detached Victorian building by Boscombe Pier.

8hc (1⇌ 2⋒) (3fb) ✗ Ⓡ ✱B&b£9–£11 Bdi£12.50–£14 WBdi£78–£92

Lic 𝍖 CTV 8P

Credit cards 1 3 Ⓥ

GH Northover Private Hotel 10 Earle Rd, Alum Chine ☎(0202) 767349 Westbourne & Branksome plan **71** *B2*
Etr–Oct

Overlooking Alum Chine, 400 yds from sea.

11hc (5⋒) (6fb) Ⓡ B&b£12–£16 Bdi£17–£21 WBdi£99–£129 LDO5pm

Lic 𝍖 CTV 11P nc5yrs

GH Oak Hall Private Hotel 9 Wilfred Rd, Boscombe ☎(0202) 35062 Boscombe & Southbourne plan **41** *C2*
Closed 6 Dec–10 Jan

Situated within easy reach of shops and Boscombe Pier and less than 5 minutes walk to Overcliff. →

10hc (3fb) Ⓡ ✱B&b£11–£12.50 Bdi£13.50–£16.50 WBdi£82–£103 (W only mid Jun–end Aug) LDO1pm

Lic ⅢⅢ CTV 9P nc6yrs

GH *Pine Beach Hotel* 31 Boscombe Spa Rd, Boscombe ☎(0202) 35902 Boscombe & Southbourne plan **42** *B1*

Situated in a quiet, elevated position overlooking Boscombe Pier and the sea.

21hc (4fb) LDO6pm

Lic CTV 17P nc4yrs

GH Ravenstone Hotel 36 Burnaby Rd, Alum Chine ☎(0202) 761047 Westbourne & Branksome plan **72** *B2*
Apr–Oct

Handsome villa near Alum Chine with pleasant garden and games room for children.

9hc (5⇔ 4fl) (3fb) CTV in all bedrooms ✈ Ⓡ B&b£14–£18 Bdi£17–£21 WBdi£98–£126 (W only mid Jul & Aug) LDO5pm

Lic ⅢⅢ 6P

Ⓥ

GH *St John's Lodge Hotel* 10 St Swithun's Rd ☎(0202) 290677 Boscombe & Southbourne plan **43** *A2*

Close to shops and within walking distance of the Chine and pier.

19hc (2fl) (4fb) ✈ Ⓡ LDO4.30pm

Lic CTV 16P

Bournemouth

GH Sea-Dene 10 Burnaby Rd, Alum Chine ☎(0202) 761372 Westbourne & Branksome plan **74** *B2*

Pleasant, detached house with forecourt parking, close to beach at Alum Chine.

7hc (4fl) (3fb) CTV in all bedrooms ✈ Ⓡ B&b£10–£14 Bdi£17–£21 WBdi£105–£133

Lic ⅢⅢ CTV 4P nc3yrs

Credit cards 1 3 Ⓥ

GH Sea Shells 203–205 Holdenhurst Rd ☎(0202) 292542 Boscombe & Southbourne plan **46** *A3*

Located near to shops on main road.

12hc (7fb) CTV in 1 bedroom TV in 8 bedrooms B&b£9.20–£10.35 W£58–£68 M

CTV 12P

Credit cards 1 3 Ⓥ

GH Sea View Court Hotel 14 Boscombe Spa Rd ☎(0202) 37197 Boscombe & Southbourne plan **47** *B1*
Apr–Oct

Two minutes walk from Boscombe Pier, an attractive gabled house with good bedrooms.

17hc (2⇔ 5fl) (7fb) ✈ Ⓡ ✱B&b£9.50–£12.50 Bdi£14.50–£17.50 WBdi£87–£105 LDO5pm

Lic CTV 20P

Ⓥ

GH *Sherbourne Hotel* 6 Walpole Rd, Boscombe ☎(0202) 36222 Boscombe & Southbourne plan **48** *B2*

Nicely-furnished detached hotel near Boscombe's main shopping street.

10hc (5fb) ✈ LDO5.30pm

Lic CTV 8P ⛳ sauna bath

GH Silver Trees Hotel 57 Wimborne Rd ☎(0202) 26040 Central plan **15** *F4*

A modernised, late Victorian house standing in its own grounds and offering comfortable accommodation.

8hc (1⇔ 4fl) (2fb) CTV in all bedrooms ✈ B&b£14–£20 WB&b£93–£133

ⅢⅢ 10P nc5yrs

Credit cards 1 3

See advertisement on page 86

GH Hotel Sorrento 16 Owls Rd, Boscombe ☎(0202) 34019 Boscombe & Southbourne plan **49** *C2*
Mar–Nov

Attractive hotel midway between Boscombe shopping centre beach and pier.

19hc (1⇔ 6fl) (5fb) Ⓡ B&b£9.50–£13 Bdi£14–£18 WBdi£82–£110 LDO6pm

Lic ⅢⅢ CTV 19P

GH Stonecroft Hotel 6 Wollstonecraft Rd, Boscombe Manor ☎(0202) 309390 Boscombe & Southbourne plan **50** *E2*
Mar–Oct

An attractive building in pleasant gardens, with comfortable rooms, 2 minutes from Boscombe Pier.

8fl (3fb) ® ✱B&b£10.50–£12 Bdi£15–£16 WBdifr£91 (W only mid Jun–mid Sep)

Lic CTV 7P

Ⓥ

GH Stratford Hotel 20 Grand Av, Southbourne ☎(0202) 424726 Boscombe & Southbourne plan **51** *E2*
Etr–Oct

13hc (5⇌) (7fb) ✱B&b£10.50–£12 Bdi£13–£14 W£89.70–£103.50 ⅉ (W only Jul & Aug) LDOnoon

Lic ♨ CTV 8P nc2yrs

Ⓥ

GH *Terrace Garden Hotel* Upper Terrace Rd ☎(0202) 25070 Central plan **16** *C2*

Centrally located for the theatre and shops.

Bournemouth

18hc (1⇌ 1fl) (2fb) CTV in 8 bedrooms LDO7pm

Lic ♨ CTV 8P ♿

Credit cards 1 2 3 5

GH Tudor Grange Hotel 31 Gervis Rd ☎(0202) 291472 Central plan **17** *F3*

Centrally located mock Tudor house with neat grounds.

12hc (3⇌) (4fb) CTV in all bedrooms ® B&b£13–£19 Bdi£18–£25 WBdi£113–£160 LDO7pm

Lic ♨ CTV 8P

Ⓥ

GH Valberg Hotel 1A Wollstonecraft Rd, Boscombe ☎(0202) 34644 Boscombe & Southbourne plan **52** *C1*

Small select private hotel near the sea and shops.

10fl (2fb) ⋈ ® ✱B&b£9.20–£12.50 WB&b£57.50–£80 (W only Jul & Aug)

♨ CTV 9P nc4yrs

GH *Vine* 22 Southern Rd, Southbourne ☎(0202) 428309 Boscombe & Southbourne plan **53** *E2*
Closed New Year

Double-fronted villa in quiet surroundings and leading to cliff top at Southbourne.

7fl

Lic ♨ CTV 7P nc

GH Waldale 37–39 Boscombe Spa Rd ☎(0202) 37744 Boscombe & Southbourne plan **54** *B1*
Mar–Oct & Xmas

Well-maintained house at Boscombe with good sea views.

19hc (8⇌ 5fl) (2fb) ® B&b£10–£15 Bdi£14–£21 WBdi£100–£140 (W only Jul & Aug)

Lic ♨ CTV 17P nc5yrs

Ⓥ

GH Weavers Hotel 14 Wilfred Rd, Boscombe ☎(0202) 37871 Boscombe & Southbourne plan **55** *C2*
Apr–Oct

In quiet residential area close to sea. A small friendly hotel offering good cooking.

7hc (4fl) (1fb) ⋈ ® ✱B&b£10–£13 Bdi£12–£15 WBdi£80–£95 (W only mid Jun–Aug) LDO5pm

Lic ♨ CTV 7P nc7yrs

Ⓥ

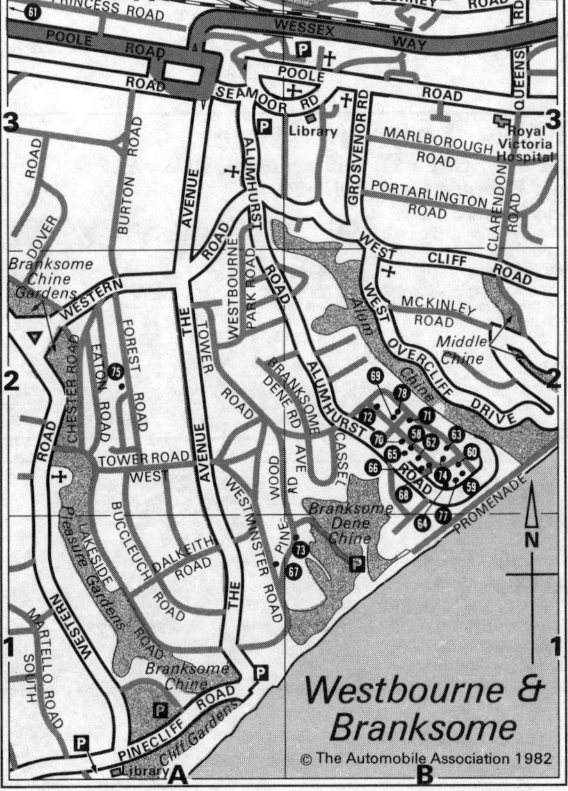

Westbourne & Branksome

58 Alum Bay Hotel
59 Alumcliff Hotel
60 Alum Grange Hotel
61 Avoncroft Private Hotel (*listed under Poole*)
62 Bay Tree Hotel
63 Chineside Private Hotel
64 Cliff House Hotel
65 Earlham Lodge
66 Golden Sands Hotel
67 Grovefield Hotel (*listed under Poole*)
68 Highclere Hotel
69 Holmcroft Hotel
70 Newfield Private Hotel
71 Northover Private Hotel
72 Ravenstone Hotel
73 Redcroft Private Hotel (*listed under Poole*)
74 Sea-Dene
75 Sheldon Lodge (*listed under Poole*)

77 West Dene Private Hotel
78 Woodford Court Hotel

GH West Dene Private Hotel
117 Alumhurst Rd, Alum Chine ☎(0202) 764843 Westbourne & Branksome plan **77** *B2*
Mar–Oct rs Nov–Feb
Overlooking sea at foot of Alum Chine.
17hc (5⇌ 7fl) (4fb) CTV in 15 bedrooms ✖ Ⓡ B&b£14–£20 Bdi£19–£25 WBdifr£119
Lic 🍽 CTV 17P
Credit cards 1 2 3 5 Ⓥ

GH Woodford Court Hotel 19–21 Studland Rd, Alum Chine ☎(0202) 764907 Westbourne & Branksome plan **78** *B2*
Mar–15 Nov
Overlooking Alum Chine enjoying a quiet location near beach.
35hc (8⇌ 18fl) (11fb) CTV in all bedrooms Ⓡ B&b£13–£16 Bdi£14–£19 WBdifr£98 LDO6.15pm
Lic 🍽 CTV 18P nc2yrs
Credit cards 1 2 Ⓥ

GH *Wood Lodge Hotel* 10 Manor Rd, East Cliff ☎(0202) 290891 Boscombe & Southbourne plan **56** *A1*
Etr–Oct
Peaceful and elegant house opposite East Cliff with attentive service and good accommodation.
15hc (7⇌ 7fl) (5fb) CTV in all bedrooms Ⓡ LDO6pm

Lic 🍽 CTV 12P
Credit cards 1 3

GH *Woodside Private Hotel* 29 Southern Rd, Southbourne ☎(0202) 427213 Boscombe & Southbourne plan **57** *E2*
Etr–Oct
9hc (1fl) ✖ LDO5pm
Lic 🍽 CTV 5P nc12yrs
Credit card 3

BOVEY TRACEY
Devon
Map **3** SX87

FH Mrs H Roberts **Willmead** *(SX795812)* ☎Lustleigh (06477) 214
Closed Xmas & New Year
Farmhouse dating from 1327 and situated on the edge of Dartmoor National Park in a delightful valley.
3hc ⊬ in all bedrooms ✖ B&b£15 WB&bfr£105
🍽 CTV P nc10yrs 32acres beef

BOW
Devon
Map **3** SS70

FH Mrs V Hill **East Hillerton House** *(SX725981)* Spreyton ☎(0633) 393
The farm is located 2m NE of Spreyton village.
3fl ⊬ in all bedrooms ✖ Ⓡ ✱B&b£8–£10 Bdi£12–£14 WBdi£75–£85 LDO4.30pm
🍽 CTV 𝐏 185acres arable beef sheep mixed

BOWNESS-ON-WINDERMERE
Cumbria
Map **7** SD49
Guesthouses are listed under **Windermere**

BRADFORD
West Yorkshire
Map **7** SE13

GH Maple Hill 3 Park Dr, Heaton ☎(0274) 44061
Large, comfortable Victorian house with many original features.
11rm (10hc) (1fb) ⊬ in 1 bedroom CTV in all bedrooms Ⓡ B&b£16.50 Bdi£21.60 WBdifr£145
Lic 🍽 15P 2🚗

BRAEMAR
Grampian *Aberdeenshire*
Map **15** NO19

GH Callater Lodge Hotel 9 Glenshee Rd (Guestaccom) ☎(03383) 275
26 Dec–mid Oct

Small friendly hotel set in own grounds with hill views.

9hc (1fb) Ⓡ B&b£12 Bdi£20 WBdifr£134.70 LDO7pm

Lic 🍽 CTV 14P

Credit cards 1 3

BRAMBER
West Sussex
Map **4** TQ11

INN Castle Hotel The Street ☎Steyning (0903) 812102

Charming old hotel with well-appointed bedrooms. Garden with small swimming pool and play area.

8hc (3⇌) (2fb) CTV in 5 bedrooms ✗ Ⓡ B&b£14–£22 Lunch£2.50–£4.50&alc Dinner9.45pm £2.50–£4.50&alc

🍽 30P 2🚗 ⇌ snooker

Credit card 3 Ⓥ

See advertisement under Steyning

BRAMPTON
Cumbria
See **Castle Carrock** and **Kirkcambeck**

BRANSCOMBE
Devon
Map **3** SY18

GH The Bulstone ☎(029780) 446
Feb–Nov

6hc (4fb) ⊬ in all bedrooms B&b£10.50–£20 Bdi£18.50–£22.50 WBdi£120–£140 LDO7.30pm

Lic 🍽 CTV 10P ⛬

BRAUNTON
Devon
Map **2** SS43

GH *Brookdale Hotel* 62 South St ☎(0271) 812075

A personally run guesthouse, situated only 200 yds from the village centre.

8hc (3fb) ✗ LDO9.30pm

Lic 🍽 CTV P 1🚗

FH Mr & Mrs Barnes **Denham** *(SS480404)* North Buckland ☎Croyde (0271) 890297

Large farmhouse, parts of which date from the 18th century, set in lovely countryside, 2 miles from Croyde and within easy reach of Barnstaple and Ilfracombe.

7hc (3fb) ✗ Ⓡ in 6 bedrooms ✱B&b£9–£10 Bdi£14.50–£15.50 WBdifr£90 (W only 18 Jul–30 Aug) LDO7.30pm

Lic CTV 8P 160acres beef

BRECHIN
Tayside
Map **15** NO56

Selected

FH Mrs M Stewart **Blibberhill** *(NO553568)* (5m WSW off B9134) ☎Aberlemno (030783) 225

This 18th century stonebuilt farmhouse enjoys a secluded setting amid rolling countryside and close to Melgund Castle. Bedrooms vary in size but all offer a high standard of decor and furnishing. The lounge is comfortable and Mrs Stewart's traditional home cooking is served at a large central table in the dining room. A friendly, informal atmosphere prevails.

3hc (1⇌) ✗ B&b£9.50–£10 Bdifr£14

🍽 CTV 4P 300acres arable beef mixed

Ⓥ

Selected

FH Mrs J Stewart **Wood of Auldbar** *(NO554556)* Aberlemno ☎Aberlemno (030783) 218

A Victorian farmhouse with open views and well-tended gardens set in the Vale of Strathmore approximately five miles from Brechin. The bedrooms are comfortably furnished in traditional style and range from small single to spacious family rooms. The lounge offers relaxation and the attractive sun lounge is where guests enjoy hearty farmhouse fare prepared by the friendly and attentive owner.

3rm (1fb) ⊬ in all bedrooms ✗ B&bfr£9.50 Bdifr£13.50

🍽 CTV 4P ⛬ 187acres arable mixed

Ⓥ

BRECON
Powys
Map **3** SO02

⟼**GH Beacons** 16 Bridge St ☎(0874) 3339

Georgian house with secluded garden beside the River Usk.

12hc (2⇌) (3fb) Ⓡ in 2 bedrooms B&b£8.50–£11.50 Bdi£13–£16 WBdi£91–£112 LDO7pm

Lic 🍽 CTV 12P

Ⓥ

BREDWARDINE
Hereford & Worcester
Map **3** SO34

GH Bredwardine Hall ☎Moccas (09817) 596
Mar–Nov

Elegant early 19th-century manor-house in tranquil garden setting.

5hc (3⇌ 1⇌) (1fb) CTV in all bedrooms ✗ (ex guide dogs) Ⓡ B&b£12–£18 Bdi£19.50–£23.50 WBdi£131.50–£138.50 LDO4.30pm

Lic 🍽 7P nc10yrs

See advertisement under Hay-on-Wye

INN Red Lion ☎Moccas (09817) 303
Mar–Oct (rs Nov–Feb party bookings only)

Charming, comfortable inn which also offers fishing and organised shoots.

7hc (4⇌) Annexe: 3hc (2⇌ 1⇌) (3fb) CTV in 5 bedrooms Ⓡ B&b£15–£30 Bdi£26–£42 WBdifr£225 Bar lunch £1–£4.50 Dinner8.30pmfr£12

🍽 35P 3🚗 ⥿

Credit cards 1 2 3 5 Ⓥ

BRENDON
Devon
Map **3** SS74

GH Brendon House ☎(05987) 206
Mar–7 Jan rs 8 Jan–Feb

Standing in ¾acre of walled gardens, ideally situated for walking or riding through wooded valleys.

5hc (1⇌) (1fb) Ⓡ B&b£10–£13 Bdi£16–£20 WBdifr£110 LDO6pm

Lic 🍽 CTV 5P ⥿

Credit card 1 Ⓥ

FH Mrs C A South ***Farley Water*** *(SS744464)* ☎(05987) 272
May–Oct

Comfortable farmhouse adjoining the moors. Good home-cooking and freedom for children. Located on west side of B3228 (sign-posted).

3rm (2hc) (2fb)

CTV P ⥿ 220acres beef sheep mixed

BRENT ELEIGH
Suffolk
Map **5** TL94

FH Mrs J P Gage **Street** *(TL945476)* ☎Lavenham (0787) 247271
Mar–Nov

A most beautiful period house, tastefully-furnished to a high standard.

4rm (3hc) ⊬ in all bedrooms ✗ Ⓡ B&b£11.50–£12

🍽 CTV 4P nc12yrs 143acres arable

BRICKHILL, GREAT
Buckinghamshire
Map **4** SP93

INN Duncombe Arms 32 Lower Way ☎(052526) 226

Cosy, comfortable and well equipped. Extensive garden leisure facilities including putting green. →

(3⋔) CTV in all bedrooms ✗ (ex guide dogs) (R) B&b£28–£30 Bdi£31.75–£40 WBdifr£225 Lunch£6.75–£7.50&alc Dinner10.30pm £6.95–£7.50&alc

⋔⋔ 12P 2🚗 ⌂ petanque

Credit cards 1 3 (V)

BRIDESTOWE
Devon
Map **2** SX58

FH Mrs M A Down **Little Bidlake** *(SX494887)* ☎(083786) 233
Whit–Sep

Neat, clean and efficient farmhouse adjacent to A30 between Bridestowe and Launceston.

2hc ✗ B&b£10–£12 Bdi£15–£18 WBdifr£98

⋔⋔ CTV P 150acres beef dairy mixed

(V)

⊢⊣**FH** Mrs J Northcott **Town** *(SX504905)* ☎(083786) 226
May–Sep

Attractive Devonshire farmhouse situated in the centre of a typical Dartmoor village. Offers comfortable accommodation and friendly service.

3hc (1fb) ✗ (R) B&b£9–£11 Bdi£13–£15 WBdifr£80 LDO6pm

⋔⋔ CTV 4P 160acres dairy

FH Mrs M Hockridge **Week** *(SX519913)* ☎(083786) 221

Large homely 17th-century stone-built farmhouse set in peaceful Devon countryside
¾ mile from A30.

6hc (3fb) (R) B&b£9.50–£10 Bdi£14–£14.50 WBdifr£94 LDO5pm

CTV 10P 183acres dairy sheep

(V)

See advertisement under Okehampton

BRIDGERULE
Devon
Map **2** SS20

⊢⊣**FH** Mrs S A Gardener **Buttsbeer Cross** *(SS266043)* ☎(028881) 210
May–Sep

Modernised farmhouse dating from 15th century. Within easy reach of Bude and North Cornish coast.

3rm (2hc) ✗ B&b£8 Bdi£12 WBdifr£80 LDO1pm

⋔⋔ CTV 6P nc6yrs 240acres mixed

BRIDGNORTH
Shropshire
Map **7** SO79

GH Severn Arms Hotel Underhill St, Low Town ☎(07462) 4616
Closed 23 Dec–2 Jan

A homely and convivial atmosphere in this early Victorian house near the River Severn.

10hc (3⋔) (5fb) (R) B&b£16–£20 Bdi£20–£27 WBdifr£125 LDO7pm

Lic ⋔⋔ CTV ⚑ ♪

Credit cards 1 3

INN King's Head Hotel Whitburn St ☎(07462) 2141

An authentic 17th-century coaching inn close to town centre.

5hc (3fb) CTV in all bedrooms ✗ (R) B&b£12.50–£13 Bdi£15.50–£21 Bar lunch £2–£6 Dinner 8pm £3–£8

⋔⋔ 8P 🚌

(V)

BRIDLINGTON
Humberside
Map **8** TA16

GH Bay Ridge Hotel Summerfield Rd ☎(0262) 673425
Closed Jan & Nov

Spacious, well-designed conversion of two semi-detached houses, close to South Bay.

14hc (6⇌ 6⋔) (5fb) CTV in all bedrooms (R) B&b£11 Bdi£14 WBdifr£88 LDO5.45pm

Lic ⋔⋔ CTV 6P ⌂

(V)

GH *Langdon Hotel* Pembroke Ter ☎(0262) 673065
May–Oct rs Mar, Apr & Nov

Comfortable hotel with smart, cosy lounge and sea views.

21hc (9⋔) (6fb) TV in 6 bedrooms ✗ LDO6pm

Lic ⋔⋔ CTV ⚑

GH *Shirley Private Hotel* 48 South Marine Dr ☎(0262) 672539

Comfortable, well-furnished guesthouse with spacious lounge and attractive dining room.

41hc (2⇌ 12⋔) (4fb) (R) LDO10pm

Lic lift ⋔⋔ CTV 7P

Credit cards 1 3

GH Southdowne Hotel South Marine Dr ☎(0262) 673270

Bright and cheerful house facing the sea.

10hc (2fb) TV in 1 bedroom ✗ (R) B&b£12.50 Bdi£15 WBdi£98

Lic ⋔⋔ CTV 10P

(V)

BRIDPORT
Dorset
Map **3** SY49
See also **Chideock Nettlecombe** & **Pilsdon**

GH Bridge House East St ☎(0308) 23371

Spacious, 18th-century, detached building on A35 on outskirts of town. Comfortable accommodation and friendly service.

11rm (10hc 6⇌ 2⋔) (3fb) (R) LDO9pm

Lic ⋔⋔ CTV 13P

GH Britmead House 154 West Bay Rd (Guestaccom) ☎(0308) 22941
Closed Jan

Between Bridport and West Bay harbour.

6hc (4⇌) (1fb) CTV in all bedrooms (R) B&b£13.25–£17.50 Bdi£20.75–£25.50 WBdi£131.60–£164.50 LDO5pm

Lic ⋔⋔ 6P nc5yrs

Credit cards 1 3 (V)

INN King Charles Tavern 114 St Andrews Rd ☎(0308) 22911

Situated a short distance from the town centre alongside the Beaminster to Yeovil road.

4hc TV in 2 bedrooms ✗ Ⓡ in 2 bedrooms ✱B&b£9–£10.50 Bdi£12–£15 WBdifr£54

CTV 6P 2🚗

BRIGHTON & HOVE
East Sussex
Map **4** TQ30

See plans **Brighton** and **Hove** on pp 91 & 92

For additional guesthouses see **Rottingdean** and **Saltdean**

Selected

GH Adelaide Hotel 51 Regency Sq ☎(0273) 205286 Telex no 877159
Brighton plan **1** *B1*
Closed 23 Dec–mid Jan

Good bedrooms with modern facilities. Cosy lounge and bar.

11hc (2⇌ 9⋒) (1fb) CTV in all bedrooms ✗ Ⓡ B&b£26–£38 Bdi£34–£46 WBdifr£266 LDO5pm

Lic 𝍊 ⁄P

Credit cards 1 2 3 5 Ⓥ

GH Ambassador Hotel 22 New Steine ☎(0273) 676869 Plan **2** *E1*

A small Victorian terraced house, recently restored to provide clean, modern accommodation.

9rm (2⇌ 5⋒) (4fb) CTV in all bedrooms ✗ Ⓡ B&bfr£14

CTV ⁄P

Credit cards 1 2 3 5

GH *Ascott House* 21 New Steine, Marine Pde ☎(0273) 688085 Brighton plan **3** *E2*

Small Victorian guesthouse run by friendly proprietors, only a short walk from shops and sea front.

10hc (4fb) CTV in all bedrooms ✗ Ⓡ

Lic 𝍊 ⁄P

Credit cards 1 2 3

GH Hotel Brunswick 69 Brunswick Pl ☎(0273) 733326 Telex no 877445 Hove Plan **1** *C1*

A large guesthouse, the Brunswick has a bar and spacious dining room.

20hc (1⇌) (3fb) CTV in all bedrooms ✗ Ⓡ B&b£15–£17 Bdi£20–£25 WBdi£125–£158 (W only Xmas) LDO10pm

Lic 𝍊 CTV 6P

Credit cards 1 2 3 5 Ⓥ

GH Cavalaire House 34 Upper Rock Gdns, Kemptown ☎(0273) 696899
Brighton plan **4** *E2*
Closed Xmas

Cheerful little terraced house close to the sea front.

9hc (2⋒) (4fb) CTV in all bedrooms Ⓡ B&b£10–£14

𝍊 ⁄P nc10yrs

GH *Charlotte House* 9 Charlotte St ☎(0273) 692849 Brighton plan **5** *F1*

Family-run commercial hotel within easy reach of the city centre.

9hc (3⋒) (1fb) CTV in all bedrooms Ⓡ

𝍊 ⁄P

GH Claremont House Second Av, Hove (Guestaccom) ☎(0273) 777748 Hove plan **2** *B1*

Gracious Victorian house retaining many original features. The bedrooms are comfortable and well appointed.

12hc (5⇌ 4⋒) CTV in all bedrooms Ⓡ ✱B&bfr£18.97 Bdifr£23.97 LDO11pm

Lic CTV ⁄P nc12yrs

Credit card 2

GH *Cornerways Private Hotel* 20 Caburn Rd, Hove ☎(0273) 731882
Brighton plan **6** *A4*

Small comfortable house with modern bedrooms and limited lounge facilities.

→

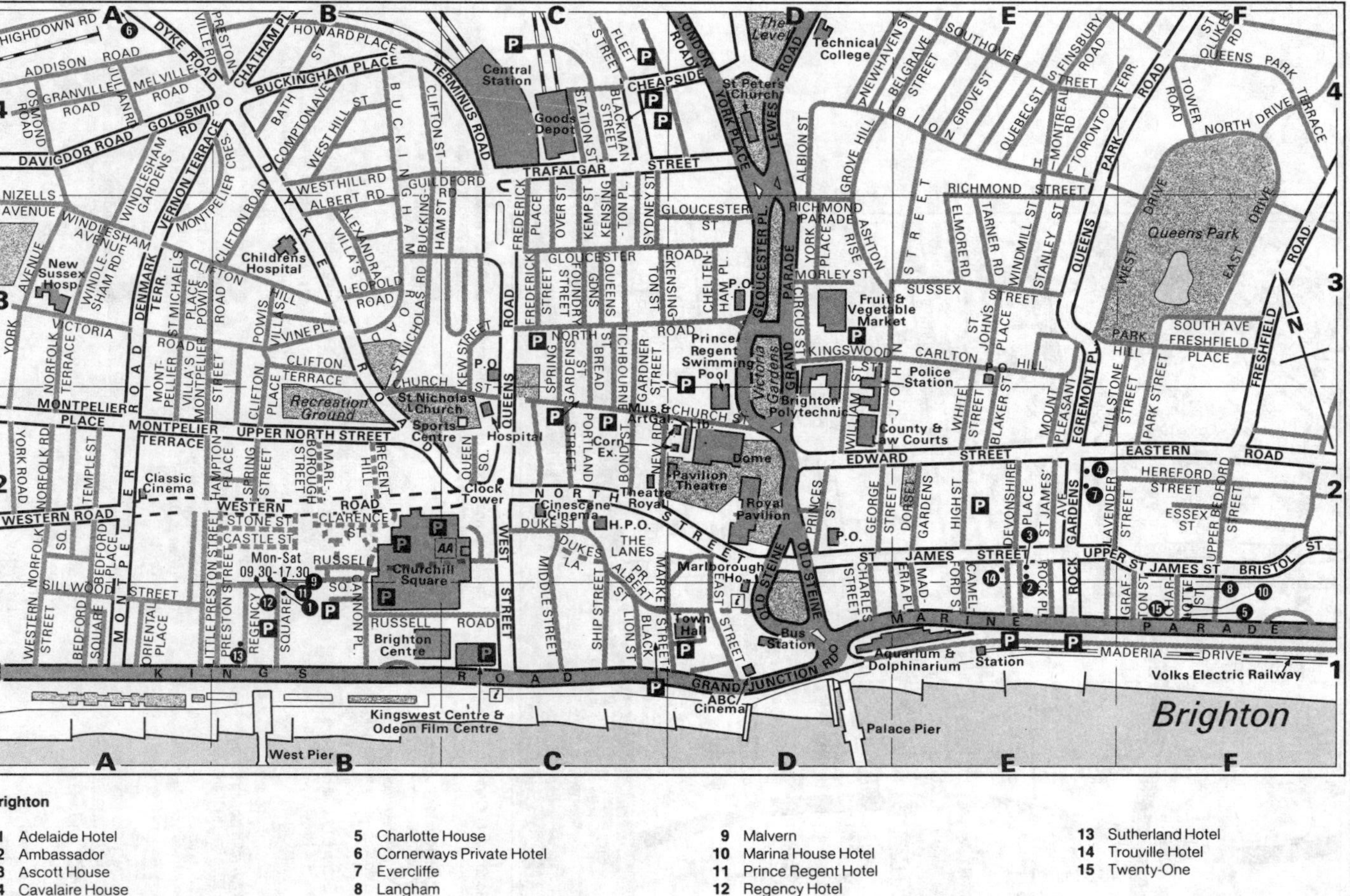

Brighton

1	Adelaide Hotel	5	Charlotte House	9	Malvern	13	Sutherland Hotel
2	Ambassador	6	Cornerways Private Hotel	10	Marina House Hotel	14	Trouville Hotel
3	Ascott House	7	Evercliffe	11	Prince Regent Hotel	15	Twenty-One
4	Cavalaire House	8	Langham	12	Regency Hotel		

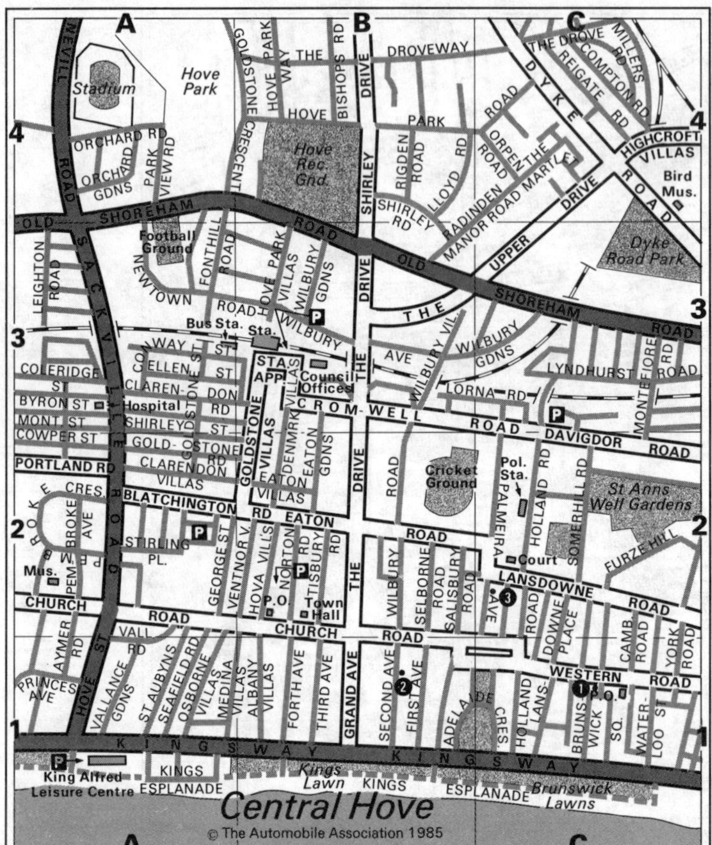

Hove

1 Brunswick
2 Claremont House
3 Croft Hotel

10hc (2fb) Ⓡ LDO4pm

Lic CTV ₱̸

GH Croft Hotel 24 Palmeira Av, Hove ☎(0273) 732860 Hove plan **3** *C2*

Well-established guesthouse, pleasantly situated within easy walking distance to the beach.

10hc (2fb) CTV in all bedrooms Ⓡ B&b£14–£16

Lic 𝍖 CTV ₱̸

ⓥ

GH Evercliff House 35 Upper Rock Gdns ☎(0273) 681161 Plan **7** *E2*

This cosy family house is situated away from the sea front. Bedrooms without private facilities are served by general showers.

10hc (3⇌) (2fb) CTV in all bedrooms ✗ Ⓡ B&b£10–£15 WB&b£66–£99

𝍖 CTV 3P (charge) nc4yrs

ⓥ

GH Langham 16 Charlotte St ☎(0273) 682843 Brighton plan **8** *F1*
Closed Dec

Victorian terraced house, comfortable and well-run establishment, just off sea front.

8hc (4fb) ✗ B&bfr£11

CTV nc7yrs

GH Malvern 33 Regency Sq ☎(0273) 24302 Plan **9** *B2*

A comfortable lounge and well-equipped bedrooms are a feature of this long-established guesthouse.

13⋒ CTV in all bedrooms ✗ Ⓡ B&b£18–£30 WB&bfr£126

Lic 𝍖 ₱̸

Credit cards 1 2 3 5 ⓥ

GH Marina House Hotel 8 Charlotte St, Marine Pde ☎(0273) 605349 Brighton plan **10** *F1*

Five-storey terraced Victorian hotel, with well-equipped accommodation, near sea front.

11hc (5⋒) (1fb) CTV in 8 bedrooms TV in 3 bedrooms ✗ Ⓡ ✱B&b£12.50–£14.50 (W only Oct–Mar) LDOnoon

Lic 𝍖 CTV ₱̸

ⓥ

GH Prince Regent Hotel 29 Regency Sq ☎(0273) 29962 Brighton plan **11** *B2*

Very comfortable Regency town house, with friendly attentive staff.

18⋒ CTV in all bedrooms ✗ Ⓡ B&b£20–£30

Lic 𝍖 CTV ₱̸ nc12yrs

Credit cards 1 3 5 ⓥ

GH Regency Hotel 28 Regency Sq ☎(0273) 202690 Brighton plan **12** *B1*

Attractive Regency house offering charm, comfort and attentive management.

14rm (4hc 1⇌ 9⋒) (1fb) CTV in all bedrooms ✗ Ⓡ ✱B&b£22–£30 Bdi£30–£40 WBdifr£200

Lic 𝍖 CTV ₱̸ nc8yrs

Credit cards 1 2 3 5 ⓥ

GH Sutherland Hotel 10 Regency Sq ☎(0273) 27055 Brighton plan **13** *B1*

Comfortable and efficiently-run hotel with well-equipped bedrooms.

26hc (12⇌ 8⋒) (3fb) CTV in all bedrooms Ⓡ B&b£18–£30 Bdi£25.95–£37.95 WBdi£160–£260 LDO4pm

Lic lift 🍽 ⁄P nc1yr

Credit cards 1 2 3 5 Ⓥ

GH Trouville Hotel 11 New Steine, Marine Pde ☎(0273) 697384 Brighton plan **14** *E2*

Well-appointed Regency house in quiet square, off the sea front.

9hc (2⫙) (2fb) CTV in 6 bedrooms ✗ B&b£9.50–£14.75 WBdi£80–£100

Lic 🍽 CTV ⁄P

Credit cards 1 2 3

Selected

GH Twenty One 21 Charlotte St, Marine Pde (Guestaccom) ☎(0273) 686450 Brighton plan **15** *F1*
Closed Xmas

Attractive rooms, tastefully furnished and decorated, one room has a fourposter bed. Dinners are well worth the experience, though not served every night.

7rm (2hc 5⫙) CTV in all bedrooms Ⓡ B&b£17–£34 Bdi£32–£49 WB&b£119–£238 LDOnoon

Lic 🍽 CTV ⁄P nc12yrs

Credit cards 1 2 3 5

BRIGSTEER (nr Kendal)
Cumbria
Map **7** SD48

FH Mrs E A Gardner **Barrowfield** *(SD484908)* ☎Crosthwaite (04488) 336
Apr–Oct

Comfortable Elizabethan farmhouse surrounded by beautiful walks and lake and sea views. 1½m N unclass road.

3rm (2hc) (1fb) ✗ B&b£9

🍽 CTV 6P 180acres dairy sheep mixed

Ⓥ

BRISTOL
Avon
Map **3** ST57

See plan on pages 94–95
See also **Redhill (Avon)**

Brighton & Hove — Bristol

GH Alandale Hotel Tyndall's Park Rd, Clifton ☎(0272) 735407 Plan **1** *C4*
Closed Xmas

Comfortable hotel near the city centre.

16hc (7⇌ 4⫙) (1fb) CTV in all bedrooms Ⓡ B&b£14.50–£25

Lic 🍽 10P

Ⓥ

GH Alcove 508–510 Fishponds Rd, Fishponds ☎(0272) 653886 Plan **2** *F4*

9hc (2⫙) (2fb) CTV in all bedrooms ✗ Ⓡ B&b£13–£18 Bdi£18–£20 LDO4pm

Lic 🍽 CTV 8P 1🚗

GH *Birkdale Hotel* 11 Ashgrove Rd, Redland ☎(0272) 733635 Plan **3** *C5*
Closed Xmas

Commercial hotel off Whiteladies Road.

18hc (4⇌ 5⫙) Annexe: 24rms CTV in all bedrooms Ⓡ LDO7.55pm

Lic 🍽 12P snooker

Credit cards 1 3

See advertisement on page 96

GH *Cavendish House Hotel*
18 Cavendish Rd, Henleaze ☎(0272) 621017 Plan **4** *C5*

Small, comfortable, friendly guesthouse in residential area near Henleaze shopping centre.

8hc (3fb) CTV in all bedrooms

🍽 5P

GH Chesterfield Hotel 3 Westbourne Pl, Clifton ☎(0272) 734606 Plan **5** *C4*
Closed Xmas

Pleasant small commercial hotel convenient to Clifton and local restaurants.

13hc CTV in all bedrooms Ⓡ B&b£12.50–£16 WB&bfr£79

Lic 🍽 ⁄P

Credit cards 1 3 Ⓥ

GH Downlands 33 Henleaze Gardens, Henleaze ☎(0272) 621639 Plan **6** *C5*

Interesting semi-detached gabled villa of varied period and design set in a select suburb. Accommodation is comfortable and the atmosphere is friendly and homely.

10hc (1⇌) (1fb) CTV in all bedrooms Ⓡ B&b£15–£20 Bdi£20–£25 LDOnoon

🍽 CTV ⁄P

Ⓥ

Selected

GH Glenroy Hotel 30 Victoria Sq, Clifton ☎(0272) 739058 Plan **7** *B3*
Closed Xmas wk

Pleasing private hotel in Clifton near to restaurants.

31rm (12hc 6⇌ 13⫙) Annexe: 17 ⫙ (9fb) CTV in all bedrooms Ⓡ B&b£21–£25.50 WB&b£140–£168

Lic 🍽 16P

Credit cards 1 3 Ⓥ

See advertisement on page 96

GH Oakdene Hotel 45 Oakfield Rd, Clifton ☎(0272) 735900 Plan **8** *C4*
Closed Xmas

Small, proprietor-run hotel.

14rm (11hc 3⫙) (2fb) CTV in all bedrooms ✗ Ⓡ ✱B&b£14–£17 WB&bfr£98 LDO6.30pm

🍽 1P

See advertisement on page 97

GH Oakfield Hotel 52–54 Oakfield Rd, Clifton ☎(0272) 735556 Plan **9** *C4*
Closed 23 Dec–1 Jan

Personally-run, private hotel.

27hc (4fb) Ⓡ B&b£15.50–£16 Bdi£19.50–£21 LDO7pm

🍽 CTV 4P 2🚗

See advertisement on page 97

GH *Rodney Hotel* 4 Rodney Pl, Clifton ☎(0272) 735422 Plan **10** *B3*
Closed Xmas

In Clifton village near to restaurants.

25hc (6fb) ✗

🍽 CTV ⁄P

GH Seeleys Hotel 19–27 St Pauls Rd, Clifton ☎(0272) 738544 Plan **11** *C4*
Closed Xmas wk

Lively hotel conveniently situated for city centre.

53hc (14⇌ 29fl) Annexe: 10hc (6⇌ 6fl) (30fb) CTV in all bedrooms ✈ Ⓡ B&b£19–£23 Bdi£25.50–£29 LDO10.30pm

Bristol

Lic 🍽 13P 22🚗 ⌂ sauna bath solarium gymnasium

Credit cards 1 2 3 Ⓥ

GH Washington Hotel 11–15 St Pauls Rd, Clifton ☎(0272) 733980 Telex no 449075 Plan **12** *C4*
Closed Xmas

Pleasant small hotel.

43rm (14hc 21⇌ 8fl) (5fb) CTV in all bedrooms Ⓡ B&b£16–£39 Bdi£22–£45 WB&bfr£100 LDO9pm

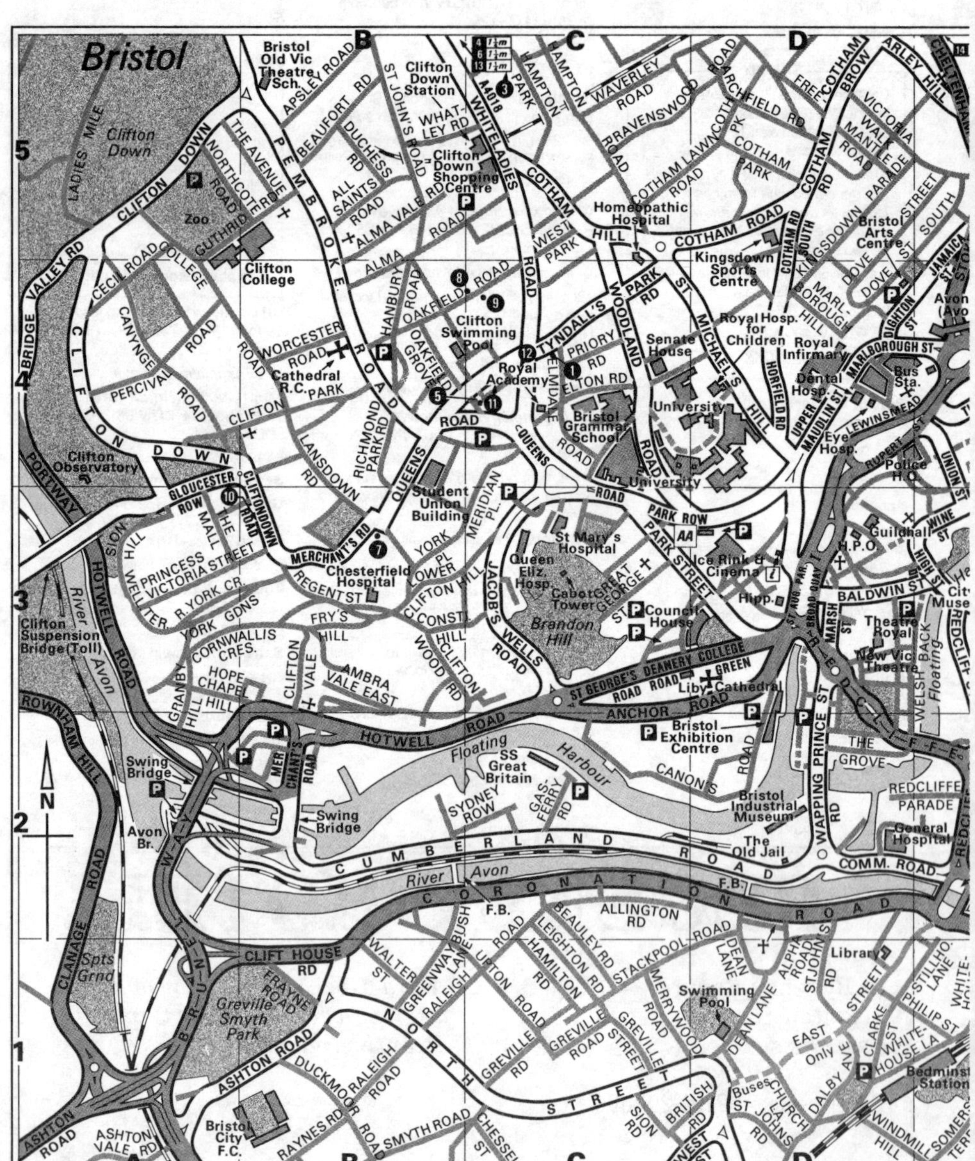

Lic 🍽 20P

Credit cards [1] [2] [3] [5] Ⓥ

GH Westbury Park Hotel
37 Westbury Rd, Westbury-on-Trym
☎(0272) 620465 Plan **13** *C5*

A high standard of both accommodation and home-cooking can be enjoyed at this hotel.

9hc (2⇌ 3fl) (2fb) CTV in all bedrooms
B&b£15–£28 Bdi£24–£38 LDO8pm

Lic 🍽 CTV 6P

Ⓥ

Bristol

1 Alandale Hotel
2 Alcove
3 Birkdale Hotel
4 Cavendish House Hotel
5 Chesterfield Hotel
6 Downlands
7 Glenroy Hotel
8 Oakdene Hotel
9 Oakfield Hotel
10 Rodney Hotel
11 Seeleys Hotel
12 Washington Hotel
13 Westbury Park Hotel
14 The Willows

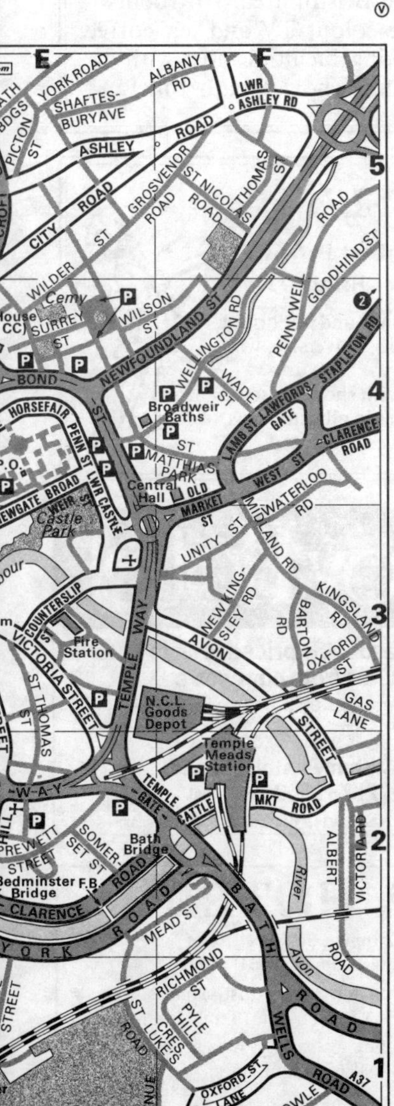

GH The Willows 209 Gloucester Rd Patchway ☎Almondsbury (0454) 6122 Plan **14** *D5*

8hc (4fl) (2fb) CTV in all bedrooms ✗ Ⓡ B&b£15.50–£17

Lic 🍽 CTV 12P

Credit card [1] Ⓥ

See advertisement on page 97

BRIXHAM
Devon
Map **3** SX95

See plan

Selected

GH Greenbrier Hotel Victoria Rd ☎(08045) 2113 Plan **2** *C1*
Mar–Nov

A small personally run hotel set in attractive gardens with commanding views of the harbour and the sea. All bedrooms are extremely well appointed and the public rooms are cosy and comfortable.

10hc (2⇌ 8fl) (2fb) CTV in all bedrooms Ⓡ ✱B&bfr£15 LDO8pm

Lic 17P

Credit cards [1] [3]

See advertisement on page 98

⊢→**GH Harbour Side** 65 Berry Head Road ☎(08045) 58899 Plan **3** *C2*

Friendly guesthouse overlooking harbour and coastline.

6hc (3fb) CTV in all bedrooms Ⓡ
B&bfr£8.50 Bdifr£13 LDOnoon

CTV P̸

GH Harbour View Hotel 65 King St ☎(08045) 3052 Plan **4** *C2*

10hc (2fb) CTV in 6 bedrooms TV in 4 bedrooms ✗ Ⓡ ✱B&b£9–£14.50 Bdi£14.50–£20 WBdi£100–£135 LDO3pm

🍽 CTV 2P

Credit cards [1] [3] Ⓥ

GH Raddicombe Lodge 105 Kingswear Rd ☎(08045) 2125 due to change to (0803) 882125 Plan **5** *A1*

9hc (2fl) (2fb) CTV in all bedrooms ✗ B&b£11–£16.60 Bdi£16.25–£23 WBdifr£125.30 LDO5pm

Lic CTV 9P

Credit cards [1] [3] Ⓥ

See advertisement on page 99

GH Ranscambe House Hotel
Ranscambe Rd ☎(08045) 2337 due to change to (0803) 882337 Plan **6** *C2*

Country-house-style property with friendly service.

10hc (6⇌ 4fl) (4fb) CTV in all bedrooms Ⓡ ✱B&b£13–£18 Bdi£18–£23 WBdi£108–£132 LDO2pm

Lic 🍽 CTV 14P

Amberley is situated in an ideal position for touring the West Country and also for the businessman who may be passing through or moving into the Bristol area. All rooms have colour TV and tea/coffee making facilities most with en suite shower/bath/toilet.

THE BIRKDALE HOTEL

Ashgrove Road (off Whiteladies Road), Redland, Bristol BS6 6LY

Proprietors: Mr & Mrs T Forde Telephone: Bristol 733635

A well appointed and moderately priced hotel, adjacent to busy and important main Whiteladies Rd, close to shops, banks, Downs, Zoo and University, with easy access to M4 and M5 motoways.

All rooms with colour TV and direct-dial telephones, most with showers, some with W/C plus bath and shower. Tea/coffee making facilities in all bedrooms. Residents Bar. Car parks. Parties welcome. Visa/Access accepted.

Glenroy Hotel

A small friendly but reasonably priced Private Hotel situated 5 minutes from city centre

A.A. Listed, (A.A. Special Merit Award), Full Central Heating, Car Park, Bar, 24 Hour Drinks Service. All Bedrooms have:- Direct Dial Telephone, Colour T.V., Four Channel Radio with Alarm Call System, Tea & Coffee Facilities.

Victoria Square, Clifton, Bristol BS8 4EW
Telephone: (0272) 739058. (Six lines).

AA Listed ETB ♛♛♛ British Hotels Restaurants and Caterers Association Member

MODA HOTEL

1 High Street, Chipping Sodbury, Avon
Telephone: Chipping Sodbury (0454) 312135

Listed Georgian residence. Privately owned, just 12 miles from Bristol City Centre, M4 and M5 interchange 10 minutes drive.

* All rooms have central heating, colour TV, direct dial telephone, clock radio and tea/coffee on request.
* À la carte restaurant.
* Lunch time carvery and salad bar.
* Small weddings or business meetings catering for.
* Easy parking.

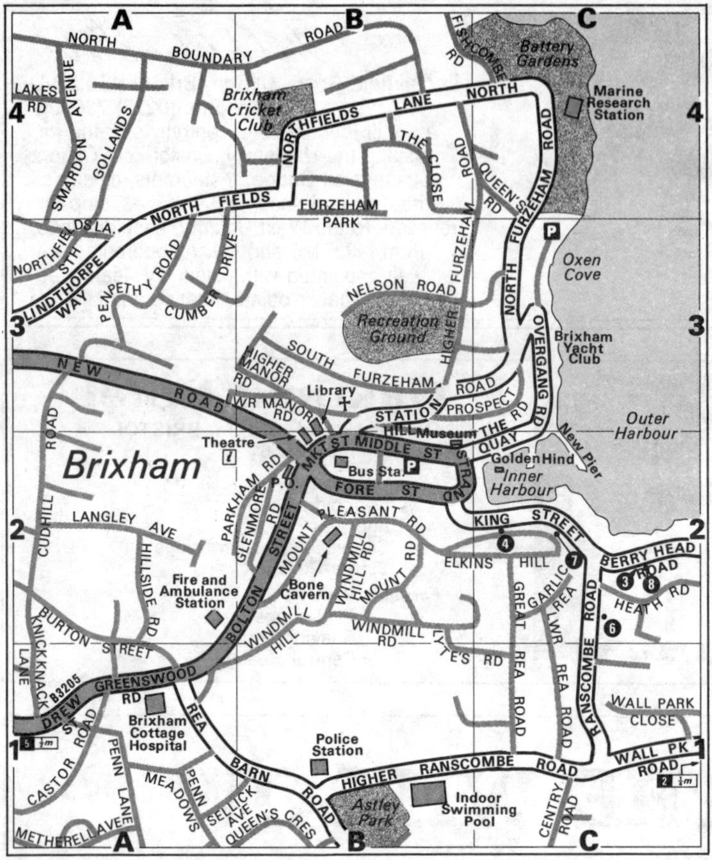

Brixham

2 Greenbrier Hotel
3 Harbour Side
4 Harbour View Hotel
5 Raddicombe Lodge
6 Ranscambe House Hotel
7 Sampford House
8 Torbay Heights Hotel

GH Sampford House 57–59 King St ☎(08045) 7761 Plan **7** *C2*
Apr–mid Oct

Small, personally-run residence. Spotless, comfortable bedrooms.

6hc (4fb) TV available in 2 bedrooms B&b£9–£12 Bdi£14–£17 WBdi£98–£119 LDO10am

CTV ⁄P

GH Torbay Heights Hotel Berry Head Rd ☎(08045) 4738 Plan **8** *C2*
Mar–Nov Closed Jan rs Dec & Feb

Small, friendly guesthouse offering good home cooking.

10hc (1⇌) (2fb) Ⓡ B&b£9–£13 Bdi£15.50–£19.50 WBdi£98–£130 (W only Aug) LDO10.30am

Lic ⫼ CTV 9P nc6yrs

Credit cards ☐1 ☐3 ☐5

BROAD CHALKE
Wiltshire
Map **4** SU02

INN Queens Head ☎Salisbury (0722) 780344

4⇌ CTV in all bedrooms ✗ Ⓡ B&b£18 Bdi£23 Lunch£4–£8&alcDinner 9.45pm £6–£8&alc

Lic 🍽 CTV 40P

Credit card ③ Ⓥ

BROAD HAVEN (nr Haverfordwest)
Dyfed
Map **2** SM81

GH Broad Haven Hotel ☎(043781) 366
Telex no 57515
Feb–Oct rs Nov–Feb

Large, lively family hotel facing beach.

39hc (32⇌ 3⋒) (12fb) CTV in all bedrooms Ⓡ ✱B&b£12–£24 Bdi£19–£31 WBdi£112–£175 LDO8.30pm

Lic CTV 100P ⩡(heated) solarium

Credit cards ① ② ③ ⑤ Ⓥ

BROAD MARSTON
Hereford & Worcester
Map **4** SP14

GH Broad Marston Manor ☎Stratford-upon-Avon (0789) 720252
Mar–Nov

7hc (2⇌) CTV in 1 bedroom TV in 6 bedrooms ✗ Ⓡ B&b£16.50–£17.50

🍽 20P nc12yrs

Credit card ③

See advertisement under Stratford upon Avon

BROADSTAIRS
Kent
Map **5** TR36

GH Bay Tree Hotel 12 Eastern Esp ☎Thanet (0843) 62502

Well-run, comfortable hotel with spacious bedrooms and sea views.

10hc (3⇌ 3⋒) (2fb) CTV in all bedrooms Ⓡ B&b£12–£15 Bdi£17.50–£20.50 WBdi£112–£134.75 LDOnoon

Lic 🍽 10P nc10yrs

Ⓥ

GH Cornerways Hotel 49–51 Westcliff Rd ☎Thanet (0843) 61612

12hc (5fb) CTV in 4 bedrooms Ⓡ B&b£12.60–£13.80 Bdi£16.10–£17.25 WBdifr£105 LDO5pm

Lic 🍽 CTV 10P

GH Dutch House Hotel 30 North Foreland Rd ☎Thanet (0843) 62824
Nov–Apr

Homely house with simple accommodation. Overlooking the sea.

10hc (2fb) ✗ Ⓡ B&b£12–£13.50 Bdi£18–£20 WBdi£125–£140 LDO8.30pm

Lic 🍽 CTV 6P

Ⓥ

GH East Horndon Hotel
4 Eastern Esp ☎Thanet (0843) 68306

Large three-storey detached house enjoying an elevated position overlooking the sea. Bedrooms are well-equipped and the hotel has a small lounge bar and television room.

11hc (1⇌ 1⋒) (4fb) CTV in 2 bedrooms TV in 9 bedrooms Ⓡ B&b£14 Bdi£20 WBdi£115

Lic 🍽 CTV P̸

Ⓥ

GH *Keston Court Hotel* 14 Ramsgate Rd ☎Thanet (0843) 62401

Comfortable, homely accommodation offering choice of menu.

9hc (2fb) ✗ Ⓡ LDO2pm

Lic 🍽 CTV 7P nc5yrs

Credit card ②

GH *St Augustines Hotel* 19 Granville Rd ☎Thanet (0843) 65017

Cheerful and bright modern bedrooms complemented by small lounge with bar. Near the sea.

15hc (4⋒) (5fb) CTV in all bedrooms Ⓡ ⱡ LDO7pm

Lic 🍽 1P

Credit cards ① ③

BROADWAY
Hereford & Worcester
Map **4** SP03

GH Leasow House Laverton Meadows ☎Stanton (038673) 526
(For full entry see **Laverton**)

See advertisement on page 100

GH Old Rectory Church St ☎Evesham (0386) 853729

(For full entry see **Willersey**)

See advertisement on page 100

GH Olive Branch 78–80 High St ☎(0386) 853440
Closed Xmas

The rooms in this fine 16th-century house are situated above both a grocery shop and an antique shop. To the rear is a secluded garden and a large car park.

8hc (2⋒) (2fb) ✗ B&b£11.50–£12.50

CTV 8P

Ⓥ

BROADWINDSOR
Dorset
Map **3** ST40

FH Mrs P Able ***Hursey*** *(ST430028)* ☎(0308) 68045
Closed Xmas & New Year

Comfortable and well-designed farmhouse accommodation enjoying quiet location in rolling Dorset countryside.

2hc ✗ Ⓡ LDOnoon

🍽 TV 2P nc5yrs 2½acres non-working

REMEMBER

Prices quoted in the gazetteer are minimum double room occupancy to maximum single room occupancy **per person.**

BROCKENHURST
Hampshire
Map **4** SU30

Selected

GH Cottage Hotel Sway Rd
☎Lymington (0590) 22296

A delightful and conveniently located cottage, parts of which date from 1600. Accommodation is very well-equipped, providing every comfort including a beamed lounge and log fires.

6hc (3⇌ 1fl) CTV in all bedrooms ✗ ® *B&b£19–£25 Bdi£29–£35 LDO7pm

Lic 6P nc

Credit cards 1 3

BROCKWEIR
Gloucestershire
Map **3** SO50

FH Mrs J Hunter **Spring** *(ST 542025)*
☎Tintern (02918) 439

A restored period farmhouse in an isolated setting but enjoying panoramic views across the Wye Valley and beyond. All rooms are tastefully appointed and comfortable.

3hc (1⇌ 1fl) no pets *B&bfr£9 Bdifr£16.50 LDO4pm
CTV 10P nc10yrs 17acres

FH Mrs M L Hitchon **Sylvia** *(SO 544024)*
☎(02918) 514
Closed Jan & Feb

16th-century farmhouse with magnificent views over surrounding countryside. Comfortable rooms.

3hc (1fb) TV in 1 bedroom ✗ B&bfr£12 Bdifr£18.50

CTV 8P

14 acres livestock

Ⓥ

BROMLEY
Gt London
London plan **4** *F2*
(pages 258–259)

GH *Glendevon House* 80 Southborough Rd, Bickley (2m E off A22)
☎01-467 2183

10hc (1fl) (1fb) CTV in 5 bedrooms LDO9pm

CTV 7P

Credit cards 1 3

GH Jasmine Villa Hotel 60 Hayes Rd
☎01-460 6821
Closed 2 wks in Dec

Mrs Vendryes runs a smart, strictly no-smoking, small hotel offering comfortable and well equipped rooms, situated in a central residential area of the town.

7hc (1fl) (1fb) CTV in all bedrooms ✗ ® *B&b£17–£23

6P nc

Ⓥ

BROMPTON REGIS
Somerset
Map **3** SS93

FH Mrs G Payne **Lower Holworthy** *(SS978308)* ☎(03987) 244
Closed Xmas

Small 18th-century hill farm overlooking and bordering Wimbleball Lake in Exmoor National Park.

3hc ✗ ® B&b£11 Bdi£18 WBdi£119.70

CTV 6P 200acres beef sheep

BROMSGROVE
Hereford & Worcester
Map **7** SO97

INN Forest 290 Birmingham Rd ☎(0527) 72063
rs Xmas

9hc CTV in all bedrooms ® B&b£16.50–£18 Lunch£2.80alcDinner 9.15pm £4.50alc

70P

Credit cards 1 2 3

BROUGH
Cumbria
Map **12** NY71

FH Mrs J M Atkinson **Augill House** *(NY814148)* ☎(09304) 305
Closed Xmas & New Year
Fine Georgian house in pleasant rural surroundings offering comfortable accommodation and good home-cooking.
3hc TV in all bedrooms Ⓡ B&b£9 Bdi£15 LDO4pm
CTV 6P nc 40acres mixed

BROUGHTON IN FURNESS
Cumbria
Map **7** SD28

INN High Cross Inn ☎(06576) 272
Closed Xmas Day
Built in 1660. Spectacular views from the attractive restaurant.
8hc (1 2) (2fb) CTV in all bedrooms Ⓡ *B&b£8–£17 Bdi£15–£18 WBdi£100–£120 Lunch fr£12alc Dinner9.30pm £6.30–£9.30alc
50P
Credit cards 1 3

BRUAR
Tayside *Perthshire*
Map **14** NN86

INN *Bruar Falls Hotel* ☎Calvine (0796) 83243
Family-run hotel in picturesque setting just off the A9. Simple accommodation with all-day meal service.
7rm (1fb) Ⓡ LDO9pm
CTV 80P
Credit cards 1 2 3 5

BRUTON
Somerset
Map **3** ST63

GH *Fryerning* Frome Rd, Burrowfield ☎(0749) 812343
4hc (3 1) CTV in 2 bedrooms TV in 2 bedrooms Ⓡ LDO7pm
Lic CTV 6P nc12yrs

BRYNGWYN
Powys
Map **3** SO14

FH Mrs H E A Nicholls **Newhouse** *(SO191497)* ☎Painscastle (04975) 671
200-year old, two-storey, stone-built farmhouse set in rolling countryside.
2hc in all bedrooms Ⓡ B&b£8.50–£9 Bdi£12–£14 LDO6pm
CTV 3P 150acres beef sheep
Ⓥ

BUCKFASTLEIGH
Devon
Map **3** SX76

GH Black Rock Buckfast Rd, Dart Bridge (at Buckfast 1m N) ☎(0364) 42343
This family-run guesthouse is an ideal location for touring Dartmoor.
10hc (4) (3fb) CTV in all bedrooms Ⓡ B&b£11.75–£12.75 Bdi£17.25–£18.25 WBdifr£115 LDO8pm
Lic CTV 43P
Credit cards 1 3 Ⓥ

GH Furzeleigh Mill Country House Hotel Dart Bridge ☎(0364) 43476
Detached house set in its own attractive gardens, close to the A38, on the edge of town.
15hc (4 2) (3fb) CTV available in bedrooms Ⓡ B&b£11.50–£12.50 Bdi£15.50–£20 WBdi£108.50–£138 LDO8pm
Lic CTV 32P
Credit cards 1 3 Ⓥ

BUCKLAND BREWER
Devon
Map **2** SS42

FH Mrs M Brown **Holwell** *(SS424159)* ☎Langtree (08055) 288
Jun–Aug rs May & Sep
16th-century farmhouse with a friendly and homely atmosphere. →

5hc (3fb) B&bfr£10 Bdifr£15 WBdifr£80 (W only Jul & Aug) LDO3pm

CTV P 310acres mixed

Ⓥ

BUCKNELL
Shropshire
Map **7** SO37

FH Mrs B E M Davies **Bucknell House** *(SO355735)* ☎(05474) 248
Closed Xmas & New Year

A large mellow, listed Georgian country house in secluded grounds on fringe of village, overlooking picturesque Teme Valley.

3rm (2⇌) Ⓡ ✱B&b£9.50–£11 WB&b£66.50–£77

CTV 3P nc12yrs (hard) 70acres grazing

FH Mrs C Price **Hall** *(SO356737)* ☎(05474) 249
Mar–Nov

A large Georgian farmhouse providing homely accommodation in peaceful rural surroundings close to village centre.

3rm (2hc) (1fb) B&b£9–£10 Bdi£14–£15 WBdifr£90

CTV 4P nc7yrs 225acres arable sheep

Ⓥ

Buckland Brewer — Bude

BUDE
Cornwall
Map **2** SS20
See plan on page 103

GH Atlantic Beach 25 Downs View ☎(0288) 3431 Plan **1** *B5*

This family-run terraced guesthouse is close to beaches and town centre. Bedrooms are comfortable and guests have a good choice of meals available.

9hc (4fl) (3fb) CTV in all bedrooms Ⓡ ✱B&b£6.50–£9 Bdi£10.50–£11 W£60–£82 LDO6.30pm

Lic CTV 1P

Credit cards 1 2 3 Ⓥ

GH Cliff Hotel Maer Down, Crooklets ☎(0288) 3110 Plan **2** *B5*
Apr–Oct

15⇌ (12fb) CTV in all bedrooms ✱B&b£10–£13.50 Bdi£14.50–£18 WBdifr£112 LDO6pm

Lic CTV 15P (heated) (hard)

GH Dorset House Hotel 47 Killerton Rd ☎(0288) 2665 Plan **3** *C3*

Charming building offering traditional English fare.

6hc (1⇌) (2fb) Ⓡ ✱B&b£12–£15 Bdi£15.50–£17.50 WBdi£80–£104 LDO6.50pm

Lic CTV 6P

Ⓥ

See advertisement on page 104

GH Flexbury Lodge Hotel Ocean View Rd ☎(0288) 3227 Plan **4** *C5*

A personally run house with its own outdoor heated swimming pool, situated just outside the town centre. Attractive gardens surround the house and home grown produce is used in the English style cooking.

15rm (4fl) (4fb) CTV in all bedrooms Ⓡ ✱B&bfr£10 Bdifr£15 LDO7pm

Lic CTV 6P (heated) pool table

Credit cards 1 2 3 5

See advertisement on page 104

GH Kisauni 4 Downs View ☎(0288) 2653 Plan **5** *C5*

A convivial atmosphere and home-cooking distinguish this semi-detached guesthouse.

7hc (4fb) CTV in all bedrooms Ⓡ ✱B&b£8.50–£10 Bdi£12.50–£14.50

Lic CTV 5P

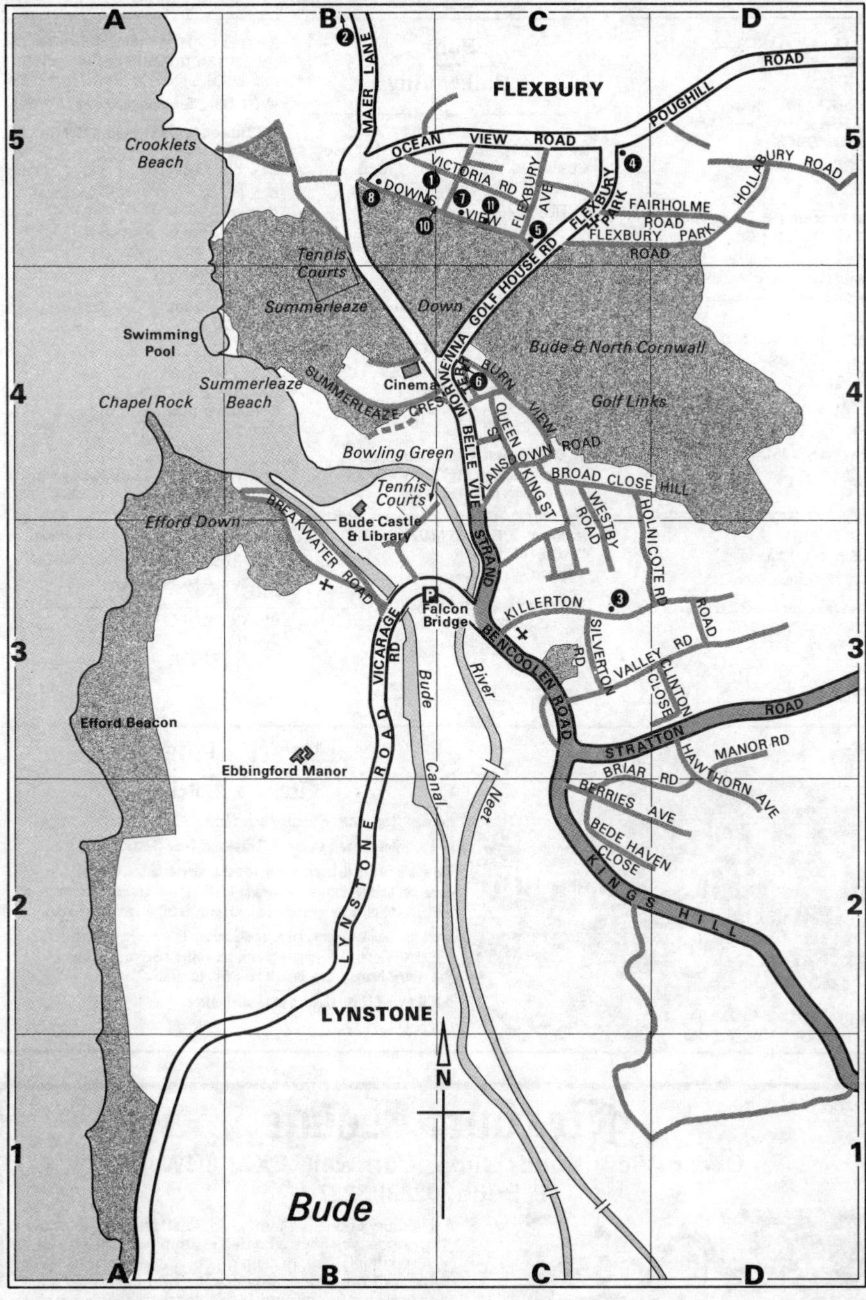

Bude

1 Atlantic Beach
2 Cliff Hotel
3 Dorset House Hotel
4 Flexbury Lodge Hotel
5 Kisauni
6 Links View
7 Pencarrol
8 Sweeneys
10 Wayfarer Hotel
11 Wyvern House

⊢⊣**GH Links View** 13 Morwenna Ter ☎(0288) 2561 Plan **6** *C4*
Closed Dec

7hc (2fb) CTV in all bedrooms ✖ Ⓡ B&b£8.50–£9.50 Bdi£13–£14.50 WBdifr£68 LDO6.30pm

Lic 🍽 CTV 2P 1🚗

Ⓥ

⊢⊣**GH Pencarrol** 21 Downs View ☎(0288) 2478 Plan **7** *C5*
Closed Xmas

Double-fronted, end of terrace Victorian house overlooking the downs and close to beaches.

8hc (1fl) (2fb) Ⓡ B&b£7.50–£11 Bdi£11.50–£15 WBdi£74–£84.50 LDO5pm

CTV 1🚗

Ⓥ

GH *Sweeney's* 35 Downs View ☎(0288) 2073 Plan **8** *B5*
Mar–Oct

Friendly guest house a short way from Crooklets Beach.

11hc (5fb) ✖ LDO5pm

Lic CTV 10P nc3yrs snooker

⊢⊣**GH Wayfarer Hotel** 23 Downs View ☎(0288) 2253 Plan **10** *B5*
Closed Xmas

9hc (2⇨ 2fl) (5fb) CTV in all bedrooms Ⓡ ✱B&b£8.50–£12.50 Bdi£14–£18.50 WBdi£87.50–£115 LDO6.30pm

Lic 🍽 CTV 4P

Ⓥ

GH *Wyvern House* 7 Downs View ☎(0288) 2205 Plan **11** *C5*

Privately run guesthouse with sea views.

8hc (3fb) ✖ LDO8pm

Lic 🍽 CTV 4P

BUDLEIGH SALTERTON
Devon
Map **3** SY08

GH Copperfields Hotel 7 Upper Stoneborough Ln ☎(03954) 3430
Closed Xmas rs Nov–mid Mar

7hc (2fl) (2fb) CTV in 2 bedrooms TV in 5 bedrooms Ⓡ B&bfr£11.50 Bdifr£17.50 WBdifr£115 LDO5pm

Lic 🍽 8P nc11yrs

GH Long Range Hotel Vale's Rd ☎(03954) 3321
Spring–Autumn

9hc (1⇨ 1fl) (1fb) CTV in all bedrooms ✖ Ⓡ B&b£12–£15 Bdi£18–£21 WBdi£130–£140 LDO8pm

🍽 CTV 8P 2🚗 (charge) nc4yrs

GH Tidwell House Country Hotel ☎(03954) 2444
Closed 24 Dec–1 Jan

Beautiful Georgian manor in extensive gardens.

9hc (3⇨ 4fl) (5fb) Ⓡ B&b£16 Bdi£22 WBdi£140 LDO9.15pm

Lic 🍽 CTV 24P 4🚗 ⌂

GH *Willowmead* 12 Little Knowle ☎(03954) 3115

6hc Ⓡ

🍽 CTV 6P nc5yrs

BUILTH WELLS
Powys
Map **3** SO05

⊢⊣**FH** Mrs Z E Hope **Cae Pandy** *(SO023511)* Garth Rd (1m W A483) ☎(0982) 553793

Cosy farmhouse near the River Irfon.

3hc (1fb) B&b£8–£8.50 Bdi£11.50–£12

🍽 CTV 10P 50acres mixed

BULKWORTHY
Devon
Map **2** SS31

⊢FH Mrs K P Hockridge **Blakes** *(SS395143)* ☎Milton Damerel (040926) 249
Etr–Sep

Pleasant, comfortable and well-decorated house in peaceful setting close to the River Torridge. Ideal touring centre for Devon and Cornwall.

2hc (1fb) ✗ B&bfr£9

CTV 4P nc12yrs 180acres arable beef sheep

BURFORD
Oxfordshire
Map **4** SP21

GH Corner House Hotel High St ☎(099382) 3151
Mar–Nov

Charming Cotswold stone building in picturesque High Street. Comfortable antique furnished bedrooms.

9hc (5⇨ 4ⓕ) (2fb) CTV in all bedrooms B&b£18–£20 LDO9pm

Lic 🏨 CTV ⅌

BURGH ST PETER
Norfolk
Map **5** TM49

FH Mrs R M Clarke **Shrublands** *(TM473926)* ☎Aldeby (050277) 241

1m SSW unclass rd.

3hc (1fb) ✗ B&b£9.50–£10.50 WB&b£66.50–£73.50

CTV 6P nc5yrs ⚲ (hard) ⚓ 480acres arable beef pigs mixed

Credit card ③ Ⓥ

BURNHAM-ON-CROUCH
Essex
Map **5** TQ99

GH Buccaneer 42 High St ☎(0621) 783654

A tastefully modernised Victorian house offering well appointed and spacious accommodation. Some rooms have retained their original Victorian fireplaces and there is also a small sun terrace to the rear.

6hc (1⇨ 5ⓕ) (1fb) CTV in all bedrooms Ⓡ B&b£12.50–£15 WB&b£75–£90

🏨 8P

Credit cards ① ② ③ ⑤

BURNSALL
North Yorkshire
Map **7** SE06

GH *Manor House* ☎(075672) 231
Closed Jan

Small private hotel whose gardens run down to River Wharfe.

7hc (2fb) ✗ LDO5pm

Lic 🏨 CTV 7P ⚓ U solarium

BURNTISLAND
Fife
Map **11** NT28

GH Forthaven 4 South View, Lammerlaws ☎(0592) 872600
Apr–Sep

Homely guesthouse looking out across the Firth of Forth.

4hc (2fb) B&b£9.50

CTV

BURTON UPON TRENT
Staffordshire
Map **8** SK22

GH Delter Hotel 5 Derby Rd ☎(0283) 35115

5hc (1fb) CTV in all bedrooms B&b£13.50 Bdi£17.50–£20 WBdifr£105 LDO7pm

Lic 🏨 ⌂

GH Edgecote Hotel 179 Ashby Rd ☎(0283) 68966

A large Victorian house situated on A50, ½ mile SE of the town centre offering a good standard of accommodation.

12hc (1ⓕ) (3fb) CTV in all bedrooms Ⓡ ✱B&b£14.50–£19.50 Bdi£22.50–£27.50 LDO 7.30pm

Lic 🏨 CTV 6P

Ⓥ

BURWASH
East Sussex
Map **5** TQ62

FH Mrs E Sirrell **Woodlands** *(TQ656242)* ☎(0435) 882794
Etr–Oct

Comfortably furnished, 16th-century cottage-style farmhouse, 1/3m down track from main road.

4rm ✗ B&b£10–£11 Bdi£14.50–£15.50 LDOam

🏨 CTV 4P

55 acres beef sheep mixed

Ⓥ

INN Admiral Vernon Etchingham Rd ☎(0435) 882230

Small 16th-century inn with beautiful gardens, overlooking Rother Valley.

5hc (2fb) CTV in 1 bedroom TV in 4 bedrooms Ⓡ in 2 bedrooms B&b£14 Bdi£18 WBdi£90 Lunch £4 Dinner 8.15pm £7

🏨 CTV 30P 2🚗 nc10yrs

INN *Bell* High St ☎(0435) 882304
rs Tue

5hc ✗ Ⓡ LDO9.30pm

Lic 15P

Credit cards ① ③

BURY ST EDMUNDS
Suffolk
Map **5** TL86

GH Chantry Hotel 8 Sparhawk St ☎(0284) 67427
rs wknds

Recent conversion of a listed Georgian house a short walk from centre.

13hc (2⇨ 8ⓕ) (2fb) CTV in all bedrooms Ⓡ B&b£18–£24 Bdi£25 LDO8.15pm

Lic 🏨 13P

Credit card ①

GH *Dunstow* 8 Springfield Rd ☎(0284) 67981

Well-extended, Victorian house with bright, well-equipped rooms. →

12hc (2⥂) (5fb) CTV in all bedrooms ✈ Ⓡ LDO6pm

Lic CTV 12P ⌂

GH White Hart 35 Southgate St ☎(0284) 5547
Closed 24–27 Dec

Old Tudor inn with original beams and chimneys, restored and converted to a guesthouse.

7hc (2⇌ 1⥂) (2fb) CTV in all bedrooms Ⓡ B&b£13–£15 Bdi£19.50–£21.50

Lic ♛ 7P

BUTLEIGH
Somerset
Map **3** ST53

FH Mrs J M Gillam **Dower House** *(ST517333)* ☎Baltonsborough (0458) 50354
Closed Dec–Jan

Attractive 18th-century farmhouse with friendly atmosphere.

3hc (1⇌) (1fb) TV available in bedrooms ✈ Ⓡ available in bedrooms B&b£9.50 Bdifr££14 LDO4.30pm

♛ CTV 6P 8acres small holding non-working

Ⓥ

BUTTERLEIGH
Devon
Map **3** SS90

FH Mrs B J Hill ***Sunnyside*** *(ST975088)* ☎Bickleigh (08845) 322
Closed Xmas

Friendly service and comfortable rooms in this Devon farmhouse 4m from M5 at Cullompton (junct 28).

5hc (3fb) ✈

CTV P 140acres mixed

Credit card ③

BUXTON
Derbyshire
Map **7** SK07

⊢⊣**GH Buxton Lodge** 28 London Rd ☎(0298) 3522
Closed 16 Dec–Jan

Spacious bedrooms, cosy lounge and dining area, forecourt parking. Near to town centre.

6hc (2fb) CTV in all bedrooms Ⓡ B&b£8.50–£9.50 Bdi£13–£14 WBdi£80–£85 LDO4pm

♛ CTV 4P

Ⓥ

⊢⊣**GH Griff** 2 Compton Rd ☎(0298) 3628

Beautifully proportioned and furnished rooms in large Victorian semi-detached house in residential area on edge of centre.

6hc (1fb) CTV in all bedrooms Ⓡ B&b£8.50–£9 Bdi£12–£13 WBdi£75–£80 LDOnoon

♛ CTV 5P

GH Hawthorn Farm Fairfield Rd ☎(0298) 3230
Mar–Oct

Charming 16th-century farmhouse retaining original features. Annexe in converted barns.

5hc Annexe: 7hc (2fb) B&b£10–£10.50 WB&b£70–£75

♛ CTV 12P 2🚗

Ⓥ

GH Hill House Private Hotel 54 London Rd ☎(0298) 4468
rs Jan & Feb

Detached Victorian house standing in own gardens a short distance from centre. Smartly furnished with lounge-bar and seminar facilities.

6hc (2fb) ✈ Ⓡ B&b£11–£17 Bdi£19–£23.50 WBdi£120–£148 LDO10pm

Lic ♛ CTV 10P nc16yrs

Ⓥ

⊢⊣**GH Kingscroft** 10 Green Ln ☎(0298) 2757
Mar–Dec

Large stone-built town house in a suburban area.

7hc (2fb) CTV in all bedrooms Ⓡ B&b£8.50 Bdi£12 WBdi£75 LDO5pm

Lic ♛ CTV 9P 2🚗 nc5yrs

Ⓥ

GH Old Manse 6 Clifton Rd, Silverlands ☎(0298) 5638
Feb–Nov

Spacious Victorian house in quiet side-road.

8hc (4⥂) (2fb) ✈ Ⓡ B&b£10–£15 Bdi£16–£20.50 WBdifr£108 LDO4pm

Lic ♛ CTV 4P nc5yrs

GH Roseleigh Private Hotel 19 Broad Walk ☎(0298) 4904
Closed Jan & Feb

Spacious accommodation overlooking the lake and Pavilion Gardens.

15hc (4⥂) (1fb) ✈ Ⓡ B&b£12–£14 Bdi£17–£21 WBdi£112–£140 LDO5pm

Lic CTV P nc7yrs

GH Swanleigh 7 Grange Rd ☎(0298) 4588

A charming three storeyed town house in a residential area close to the town centre.

4rm (1fb) TV in all bedrooms ✈ Ⓡ ✱B&bfr£8.50 Bdifr£13.50 LDO6.30pm

CTV 6P

GH *Templeton* 13 Compton Rd ☎(0298) 5275
Mar–Oct

On edge of centre, Victorian house of character with good-sized, well-appointed rooms.

6hc LDO5.30pm

♛ CTV 10P nc5yrs

GH Thorn Heyes Private Hotel 137 London Rd (Guestaccom) ☎(0298) 3539
Closed last 2 wks Jan & Nov

Local stone-built house dating from 1860, once a gentlemans residence, it still retains a Victorian theme throughout. Set in gardens.

8⥂ (2fb) CTV in all bedrooms Ⓡ ✱B&bfr£15.50 Bdifr£22.90 WBdifr£135 LDO6pm

Lic ♛ 11P

GH *Westminster Hotel* 21 Broadwalk ☎(0298) 3929
Feb–Nov & Xmas

Overlooking Pavilion Gardens lake, a large, double-fronted, Victorian town house with good, well-furnished rooms.

12hc (4⇌ 8⥂) (2fb) CTV in all bedrooms Ⓡ LDO3pm

Lic ♛ CTV 10P

Credit cards ① ② ③ ⑤

FH Mrs M A Mackenzie **Staden Grange** *(SK075717)* Staden Ln (1½m SE off A515) ☎(0298) 4965

Friendly proprietors run this well-converted, hillside farmhouse, offering spacious accommodation. Good scenic views.

3hc (1⇌ 1⥂) (1fb) Ⓡ ✱B&b£13.50–£17.50 Bdi£19–£23 WBdifr£133 LDO4.30pm

Lic ♛ CTV 20P Ս 250acres mixed

Ⓥ

BYRNESS
Northumberland
Map **12** NT70

⊢⊣**FH** Mrs A Anderson **Blakehope Burnhaugh** *(NT783002)* (1½m along A68 towards Rochester) ☎Otterburn (0830) 20267
Mar–Oct

Farmhouse in the Redesdale forest offering comfort and tranquility.

3hc (1fb) ✱B&b£8.50 Bdi£13.50 WBdifr£90 LDO4pm

♛ CTV 5P 3🚗 ⌂ 150acres beef

CADNAM
Hampshire
Map **4** SU21

FH Mrs A M Dawe **Budds** *(SU310139)* Winsor Rd, Winsor ☎Southampton (0703) 812381
Apr–Oct

Picturesque dairy farmhouse with thatched roof and attractive gardens, adjacent to the New Forest.

2hc (1fb) ✈ ✱B&b£9.50–£10 WB&bfr£63

♛ CTV 3P 200acres dairy beef

FH Mr & Mrs R D L Dawe **Kents**
Winsor Rd, Winsor
☎Southampton (0703) 813497
May–Sep

Picturesque thatched farmhouse, recently renovated. Accommodation of a high standard. 2m NE unclass rd.

2hc (1⇌ 1fl) (1fb) ✗ B&b£9.50–£10 WB&bfr£65

M CTV 4P nc2yrs 200acres beef dairy

CAERNARFON
Gwynedd
Map **6** SH46
See also **Llanddeiniolen**

GH Caer Menai 15 Church St
☎(0286) 2612
Mar–Dec

Mid-terrace Victorian building situated a short walk from the castle.

7hc (3fb) ✗ B&b£9–£9.50

CTV P̸

Ⓥ

GH Menai View Hotel North Rd
☎(0286) 4602

Single-fronted mid-terrace Victorian building overlooking the Menai Straits.

6hc (3fb) B&b£9–£10.50 Bdi£14.50–£16 WBdifr£100 LDO6pm

Lic M CTV P̸

Credit card 1

Credit Cards

1 Access/Euro/Mastercard

2 American Express

3 Barclaycard/Visa

5 Diners

Cadnam — Callander

GH Plas Treflan Motel Caethro ☎(0286) 2542
14 Mar–14 Nov

2fl Annexe: 7fl (2fb) CTV in all bedrooms Ⓡ B&b£12.50 Bdi£19.50 WBdi£115–£135 (W only Jul & Aug) LDO8.30pm

Lic M 20P nc7yrs grass solarium

Credit cards 1 2 3 Ⓥ

FH Mr & Mrs D Mackinnon **Plas Tirion** *(SH524628)* (Llanrug 3m E A4086)
☎(0286) 3190
Whit–Oct

4hc (2fb) ✗ Ⓡ B&b£10–£12

Lic M CTV 6P 450acres mixed

CAERSWS
Powys
Map **7** SO09

FH Mrs J Williams **Cefn-Gwyn** Trefeglwys (3m W along B4569) *(SO993923)*
☎Trefeglwys (05516) 648

2hc (1fb) ✗ ✻B&b£7.50–£8.50 Bdi£11.50–£12.50 WBdi£77–£84

M CTV 12P 2 80 acres mixed

Ⓥ

CAIRNRYAN
Dumfries & Galloway *Wigtownshire*
Map**10** NX06

INN Loch Ryan Hotel ☎(05812) 275

Neat roadside hotel with modest but spotless bedrooms and a pleasant bar. Its situation, opposite the Irish ferry terminal, make it an ideal location for the traveller.

12hc (4fl) CTV in 4 bedrooms ✗ Ⓡ B&b£18–£20 Bar lunch £1–£8 Dinner10pm£1–£8

M CTV 50P

CALDBECK
Cumbria
Map **11** NY33

GH High Greenrigg House
(Guestaccom)☎(06998) 430
Mar–Oct

Delightful 17th-century farmhouse offering good standard of accommodation. Well-equipped games room.

8hc (2⇌ 2fl) (1fb) ⊬ in 8 bedrooms B&b£14–£17 Bdi£23–£26 WBdi£138–£156 LDO5pm

Lic M CTV 8P

GH Riverside Lodge ☎(06998) 234
Mar–Dec

6fl (1fb) ⊬in all bedrooms CTV in all bedrooms ✗ Ⓡ B&b£17.25–£20.25 Bdi£24.25–£27.25 WBdifr£155.75 LDO7.30pm

Lic M 6P

Credit cards 1 3

FH Mrs D H Coulthard **Friar Hall** *(NY324399)* ☎(06998) 633
Mar–Oct

Modernised two-storey stone-built farmhouse, well-decorated and containing good quality furniture. Overlooks river and village church.

3hc (2fb) ✗ B&b£10–£11 Bdi£15.50–£16.50

CTV 3P 140acres dairy mixed sheep

Ⓥ

See advertisement on page 108

FH Mr & Mrs N M Savage **Swaledale Watch** Whelpo *(NY308398)* ☎(06998) 409
Closed Xmas

A spacious and comfortable bungalow offering a friendly atmosphere and excellent home made food.

3hc (1fb) ⊬ in all bedrooms ✗ Ⓡ ✻B&bfr£7.50 Bdifr£12 LDO2pm

CTV 12P 300acres sheep mixed

CALLANDER
Central *Perthshire*
Map **11** NN60

GH *Abbotsford Lodge* Stirling Rd
☎(0877) 30066

Large stone house on main street in its own grounds, at S entrance to the town. →

18hc (2⇌) (7fb) Ⓡ LDO7pm
Lic 🍽 CTV 20P

⊢ GH Annfield 18 North Church St ☎(0877) 30204
Mar–Oct
Attractive stone-built house on quiet street in the town centre.
8hc (2fb) B&b£8.50 WB&b£59.50
🍽 CTV 9P
Ⓥ

⊢ **GH Arden House** Bracklinn Rd ☎(0877) 30235
Feb–Nov
Attractive stone house standing on hillside close to golf course, formerly used in the making of 'Dr Finlay's Casebook'.
9hc (3fl) (3fb) Ⓡ B&b£9–£10 Bdi£15–£16.50 WBdi£95–£105 LDO7pm
🍽 CTV 12P
Ⓥ

⊢ **GH Brook Linn Country House** Leny Feus ☎(0877) 30103
Etr–Oct
Country house in own grounds with fine views over town and surrounding hills specialising in wholefood and vegetarian cooking.
7hc (4fl) (2fb) in all bedrooms Ⓡ B&b£9–£9.50 Bdi£16–£17 WBdifr£108 LDO6pm
🍽 CTV 10P

GH Edina 111 Main St ☎(0877) 30004
Pleasant stone-built guesthouse in main street.
9hc (1⇌) Annexe: 2hc (1⇌ 1fl) (2fb) Ⓡ B&b£9.50 Bdi£14.50 WBdifr£93.50
CTV 7P
Ⓥ

GH Greenbank 143 Main St ☎(0877) 30296
Closed Xmas & New Year rs Nov–Etr
Pleasant house standing in the main street.
6hc (2fb) *B&b£8.50–£10 Bdi£13.50–£15 WBdifr£90 LDO7pm
Lic 🍽 CTV 5P
Ⓥ

Selected

GH Highland House Hotel South Church St ☎(0877) 30269
Mid Mar–mid Nov
This charming, white painted house changed hands recently. However, new owners Keith and Pat Cooper have maintained the warmth and friendliness for which the house is renowned. Conveniently situated in a quiet street in the centre of town. The smartly-decorated public rooms are cosy and the bedrooms are attractive. Menus offer traditional Scottish dishes.
10hc (3fl) (1fb) Ⓡ *B&b£11–£12.75 Bdi£21.50–£23.25 WBdifr£142.95 LDO7pm
Lic 🍽 CTV
Ⓥ

GH Kinnell 24 Main St ☎(0877) 30181
Friendly house in main street, also functions as a tea room.
7hc (2fb) *B&b£9–£9.25 Bdi£14–£14.25 LDO7pm
CTV 7P

GH *Riverview House Private Hotel* Leny Rd ☎(0877) 30635
Etr–Oct
6hc (2fl) (2fb) Ⓡ LDO7.15pm
Lic 🍽 CTV 8P

GH *Rock Villa* 1 Bracklinn Rd ☎(0877) 30331
May–Sep
Detached house in corner site set back from the main road.
7hc (1fb)
🍽 7P

CALSTOCK
Cornwall
Map **2** SX46

INN Boot Fore St ☎Tavistock (0822) 832331
3hc (1⇌) (1fb) CTV in 2 bedrooms Ⓡ B&b£11.50–£17.50 Bdi£16.50–£22.50 WBdifr£103 Lunch fr£5.95&alc Dinner 10pmfr£5.95&alc
🍽 6P
Credit cards 1 2 3 5 Ⓥ

CALVINE
Tayside *Perthshire*
Map **14** NN86

FH Mrs W Stewart ***Clachan of Struan*** *(NN802654)* ☎(079683) 207
rs Oct–Etr
½m S on B847
2rm (1fb)
CTV 10P 10,000acres sheep

CAMBRIDGE
Cambridgeshire
Map **5** TL45

GH Antwerp 36 Brookfields ☎(0223) 247690
Converted period house with modern extension.
9hc (2fl) (1fb) TV in all bedrooms Ⓡ B&b£11–£20 Bdi£15–£24 WBdifr£105 LDO5pm
Lic 🍽 CTV 9P
Ⓥ

GH Ayeone Cleave 95 Gilbert Rd ☎(0223) 63387
6hc (2fl) (1fb) in 2 bedrooms CTV in all bedrooms Ⓡ B&b£15–£16
🍽 CTV 7P

GH Barnwell Lodge Hotel 627–631 Newmarket Rd ☎(0223) 249791
Closed Xmas Day
This personally-run guesthouse is easily accessible via the ring road on the outskirts of the city. Accommodation is compact and well-equipped.
18hc (3⇌ 6fl) (4fb) CTV in all bedrooms Ⓡ *B&b£20–£25
🍽 CTV 18P
Credit cards 1 3

GH Belle Vue 33 Chesterton Rd ☎(0223) 351859
Closed Xmas

7hc (2fb) CTV in all bedrooms ® B&b£10–£12

⚲ 4P 2🚗

GH Bon Accord House 20 St Margarets Av ☎(0223) 411188
Closed Xmas

A small friendly, family run hotel situated in a quiet cul-de-sac about 1½m to the south of this historic city.

12hc (1fl) (1fb) CTV in all bedrooms ⚟ in 2 bedrooms ✗ ® ✱B&bfr£11
12P 2🚗

Credit cards 1 3

Cambridge

GH *Fairways* 143 Cherryhinton Rd ☎(0223) 246063
Closed 24–26 Dec

14hc (4fl) (4fb) CTV in all bedrooms ✗ ®

⚲ CTV 20P

See advertisement on page 110

GH Hamilton Hotel 156 Chesterton Rd ☎(0223) 65664

Detached house in busy city road with car-parking at rear.

10hc (5fl) (3fb) CTV in all bedrooms ✗ ® B&b£14–£16 Bdi£19–£22 WBdi£133–£154

Lic ⚲ 10P nc4yrs

See advertisement on page 110

GH Helen Hotel 167–169 Hills Rd ☎(0223) 246465
Closed 16 Dec–5 Jan

23hc (3⇨ 20fl) Annexe: 6fl (4fb) CTV in all bedrooms B&b£22–£25 Bdi£31–£34 WBdifr£210

Lic ⚲ CTV 20P

Credit cards 1 3

See advertisement on page 110

GH Lensfield Hotel 53 Lensfield Rd
☎(0223) 355017
Closed 2wks Xmas

36hc (2⇌ 18⋒) (4fb) CTV in all bedrooms
✕ B&b£23–£30 Bdi£29–£36 LDO8.45pm

Lic ⅏ CTV 5P

Credit cards [1] [2] [3] [5]

GH Sorrento Hotel 196 Cherry Hinton Rd
☎(0223) 243533

A family-run hotel in a residential area with ample private parking.

22hc (3⇌ 19⋒) (2fb) CTV in all bedrooms
B&b£18–£30 Bdi£31.50–£41.50
WBdi£210–£260 LDO8.30pm

Lic ⅏ CTV 25P

Credit cards [1] [3] ⓥ

GH Suffolk House Private Hotel
69 Milton Rd ☎(0223) 352016

A substantial detached house with spacious rear garden and comfortable bedrooms on the outskirts of the town centre.

9hc (1⇌) (2fb) CTV in all bedrooms ✕ ®
B&b£15–£43 Bdi£24–£52 LDOnoon

Lic ⅏ CTV 10P

Credit cards [1] [3]

CAMELFORD
Cornwall
Map **2** SX18

GH Sunnyside Hotel Victoria Rd
☎(0840) 212250
Closed Nov

An impressive stone-built hotel standing on the outskirts of the small market town. →

10hc (2⇌) (6fb) CTV in all bedrooms B&b£12–£13.50 Bdi£18–£20.50 WBdi£95–£105 LDO7pm

Lic 🍴 CTV 12P

Ⓥ

GH Warmington House 32 Market Pl ☎(0840) 213380

Creeper-hung, large double-fronted house set in the middle of Camelford.

6hc (2fb) Ⓡ ✱B&b£10–£13 WB&b£66–£88 LDO9.30pm

Lic 🍴 CTV 3P 3🚗

Credit card ③

FH Mrs R Y Lyes **Pencarrow** *(SX108825)* Advent ☎(0840) 213282
Apr–Oct

Large stone farmhouse in pretty hamlet, 1½miles from Camelford.

2hc ✗ ✱B&b£7–£8 Bdi£11–£12 WBdi£75–£82 LDO10am.

TV 2🚗 40acres dairy

Ⓥ

CANTERBURY
Kent
Map **5** TR15

GH Abba Hotel Station Road West ☎(0227) 464771
Closed Xmas wk

Comfortable, modern, well-maintained accommodation with cellar restaurant.

19hc (2⫼) (4fb) ✗ Ⓡ available in bedrooms B&b£12.50–£17 Bdi£18.50–£32.50 WBdi£95–£110 LDO9.30pm

Lic 🍴 CTV 7P

Credit card ③ Ⓥ

GH Ebury Hotel New Dover Rd ☎(0227) 68433
Closed 25 Dec–16 Jan

Large Victorian gabled building in two acres of grounds. Cheerfully decorated spacious well-equipped accommodation.

17hc (15⇌ 2⫼) (6fb) CTV in all bedrooms Ⓡ B&b£19–£29 Bdi£27.50–£39.50 WBdi£130–£200 LDO8.30pm

Lic 🍴 CTV 20P 1🚗(charge) ▭(heated)

Credit cards ① ② ③ Ⓥ

GH Ersham Lodge 12 New Dover Rd (Minotels) ☎(0227) 463174 Telex no 965536
Apr–Dec

Comfortable modern accommodation with well-equipped bedrooms.

14hc (2⇌ 11⫼) (2fb) CTV in all bedrooms ✗ B&b£16–£30 WB&b£112–£210

Lic 🍴 11P 1🚗(charge)

Credit cards ① ② ③ Ⓥ

GH Highfield Hotel Summer Hill, Harbledown ☎(0227) 462772
Mar–Nov

Georgian-style country house, family-run and providing value for money.

10hc (1⫼) (2fb) ✗ Ⓡ B&b£12–£17

Lic 🍴 12P nc5yrs

Credit cards ① ③

GH Kingsbridge Villa Hotel 15 Best Ln ☎(0227) 66415

Modern guesthouse with 'Il Pozzo' basement restaurant and lounge bar.

12hc (4⇌) (4fb) CTV in 7 bedrooms B&b£13–£15 LDO10pm

Lic 🍴 CTV 8P

Ⓥ

GH Magnolia House 36 St Dunstans Ter ☎(0227) 65121

This small, homely guesthouse is in a quiet and pleasant residential area close to the Westgate Towers. Family-run, the accommodation is comfortable and well-maintained.

6hc (3fb) ⚟ in all bedrooms ✗ B&b£12–£14 WB&b£77–£91

🍴 CTV 3P

GH *Pilgrims* 18 The Friars ☎(0227) 464531

Compact city-centre guesthouse with simple but comfortable accommodation. Smoking is not encouraged.

14hc (2fl) ✗ (2fb)
ꟗ CTV 2P 4🚗

GH Pointers Hotel 1 London Rd ☎(0227) 456846
Closed Xmas & New Year
Tastefully furnished and well-equipped Regency-style hotel.
14hc (4⇨ 8fl) (2fb) CTV in all bedrooms Ⓡ ✱B&b£16–£26 Bdi£25–£35 WBdifr£147 LDO8.15pm
Lic ꟗ 10P
Credit cards 1 2 3 5 Ⓥ

CAPUTH
Tayside *Perthshire*
Map **11** NO04

FH Mrs R Smith **Stralochy** *(NO086413)* ☎(073871) 250
May–Oct
Situated in a lovely spot looking down a valley with trees merging in Sidlaw hills.
2rm ✗ Ⓡ B&bfr£8 Bdifr£12 WBdifr£84 LDO4pm
CTV 2P 239acres arable beef sheep

CARDIFF
South Glamorgan
Map **3** ST17

GH Ambassador Hotel 4 Oakfield St Roath ☎(0222) 491988
Closed Xmas

Canterbury — Cardiff

A friendly but modestly-appointed hotel; bar for residents.
12hc (4fb) CTV in all bedrooms ✗ Ⓡ ✱B&b£12–£15
ꟗ 12P

GH Balkan Hotel 144 Newport Rd ☎(0222) 463673
Modest commercial hotel convenient to city.
14hc (5fl) (3fb) CTV in all bedrooms ✗ Ⓡ in 6 bedrooms B&b£12–£16 Bdi£17–£21 LDO7pm
ꟗ CTV P
Credit cards 1 2

GH Domus 201 Newport Rd ☎(0222) 495785
Closed Xmas & New Year
Personally-run Victorian house with comfortable lounge and small bar.
10hc (2fl) (2fb) ✗ Ⓡ B&b£12.50–£17 Bdi£16.50–£21 LDOnoon
Lic ꟗ CTV 10P nc2yrs

GH Ferrier's (Alva Hotel) 130/132 Cathedral Rd ☎(0222) 383413
Closed 2 wks Xmas & New Year
Well-equipped and comfortable family-run hotel offering a good standard of service.
26hc (1⇨ 3fl) (4fb) CTV in all bedrooms B&b£15–£30 LDO7.45pm
Lic ꟗ CTV 10P
Credit cards 1 2 3 5
See advertisement on page 114

GH Princes 10 Princes St, Roath ☎(0222) 491732
Proprietor run guest house.
6hc (1fb) CTV in all bedrooms ✗ Ⓡ ✱B&b£11–£12.50 Bdi£18–£19.50 WBdifr£119 LDOnoon
ꟗ CTV 3🚗
Ⓥ

GH Tane's Hotel 148 Newport Rd ☎(0222) 491755
Within easy distance of the city centre, a proprietor-run establishment.
9hc (1fb) ✗ LDO7pm
ꟗ CTV 9P nc3yrs

Cardigan — Carradale

CARDIGAN
Dyfed
Map **2** SN14

GH Brynhyfryd Gwbert Rd ☎(0239) 612861
Small guesthouse run by enthusiastic family on pleasant outskirts of town.
6hc (2fb) Ⓡ B&b£9–£9.50 Bdi£13.50–£14.50 WBdi£85–£90 LDO7.30pm
CTV
Ⓥ

CARLISLE
Cumbria
Map **12** NY45

GH Angus Hotel 14 Scotland Rd ☎(0228) 23546
Closed 24–31 Dec
A neat, mid-terrace house on N side of centre.
9hc (2fb) CTV in 1 bedroom ✱B&b£11–£14 Bdi£14–£20 LDO7.45pm
Lic CTV

GH East View 110 Warwick Rd ☎(0228) 22112
Closed Xmas & New Year
Family-run, friendly guesthouse offering good value.
8hc (2fl) (2fb) ✱B&b£9–£10.50 Bdi£12.50–£14 LDO5pm
CTV

GH Kenilworth Hotel 34 Lazonby Ter ☎(0228) 26179
Small, friendly, guesthouse, family-run.
6hc (2fb) Ⓡ B&b£8.50–£10 WB&bfr£56
CTV 5P
Ⓥ

CARLOPS
Borders *Peeblesshire*
Map **11** NT15

FH Mrs J Aitken **Carlophill** *(NT155556)* (½m SW unclass) ☎West Linton (0968) 60340
Jun–Oct (rs May)
Compact, homely bungalow with attractive residents' lounge. Reached by private track at S end of village.
3rm Ⓡ in 2 bedrooms ✱B&b£9–£11 WB&bfr£55
CTV 6P 1800acres beef sheep mixed
Ⓥ

CARNO
Powys
Map **6** SN99

FH P M Lewis **Y Grofftydd** *(SN981965)* ☎Newtown (0686) 420274
Farmhouse is situated off A470 overlooking typical mid-Wales scenery. Ideal centre for walking. Sporting clay-pigeon shooting on premises.
3hc (1fb) B&b£10 Bdi£14.50 WBdi£98
CTV 4P 180acres beef sheep
Ⓥ

CARRADALE
Strathclyde *Argyllshire*
Map **10** NR83

GH Ashbank Hotel ☎(05833) 650
Adjacent to golf course offering comfortable but compact accommodation.
6hc (3fl) (1fb) Ⓡ B&bfr£10 Bdifr£16.50 WBdifr£90 LDO7pm
Lic 6P

GH Drumfearne ☎(05833) 710
Apr–Sep
Detached stone house in own grounds on a hill behind the harbour.
6rm (5hc) (1fb) B&b£9 Bdi£14 WBdifr£84 LDO6pm
CTV P
Ⓥ

Craigburn Farm

Catlowdy, Penton, Carlisle
Telephone: 0228 77214

A friendly atmosphere and personal attention awaits you at this 18th Century, 250 acre farm. Situated in a quiet setting. Delicious home cooking with fresh produce. Small Farmhouse Restaurant with Licence. All bedrooms with bathroom-en-suite, and tea making facilities. Central Heating. Pool table, darts, some gym equipment, ponies and shooting on farm, Fishing nearby. Excellent for touring, and stop overs to and from Scotland.

Member English and Cumbria Tourist Board and Farm Holiday Bureau.
Winter Bargain Breaks.

See gazetteer under Catlowdy

Bessiestown Farm

Catlowdy, Penton, Carlisle. CA6 5QP
Telephone no: Nicholforest (0228 77) 219
Your hosts: Jack and Margaret Sisson

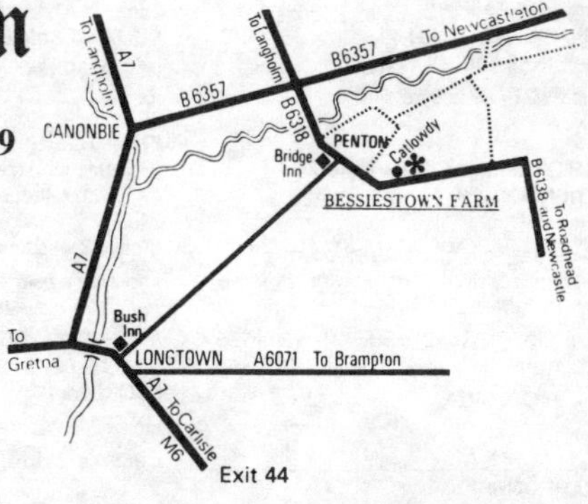

Small beef/sheep rearing farm offering friendly, relaxing atmosphere combined with delicious home cooking in delightful Farmhouse overlooking Scottish Borders.

Seven bedrooms - all ensuite. Tea/coffee making facilities.
Residential licence. Lounge. Separate T.V. lounge.
Dining room with open fire. Central heating throughout.

Three self catering cottages with option of evening meal in the Farmhouse.

Indoor Heated Swimming Pool (Pool open mid May-mid Sept)

Pony Riding. Games Room.

Ideal for family holiday, touring Lake District, Roman Wall, Solway and Galloway Coasts and as 'stop over' enroute to and from Scotland. **Winter breaks.**

AWARD WINNER
AA
1984

GH Dunvalanree Portrigh ☎(05833) 226
Etr–Oct

Large house with attractive rockery garden beside small sandy bay to the south of Carradale Harbour.

12hc (3fb) B&bfr£9.50 Bdifr£12.50 WBdifr£80 LDO4pm

Lic 🍽 CTV 9P

CARRBRIDGE
Highland *Inverness-shire*
Map **14** NH92

GH Ard-na-Coille Station Rd ☎(047984) 239

6hc (2fb) B&b£9.50–£10.50 Bdi£14.50–£15.50 WBdifr£98 LDO 6pm

Lic 🍽 CTV 6P

Ⓥ

GH Carrmoor Carr Rd ☎(047984) 244

A charming little house where you will get a warm welcome from the owners, with bright, airy cottage-style bedrooms and comfortable lounge in which to relax. Good home-cooking.

4hc (1fb) Ⓡ B&b£10 Bdi£15 WBdifr£98 LDO5.30pm

Lic 🍽 CTV 4P

Ⓥ

GH Mountain Thyme Country Station Rd ☎(047984) 696
Closed Nov–25 Dec

A comfortable and nicely-appointed country guesthouse. Situated ½m W of Carrbridge station.

6hc (3⇌ 3fl) (1fb) ✗ Ⓡ ✱B&b£9.50–£10 Bdi£15.50–£16 LDO5pm

Lic 🍽 CTV 8P nc9yrs

Ⓥ

GH Old Manse Private Hotel Duthil ☎(047984) 278
Nov–26 Dec

Personally-run, modernised, country manse in secluded setting with attractive, comfortable rooms.

8hc (3fb) Ⓡ B&bfr£10 Bdifr£15 WBdifr£95 LDO1pm

Lic 🍽 CTV 9P

Ⓥ

CARRONBRIDGE
Central *Stirlingshire*
See **Denny**

CARRUTHERSTOWN
Dumfries & Galloway *Dumfriesshire*
Map **11** NY17

FH Mrs J Brown **Domaru** *(NY093716)* ☎(038784) 260
Apr–Oct

Modern farmhouse set back from main road. Good home-cooking by Mrs Brown, a highly qualified chef.

3rm (2hc) TV in all bedrooms B&bfr£9 Bdifr£13.50 WBdifr£94.50 LDO7pm

🍽 3P nc5yrs 150acres dairy Ⓥ

CASTLE CARROCK
Cumbria
Map **12** NY55

FH B W Robinson **Gelt Hall** *(NY542554)* ☎Hayton (022870) 260

An olde-worlde farmhouse built around a courtyard directly off the main street of this tiny village.

3rm (1⇌) (1fb) ⊁ in 1 bedroom TV in 1 bedroom Ⓡ in 1 bedroom B&b£9–£10 Bdi£14.50–£15 WBdifr£85 LDO5pm

CTV 6P 1🚗 250acres beef dairy sheep

Ⓥ

CASTLE DONINGTON
Leicestershire
Map **8** SK42

GH Delven Hotel 12 Delven Ln ☎Derby (0332) 810153

7hc (2⇌) (1fb) CTV in all bedrooms ✗ Ⓡ in 2 bedrooms ✱B&b£10.64–£21.28 LDO10.30pm

Lic 🍽 5P 2🚗

Credit cards 1 2 3 5 Ⓥ

GH Four Poster 73 Clapgun St ☎Derby (0332) 810335

Tastefully restored and modernised old ivy-clad house in quiet street.

7hc ⊁ in all bedrooms ✗ ✱B&b£11.50–£13.50 WB&bfr£80.50

🍽 CTV 8P 4🚗

Ⓥ

FH Mr J C G Shields **Park** *(SK417253)* (Guestaccom) Melbourne Rd (1½m S A453) ☎Melbourne (Derbys) (03316) 2409
Closed 2 wks Xmas

Impressive half-timbered farmhouse dating from the 18th-century.

8hc (2⇌ 2fl) (3fb) CTV in all bedrooms Ⓡ B&b£15–£24 Bdi£19–£35 WB&bfr£90 LDO8.30pm

Lic 🍽 20P 40acres non-working

Credit cards 1 2 3 5 Ⓥ

Credit Cards

1 Access/Euro/ Mastercard

2 American Express

3 Barclaycard/Visa

5 Diners

CATLOWDY
Cumbria
Map **12** NY47

FH Mr & Mrs Lawson **Craigburn** *(NY474761)* ☎Nicholforest (022877) 214
Mar–Nov

Attractive farmhouse dating from 1760 with friendly atmosphere and good home-cooking.

7hc (4⇌ 3fl) (4fb) Ⓡ B&b£10–£11 Bdi£16–£17 WBdi£112–£119 LDO6.30pm

Lic 🍽 CTV 20P 250acres beef sheep

Ⓥ

See advertisement on page 115

Selected

FH Mr & Mrs J Sisson **Bessiestown** *(NY457768)* ☎Nicholforest (022877) 219

This truly delightful farmhouse has many facilities including an indoor heated swimming pool, games room and childrens play area. There is a friendly relaxed atmosphere and guests are free to wander about the farm or enjoy the many country walks nearby. The bedrooms and public rooms are comfortable and well-appointed. The delicious home cooking of Margaret Sisson is also highly recommended..

7rm (3⇌ 4fl) (2fb) ✗ Ⓡ B&b£12.50–£14 Bdi£19.50–£21 WBdi£120–£125 (W only mid Jul–Aug) LDO4pm

Lic 🍽 CTV 10P (heated) U gymnasium 55acres beef sheep mixed

Ⓥ

See advertisement on page 115

CEMMAES
Powys
Map **6** SH80

FH Mrs D Evans-Breese **Rydygwiel** *(SH826056)* ☎Cemmaes Road (06502) 541

Remote, detached, stone-built farmhouse on north side of the Dovey Valley with attractive gardens to rear of the house.

3rm (1fb) B&b£7–£8.50

P 200acres mixed

CHAGFORD
Devon
Map **3** SX78

GH Bly House Nattadon Hill ☎(06473) 2404
Jan–10 Nov

Lavishly furnished with antiques, this elegant former rectory is set in five acres of grounds.

8hc (5⇌) CTV in 4 bedrooms Ⓡ B&b£12–£16 WB&b£77–£105

🍽 CTV 10P nc12yrs

Ⓥ

GH Glendarah ☎(06473) 3270
Closed Jan & Feb
7rm Annexe: 1⇌ (2fb) CTV in 1 bedroom ® B&b£10.50–£12.50 Bdi£17–£19 WBdifr£115 LDO6.30pm
Lic 🍽 CTV 9P
Ⓥ

INN *Globe* ☎(06473) 3485
Friendly inn of character in the centre of this small Devonshire town.
3⇌ CTV in all bedrooms ® LDO9pm
🍽

CHALE
Isle of Wight
See **Wight, Isle of**

CHANNEL ISLANDS
Map **16**

GUERNSEY

L'ANCRESSE VALE

GH Lynton Park Hotel Hacsé Ln ☎(0481) 45418
14hc (5⇌ 7fl) (2fb) CTV in all bedrooms ✱ ® B&b£13–£19 Bdi£16.50–£22.50 LDO9pm
Lic 🍽 CTV 20P nc5yrs solarium
Credit cards 1 2 3 5 Ⓥ

GRANDES ROCQUES

GH *La Galaad Hotel* Rue Des Français ☎(0481) 57233
Etr–Oct
Only 10 mins walk from the sea, a modernised hotel in quiet residential area.
12hc (2⇌ 10fl) (3fb) CTV in all bedrooms LDO5.30pm
Lic 🍽 CTV 14P nc4yrs

GH Hotel le Saumarez Rue de Galad ☎(0481) 56341
Apr–Oct
Detached hotel in residential area, with spacious bar, separate lounge and modest bedrooms.
21hc (11⇌ 5fl) (6fb) ✱ ® available in bedrooms Bdi£13.50–£21.50 LDO6.30pm
Lic 🍽 CTV 30P nc5yrs

ST PETER PORT

GH Changi Lodge Hotel Les Baissieres ☎(0481) 56446
Apr–Oct
13hc (2⇌ 5fl) (7fb) ✱ ® B&b£9.50–£14.50 Bdi£13.50–£18.50 WBdifr£94.50 LDO7pm
Lic 🍽 CTV 15P (heated)
Credit card 3

GH Les Ozovets Lodge Ozovets Rd ☎(0481) 21288
Etr–Sep
12hc (5⇌ 6fl) CTV in all bedrooms ✱ ® ✱B&b£10.50–£14 Bdi£14.50–£18.50 LDO7.45pm
Lic 15P nc5yrs (grass)
Credit card 3

Selected

GH Midhurst House Candie Rd ☎(0481) 24391
25 Mar–15 Oct
5hc (2⇌ 3fl) Annexe 3fl (1fb) CTV in all bedrooms ✱ ® B&b£15–£19.50 Bdi£20–£25 WBdi£140–£161 LDO7pm
Lic 🍽 nc8yrs

ST SAMPSON'S

GH Ann-Dawn Private Hotel Route Des Capelles ☎(0481) 25606
30 Apr–4 Oct
Traditional Guernsey house with informal atmosphere, large lawned and landscaped gardens.
14hc (3⇌ 7fl) CTV in all bedrooms ✱ ® ✱B&b£10.50–£15.50 Bdi£15.50–£20.50 WBdi£143.50 LDO5pm
Lic 🍽 12P nc10yrs

ST SAVIOUR

GH La Girouette House Hotel ☎ (0481) 63269
mid Mar–Oct
14hc (6⇌ 6fl) (2fb) CTV in all bedrooms ✱ ® B&b£13.50–£18.50 Bdi£20–£25 WBdifr£140 LDO7.30pm
Lic 🍽 15P nc5yrs
Credit cards 1 2 3

JERSEY

GOREY

GH *Royal Bay Hotel* ☎(0534) 53318
May–Sep
Family-run hotel near the beach in this picturesque village.
16hc (6⇌ 10fl) (2fb) ✱ LDO7.30pm
Lic 🍽 CTV P nc6yrs

ST AUBIN

Selected

GH Panorama St Aubin High St ☎(0534) 42429 Telex No 4192341
Apr–Nov
Attractive property in elevated position with terraced tea garden and Victorian style summerhouse. Beautiful views across the bay. Friendly service.
16hc (7⇌ 9fl) (3fb) CTV in all bedrooms ✱ ® B&b£14–£35 WB&b£98–£245 (W only Jun–Sep)
🍽 nc6yrs
Credit cards 1 2 3 5 Ⓥ

ST CLEMENT

GH *Belle Plage Hotel* Green Island ☎(0534) 53750
Etr–Oct
Family-run hotel backing onto beach in a lovely part of the island.
20hc (4⇌ 16fl) (2fb)
Lic CTV 18P nc8yrs
Credit cards 1 3

ST HELIER

GH *Almorah Hotel* La Pouquelaye ☎(0534) 21648
Etr–Oct

Small, well-appointed hotel overlooking the bay with oak-panelled lounge and Breton dining room.

16hc (11⇌) (4fb) ✗ LDO6.30pm

Lic lift 🍽 CTV 10P ⛳

GH Cliff Court Hotel St Andrews Rd, First Tower ☎(0534) 34919
Feb–Oct

Good, comfortable accommodation and lovely views over the bay.

17hc (15⇌) (6fb) CTV in all bedrooms ✗ Ⓡ B&b£12.50–£20 Bdi£16–£24 WB&b£87.50–£140 (W only Jul & Aug) LDO7.15pm

Lic 🍽 CTV 12P ⇌(heated)

Ⓥ

GH Millbrook House Rue de Trachy ☎(0534) 33036
May–Sep

24hc (17⇌ 6⋔) ✗ Ⓡ ✱B&b£9.25–£20.50 Bdifr£9.75

Lic lift CTV P

GH Runneymede Court Hotel 46–52 Roseville St ☎(0534) 20044
mid Mar–5 Nov

Large family-run hotel within walking distance of town centre.

Channel Islands — Chapelton

57hc (41⇌ 16⋔) (6fb) CTV in all bedrooms ✗ Ⓡ B&b£10–£18 Bdi£13.50–£22.50 WBdi£94.50–£157.50

Lic lift 🍽 CTV ₱ nc5yrs

Credit card ③

ST MARTIN

GH Le Relais de St Martin ☎(0534) 53271
Apr–Oct

12hc (2⇌ 10⋔) (4fb) ✗ (ex guide dogs) Ⓡ B&b£13.75–£16 Bdi£17.25–£21

Lic 🍽 CTV 16P ⇌ snooker

ST PETER'S VALLEY

GH Midvale Private Hotel ☎(0534) 42498
Etr–Oct

Impressive 19th-century hotel in beautiful woodlands and water meadows.

20hc (7⇌) (3fb) ✗ B&b£13.10–£15.85 Bdi£15.10–£18.85 WBdi£105.70–£131.95 LDO6.30pm

Lic CTV 15P nc3yrs

Ⓥ

TRINITY

GH Highfield Country Hotel Route du Ebenezer ☎(0534) 62194
30 Mar–Oct

25hc (14⇌ 11⋔) (4fb) CTV in all bedrooms ✗ Ⓡ ✱B&b£17–£26.50 Bdi£19–£28.50 LDO7.45pm

Lic 🍽 25P ⛳ ⇌

Credit cards ① ② ③ ⑤ Ⓥ

CHAPELHALL
Strathclyde *Lanarkshire*
Map **11** NS76

GH Laurel House Hotel 101 Main St ☎Airdrie (02364) 63230

A comfortable house with good standards, run by friendly proprietors.

6rm (5hc) (1fb) B&bfr£12.50 Bdifr£16.50 LDO6.30pm

Lic 🍽 CTV 6P

CHAPELTON
Strathclyde *Lanarksire*
Map **11** NS64

FH Mrs E Taylor ***Millwell*** *(NS653496)* ☎East Kilbride (03552) 43248

Small, 18th-century farmhouse set in tree-studded land.

3rm (1fb) LDO5pm

🍽 CTV 5P 94acres dairy

Chapmanslade — Cheltenham

CHAPMANSLADE
Wiltshire
Map **3** ST84

FH Mrs M Hoskins **Spinney** *(ST839480)* ☎(037388) 412

Two-storey stone-built farmhouse surrounded by fields and woodland.

3hc (1fb) Ⓡ B&b£9.50–£12 Bdi£15.50–£18 WBdifr£90 ⱡ LDO4pm

⊞ TV 12P 1🚗 ⌂ 4acres poultry

Ⓥ

CHARD
Somerset
Map **3** ST30

GH Watermead 83 High St ☎(04606) 2834

9hc (1🛁 1🚿) (1fb) 🚭 in 3 bedrooms CTV in 5 bedrooms Ⓡ B&b£11–£13 Bdi£14.50–£17 WBdi£105–£120 LDOnoon

Lic ⊞ CTV 9P 2🚗

Ⓥ

CHARFIELD
Gloucestershire
Map **3** ST79

INN Huntingford Mill Hotel ☎Dursley (0453) 843431

Pleasant converted mill, enthusiastically-run and having a good steak restaurant.

5hc (1fb) CTV in all bedrooms ✘ Ⓡ B&b£15–£20 Bdi£25.95–£30.95 WBdi£164–£195 Lunch £10.95–£15&alc Dinner 10pm £10.95–£15&alc

⊞ 25P ⛟ ✓

Credit cards 1 2 3 5 Ⓥ

CHARLTON MUSGROVE
Somerset
Map **3** ST72

FH Mrs A Teague **Lower Church** Rectory La *(ST721302)* ☎Wincanton (0963) 32307
Apr–Oct

18th-century brick-built farmhouse with inglenook fireplace and beams.

2hc (1fb) Ⓡ ✱B&b£8.50 Bdi£13.50 WBdi£85 LDO10am

⊞ CTV 3P 60acres dairy sheep

CHARLWOOD
Surrey
Map **4** TQ24
For accommodation details see under **Gatwick Airport**

CHARMOUTH
Dorset
Map **3** SY39

GH Newlands House Stonebarrow Ln ☎(0297) 60212
Mar–Oct

Sixteenth-century farmhouse standing in own grounds on edge of village at the foot of National Trust land and minutes walk from beach.

12hc (7🛁 4🚿) (2fb) CTV in all bedrooms Ⓡ B&b£14–£16 Bdi£21.50–£23.50 WBdi£143–£157 LDOnoon

Lic ⊞ CTV 12P

Ⓥ

CHEDINGTON
Dorset
Map **3** ST40

FH Lt Col & Mrs E I Stanford **Lower Farm** *(ST485054)* ☎Corscombe (093589) 371
Closed Xmas

16th-century thatched farmhouse with extensive views over unspoilt Dorset and Somerset countryside. Jacob sheep, Suffolk Punch horses and ornamental waterfowl can be seen. Boating available on farm lakes.

3hc (1fb) 🚭 in all bedrooms ✘ Ⓡ B&bfr£12.50 WB&bfr£80

⊞ CTV 4P nc6yrs ✓ 120acres beef pig sheep

CHELMSFORD
Essex
Map **5** TL70

GH Beechcroft Private Hotel 211 New London Rd ☎(0245) 352462
Closed Xmas–New Year

Friendly, traditional-style guesthouse.

23hc (2🚿) (2fb) Ⓡ B&bfr£18.50

⊞ CTV 15P

Selected

GH Boswell House Hotel 118–120 Springfield Rd ☎(0245) 287587
Closed 10 days Xmas

Renovated Victorian town house, run by young and enthusiastic proprietors. Accommodation is of a good standard, modern and well-equipped.

13hc (9🛁 4🚿) (2fb) 🚭 in 2 bedrooms CTV in 9 bedrooms Ⓡ ✱B&b£22–£30 Bdi£28–£36 WBdi£196–£252 LDO8.30pm

Lic ⊞ CTV 15P

Credit cards 1 2 3 5 Ⓥ

GH Tanunda Hotel 219 New London Rd ☎(0245) 354295
Closed 2 wks Xmas

Fairly large modern hotel with good restaurant facilities and effective management.

20hc (2🛁 9🚿) CTV in 12 bedrooms B&b£18.25–£23 WB&b£127.75–£161 LDO7.25pm

Lic ⊞ CTV 20P

CHELTENHAM
Gloucestershire
Map **3** SO92
See also **Bishop's Cleeve**

GH Allards Shurdington Rd ☎(0242) 862498

Mr and Mrs Castle offer a warm welcome to this elegant period villa which has attractive and spacious accommodation and is situated two miles from the town.

11🚿 (2fb) CTV in all bedrooms ✘ Ⓡ B&b£15–£16 WB&bfr£112

⊞ 15P 1🏠

Credit cards 1 3 Ⓥ

GH Askham Court Hotel Pittville Circus Rd ☎(0242) 525547
rs Xmas

Regency house within walking distance of the town centre. →

18hc (4⇌ 4fl) (3fb) CTV in 8 bedrooms Ⓡ
✱B&b£16.50–£23 Bdi£23.50–£30.50
WBdifr£148 LDO6.30pm

Lic 🍽 CTV 20P

ⓥ

GH Beaumont House Hotel
56 Shurdington Rd ☎(0242) 245986

A listed Victorian house with picturesque garden, and spacious attractive bedrooms, close to town centre.

14hc (6⇌ 7fl) (2fb) CTV in 12 bedrooms TV in 2 bedrooms Ⓡ B&b£11.50–£20 Bdi£18–£26.50 WBdi£119–£178.50 LDO4pm

Lic 🍽 CTV 14P 2🚗

Credit cards 1 3 ⓥ

GH Beechworth Lawn Hotel 133 Hales Rd ☎(0242) 522583

Pleasantly furnished detached Victorian town-house with good parking.

7hc (3fl) (2fb) CTV in all bedrooms
B&b£12–£16 Bdi£17.50–£21.50
WBdifr£115 LDO4pm

🍽 CTV 10P

ⓥ

GH Bowler Hat Hotel 130 London Rd
☎(0242) 577362

Proprietor-run guesthouse.

Cheltenham

6hc (1⇌) (2fb) CTV in all bedrooms ✗ Ⓡ available in bedrooms B&b£12–£14 Bdi£18–£20 LDOam

Lic 🍽 CTV 8P

GH Carrs Hotel 42 Clarence St ☎(0242) 524003
Closed Xmas

15hc (2fl) (3fb) CTV in all bedrooms Ⓡ B&b£15–£20 Bdi£20–£25 LDO6.30pm

Lic CTV P

Credit cards 1 2 3 5 ⓥ

GH Central Hotel 7/9 Portland St
☎(0242) 582172

Recently refurbished and altered town-centre hotel.

17hc (8fl) (3fb) CTV in 8 bedrooms
B&b£14–£25 Bdi£20.50–£31.50
WBdi£140–£210 LDO9pm

Lic CTV 6P

Credit cards 1 2 3 5 ⓥ

GH Cleevelands House 38 Evesham Rd
☎(0242) 518898

16hc (6⇌ 6fl) (4fb) CTV in all bedrooms Ⓡ B&b£13.80–£16.50 Bdi£18–£21.50 WBdifr£115 LDO10pm

Lic 🍽 CTV 10P ♿

Credit cards 1 2 3 5

GH Cotswold Grange Hotel Pittville Circus Rd ☎(0242) 515119
Closed Xmas wk

Cotswold-stone house, attractively appointed.

26hc (9⇌ 12fl) (3fb) CTV in 21 bedrooms Ⓡ B&b£14–£26 WB&b£119–£182 LDO7.15pm

Lic 🍽 CTV 27P

Credit cards 1 3 ⓥ

GH Eton House Wellington St ☎(0242) 523272

Enthusiastic owners ensure guests a friendly welcome and personal attention at this tastefully appointed, end-of-terrace Georgian house. Enjoys a central location.

7hc (2⇌ 2fl) (1fb) CTV in all bedrooms ✗ Ⓡ B&b£14–£20 Bdi£21.95–£27.95 WBdifr£142.70 LDO8.30pm

Lic 🍽 P nc12yrs

Credit cards 1 3

GH Hallery House 48 Shurdington Rd
☎(0242) 578450

Victorian Grade II listed home on main Stroud road out of town. Friendly atmosphere.

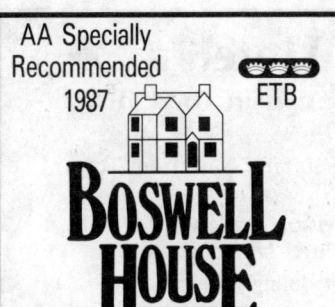

16hc (4fl) (3fb) ⅄ in 2 bedrooms CTV in 4 bedrooms TV in 1 bedroom Ⓡ B&b£13–£17 Bdi£18–£22 WBdi£120–£145 LDO5.30pm

M CTV 20P 3garages(charge) ⌂

Ⓥ

GH Hannaford's 20 Evesham Rd ☎(0242) 515181
Closed Xmas wk

Attractive, comfortable, terrace house, near centre and public car park. Personally-run.

10hc (1⇌ 8fl) (1fb) CTV in all bedrooms ✕ Ⓡ B&b£14–£23 Bdi£22.50–£31.50 (W only 2 wks in Mar) LDO5pm

Cheltenham

Lic M CTV ₽ nc7yrs

Ⓥ

GH Hollington House Hotel 115 Hales Rd ☎(0242) 519718
Closed Xmas

Attractive Cotswold-stone detached house in small pleasant gardens.

7hc (3fl) (2fb) CTV in all bedrooms Ⓡ B&b£13–£20 Bdi£20.50–£29 LDO6.30pm

Lic M CTV 12P ⌂

Ⓥ

⊢⊣**GH Ivy Dene** 145 Hewlett Rd ☎(0242) 521726

Proprietor-run guesthouse, modestly appointed.

10hc (2fb) CTV in all bedrooms Ⓡ B&b£8.50–£9.50 WB&b£59.50–£66.50

M CTV 8P

See advertisement on page 122

GH Knowle House 89 Leckhampton Rd ☎(0242) 516091
Closed 24–27 Dec →

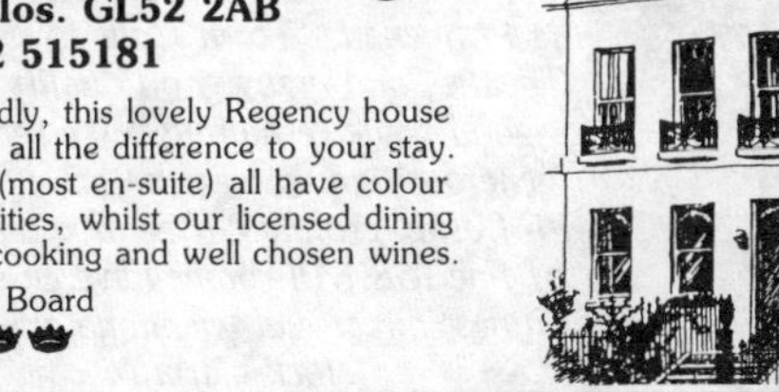

Double-fronted, red-brick house in residential suburb. Bright, neat interior.

5hc (1ꟷ) (1fb) ✻B&b£10 WB&bfr£63

CTV 6P

Ⓥ

GH Lawn Hotel 5 Pittville Lawn ☎(0242) 526638

9hc (2fb) CTV in 5 bedrooms ✗ Ⓡ B&b£11.50–£12.50 Bdi£17.50–£18.50 WBdifr£110 LDOnoon

Lic CTV 8P

Ⓥ

GH Milton House 12 Royal Pde, Bayshill Rd ☎(0242) 582601

Cheltenham

Elegant Regency terraced house, recently converted, with comfortable bedrooms.

9hc (1⇌ 8ꟷ) (4fb) CTV in all bedrooms Ⓡ B&b£14–£30

5P

Credit cards 1 3 Ⓥ

GH North Hall Hotel Pittville Circus Rd ☎(0242) 520589

Closed Xmas

Detached house with large bedrooms.

19hc (5⇌ 6ꟷ) (1fb) CTV in all bedrooms Ⓡ B&b£13.80–£19.55 Bdi£19.55–£25.30 WBdifr£117.30 LDO6.45pm

Lic CTV 20P

Credit cards 1 3 Ⓥ

GH Regency 50 Clarence Sq ☎(0242) 582718

Closed Xmas & New Year

8ꟷ (2fb) CTV in all bedrooms Ⓡ B&b£17–£20 Bdi£25–£28 WBdifr£155 LDO4pm

Lic CTV 3P nc7yrs

GH Stretton Lodge Western Rd ☎(0242) 528724

Elegant 19th-century house in a residential area. There is a friendly atmosphere and accommodation is comfortable with well-equipped bedrooms and a spacious lounge.

12hc (2⇌ 5⛆) (3fb) CTV in all bedrooms ✈ ® B&b£14.50–£25 Bdi£21.50–£32 LDOnoon

🍽 CTV 6P

Credit cards [1] [3]

GH Willoughby 1 Suffolk Sq ☎(0242) 522798
Closed Xmas & New Year

Proprietor run Regency house.

11hc (5⛆) (1fb) CTV in all bedrooms ® B&b£15.50–£18.50 Bdi£20.50–£23.50 WBdi£130–£145 LDO4pm

🍽 CTV 10P

CHERITON FITZPAINE
Devon
Map **3** SS80

FH Mrs D M Lock **Brindiwell** *(SS896079)* ☎(03636) 357

Period farmhouse with oak beams and panelling; on the side of a valley with views of the Exe Valley and Dartmoor.

4rm (1hc) (1fb) ⚟ in 1 bedroom ✈ ® ✱B&b£8.50–£9 Bdi£13.50–£15 WBdifr£84

CTV 4P 1🚗 120acres sheep

Ⓥ

CHESTER
Cheshire
Map **7** SJ46

GH Brookside Private Hotel 12 Brook Ln (Exec Hotels) ☎(0244) 381943
Closed Xmas wk

Large, well-furnished hotel with attractive restaurant and Victorian-style lounges.

24hc (16⇌ 8⛆) (6fb) CTV in all bedrooms ® B&b£15–£19.50 Bdi£21.95–£25.95 WBdi£138.29–£163.49 LDO8.30pm

Lic 🍽 CTV 14P ⌂ sauna bath solarium

Credit cards [1] [3] Ⓥ

GH *Cavendish Hotel* 44 Hough Green ☎(0244) 675100

Comfortable, elegantly furnished Victorian house in own grounds.

20hc (4⇌ 12⛆) CTV in all bedrooms LDO9pm

Lic 🍽 CTV 30P ⌂

Credit cards [1] [2] [3] [5]

GH Chester Court Hotel 48 Hoole Rd ☎(0244) 20779
Closed 24 Dec–5 Jan

A half-timbered characterful detached building with modern chalets to rear, set in its own grounds.

8hc (1⇌ 4⛆) Annexe: 12hc (6⇌ 6⛆) (7fb) CTV in all bedrooms ® ✱B&b£14–£26 Bdi£23–£35 LDO8pm

Lic 🍽 25P

Credit cards [1] [2] [3] [5]

GH Devonia 33–35 Hoole Rd ☎(0244) 22236

A small family-run establishment catering for tourists and business people. On A56, ½m from city centre.

10hc (6fb) CTV in all bedrooms ® ✱B&b£11.50–£13.50 Bdi£17–£19 WBdifr£115 LDO4pm

Lic 🍽 CTV 15P

Ⓥ

See advertisement on page 124

GH Eaton Hotel 29 City Rd ☎(0244) 312091

Family-run canal-side hotel close to city centre and station.

21hc (5⇌ 7⛆) (3fb) CTV in all bedrooms ® B&b£13–£20 Bdi£17.50–£26 WBdifr£122.50 LDO8pm

Lic 🍽 CTV 8P 1🚗

Credit cards [1] [2] [3] [5] Ⓥ

See advertisement on page 124

GH Egerton Lodge Hotel 57 Hoole Rd, Hoole ☎(0244) 20712
Closed 19 Dec–3 Jan

Attractive and well-furnished Victorian terraced house close to city centre.

6hc (4fl) (3fb) CTV in all bedrooms ✗ ® available in bedrooms B&b£12.50–£19.50 WB&b£87.50–£101.50

5P nc3yrs

Credit cards 1 2 3

GH *Elizabethan Park Hotel* 78 Hoole Rd ☎(0244) 310213

Charming, well-furnished house in own grounds, with good service only 1 mile from city.

Chester

7hc (2⇌ 5fl) (3fb) ® LDO6.30pm

Lic 20P 1 garage

GH Eversley Hotel 9 Eversley Park ☎(0244) 373744

Small, privately owned hotel with relaxing atmosphere.

11hc (4⇌ 5fl) (3fb) CTV in all bedrooms ✗ ® B&b£15–£16 WB&b£94.50–£100.80 LDO8pm

Lic CTV 12P

Credit card 1

GH Gables 5 Vicarage Rd, Hoole ☎(0244) 23969 due to change to 323969

Modern guesthouse in quiet road outside the city centre.

7hc (4fb) ® B&b£10–£12 WB&b£70–£77

CTV 7P

Credit card 1 Ⓥ

GH Hamilton Court 5–7 Hamilton St ☎(0244) 45387
Closed Xmas wk

A comfortable, family-run hotel in a quiet side road.

12hc (6fl) (5fb) CTV in all bedrooms Ⓡ
✱B&b£10–£12.50 Bdi£14–£16
WBdifr£160 LDO6.30pm

Lic 🏛 CTV 5P 10🚗

Credit card [3] Ⓥ

GH Malvern 21 Victoria Rd ☎(0244) 380865

Conveniently situated guesthouse opposite Northgate.

8hc (2fb) ✈ Ⓡ B&b£10 Bdi£13.50
WBdifr£94.50 LDO5pm

🏛 CTV ℗ nc2yrs

Ⓥ

GH Redland Private Hotel 64 Hough Green ☎(0244) 671024

Chester

Attractive, well-furnished house in own grounds with comfortable sitting rooms.

10hc (2⇌) (3fb) CTV in all bedrooms
B&b£15–£17.50

Lic 🏛 CTV 10P 3🚗 snooker

Credit cards [1] [3]

GH Riverside Recorder Hotel 19 City Walls ☎(0244) 311498

Small hotel with good facilities, newly furnished, on Roman Wall.

10⇌ fl (2fb) CTV in all bedrooms Ⓡ
✱B&b£18–£26 Bdi£25.50–£33.50
LDO8.30pm

Lic 🏛 CTV 15P

Ⓥ

See advertisement on page 126

GH Riverside Private Hotel 22 City Walls, off Lower Bridge St ☎(0244) 26580

Well-furnished modern hotel on City Walls next to the River Dee.

13hc (11⇌) (2fb) CTV in all bedrooms Ⓡ
B&b£16–£20 Bdi£23.50–£27.50
WBdi£168.50–£198.50 LDO9pm

Lic 🏛 CTV 25P

Credit card [3] Ⓥ

Chichester — Chislehampton

CHICHESTER
West Sussex
Map **4** SU80

GH Bedford Hotel Southgate ☎(0243) 785766

Small comfortable hotel. Personally run.

26hc (1⇨ 4fl) (2fb) CTV in all bedrooms Ⓡ in 5 bedrooms B&b£20–£35 LDO9pm

Lic 🍽 CTV 5P

Credit cards 1 2 3 5

CHICKERELL
Dorset
Map **3** SY68

INN Turks Head Hotel & Restaurant 6–8 East St ☎Weymouth (0305) 783093

Converted cottage extension to small hotel & restaurant, only 3 miles from Weymouth, offers comfortable bedrooms with own bathrooms.

4⇨ fl CTV in all bedrooms ✗ Ⓡ *B&b£20 Bdi£28.50 WBdifr£165 LDO9.30pm

🍽 CTV 12P

Credit cards 1 3 Ⓥ

CHICKLADE
Wiltshire
Map **3** ST93

GH Old Rectory ☎Hindon (074789) 226

6hc (2fb) B&b£10–£13 Bdi£16–£18 WBdi£90 LDO9pm

Lic CTV 14P

Credit card 1 Ⓥ

REMEMBER

Prices quoted in the gazetteer are minimum double room occupancy to maximum single room occupancy **per person.**

CHIDEOCK
Dorset
Map **3** SY49

Selected

GH Betchworth House Hotel ☎(0297) 89478

Cosy cottage-style guesthouse located in a most beautiful part of Dorset. Bedrooms are comfortable, public areas attractive, food home-cooked and the atmosphere is friendly.

6hc (3fl) (1fb) ✗ Ⓡ B&b£13–£15 Bdi£21–£23 WBdi£132.50–£153 LDO6pm

Lic 🍽 CTV 15P nc7yrs

Ⓥ

CHIPPENHAM
Wiltshire
Map **3** ST97

GH Oxford Hotel 32/36 Langley Rd ☎(0249) 652542
rs Xmas–New Year

Tidy, detached guesthouse on edge of town on Swindon Road.

13hc (7fl) (1fb) CTV in all bedrooms ✗ (except guide dogs) Ⓡ B&b£13–£21 Bdi£19.50–£27.50 WBdifr£135 LDO5.30pm

Lic 🍽 9P

Credit cards 1 2 3 Ⓥ

CHIPPING SODBURY
Avon
Map **3** ST78

GH Moda Hotel 1 High St ☎(0454) 312135
Closed 25 Dec–10 Jan

On High Street, a large well-maintained Georgian house, personally-run.

8hc Annexe: 3hc CTV in all bedrooms Ⓡ B&b£23 Bdi£30–£35 LDO7.30pm

Lic 🍽 20P nc

See advertisement under Bristol

CHIRNSIDE
Borders *Berwickshire*
Map **12** NT85

INN *Mitchell's Hotel* West End ☎(089081) 507

Small, friendly family-run inn. Modern conversion of six stone houses.

4hc (1fb) TV in all bedrooms ✗ LDO9.30pm

🍽 CTV 15P

CHISELBOROUGH
Somerset
Map **3** ST41

FH Mrs E Holloway **Manor** *(ST468151)* ☎(093588) 203
Apr–Oct

Comfortable 19th-century house built of ham stone with well appointed rooms.

4hc (1fb) ✗ Ⓡ B&b£10.50–£11.50 Bdi£17.50–£18.50 WBdifr£106 LDO5pm

CTV 4P 450acres mixed

Ⓥ

CHISELDON
Wiltshire
Map **4** SU17

FH Parsonage *(SU185799)* ☎Swindon (0793) 740204

16th-century building with spacious rooms. Pleasant lawned gardens back on to church.

5rm (4hc 1⇨) Ⓡ B&b£15–£17.50 Bdi£18.50–£21 LDO6pm

🍽 CTV 8P 2🚗 U

400acres arable

CHISLEHAMPTON
Oxfordshire
Map **4** SU59

INN Coach & Horses Stadhampton Rd ☎Stadhampton (0865) 890255

Hospitable, old-world country inn with very pleasant bedrooms.

9hc (2⇌ 7fl) CTV in all bedrooms ✈ (except guide dogs) Ⓡ B&b£24.50–£39 Bdi£34.50–£49 WBdi£214–£298 Lunch £11–£12&alc Dinner 10pm £11–£12&alc

42P

Credit cards ① ② ③ ⑤ Ⓥ

CHRISTCHURCH
Dorset
Map **4** SZ19
For additional guesthouses see **Bournemouth**

GH Belvedere Hotel 59 Barrack Rd ☎(0202) 485978

Large Victorian hotel on main Christchurch to Bournemouth road.

7hc (3fb) CTV in 4 bedrooms TV in 3 bedrooms B&b£12 Bdi£18 WBdifr£116 LDO4pm

Lic ꟾ CTV 12P ♘

GH Pines Private Hotel 39 Mudeford Rd ☎(0202) 482393

Quiet location close to Mudeford Quay and beaches.

12hc (6fl) (3fb) CTV in 6 bedrooms Ⓡ B&b£14.50–£16 Bdi£19–£20 WBdifr£121 LDO2.30pm

Lic ꟾ CTV 16P

Credit card ③ Ⓥ

GH Sea Witch Hotel 153/5 Barrack Rd ☎(0202) 482846

Friendly and efficient guesthouse on main Bournemouth road.

9hc (2fb) B&bfr£11.50 Bdifr£17 WBdifr£102 LDOnoon

Lic ꟾ CTV 15P

Ⓥ

GH Shortwood House Hotel 1 Magdalen Ln ☎(0202) 485223

Attractive, detached house in own garden in a cul-de-sac off main Bournemouth Road.

7hc (1⇌ 3fl) Annexe: 1fl (3fb) CTV in 7 bedrooms TV in 1 bedroom ✈ Ⓡ B&b£11–£16 Bdi£16–£22 WBdi£88–£120 LDO5pm

Lic ꟾ CTV 12P

CHURCHILL
Avon
Map **3** ST45

FH Mrs S Sacof **Churchill Green** *(ST429602)* ☎(0934) 852438

Modernised 16th-century farmhouse still retaining its character, the large garden faces south overlooking the foothills of the Mendips.

7hc (1fl) (2fb) ⁄ in 1 bedroom ✈ Ⓡ B&b£14.38 Bdi£18.50 WBdi£102.35

Lic ꟾ TV 30P ♘ ⩫(heated) U 25acres arable beef

CHURCHINFORD
Somerset
Map **3** ST21

⊢⊣**FH** M Palmer **Hunter Lodge** *(ST212144)* ☎Churchstanton (082360) 253

Detached, two-storey farmhouse with slate roof and large garden. Set in the Blackdown Hills.

4rm (3hc) (3fb) B&b£7–£8 Bdi£11–£12 WBdi£77–£84 LDOnoon

ꟾ CTV 6P ⩫(heated) U 30acres mixed

Ⓥ

CHURCH STOKE
Powys
Map **7** SO29

⊢⊣**FH** Mrs C Richards **Drewin** *(SO261905)* ☎(05885) 325 Apr–Oct

A border farmhouse with beams and inglenook fireplace. Fine views of surrounding countryside. Offa's Dyke footpath runs through the farm.

2hc (1fb) CTV in 1 bedroom TV in 1 bedroom ✈ Ⓡ B&b£9–£10 Bdi£13–£15 WBdi£90–£100 LDO6pm

ꟾ CTV 6P ♘ 102acres mixed

CHURCH STRETTON
Shropshire
Map **7** SO49

GH Dudgeley Mill All Stretton (2mN B4370) ☎(0694) 723461

Tastefully modernised old mill in peaceful, picturesque setting.

7hc (1fl) (1fb) ✈ Ⓡ B&b£11.50–£12 Bdi£17.50–£18 WBdi£115 LDO6pm

Lic 8P Ⓥ

GH Mynd House Private Hotel Ludlow Rd, Little Stretton (2m S B4370) ☎(0694) 722212
Closed Jan

13hc (3⇌) (1fb) Ⓡ B&b£13.75–£17.50 Bdi£25.50–£26 WBdi£143–£165 LDO12.30pm

Lic ꟾ CTV 16P

Credit cards ① ③

⊢⊣**FH** Mrs C J Hotchkiss **Olde Hall Farm** *(SO509926)* Wall-under-Heywood ☎Longville (06943) 253 Feb–Nov

Beautifully preserved Elizabethan farmhouse with cruck timbers and fine Jacobean staircase.

3hc (1fb) ✈ Ⓡ B&b£8.50–£10 WB&bfr£60

ꟾ CTV 6P 180acres dairy

FH Mrs J C Inglis **Hope Bowdler Hall** *(SO478925)* Hope Bowdler (1m E B4371) ☎(0694) 722041 Mar–Oct rs Nov

17th-century manor-house which has recently been modernised to a high standard. Set on the edge of the tiny village of Hope Bowdler and surrounded by hills.

3hc ✈ ✱B&b£10–£12

ꟾ 6P nc10yrs ℘(hard) 22acres sheep Ⓥ

Selected

FH Mrs J A Davies **Rectory** *(SO452985)* Woolstaston (3½m off B4370 at All Stretton) ☎Leebotwood (06945) 306
Mar–Oct

3⇌ ✈ B&b£10–£12

ꟾ CTV 10P nc12yrs 170acres beef dairy

FH Mr P W Secrett **Willowfield** *(SO464975)* Lower Wood All Stretton ☎Leebotwood (06945) 471

3rm (2hc) ✱B&bfr£8.50 Bdifr£12.50 LDO9pm

5P 40acres mixed

CINDERFORD
Gloucestershire
Map **3** SO61

INN *White Hart Hotel* St White's Rd, Ruspidge (B4227) ☎Dean (0594) 23139

Satisfactory inn with good-value restaurant.

4hc (2) (2fb) CTV in all bedrooms Ⓡ LDO9.45pm

CTV P

Credit card 1

CIRENCESTER
Gloucestershire
Map **4** SP00

GH Raydon House Hotel 3 The Avenue (Guestaccom) ☎(0285) 3485 due to change to 653485

Pleasant, small guesthouse, run by proprietors.

10hc (4 3) (2fb) CTV in all bedrooms Ⓡ B&b£16–£27 WBdi£100.80–£188.10 LDO9.45pm

Lic 7P

Credit cards 1 3

Church Stretton — Clacton-on-Sea

GH Rivercourt Beeches Rd ☎(0285) 3998 (due to change to 653998)

Comfortable homely guesthouse in pleasant garden setting.

6hc (2) Annexe: 4hc Ⓡ B&bfr£11 Bdifr£17.90 WBdifr£120.75 LDO7pm

Lic CTV 12P 1

GH La Ronde Hotel 52–54 Ashcroft Rd ☎(0285) 4611 (due to change to 654611)

An enthusiastically run comfortable guesthouse with attractive dining room.

10hc (1 6) (3fb) CTV available in all bedrooms Ⓡ B&b£15.25–£19.25 Bdi£29–£36 WBdifr£152 LDO8.15pm

Lic CTV 9P

Ⓥ

GH Wimborne 91 Victoria Rd ☎(0285) 3890 due to change to 653899

A neat and modestly appointed guesthouse. Strictly non-smoking.

5 (1fb) in all bedrooms CTV in all bedrooms Ⓡ B&b£11.50–£14 Bdifr£18 WB&bfr£80 LDO4pm

CTV 6P nc5yrs

CLACTON-ON-SEA
Essex
Map **5** TM11

GH Chudleigh Hotel Agate Rd ☎(0255) 425407

Well-kept family hotel near sea and shops.

13hc (1 5) (5fb) CTV in all bedrooms Ⓡ B&b£15.50–£19 Bdi£21–£24.50 WBdifr£130 LDO6.15pm

Lic 7P

Credit cards 1 2 3 Ⓥ

GH *Sandrock Hotel* 1 Penfold Rd ☎(0255) 428215

Detached house close to pier offering sound accommodation.

6hc (4) (3fb) Ⓡ LDO6pm

Lic CTV 6P

GH Stonar Private Hotel 19 Agate Rd ☎(0255) 426554

Small beautifully kept hotel, close to the sea and pier.

9hc (1fb) in 4 bedrooms Ⓡ ✱B&b£10–£13 Bdi£14.50–£16 WBdi £112–£120 LDO1pm

CTV 2P (charge) Ⓥ

WIMBORNE HOUSE

91 Victoria Road, Cirencester, Glos GL7 1ES
Telephone: (0285) 3890 or 653890

Dianne and Marshall Clarke invite you to enjoy the comfort of their house with good home cooking.

ALL ROOMS

En suite bathroom & shower. Colour TV. Tea/Coffee making facilities. Clock radio alarm. Full central heating. Free car park.

BED & BREAKFAST

Double or Twin room	*£22.00 to £28.00*	ALL PRICES
Single room	*£17.50 to £20.00*	INCLUDE
Evening Meal	*£6.50 per person*	V.A.T.

SAE please for brochure A NON-SMOKING HOUSE 

CHUDLEIGH HOTEL

Agate Road, Clacton-on-Sea CO15 1RA Tel: (0255) 425407

The Hotel is central, near the Pier and Seafront gardens and within easy reach of Theatres, Cinemas, Shops and Coach and Bus Station. Expert attention is given to the planning of the Menus and preparation of all meals.

- 13 well appointed bedrooms, most with private bath/shower/toilet
- All bedrooms with colour TV, radio/alarm/intercom and tea/coffee making facilities
- Residential licensed bar
- Full English breakfast menu
- Free heating in bedrooms
- Pleasant and relaxing lounge
- Parking on premises

Further details from resident proprietors: Carol & Peter Oleggini

La Ronde Hotel

52/54 ASHCROFT ROAD
CIRENCESTER
GLOS. GL7 1QX
Telephone: (0285) 4611
Due to change in 1988 to (0285) 654611

A detached Victorian Cotswold stone house well situated just off the town centre. Within minutes of Cirencester Park, Abbey grounds, Corinium museum, and the Cirencester leisure centre. The ideal base for touring the Cotswolds.

★ Renowned for the warmth of welcome and excellent freshly prepared food.
★ Attractive candlelit dining room. Dinner except Sunday. Bar snacks. Chilled beer.
★ Varied menu with extensive wine list.
★ Cosy beamed cocktail bar.
★ Colour TV lounge.
★ Full central heating.
★ Fully fire protected & certificated.
★ Most rooms with en-suite facilities.
★ Private parking at rear of hotel.
★ TV and tea/coffee making facilities available.
★ Fully licensed.

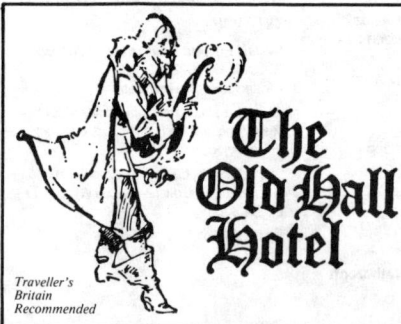

Owned and managed by
Norman & Judith Shales.
Travellers Britain (Arthur Eperon)
Member of the Heart of England Tourist Board
Listed by Arthur Frommer in U.S.A.

CLARENCEFIELD
Dumfries & Galloway *Dumfriesshire*
Map **11** NY16

Selected

GH Comlongon Castle ☎(038787) 283

Formerly the summer home of the Earl of Mansfield, this outstanding residence has an adjoining 15th-century Castle Tower and is a listed Ancient Monument. The bedrooms are opulent and comfortable, whilst the public rooms are spacious and grand featuring an abundance of splendid oak panelling. Guests are invited on a tour of the haunted castle before an enjoyable candle-lit dinner.

7hc (4⇌) (1fb) CTV in all bedrooms ✗ ✱B&bfr£20 LDO8.15pm

Lic 50P 1🚘

See advertisement under Dumfries

CLAVERDON
Warwickshire
Map **4** SP16

FH Mr & Mrs F E Bromilow **Woodside** *(SP186644)* Langley Rd (¾m S of B4095) ☎(092684) 2446
Closed 25 Dec–1 Jan

Quiet, comfortable house set in attractive gardens and adjacent to a 17-acre woodland nature conservancy. Close to Stratford and the tourist routes yet well off the beaten track.

3hc (1fb) CTV in 1 bedroom Ⓡ B&b£10–£13 Bdi£18.50–£21.50 WBdifr£125 LDO2pm

🍽 CTV 12P 1🚘 ⌂ croquet 22acres Bee hives dogs

CLEARWELL
Gloucestershire
Map **3** SO50

GH Tudor Farm ☎Dean (0594) 33046
Closed Jan

Farmhouse dates back to the 13th century and features oak beams, panelling and inglenook fireplace.

6hc (4⚑) Annexe: 1⚑ (1fb) CTV in all bedrooms dogs in annexe only Ⓡ B&b£12.50–£18.50 Bdi £20–£26 WBdifr£130

Lic 🍽 15P 2🚘

Ⓥ

Selected

INN Wyndham Arms ☎Dean (0594) 33666
Closed Xmas

A comfortable inn with good atmosphere.

5⇌ ⚑ (2fb) CTV in all bedrooms Ⓡ B&b£20.35–£33 Lunch£7–£8.75&alc Dinner9.30pm£9.75&alc

🍽 30P 1🚘 🚗

Credit cards 1 3

Clarencefield — Clunton

CLEVEDON
Avon
Map **3** ST47

GH Amberley 146 Old Church Rd ☎(0272) 874402
Closed Xmas

A comfortable stone-built house enthusiastically run by proprietor.

8hc (3⇌) (1fb) CTV in all bedrooms ✗ Ⓡ B&b£15–£18 Bdi£21.50–£28.50 WBdi£150.50–£171.50 LDO7pm

Lic 🍽 CTV 2P

Credit card 2

See advertisement under Bristol

CLIFTONVILLE
Kent
Map **5** TR37

See **Margate**

CLITHEROE
Lancashire
Map **7** SD74

INN *Swan & Royal* Castle St ☎(0200) 23130

Town centre inn with good, all-round furnishings. Reputedly one of the oldest buildings in Clitheroe.

5hc (3⇌) (3fb) CTV in all bedrooms Ⓡ LDO10pm

🍽 🅿̸ solarium

Credit cards 1 2 3 5

INN White Lion Hotel Market Pl (Whitbread) ☎(0200) 26955

Reputed to be the oldest alehouse in Clitheroe, now a well-furnished and comfortable inn.

4hc CTV in all bedrooms ✗ Ⓡ ✱B&b£11.50 Bdi£16.50 WBdifr£115.50 Lunch £1.50–£5.95 Dinner 10pm £1.50–£5.95

🍽 6P Ⓥ

CLOUGHTON
North Yorkshire
Map **8** TA09

Credit Cards

1 Access/Euro/Mastercard

2 American Express

3 Barclaycard/Visa

5 Diners

GH Cober Hill Newlands Rd ☎Scarborough (0723) 870310

A large country house in a rural setting between Whitby and Scarborough. Accommodation offered is comfortably old fashioned and the atmosphere most tranquil.

48hc (10fb) B&b£10.50–£12 Bdi£15–£17 WBdifr£95.50

🍽 70P 🎾(hard)

See advertisement under Scarborough

CLOVELLY
Devon
Map **2** SS32

⊢⊣**FH** Mrs G Symons **Burnstone** *(SS325233)* Higher Clovelly ☎(02373) 219

Large, comfortably furnished farmhouse with open fires in spacious lounge. Good farmhouse fare.

2hc (2fb) Ⓡ B&b£9–£9.50 Bdi£14.50–£15.50 WBdi£90–£95 LDO5pm

🍽 CTV 2P 500acres arable dairy mixed

Credit card 3 Ⓥ

INN *New Inn* Main St ☎(02373) 303

4hc ✗ LDO9.30pm

CTV P ⌂ snooker

Credit card 1

INN Red Lion The Quay ☎(02373) 237
Apr–Oct

11hc (1⇌) ✗ Ⓡ B&b£13–£16.50 Bdi£20–£23.50 WBdi£140–£164 Lunchfr£4 Dinner8.30pmfr£7

🍽 CTV P

Credit cards 1 3

CLOVENFORDS
Borders *Selkirkshire*
Map **12** NT43

INN Thornielee House ☎(089685) 350

18th-century stone-built inn situated in landscaped gardens overlooking the Tweed valley 3m W of Clovenfords on the A72. Good home cooking using fresh produce.

4hc CTV in all bedrooms Ⓡ B&bfr£13.50 Bdifr£19.50 Lunch £3.50alc Dinner10pm £6alc

🍽 CTV 20P

Ⓥ

CLUN
Shropshire
Map **7** SO38

INN Sun ☎(05884) 277

4hc Annexe: 3⚑ (1fb) ✗ Ⓡ B&b£14–£16 Bdi£21–£23 Lunch£3–£5 Dinner9pm£4–£7&alc

🍽 CTV 7P 🚗 nc10yrs

CLUNTON
Shropshire
Map **7** SO38

⊢⊣**FH** Mrs J Williams **Hurst Mill** *(SO318811)* ☎Clun (05884) 224

Stone-built farmhouse in picturesque setting with a river running through, surrounded by tree-clad hills. Friendly atmosphere.

4rm (2hc) (1fb) ⅟ in 1 bedroom TV in 1 bedroom Ⓡ in 1 bedroom B&b£8–£10 Bdi£12.50–£14 LDO6.30pm

CTV 4P 2🚗 ⌂ ↲ pony riding 100acres mixed

Credit cards 1 3 Ⓥ

COCKERMOUTH
Cumbria
Map **11** NY13

Selected

GH Low Hall Country Brandlingill (3m S on unclass off A5086) ☎(0900) 826654

A delightful 17th-century converted farmhouse set in a peaceful location. Accommodation is of a high standard, each bedroom being individually furnished and decorated with fully co-ordinating Laura Ashley designs. The two lounges are extremely comfortable and feature real fires. Vegetarian meals are available as well as the imaginative home cooked meals, and are served in the charming oak beamed dining room.

6hc (1⇌ 2⋔) ✗ Ⓡ B&b£13.50–£17 Bdi£21.50–£25 WBdifr£144 LDO3pm

Lic ⅏ CTV 12P nc10yrs

Credit cards 1 3 Ⓥ

CODSALL
Staffordshire
Map **7** SJ80

FH Mrs D E Moreton **Moors Farm & Country Restaurant** *(SJ859048)* Chillington Ln ☎(09074) 2330

Modernised and extended old farmhouse in pleasant rural location.

6hc (1⋔) (3fb) ✗ Ⓡ B&b£12–£22 Bdi£18.50–£28.50 WBdi£125–£195 LDO9pm

Lic CTV 20P nc4yrs 100acres beef dairy mixed sheep

COLD KIRBY
North Yorkshire
Map **8** SE58

FH Mr & Mrs K M Hope **High House** *(NZ538843)* Sutton Bank (1m from Sutton Bank incline on A170) ☎Thirsk (0845) 597557
Mar–Nov

3rm (2hc) (2fb) ✗ Ⓡ ✱B&bfr£8 Bdifr£13 LDO 7pm

⅏ CTV 6P 113acres beef dairy

COLESHILL
Warwickshire
Map **4** SP28

INN *George & Dragon* 154 Coventry Rd ☎(0675) 62249

Large half-timbered roadside inn near M6 Junction 4.

4hc (3fb) TV in all bedrooms ✗ LDO9.45pm

⅏ 50P 🚌

COLL (Island of)
Strathclyde *Argyllshire*
Map **13** NM25

Car Ferry from Oban. (Some services via Lochaline/Tobermory. Also linking with Tiree)

Selected

GH Tigh-na-Mara Arinagour ☎(08793) 354
Closed Dec–14 Jan

A modern guesthouse beautifully situated, with commanding views towards Mull and the Treshnish Isles. The house is tastefully decorated and furnished and has a relaxed and friendly atmosphere. Facilities include cycle and boat hire, sea-angling trips, with putting and croquet on the front lawn.

8hc (2⋔) (2fb) ⅟ in 1 bedroom TV in 2 bedrooms Ⓡ Bdi£18–£19 WBdi£119–£126 LDO6pm

Lic ⅏ CTV 10P ↲

COLLYWESTON
Northamptonshire
Map **4** TF00

INN Cavalier Main St ☎Duddington (078083) 288
Closed Xmas Day

7hc (3⇌ 2⋔) CTV in all bedrooms B&b£15.50–£16.50 Lunch£1.95–£9&alc Dinner9.30pm£1.95–£9&alc

⅏ 60P no babies

Credit cards 1 3 5

COLMONELL
Strathclyde *Ayrshire*
Map **10** NX18

⊢⊣**FH** Mrs G B Shankland **Burnfoot** *(NX162862)* ☎(046588) 220
Apr–Oct

Welcoming farmhouse in peaceful country setting beside River Stinchar.

2hc (1fb) Ⓡ B&b£9–£10 Bdi£14–£15 WBdifr£90 LDO4.30pm

CTV 2P 157acres beef dairy

Ⓥ

COLNE
Lancashire
Map **7** SD84

Selected

FH Mrs C Mitson **Higher Wanless** *(SD873413)* Red Ln ☎(0282) 865301
Closed Dec

Charming farmhouse in an idyllic setting. There is a cosy atmosphere and guests are made to feel like part of the family by friendly owners. There are only two bedrooms but both are spacious and well-decorated. A roaring log fire in the lounge is a welcoming sight on cool evenings and oak beams add to the character.

2hc (2fb) CTV in 1 bedroom ✗ Ⓡ WB&b£12.50–£15 Bdi£18.50–£21 WBdifr£115 LDO9am

⅏ CTV 4P nc3yrs
25acres sheep shire horses

Ⓥ

COLWYN BAY
Clwyd
Map **6** SH87

See plan

GH Cabin Hill Private Hotel College Av, Rhos-on-Sea ☎(0492) 44568 Plan **1** *A4*
Mar–Oct

Detached Edwardian house in residential area, off Marine Drive.

10hc (7⋔) (2fb) CTV in all bedrooms ✗ Ⓡ B&b£11–£15 Bdi£15.50–£20.50 WBdi£93–£110 LDO5pm

Lic ⅏ 6P nc3yrs Ⓥ

GH *Grosvenor Hotel* 106–108 Abergele Rd ☎(0492) 530798 Plan **2** *B1*

Large family-run Victorian house set back from the A55. Close to shops, Eirias Park and Leisure Centre.

18hc (2⇌) (8fb) Ⓡ LDO10pm

Lic ⅏ CTV 16P ⌂

Credit card 3

See advertisement on page 133

GH Northwood Hotel 47 Rhos Rd, Rhos-on-Sea ☎(0492) 49931 Plan **3** *A4*

Detached Edwardian hotel, a short walk from village and promenade.

14hc (1⇌ 7⋔) (3fb) CTV in all bedrooms Ⓡ B&b£11–£13 Bdi£17–£19 WBdi£90–£114 (WB&b only high season) LDO6pm

Lic ⅏ CTV 10P

Ⓥ

See advertisement on page 133

GH Southlea 4 Upper Prom ☎(0492) 532004 Plan **4** *B1*
Closed 2 wks Oct

Single-fronted mid-terrace Victorian house adjacent to beach.

10hc (5fb) Ⓡ ✱B&b£10–£11 Bdi£14–£15 WBdifr£84 LDO6pm

Lic ⅏ CTV ⅌

Ⓥ

See advertisement on page 133

COLYFORD
Devon
Map **3** SY29

Selected

GH Swallows Eaves Hotel Swan Hill Rd ☎Colyton (0297) 53184

Comfortable accommodation in attractive gabled property in village centre.

6hc (5⇌ 1⋒) (2fb) CTV in all bedrooms ✈ ® B&b£18.50–£25 Bdi£24–£29 WBdi£154–£165 LDO8pm

Lic ⅏ 10P nc6yrs Ⓥ

COLYTON
Devon
Map **3** SY29

GH Old Bakehouse Lower Church St ☎(0297) 52518

Former 17th-century bakery with attractive beamed dining room. Personal service and good food.

6hc (5⇌ 1⋒) (1fb) CTV in all bedrooms ® B&bfr£19 Bdifr£26 WBdifr£147 LDO9.30pm

Lic ⅏ 8P

Credit card ③

COMBE MARTIN
Devon
Map **2** SS54

GH *'Almaza'* 3 Woodlands ☎(027188) 3431

Friendly, family-run guesthouse, 150 yds from beach and local amenities.

7hc (2fb) ✈ LDO6.30pm

Lic CTV 5P

⊢⊸**GH Channel Vista** ☎(027188) 3514
Apr–Oct

Family-run Edwardian establishment, just 150 yds from secluded cove. Tastefully refurnished, with comfortable bedrooms. Good home cooking and friendly service.

8hc (1⇌ 4⋒) (3fb) CTV in 1 bedroom ✈ ® in 1 bedroom B&b£8.50–£10.50 Bdi£13.50–£15.50 WBdifr£80 LDO6pm

Lic ⅏ CTV 9P 1🚗 nc3yrs

Credit cards ① ③ Ⓥ

GH *Firs* Woodlands ☎(027188) 3404
Mar–Oct

9hc (4fb) ✈ LDO5pm

Lic ⅏ CTV 10P ⌂

GH Lodge Country House Berrynarbor (Berrynarbor 1½mW of A399) ☎(027188) 3246
Closed Xmas

6hc (2⋒) (1fb) CTV in 2 bedrooms B&b£9.50–£10.50 Bdi£13.50–£15.50 WBdi£85–£95 LDO5.30pm

Lic ⅏ CTV 7P nc2yrs

Ⓥ

Colwyn Bay

1 Cabin Hill Private Hotel
2 Grosvenor Hotel
3 Northwood Hotel
4 Southlea

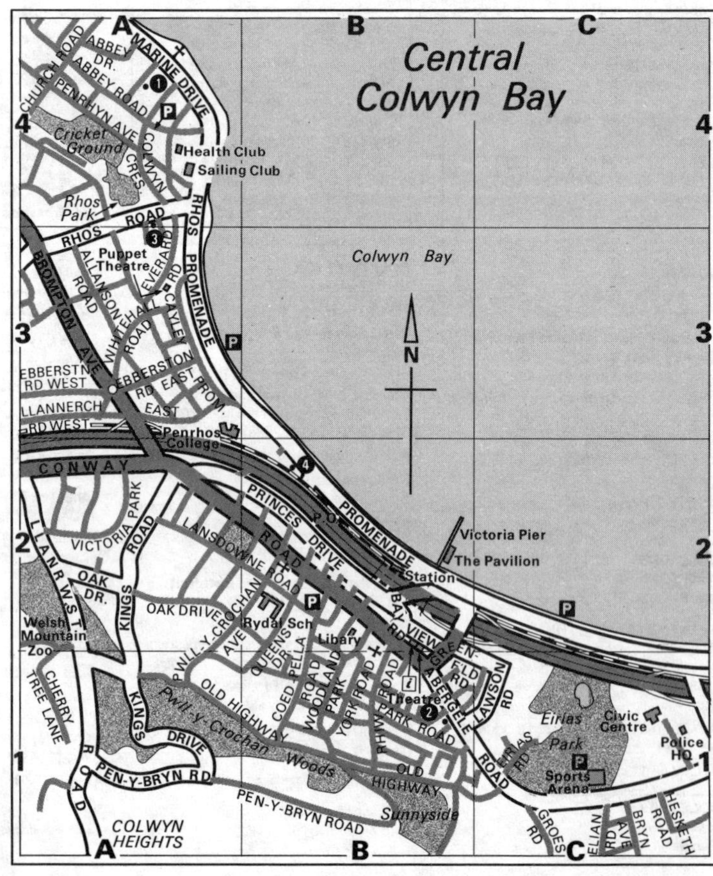

Grosvenor Hotel

ABERGELE ROAD, COLWYN BAY, CLWYD
Tel: Colwyn Bay 530798 Reception 531586 Office.

We have a friendly family hotel of 16 bedrooms, many with bathroom, all with tea making facilities and Radio/Intercom, ideally situated for the beach, shopping centre, beautiful Eirias Park and Leisure Centre. Children of all ages are welcome here and we will gladly baby listen on request. There is a residents' cosy "Olde Worlde" bar and games room. Ideal base for touring scenic North Wales. À la carte menus. Large free Car Park.

Northwood Hotel

47 Rhos Road, Rhos-on-Sea, Colwyn Bay, Clwyd, LL28 4RS
Telephone: (0492) 49931

Family business in centre of Rhos-on-Sea, 175 yards from Promenade and High Class Shopping Centre.

* Open all year * Wales Tourist Board 3 Crowns Verification * 14 bedrooms, all with Colour TV, clock radios, tea and coffee making facilities, many en-suite * Excellent food with wide choice of menu * Private Car Park * Attractive Lounge Bar with Colour TV * Residents Colour TV Lounge * Early/Late Season Breaks * Mid week bookings accepted * Car to Railway/Bus Station Service * Pets by arrangement * Special Promotion Holidays — Golf, Fishing, Drama and Bowls Festivals, Heritage Wales & Honeymooners * Festive Christmas Programme.

Brochure from proprietors — Gordon & Agnes Palliser.

SOUTHLEA Hotel

4 Upper Promenade, Colwyn Bay. Telephone: (0492) 532004

A small family run hotel situated 75yds Beach, 300yds shops, entertainment etc. An ideal base for seeing the sights of North Wales. Open all year with full gas central heating. Residential licence with a well stocked Cosy Bar, with separate lounge with Colour TV. Baby listening/radio/intercom in all rooms plus tea & coffee making facilities, some with private showers. Children & pets made most welcome. Choice of Menu at all meals including Childrens menu.
Highly recommended. Send stamp for colour brochure etc.
Bed, breakfast & evening meal from £84 per week. Good reductions for children, fortnightly, OAP & Party bookings.

Don't take chances!

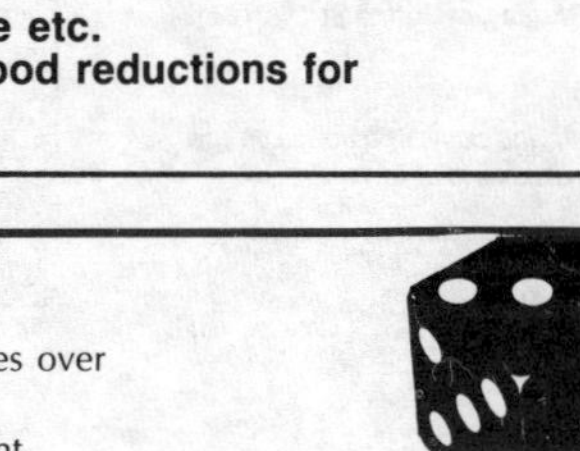

A holiday is something one works and saves for — don't take chances over your choice of accommodation.
Here at The Lodge Country Guest House your comfort and enjoyment is our prime consideration, situated in the picturesque village of **Berrynarbor** *1985 winner of Best kept village competition.* (1 mile from Watermouth Cove, 2½ miles Ilfracombe Golf Course and 2 miles Combe Martin — Gateway to Exmoor).
A family run licensed guest house offering double, single and en suite rooms. The Lodge is set in 1 acre of beautiful grounds overlooking the Sterridge Valley, where you can enjoy peace and tranquillity, excellent food, comfort and a warm friendly atmosphere.
For illustrated brochure, please write or 'phone Mrs. Doreen Prater,
The Lodge Country Guest House, Berrynarbor. (027 188) 3246.

GH Mellstock House Woodlands ☎(027188) 2592
Mar–Oct

6hc (3⫬)1fb) ✗ Ⓡ B&b£12–£18.50 Bdi£17–£23.50 WBdi£110–£155 LDO4.30pm

Lic 🍽 CTV 6P 1🚗 nc

⊢GH **Miramar Hotel** Victoria St ☎(027188) 3558

9hc (4⫬) (4fb) CTV in all bedrooms Ⓡ B&b£9–£12 Bdi£13–£16 WBdifr£89 LDO6pm

Lic 🍽 CTV 10P 2🚗 ⛳ ⛆(heated) Ⓥ

GH *The Woodlands* 2 The Woodlands ☎(027188) 2769
Mar–Nov

Comfortable, family-run guesthouse offering good home cooking.

8hc (2fb) ✗ LDO5pm

Lic CTV 7P 2🚗 nc5yrs

Credit card ③

FH Mrs M A Peacock ***Longlands*** *(SS614451)* Easterclose Cross ☎(027188) 3522
Mar–Oct

Situated in unspoilt woods and valleys with fine views.

6hc (2fb) LDO6.30pm

Lic 🍽 CTV 15P ♪ 27acres sheep mixed

COMPTON
Berkshire
Map **4** SU57

INN *Swan Hotel* ☎(063522) 269

Friendly warm atmosphere with bar and restaurant menus.

3hc (1fb) Ⓡ LDO8.15pm

TV 40P 🚌

Credit cards ① ② ③ ⑤

COMRIE
Tayside *Perthshire*
Map **11** NN72

⊢**GH Mossgiel** Burrell St ☎(0764) 70567
Etr–Oct

A homely and cosy little house on the western outskirts of town.

Combe Martin — Conwy

6hc B&bfr£7.50 Bdifr£11 WBdifr£77 LDO5.30pm

🍽 CTV 6P nc5yrs

FH Mrs J H Rimmer **West Ballindaloch** *(NN744262)* Glenlednock ☎(0764) 70282
Mar–Nov

Cosy, small farmhouse with neat garden set amid hills in secluded glen, 4m from Comrie.

2rm (1fb) ✗ Ⓡ ✱B&b£8–£8.50

CTV 3P 1500acres sheep hill farm Ⓥ

CONISTON
Cumbria
Map **7** SD39

INN Crown ☎(05394) 41243

Cheerful village inn near lake.

7hc (4fb) CTV in all bedrooms Ⓡ B&b£13–£15 Bdi£19–£22 WBdifr£130 Lunch£3.50–£5.50 High tea £1.10–£5.50 Dinner 9pm £8.50–£10.50

🍽 CTV 30P Ⓥ

CONNEL
Strathclyde *Argyllshire*
Map **10** NM93

Selected

GH Loch Etive Private Hotel Main St ☎(063171) 400
mid Apr–mid Oct

A warm welcome is offered by proprietor Francoise Weber to this small friendly hotel. The bright and cheerful bedrooms are comfortably furnished and excellent home cooking is served in the cosy dining room adjoining the lounge.

6hc (2⇌ 2⫬)(2fb) CTV in all bedrooms Ⓡ ✱B&b£11.50–£14 Bdi£18–£20.50 WBdi£112–£129 LDO7pm

Lic 🍽 8P

Ⓥ

CONSTANTINE
Cornwall
Map **2** SW72

INN *Trengilly Wartha* Nancenoy ☎Falmouth (0326) 40332

Popular country inn serving good value country fare. Well-appointed bedrooms.

6hc (4⇌) Ⓡ LDO9.30pm

🍽 60P

Credit cards ① ② ③

See advertisement under Falmouth

CONWY
Gwynedd
Map **6** SH77

GH Cyfnant Private Hotel Henryd Rd, Gyffin (1m S B5106) ☎(0492) 592442
Mar–Oct

Large, semi-detached house close to castle and town. Bright, clean accommodation.

5hc (2fb) TV in all bedrooms ✗ B&b£10–£11 Bdifr£14.75 WBdifr£93

Lic CTV 6P Ⓥ

⊢**GH Llys Gwilym** 3 Mountain Rd, off Cadnant Park ☎ (0492) 592351

Semi-detached house ½m from the Castle.

6hc (3fb) ✗ B&b£9–£10 Bdi£12–£13WBdifr£84 LDO5pm

Lic 🍽 CTV 2P

⊢**GH Sunnybanks** Llanrwst Rd, Woodlands ☎(0492) 593845
Etr–Oct

A small family run hotel situated in an elevated position close to the Castle Walls.

6hc (2fb) CTV in all bedrooms Ⓡ ✱B&bfr£7.50 Bdifr£12 LDO8.30pm

Lic 🍽 CTV 8P Ⓥ

⊢**FH** Mrs C Roberts **Henllys** *(SH767758)* Llechwedd (2m W unclass rd) ☎ (0492) 593269
Apr–Oct

Large, stone-built farmhouse, signposted from main road.

2hc (1fb) Ⓡ B&b£9–£12 Bdi£12.50–£16 WBdi£80–£100 LDO7pm

CTV 4P 150acres mixed Ⓥ

COOKLEY
Suffolk
Map **5** TM37

FH Mr & Mrs A T Veasy **Green** *(TM337772)* ☎Linstead (098685) 209
Apr–Oct

17th-century farmhouse with exposed timbers. Situated in an area of rural peace and quiet. Friendly atmosphere.

3hc (1fb) ✗ B&bfr£10 Bdifr£15.50 LDO3pm

CTV 3P nc8yrs 45 acres mixed

COOMBE
Cornwall
Map **2** SW95

FH Mrs J Scott ***Treway*** *(SW935505)* ☎St Austell (0726) 882236

Pleasant, comfortable farmhouse in isolated rural setting approx 8m from St Austell.

3rm (2hc) (2fb)

▥ CTV 3P ⌂ 180acres arable beef dairy

COPMANTHORPE
North Yorkshire
Map **8** SE54

GH Duke of Connaught Copmanthorpe Grange (Guestaccom/Minotels) ☎Appleton Roebuck (090484) 318
Closed Xmas wk

Nicely converted former stables in open rural surroundings.

11⋒ (1fb) 🚭 in 3 bedrooms CTV in all bedrooms ✗ Ⓡ ✱B&b£13–£15 Bdi£20–£22 WBdifr£140 LDO6pm

Lic ▥ CTV 40P

CORRIE
Isle of Arran, Strathclyde *Buteshire*
See **Arran, Isle of**

CORSLEY
Wiltshire
Map **3** ST84

FH Mrs M A Cottle **Sturford Mead** *(ST834456)* ☎Chapmanslade (037388) 213

Attractive detached brick and rendered house in a peaceful countryside location adjacent to Longleat Safari Park. Well-furnished comfortable bedrooms. Strictly non-smoking.

3hc (1⋒) (1fb) CTV available in bedrooms ✗ Ⓡ B&b£10–£15

▥ CTV 10P ⌂ 5acres pig

CORTACHY
Tayside *Angus*
Map **15** NO35

⊢⊣**FH** Mrs J Grant **Cullew** *(NO387609)* ☎(05754) 242
Apr–Oct

Substantial stone farmhouse in lovely hill country.

2rm (1fb) 🚭 in bedrooms ✗ B&b£8–£8.50 Bdi£12–£13 WBdifr£112 LDO9pm

▥ CTV 3P ⌂ arable 850acres arable mixed Ⓥ

CORWEN
Clwyd
Map **6** SJ04

GH Coleg-y-Groes ☎(0490) 2169

Small, Christian guesthouse, originally 18th-century almshouses, in quiet part of town.

6hc (2fb) Ⓡ B&b£10–£12 Bdi£14.50–£17 WBdifr£96.50

▥ CTV 6P Ⓥ

GH Corwen Court Private Hotel London Rd ☎(0490) 2854
Mar–Nov rs Dec–Feb

10hc (4⇌ 4⋒) B&b£10 Bdi£15 WBdifr£99.75 LDO7pm

▥ CTV 🅿 Ⓥ

COTHERIDGE
Hereford & Worcester
Map **3** SO75

FH Mr & Mrs V A Rogers **Little Lightwood** *(SP798554)* ☎(090566) 236
Feb–Nov

Welcoming and relaxed farmhouse offering good home-cooking.

3hc (fb) 🚭 in all bedrooms ✗ Ⓡ B&b£8–£9.50 Bdi£13–£14 WBdi£85–£90 LDO10am

▥ CTV 6P 60acres dairy Ⓥ

COUNTISBURY (nr Lynton)
Devon
Map **3** SS74

FH Mrs R Pile **Coombe** *(SS766489)* ☎Brendon (05987) 236
Apr–Oct rs Nov–Dec

5hc (2 ⋒) (2fb) ✗ Ⓡ ✱B&b£10.50–£15 Bdi£17.50–£22 WBdi£109–£135 LDO5pm

Lic ▥ CTV 6P 365acres hill-stock sheep

COVENTRY
West Midlands
Map **4** SP37

GH Ashleigh House 17 Park Rd ☎(0203) 23804
Closed 2 wks Xmas

Popular guesthouse close to the city centre with its own car park at rear.

10hc (5fb) CTV in all bedrooms ✗ Ⓡ B&bfr£11

CTV 12P

Credit card 2

GH Croft Hotel 23 Stoke Gn, off Binley Rd ☎(0203) 457846

12hc (1⋒) (1fb) CTV in 5 bedrooms Ⓡ B&b£19–£23.50 Bdi£26.48–£30.98 LDO9.30pm

Lic ▥ CTV 20P solarium Ⓥ

GH Fairlight 14 Regent St ☎(0203) 24215
Closed 24 Dec–2 Jan

Victorian terraced house near city centre and railway station.

12hc (3fb) Ⓡ B&b£10–£12

▥ CTV 7P

GH Hearsall Lodge Hotel 1 Broad Ln ☎(0203) 74543

Large detached house with modern bedroom extension. Close to common and town centre.

13hc (2fb) CTV in all bedrooms Ⓡ B&b£14.95–£16.10 Bdi£21–£28 LDO7.30pm

Lic ▥ CTV 13P solarium

See advertisement on page 136

GH Northanger House 35 Westminster Rd ☎(0203) 26780

Comfortable, welcoming, Victorian terrace house near city centre.

9hc (3fb) ® available in bedrooms B&b£9.50–£11

♨ CTV 1🚗

GH Spire View 36 Park Rd ☎(0203) 51602

RS Xmas day

Large and comfortable Victorian house near City centre.

7hc (3⥾) (3fb) CTV in all bedrooms ✖ ® ✱B&b£11–£13 Bdi£16–£19

♨ CTV 3P Ⓥ

GH Trinity House Hotel 28 Lower Holyhead Rd ☎(0203) 555654

Closed 10 days Xmas

Tall, bay-windowed house with bright modern interior, situated in a cul-de-sac, close to the town centre.

7hc (1fb) TV in 1 bedroom ✖ (ex guide dogs) ® B&b£13–£16 Bdi£20–£23 WBdi£125–£145 LDO9.30pm

Lic ♨ CTV 2P nc5yrs

Credit cards 1 3

COVERACK BRIDGES (nr Helston)
Cornwall
Map **2** SW63

⊢⊣**FH** Mr & Mrs E Lawrance **Boscadjack** *(SW673311)* ☎Helston (0326) 572086

Etr–Oct

Modernised farmhouse situated in Cober Valley amidst delightful unspoilt countryside.

4hc (2fb) ✖ B&b£8.50–£9.50 Bdi£13.50–£14.50 WBdi£90–£100 LDOnoon

♨ CTV P 92acres dairy

COWDENBEATH
Fife
Map **11** NT19

GH Glenbank House 36 Foulford Rd ☎(0383) 515466

Detached house in elevated position in residential area.

5hc (3fb) CTV in 2 bedrooms ® B&b£10–£12 Bdi£15–£17 WBdi£105 LDO9pm

Lic ♨ CTV 10P Ⓥ

GH Struan Bank Private Hotel 74 Perth Rd ☎(0383) 511057

A small pleasantly-appointed hotel on outskirts of town.

8hc ✱B&b£10–£12 Bdi£15–£17 LDO6pm

Lic ♨ CTV 8P Ⓥ

CRACKINGTON HAVEN
Cornwall
Map **2** SX19

Selected

FH Mrs M Knight **Manor** *(SX159962)* ☎St Gennys (08403) 304

Dating from the 12th century and mentioned in the Domesday Book. Attractive gardens with beautiful view, in secluded position. Guests are not permitted to smoke in the house.

4hc (2⇌ 1⥾) ✖ B&b£13–£16 Bdi£20–£23 WBdi£130–£144 LDO5pm

♨ CTV 6P nc16yrs snooker 40acres beef

CRAFTHOLE
Cornwall
Map **2** SX35

INN Finnygook ☎St Germans (0503) 30338

Well-modernised, country inn with pleasant views and comfortable bedrooms.

6hc (5⇌) CTV in all bedrooms ✖ ® B&b£9.50–£29 Lunch £1.50–£4.50 Dinner 9.30pm £1.50–£4.50&alc

♨ 30P nc14yrs

Credit cards 1 3

CRAIL
Fife
Map **12** NO60

GH Caiplie 51–53 High St ☎(0333) 50564
Mar–Sep
Neatly maintained guesthouse in main street, with well-furnished bedrooms, shower-rooms and bistro-style dining room.
7hc (1fb) ® B&b£10.50–£12.50 Bdi£18–£20 WBdifr£105 LDO4pm
Lic 🍽 CTV 🚫

GH *Hazelton Private Hotel* 29 Marketgate ☎(0333) 50250

Comfortable, welcoming house off main street.
5hc (1fb) LDO8pm
Lic 🍽 CTV 🚫

CRAVEN ARMS
Shropshire
Map **7** SO48

FH Mrs C Morgan **Strefford Hall** *(SO444856)* ☎(05882) 2383
Etr–Oct
Large, comfortable, stone-built, Victorian farmhouse, north of town off A49.
3rm (2hc) (1fb) ⚟ in 3 bedrooms B&b£8.50–£9 Bdi£13.50–£14 WBdifr£90 LDO6pm
CTV 3P 🚜
350acres arable beef sheep
Ⓥ

CRAWLEY
West Sussex
Map **4** TQ23

For accommodation details see **Gatwick Airport**

CREDITON
Devon
Map **3** SS80

FH Mr & Mrs M Pennington **Woolsgrove** *(SS793028)* Sandford ☎Copplestone (03634) 246
Mar–Oct
17th-century farmhouse overlooking grassland. 3m NW on unclass road and 1m N of A377.
3hc (2fb) B&b£8.50–£9.50 Bdi£12.50–£13 LDO4pm
CTV P 150acres mixed
Ⓥ

CRIANLARICH
Central *Perthshire*
Map **10** NN32

GH Glenardran ☎(08383) 236
Stone house in scenic village with good accommodation.
6hc (2⫿) (1fb) ✱B&b£9.50–£10.50 Bdi£16–£18 WBdifr£108 LDO7pm
Lic ₶ CTV 9P
Credit cards 1 3

GH Moungreenan ☎(08383) 286
Friendly little guesthouse with good views of Ben More.

Crediton — Criccieth

5hc (1fb) ✗ B&bfr£9.50 Bdifr£15.50 LDO4pm
₶ CTV 10P
Ⓥ

CRICCIETH
Gwynedd
Map **6** SH53

GH Glyn-y-Coed Private Hotel Portmadoc Rd ☎(076671) 2870
Closed Xmas & New Year
10hc (1⇌ 5⫿) (5fb) Ⓡ B&bfr£11 Bdifr£16 WBdifr£108 LDO4pm
Lic CTV 14P

GH Min-y-Gaer Private Hotel Porthmadoc Rd ☎(076671) 2151
Mar–Oct
Substantial Victorian semi-detached house with coastal views.
10hc (1⇌ 4⫿) (3fb) CTV in 3 bedrooms TV in 2 bedrooms (charge) Ⓡ B&b£10–£12 Bdi£15.50–£17.50 WBdi£105–£119 LDO4pm
Lic ₶ CTV 12P
Ⓥ

GH *Moorings* 20 Marine Ter ☎(076671) 2802
Mar–Oct (rs Mar & Oct)
Victorian mid terrace on the front, adjacent to the castle.
6hc TV in 1 bedroom ✗ LDO6pm
Lic CTV 20P

GH *Môr Heli Hotel* Marine Ter ☎(076671) 2878
Mar–Oct (rs Mar & Oct)
Victorian mid terrace house on the sea front, ¼ mile from shops.
10hc (1⇌) (4fb) LDO6pm
Lic CTV 20P

GH Neptune Hotel Marine Ter (Guestaccom) ☎(076671) 2794
Mar–Oct
Victorian mid-terrace house on sea front adjacent to the castle.
20hc (4⇌) (8fb) B&bfr£10.50 Bdifr£15.50 WBdifr£105.50 LDO6pm
Lic CTV 20P
Ⓥ

CRICKHOWELL
Powys
Map **3** SO21

GH Dragon Country House Hotel High St ☎(0873) 810362

Friendly, informal hotel catering for tourists and commercial trade. Vegetarian meals served.

10hc (1⇌ 1fl) (2fb) CTV in 6 bedrooms ✈ ® in 8 bedrooms ✱B&b£11.50–£22.50 WBdifr£133 LDO8.30pm

Lic 𝔐 CTV 15P

Credit cards 1 3 Ⓥ

CRIEFF
Tayside *Perthshire*
Map **11** NN82

GH Heatherville 29–31 Burrell St ☎(0764) 2825

Comfortable, privately owned house forming part of a terrace.

5hc (2fb) ✱B&b£8.50–£9 Bdi£13–£13.50 LDOnoon

Lic 𝔐 CTV 5P

REMEMBER

Prices quoted in the gazetteer are minimum double room occupancy to maximum single room occupancy **per person.**

INN Meadow 38 Burrell St ☎(0764) 3261

4hc (1⇌ 2fl) ® in 3 bedrooms ✱B&b£10–£15 Lunch£4–£6&alc Dinner10pm £7.50–£9&alc

𝔐 CTV 8P

Credit card 3 Ⓥ

CROESGOCH
Dyfed
Map **2** SM83

GH Cwmwdig Water Berea ☎(03483) 434
Mar–Oct

Bedrooms have charm and individuality in this lovely converted farmhouse overlooking the sea.

2hc Annexe: 8hc (2fb) ® ✱B&b£10–£13 Bdi£16.50–£19.50 WBdi£110–£130 (W only 23 Jul–27 Aug) LDO6pm

Lic CTV 15P

Credit cards 1 2 3 5 Ⓥ

FH Mrs A Charles **Torbant** *(SM845307)* ☎(03483) 276
Etr–Sep (rs Oct–Etr, except closed Xmas)

Larger than average farm guesthouse in pleasant position overlooking open country.

7hc (3fb) ✈ ✱B&b£10.50–£11.50 Bdi£14.50–£15.50 WBdi£95–£105 LDO6pm

Lic 𝔐 CTV 40P 110acres dairy

Ⓥ

FH Mrs M B Jenkins **Trearched** *(SM831306)* ☎(03483) 310
Etr–Oct

Cosy character farmhouse overlooking St George's Channel. Reading room and patio gardens.

7hc B&b£10–£12 Bdi£15–£17 WBdi£100–£102 LDOnoon

𝔐 CTV 12P 100acres arable

Ⓥ

CROMER
Norfolk
Map **9** TG24

GH Brightside 19 Macdonald Rd ☎(0263) 513408
Apr–Oct

7hc (3fb) ⊁ in all bedrooms ✈ B&b£9.50 Bdi£13 WBdifr£76 LDO3.30pm

Lic 𝔐 CTV P nc3yrs

GH Chellow Dene 23 Macdonald Rd ☎(0263) 513251 →

7hc (2fb) CTV in all bedrooms Ⓡ
✱B&bfr£9 Bdifr£14 WBdifr£79 LDO5pm

Lic ▥ 6P

GH Morden 20 Cliff Av ☎(0263) 513396

Smart late Victorian house in a quiet residential avenue.

7hc (3🚿) (2fb) Ⓡ B&b£9.75–£11.25 Bdi£14.50–£16 WBdifr£91 LDO5pm

Lic ▥ CTV 3P

Ⓥ

GH Sandcliff Private Hotel Runton Rd ☎(0263) 512888
Closed 10 Dec–Jan

Friendly-run private hotel situated on the coast road, conveniently placed for access to town centre.

23hc (8🛁 10🚿) (10fb) Ⓡ ✱B&bfr£14.20 Bdifr£18.20 WBdifr£100

Lic CTV 10P

GH Westgate Lodge Private Hotel 10 Macdonald Rd ☎(0263) 512840

12hc (8🚿) (4fb) CTV in all bedrooms ✗ B&bfr£12.65 Bdifr£19 WBdifr£120.75 LDO7pm

Lic ▥ 14P nc3yrs

Credit cards [1] [3]

CROMHALL
Avon
Map **3** ST69

FH Mrs S Scolding **Varley** *(ST699905)* Talbot End ☎Wickwar (045424) 292
Etr–Aug

Spacious, two-storey stone-built farmhouse with garden. Well-maintained and neatly decorated throughout.

4hc (4fb) 🚭 in all bedrooms ✗ Ⓡ in 2 bedrooms ✱B&b£9–£10.50 Bdi£13.50–£15 WBdifr£90 LDO3.30pm

▥ CTV 5P 75acres dairy

CROOK
Cumbria
Map **7** SD49

FH Mrs I D Scales **Greenbank** *(SD462953)* ☎Staveley (0539) 821216
Closed Dec

Good home-cooking is a feature of this attractive, comfortable farmhouse.

5hc (1🚿) Ⓡ B&b£12–£13 Bdi£22–£24 WBdifr£150 LDO5pm

Lic ▥ CTV 12P nc12yrs 14½acres mushrooms

Credit card [3] Ⓥ

CROSCOMBE
Somerset
Map **3** ST54

FH Mrs Keen ***Upper Thrupe*** Maesbury *(ST604457)* (1½m NE of Croscombe unclass) ☎Shepton Mallet (0749) 2697

Comfortable accommodation at a peaceful dairy farm.

3rm (2hc) 🚭 in 2 bedrooms ✗

160acres dairy

CROSSGATES
Powys
Map **3** SO06

GH Guidfa House ☎Penybont (059787) 241

Exquisite country house offering very agreeable accommodation.

7hc (1🛁 2🚿) (3fb) Ⓡ ✱B&b£11–£13.50 Bdi£20.50–£23

Lic ▥ CTV 10P

Ⓥ

⊢⊣**FH** Mrs M A Davies **Bryn Nicholas** *(SJ075658)* (Gwystre 2m W A44) ☎Penybont (059787) 447
Apr–Oct

Cosy farmhouse accommodation in this convenient touring location.

3hc Ⓡ B&b£8.50 Bdi£15 WBdifr£97 LDO4pm

▥ CTV 6P 161acres beef sheep

Ⓥ

⊢⊣**FH** Mrs C Drew **Gwystre** *(SO070656)* (Gwystre 2m W A44) ☎Penybont (059787) 316
Mar–Oct

Modestly appointed small farmhouse.

2rm TV in all bedrooms Ⓡ B&b£7.50–£8.50 Bdi£13–£14 WBdifr£90 LDO4pm

▥ CTV ₱ 200acres mixed

Ⓥ

CROYDE
Devon
Map **2** SS43

GH *Moorsands House Hotel* Moor Ln ☎(0271) 890781
Apr–Oct

8hc (3fb) ✗ LDO1pm

Lic ▥ CTV 8P nc4yrs

Selected

GH Whiteleaf at Croyde ☎(0271) 890266

This 1930's detached house set in attractive gardens is run by Flo and David Wallington. The bedrooms and public rooms are well appointed and guests can enjoy a five course menu in the attractive dining room prepared by their affable host.

5hc (4🛁 1🚿) (2fb) CTV in all bedrooms Ⓡ ✱B&b£14–£28 Bdi£23.50–£37.50 LDO8.30pm

10P ♧

Credit cards [1] [3]

INN *Thatched Barn* ☎Barnstaple(0271) 890349

16th-century, thatched free house in centre of pretty village.

4hc (1🚿) (1fb) ✗ LDO10.15pm

▥ 30P

CROYDON
Gt London
London plan **4** D1 (pages 258–259)

GH Lonsdale Hotel 158 Lower Addiscombe Rd ☎01-654 2276
Closed 24 Dec–4 Jan

Family-run hotel with a warm, homely atmosphere.

12hc (3🚿) CTV in all bedrooms ✗ Ⓡ ✱B&b£24–£27 Bdi£33–£36 WB&b£144–£162 LDO6.30pm

Lic 🍽 CTV 12P snooker

Credit card 3

GH Markington Hotel 9 Haling Park Rd ☎01-681 6494
Closed Xmas

Well-equipped family run guesthouse with relaxing atmosphere.

21hc (2⇌ 18🚿) (2fb) ⊬ in 4 bedrooms CTV in all bedrooms ✗ Ⓡ ✱B&b£18–£35 LDO8pm

Lic 🍽 CTV 7P

Credit cards 1 2 3 Ⓥ

GH Oakwood Hotel 69 Outram Rd ☎01-654 2835

Near town centre, Victorian house with bay windows, offering comfortable rooms.

14hc (8⇌ 6🚿) (4fb) CTV in all bedrooms Ⓡ B&b£25–£43 Bdi£32.50–£51 LDO8pm

Lic 🍽 CTV 7P sauna bath solarium

Credit cards 1 2 3 5 Ⓥ

CRUCKTON
Shropshire
Map **7** SJ41

FH Mrs M L Birchall **Woodfield** *(SJ432108)* ☎Shrewsbury (0743) 860249
Jun–Oct

Large, modern detached farmhouse with neat gardens.

3rm (1⇌) ✗ ✱B&bfr£9

🍽 CTV 3P 84acres

CULLEN
Grampian *Banffshire*
Map **15** NJ56

GH Wakes Hotel Seafield Pl ☎(0542) 40251

Spacious guesthouse set in a residential area of this attractive coastal resort.

23rm (22hc) (5fb) Ⓡ available in bedrooms B&bfr£9.50 Bdifr£14 WBdifr£80 LDO7.30pm

Lic CTV 20P ⌂

Ⓥ

CULLODEN MOOR
Highland *Inverness-shire*
Map **14** NH74

⊢⊣**FH** Mrs E M C Alexander **Culdoich** *(NH755435)* ☎Inverness (0463) 790268
Apr–Oct

18th-century farmhouse in a position near Culloden battlefield and Clava standing stones

2hc (1fb) ✗ B&b£8.50–£9 Bdi£14–£15 WBdi£85–£90 LDO5pm

CTV P 200acres mixed

Ⓥ

CULLOMPTON
Devon
Map **3** ST00

⊢⊣**FH** Mrs A C Cole **Five Bridges** *(ST026095)* ☎(0884) 33453
Etr–Oct

Well-maintained, brick-built farmhouse.

4hc (3fb) B&b£8 Bdi£12 WBdifr£80 LDO5pm

CTV 6P 1🚗 ⚲ 22acres non-working

Ⓥ

CUPAR
Fife
Map **11** NO31

FH Mr & Mrs E Kay **Blebo Mains** *(NO428140)* ☎Ceres (033482) 266
Etr–Sep

A comfortable and attractive house standing on the hillside above the B939, 5 miles E of Cupar.

2rm (1fb) ✗ ✱B&bfr£9.50

CTV 4P 200acres arable

CURY
Cornwall
Map **2** SW62

⊢⊣**FH** Mrs M F Osborne **Polglase** *(SW686213)* Cross Lanes (1m E) ☎Mullion (0326) 240469
Etr–Sep

Comfortable working farm with modern accommodation and good food. 5m from Helston.

6rm (5hc) (2fb) ✗ B&b£9 Bdi£14 WBdifr£98

CTV P 65acres mixed

FH Mrs H Lugg ***Tregaddra*** *(SW701219)* ☎Mullion (0326) 240235
Mar–Oct

A delightful 18th-century stone farmhouse with glorious views.

5hc (2🚿) (2fb) ✗ LDO10am

CTV 8P ⛱

120acres arable beef

See advertisement under Mullion

CWMBRAN
Gwent
Map **3** ST29

FH Mrs B Watkins **Glebe** *(ST325965)* Croes-y-Ceiliog (1½m E unclass towards Llandedveth village) ☎Tredunnock (063349) 251
Closed 21 Dec–7 Jan

Modern ranch-house-style building in lovely countryside, offering a friendly welcome.

3rm (2hc) (1fb) ✗ B&b£10–£10.50

🍽 CTV P

100acres beef dairy

Ⓥ

CWMDUAD
Dyfed
Map **2** SN33

⊢⊣**GH Neuadd-Wen** ☎Cynwyl Elfed (026787) 438

A welcoming, family-run rural guesthouse, in village set in wooded valley. An ideal base for seeing West Wales.

6hc (2fb) B&b£8–£10 Bdi£12.50–£14.50 WBdi£70–£85 LDO10.30pm

Lic 🍽 CTV 12P

Ⓥ

DALMALLY
Strathclyde *Argyll*
See Ardbrecknish

See advertisment on page 142

DALWOOD (nr Axminster)
Devon
Map **3** ST20

⊢⊣**FH** Mr & Mrs Cobley **Elford** *(ST258004)* ☎Axminster (0297) 32415
Mar–Oct

Listed farmhouse of historic interest with parts dating from the 12th century. Panoramic and pastoral views.

7rm (4hc 2⇌) (2fb) ✗ B&b£9–£11.50 Bdi£14–£15.50 WBdifr£84 LDO5.30pm

Lic 🍽 CTV 8P 37acres dairy

Ⓥ

DARLINGTON
Co Durham
Map **8** NZ21

GH Raydale Hotel Stanhope Road South ☎(0325) 58993
Closed 24 Dec–1 Jan

Impressive house with friendly and relaxed atmosphere, standing within walled garden.

11hc (3fb) TV in 1 bedroom B&b£14.95–£18.40 Bdi£20.95–£24.40 LDO3.30pm

Lic 🍽 CTV 12P

Credit cards 1 3 5

DARTINGTON
Devon
Map **3** SX76

INN Cott ☎Totnes (0803) 863777

Character inn with lively bars and cosy restaurant. Food standards are high with an imaginative menu relying strongly on quality local produce. Attractive garden and patio area.

6hc ✗ Ⓡ B&b£20–£25 Bdi£30–£35 WBdifr£210 Lunch£5.75–£7 Dinner 9pm £12.50–£15&alc

CTV 50P nc10yrs

Credit cards 1 2 3 5

See advertisement on page 142

DARTMOUTH
Devon
Map **3** SX84

GH Captains House 18 Clarence St ☎(08043) 2133

A charming small Georgian listed house built around 1760 situated close to the shops and River Dart frontage. Cosy well appointed bedrooms and friendly service.

5hc (3⇌ 2fl) CTV in all bedrooms Ⓡ ✱B&bfr£12

🍽

GH Orleans 24 South Town ☎(08043) 2967

Listed Georgian terraced house overlooking estuary. Simply furnished with warm, relaxed atmosphere.

5hc ✘ B&b£10.50–£12 WB&b£70–£77

🍽 CTV ₱

GH Sunny Banks 1 Vicarage Hill ☎(08043) 2766

Small friendly guesthouse close to town centre and quay.

7hc (1⇌ 1fl) (2fb) CTV in all bedrooms ⅟ in 2 bedrooms Ⓡ B&b£10.50–£12.50 Bdi£16–£18 WBdi£105–£120 LDO7.30pm

🍽 CTV

DAVENTRY
Northamptonshire
Map **4** SP56

GH Abercorn Hotel Warwick St ☎(0327) 703741

Commercial hotel in residential street a short way from town centre

32hc (2⇌ 30fl) (1fb) CTV in all bedrooms ✘ ✱B&bfr£29 Bdifr£38 LDO8.30pm

Lic 🍽 CTV 20P

DAVIOT
Highland *Inverness-shire*
Map **14** NH73

⊢⊣**FH** Mrs E M MacPherson **Lairgandour** *(NH720376)* ☎(046385) 207
Apr–Sep

In a quiet location near to Culloden Moor, Loch Ness and the Cairngorms. Situated east of A9 at junction with B9154.

5rm (4hc) (3fb) B&bfr£8 Bdifr£12 WBdifr£80

CTV P 1000acres beef sheep mixed

DAWLISH
Devon
Map **3** SX97

GH Broxmore Private Hotel
20 Plantation Ter ☎(0626) 863602
Closed Jan & Feb

8hc (3fb) (ex guide dogs) Ⓡ B&b£9.50–£11.20 Bdi£14–£16.50 WBdi£93–£107 LDO4.30pm

Lic CTV nc5yrs

Credit cards 1 3 Ⓥ

GH Lynbridge Private Hotel Barton Villas ☎(0626) 862352
Apr–Oct

8hc (2fb) in 2 bedrooms *B&b£9–£10 Bdi£12.50–£13 WBdifr£84 LDO5pm

CTV 6P nc2yrs

Ⓥ

⊢⊣**GH Mimosa** 11 Barton Ter ☎(0626) 863283

9hc (1) (4fb) B&b£8–£9 Bdi£11.50–£12.50 WBdifr£72 LDO3pm

Lic CTV 4P nc4yrs

Ⓥ

GH Radfords Hotel Dawlish Water ☎(0626) 863322
Apr–Sep rs Mar, Oct, Nov

Fine, old-world, thatched building with modern extension, ideal for family holidays.

34 (34fb) Ⓡ Bdi£20–£29 WBdi£145–£186 (W only Whit–Sep) LDO7pm

Lic CTV 40P (heated) snooker solarium

Ⓥ

DEBDEN GREEN
Essex
Map **5** TL53

FH Mrs K M Low **Wychbars** *(TL564313)* ☎Bishop's Stortford (0279) 850362

Moated farmhouse in 3½ acres. Down unclassified Debden Green road, off B1051. Farmhouse through Scotts Farm.

2rm CTV in all bedrooms Ⓡ available in bedrooms B&b£11–£13.50

lift CTV 10P 2 600acres arable

Ⓥ

DEDHAM
Essex
Map **5** TM03

Selected

GH Dedham Hall ☎Colchester (0206) 323027
Closed 20 Dec–Feb

Beautiful timber-framed house in six acres of grounds providing comfortable accommodation and good home-cooking.

7hc (3) (1fb) TV in 1 bedroom Ⓡ *B&b£14.25–£22.50 Bdi£25.25–£33.50 WBdi£167.91–£222.78 LDO4pm

Lic CTV 10P 2 nc6yrs

DENBIGH
Clwyd
Map **6** SJ06

GH Cayo 74 Vale St ☎(074571) 2686
Closed Xmas

5hc (2fb) B&b£10–£10.50 Bdi£14–£14.50 WBdifr£98 LDO2pm

Lic CTV

Ⓥ

DENNY
Central *Stirlingshire*
Map **11** NS88

⊢⊣**FH** Mrs J Morton **Lochend** *(NS759856)* ☎(0324) 822778
rs Oct–Apr

4m W along B818, then turn right at Carronbridge on unclass road for 2 miles.

2hc Ⓡ B&b£9–£9.50 Bdi£14–£15 LDO3pm

CTV P nc3yrs

650acres sheep

Ⓥ

DERBY
Derbyshire
Map **8** SK33

GH *Ascot Hotel* 724 Osmaston Rd ☎(0332) 41916

20hc (1fb) CTV in 2 bedrooms TV in 4 bedrooms

Lic CTV 15P

GH Dalby House 100 Radbourne St (off Windmill Hill Ln) ☎(0332) 42353

Lovely old house in residential area. Popular with tourists and business travellers.

9hc (2fb) CTV in all bedrooms Ⓡ *B&b£10.50–£13.50 Bdi£16–£19 WBdi£112–£133 LDO6pm

CTV 9P 1

Ⓥ

See advertisement on page 144

GH Georgian House Hotel 32/34 Ashbourne Rd ☎(0332) 49806

Beautifully maintained house offering a high standard of accommodation.

20hc (2 8) (5fb) CTV in all bedrooms Ⓡ B&b£14–£30 Bdi£24–£28 LDO9.30pm

Lic CTV 24P

See advertisement on page 144

GH Rangemoor Hotel 67 Macklin St ☎(0332) 47252

Simple accommodation in a terraced house near town centre.

12hc Annexe: 8hc (3fb) Ⓡ B&b£11.50–£12.50 WB&b£80.50–£87.50

CTV 18P 2

Credit card 3

Dersingham — Diddlebury

DERSINGHAM
Norfolk
Map **9** TF63

GH *Westdene House Hotel* 60 Hunstanton Rd ☎(0485) 40395
rs Nov–Feb

5hc (1⇌) (1fb) Ⓡ LDO9pm

Lic ⊞ CTV 12P

DEVIL'S BRIDGE
Dyfed
Map **6** SN77

FH Mrs E E Lewis **Erwbarfe** *(SN749784)*
☎Ponterwyd (097085) 251
Etr–Oct

A traditional stone-built farmhouse with oak-beamed ceiling in the lounge. 2m NE of Devil's Bridge on A4120.

2hc (1fb) ✗ Ⓡ B&b£9.50–£11 Bdi£14–£16 WBdifr£100 LDO4pm

⊞ CTV 4P 400acres mixed

Credit cards 1 2 3 5 Ⓥ

DEVIZES
Wiltshire
Map **4** SU06

INN *Castle Hotel* New Park St ☎(0380) 2902
Closed Boxing Day

17hc (2⇌) (2fb) CTV in all bedrooms Ⓡ LDO10pm

⊞ 8⌂

Credit cards 1 2 3 5

DEVORAN
Cornwall
Map **2** SW73

GH Driffold Lodge Hotel 8 Devoran Ln (Guestaccom) ☎Truro (0872) 863314
Closed Nov–Dec rs Jan–Feb

Attractive small hotel overlooking Devoran Creek. Friendly, personally-run and good food.

9hc (1⇌ 4⫴) (1fb) TV in all bedrooms ✗ B&b£12–£15 Bdi£19–£22 WBdi£125–£145 LDOnoon

Lic ⊞ 12P

Ⓥ

See advertisement under Truro

DIBDEN
Hampshire
Map **4** SU40

⊢⊣**GH Dale Farm** Manor Rd
☎Southampton (0703) 849632
Closed Xmas

18th-century farmhouse on edge of the New Forest with modern bedrooms and fresh home-cooking.

6hc (1fb) CTV in 1 bedroom TV in 1 bedroom ✗ Ⓡ B&b£8.50–£11 Bdi£13.50–£16.50 WBdifr£90 LDO11am

⊞ CTV 10P ⌂ U

Ⓥ

DIDDLEBURY
Shropshire
Map **7** SO58

Selected

FH Mrs E Wilkes **Glebe** *(SO507856)*
☎Munslow (058476) 221
Mar–7 Nov (closed 10 days early Jun)

'Pride of Place' national winner in 1983 Glebe Farm is a Tudor farmhouse in the village centre. Rooms are divided between the main house with its ancient timbers and a cottage annexe recently converted to provide more modern surroundings. British country cooking is a speciality, with warm, friendly service.

3hc (1⫴) Annexe: 3hc (1⫴) ✗ Ⓡ ✱B&b£17–£21 Bdi£27.50–£31.50 WBdifr£175 LDO6pm

Lic ⊞ CTV 10P 2⌂ nc10yrs 123acres mixed

DINDER
Somerset
Map **3** ST54

FH Mrs P J Keen ***Crapnell*** *(ST597457)* ☎Shepton Mallet (0749) 2683
Mar–Oct

Pleasant farm with comfortable bedrooms and friendly atmosphere.

3hc (1fb) ✗ Ⓡ LDOnoon

🛏 CTV P ⛳ ⛀ snooker 300acres dairy mixed

DIRLETON
Lothian *East Lothian*
Map **12** NT58

INN Castle ☎(062085) 221
Closed 21 Dec–5 Jan

Plain but comfortable inn in attractive setting on village green.

4hc (3⇌ 1🚿) Annexe: 4hc Ⓡ B&b£14–£18 Bdi£21–£25 WBdifr£150 Bar lunch £1.50–£5 Dinner 8.30pm £7–£10

🛏 CTV 20P

Credit card ② Ⓥ

DITCHLING
East Sussex
Map **4** TQ31

INN *Bull Hotel* 2 High St ☎Hassocks (07918) 3147

Beautifully restored country inn with comfortable accommodation and welcoming bars.

3⇌ CTV in all bedrooms Ⓡ LDO9.30pm

🛏 50P 🚸

Credit cards ① ② ③ ⑤

DOCKLOW
Hereford & Worcester
Map **3** SO55

⊢⊣**FH** Mrs M R M Brooke **Nicholson** *(SO584581)* ☎Steens Bridge (056882) 269

Typical Herefordshire farmhouse, about 350 years old.

3rm (1hc) (1fb) B&b£8.80–£9.25 Bdi£12.80 WB&bfr£61 LDOam

🛏 CTV P ⚓ 200acres dairy mixed

Credit cards ① ③ Ⓥ

DODDISCOMBSLEIGH
Devon
Map **3** SX88

INN Nobody ☎Christow (0647) 52394
rs Sun & Mon (closed Xmas Day)

Attractive inn dating from the 16th century retaining many original features.

4hc (2🚿) Annexe: 3⇌ 🚿 CTV in all bedrooms ✗ Ⓡ B&b£12–£17 WB&b£70–£105 Bar lunch £5alc Dinner 9.30pm £9alc

50P 🚸 nc14yrs

Credit cards ① ③

DOLGELLAU
Gwynedd
Map **6** SH71

GH Clifton Private Hotel Smithfield Sq ☎(0341) 422554

6hc (2🚿) (1fb) CTV in 2 bedrooms ✗ Ⓡ B&b£11–£16 Bdi£16–£24 WBdi£115.50–£161 LDO9pm

Lic 🛏 CTV 3P

Ⓥ

FH Mrs E W Price **Glyn** *(SH704178)* ☎(0341) 422286
Mar–Nov

Stone-built farmhouse of historical interest with oak beams and dressers. Well-situated for coastal resorts.

4rm (3hc) (2fb) Ⓡ ✱B&b£8.50–£9 Bdi£12.50–£14 WB&bfr£58 LDOprevious day

🛏 CTV 6P 150acres mixed

Ⓥ

⊢⊣**FH** Mrs C Tudor-Owen **Rhedyncochion** *(SH693156)* Llanfachreth (3m NE unclass) ☎Rhydymain (034141) 600
Etr–Oct

→

100-year-old, stone-built farmhouse with extensive views of surrounding countryside and mountains.

2rm (1hc) (1fb) ✖ B&bfr£8.50 Bdifr£13

🍽 CTV P 120acres mixed

DOLWYDDELAN
Gwynedd
Map **6** SH75

INN *Gwydyr* ☎(06906) 209
rs Oct–May

Victorian detached inn in centre of village, set in peaceful valley.

3hc CTV in all bedrooms LDO10pm

🍽 CTV 6P nc

DORSINGTON
Warwickshire
Map **4** SP14

FH Mrs M J Walters **Church** *(SP132495)*
☎Stratford-upon-Avon (0789) 720471

Homely Georgian house on village outskirts.

4hc (1fb) ⚟ in all bedrooms ✖ Ⓡ available in bedrooms B&bfr£10 Bdifr£16 LDO5.30pm

🍽 CTV 6P 127acres arable beef horses

DOUGLAS
Isle of Man
See **Man, Isle of**

DOUGLAS WATER
Strathclyde
Map **11** NS83

FH Mrs J Tennant **Eastertown**
Sandilands *(NS874377)* ☎(055588) 236
Closed Nov

A substantial stone built house standing on the northern outskirts of the village. The accommodation is attractive and comfortable and Mrs Tennants 'Taste of Scotland' meals are a welcome bonus.

5hc (1fb) CTV in all bedrooms Ⓡ B&b£10–£12 Bdi£15–£17 WBdifr£98 LDO5pm

🍽 CTV 12P 300acres sheep

DOVER
Kent
Map **5** TR34

GH Beaufort House 18 East Cliff, Marine Pde ☎(0304) 216444

18⋔ (6fb) CTV in all bedrooms
✱B&b£11.50–£21 Bdi£18–£28 WBdi£162–£199 LDO9.30pm

Lic 🍽 CTV 18P 5🚗

Credit cards 1 2 3 Ⓥ

GH Beulah House 94 Crabble Hill, London Rd ☎(0304) 824615

Cosy, homely compact accommodation with limited lounge facilities. Extensive lawns and gardens to rear with open aspect.

8hc (3fb) ✖ B&b£12–£15 WB&bfr£77

🍽 CTV 8P 2🚗

Ⓥ

GH Castle 10 Castle Hill Rd ☎(0304) 201656
Closed Xmas

6hc (4⋔) (1fb) CTV in all bedrooms ✖ Ⓡ
✱B&b£10–£13 WB&b£69.30–£81.90 LDO5pm

Lic 🍽 3P 1🚗(charge)

Credit card 3

⊢⊣ **GH Dell** 233 Folkestone Rd
☎(0304)202422

Victorian terraced house with good family accommodation.

6hc (4fb) ✖ Ⓡ B&b£9–£11.50

🍽 CTV 6P

Ⓥ

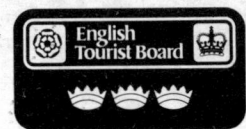

GH Gateway Hovertel Snargate St
☎(0304) 205479
Closed 23 Dec–Feb

Immaculate, well-equipped family-run hotel. Conveniently situated for town and beach.

27hc (4⇌ 23⫫) (7fb) CTV in all bedrooms ✗ B&b£16.50–£20 LDO6pm

Lic ⫫ CTV 24P

Ⓥ

GH Kernow 189 Folkestone Rd ☎(0304) 207797

6hc (2fb) CTV in all bedrooms Ⓡ B&b£9–£12

⫫ CTV 4P 1🚗 (charge)

Credit cards 1 3 Ⓥ

See advertisement on page 148

Dover

GH Number One 1 Castle St ☎(0304) 202007

Conveniently situated, nicely furnished, friendly and efficient establishment complemented by a cosy Victorian atmosphere.

5hc (3⫫) (3fb) CTV in all bedrooms ✗ Ⓡ B&b£12–£14

⫫ 2P 4🚗 (charge)

Ⓥ

See advertisement on page 148

GH Peverall House Hotel 28 Park Av ☎(0304) 202573

Closed Dec

Comfortable, well-appointed accommodation and a cheerful, pleasant welcome.

6hc (2⇌ 2⫫) (3fb) CTV in all bedrooms Ⓡ ✱B&b£13–£16 Bdi£20–£23 WBdifr£120 LDOnoon

Lic ⫫ CTV 6P

See advertisement on page 148

GH St Brelades 82 Buckland Av ☎(0304) 206126

Mar–Nov rs Dec–Feb

Family accommodation with friendly attentive service.

→

8hc (4fb) CTV in 5 bedrooms ✖ ® B&b£10–£12

Lic 🍴 CTV 6P

GH St Martins 17 Castle Hill Rd ☎(0304) 205938
Closed Xmas

8hc (2fb) CTV in all bedrooms ✖ B&b£10–£13 WB&b£70–£91

Lic 🍴 1🚗

Credit card 1

GH Walletts Court West Cliffe, St Margarets-at-Cliffe (1½m NE of A2/A258 junction, off B2058) ☎(0304) 852424
Closed Xmas Day & Boxing Day

A restored 17th-century farmhouse with large beamed bedrooms, inglenooks and oak staircase. Situated on the white cliffs of Dover, 3m from harbour.

3⫿ Annexe: 4⫿ (2fb) CTV in all bedrooms ✖ ® B&b£24–£34 Bdi £34–£44 WBdifr£168 LDO8pm

Lic 🍴 16P 10🚗 ⛳

Ⓥ

DOWNHAM MARKET
Norfolk
Map **5** TF60

GH Cross Keys Riverside Hotel Hilgay (Guestaccom) ☎(0366) 387777
Closed 24 Dec–22 Jan

Once a coaching inn, now a small attractive and comfortable hotel, adjacent to the A10 and on the banks of the River Wissey. 3m S off A5012.

3⇌ Annexe: 2⇌ (1fb) CTV in all bedrooms ✖ ® B&b£17–£23 Bdi£22.60–£29.90 WBdi£137.55 LDO8.30pm

Lic 🍴 10P ✓

Ⓥ

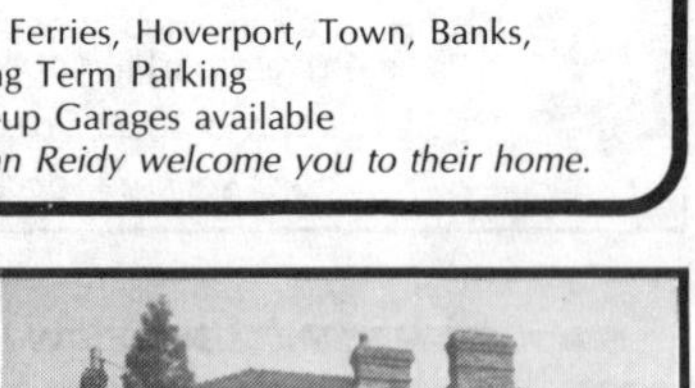

DOWNTON
Wiltshire
Map **4** SU12

GH Warren High St ☎(0725) 20263
Closed 15 Dec–15 Jan

A charming period house, comfortably furnished, with a warm welcome.

7hc (1⇌) (1fb) Ⓡ B&b£12.50–£14.50 WB&bfr£87.50

ꟼ CTV 8P nc5yrs

Ⓥ

See advertisement under Salisbury

DROXFORD
Hampshire
Map **4** SU61

GH Little Uplands Country Motel
Garrison Hill ☎(0489) 878507 Telex no 477046
Closed 24 Dec–2 Jan

Annexe: 15hc (11ꟼ) (2fb) CTV in all bedrooms ✗ Ⓡ B&b£18.50–£30 WB&b£116–£189 LDO9pm

Lic ꟼ CTV 25P ⇌(heated) ℘(hard) ⌐ snooker sauna bath solarium gymnasium

Credit cards 1 2 3 5 Ⓥ

DRUMNADROCHIT
Highland *Inverness-shire*
Map **14** NH53

INN Lewiston Arms Lewiston ☎(04562) 225

A comfortable and cosy old inn with a friendly relaxed atmosphere and a reputation for good food.

4rm (3hc) Annexe: 4hc (1fb) Ⓡ ✱B&b£13–£15 Bdi£19–£25 Bar lunch £2.50alc Dinner 8.30pm £7.50alc

CTV 30P

Credit card ③ Ⓥ

DULVERTON
Somerset
See **Oakford**

DUMFRIES
Dumfries & Galloway *Dumfriesshire*
Map **11** NX97

GH *Fulwood Private Hotel* 30 Lovers Walk ☎(0387) 52262

Compact neat homely villa lying opposite railway station.

6hc (2fb)

CTV 1

GH *Newall House* 22 Newall Ter ☎(0387) 52676

Neatly appointed house with spacious airy bedrooms in residential area between station and town centre.

7rm (6hc) (3fb) TV in 3 bedrooms Ⓡ LDO5pm

Lic CTV 7P

DUNBAR
Lothian *East Lothian*
Map **12** NT67

GH Courtyard Woodbush Brae ☎(0368) 64169
Closed 3wks Jan

Delightful modernised guesthouse in cobbled courtyard on sea-front. It offers excellent home-cooking and has well-equipped bedrooms.

7hc (2⫶) CTV in all bedrooms Ⓡ B&b£13–£18 WB&b£86.45–£119.60 LDO8.30pm

Lic 7P

Credit cards ① ③ Ⓥ

GH Marine 7 Marine Rd ☎(0368) 63315

A friendly, comfortable seaside guesthouse in a quiet residential area on the west side of town.

10hc (3fb) Ⓡ B&b£10–£12.50 Bdi£15–£18 WBdifr£100 LDO4pm

CTV

GH Springfield House Edinburgh Rd ☎(0368) 62502
Mar–Oct

Attractive, family-run detached house set in own grounds a short walk from the town centre.

6hc (2fb) CTV in all bedrooms Ⓡ B&b£14–£15 Bdi£22–£23 WBdifr£138.60 LDO5pm

Lic CTV 7P

Credit cards ① ③

Selected

GH St Beys 2 Bayswell Rd ☎(0368) 63571

Situated close to the town centre, this comfortable house enjoys magnificent sea views. The bedrooms are attractively furnished and well appointed with many thoughtful extras. The smart lounge features a log-burning stove and in the neat dining room guests can enjoy excellent breakfasts and evening meals.

6hc (3fb) CTV in all bedrooms Ⓡ B&b£15.50–£17 Bdi£22.50–£25 WBdifr£135 LDO6pm

CTV

Credit card ③ Ⓥ

DUNDEE
Tayside *Angus*
Map **11** NO43

GH Beach House Hotel 22 Esplanade, Broughty Ferry ☎(0382) 76614

Compact, friendly tourist/commercial guesthouse with well-equipped, modern bedrooms.

4hc (2fb) CTV in all bedrooms ® B&b£12.50–£15 Bdi£17–£20 LDO8.30pm

Lic 🛏 ✗

DUNLOP
Strathclyde *Ayrshire*
Map **10** NS44

FH Mr & Mrs R B Wilson **Struther** *(NS412496)* ☎Stewarton (0560) 84946

Closed 2wks Spring & Autumn

Large farmhouse in its own gardens. On edge of Dunlop village.

6hc (2fb) B&bfr£10 Bdifr£19.50 WBdifr£120 LDO8.30pm

CTV 16P 16acres non-working

DUNOON
Strathclyde *Argyllshire*
Map **10** NS17

GH Cedars Hotel 51 Alexandra Pde, East Bay ☎(0369) 2425

Small family hotel on seafront. Home-cooking and warm welcome.

13hc (4⇌ 5🚿) (1fb) CTV in all bedrooms ✗ ® ✱B&bfr£11 Bdifr£17 WBdifr£107 LDO6.30pm

Lic 🛏 CTV ✗

Credit cards 1 3 Ⓥ

DUNSYRE
Strathclyde *Lanarkshire*
Map **11** NT04

FH Mrs L Armstrong **Dunsyre Mains** *(NT074482)* ☎(089981) 251

Mar–Oct

Two-storey stone farmhouse dating from 1800 in courtyard-style with splendid views and small garden.

3hc (1fb) ✗ B&b£9.50 Bdi£14.50 WBdifr£100 LDO7pm

🛏 CTV P 400acres beef sheep

DUNURE
Strathclyde *Ayrshire*
Map **10** NS21

⊢⊣**FH** Mrs R J Reid **Lagg** *(NS281166)* ☎(029250) 647

Apr–Oct

Extensively renovated and modernised farmhouse overlooking the coast.

3hc B&bfr£9 Bdifr£15 WB&b£60 LDOnoon

🛏 CTV 6P 480acres dairy sheep

DUNVEGAN
Isle of Skye, Highland *Inverness-shire*
See **Skye, Isle of**

DURHAM
Co Durham
Map **12** NZ24

INN Croxdale Croxdale (3m S A167) ☎Spennymoor (0388) 815727

Comfortable inn offering spacious and attractive bedrooms and friendly service.

9hc (1⇌) (1fb) CTV in all bedrooms ® in 5 bedrooms ✱B&bfr£15 WB&bfr£90 Lunch£2.50–£4 Dinner10pm£4.50–£5&alc

🛏 30P

Credit cards 1 3

DURSLEY
Gloucestershire
Map **3** ST79

FH Mrs C St John-Mildmay **Drakestone House** *(ST734977)* Stinchcombe (2½m W off B4060) ☎(0453) 2140

Apr–Oct

Charming country house on the edge of beechwoods with superb views, gardens, and a warm welcome.

3rm (1hc) ✗ ✱B&b£14 Bdi£22.50 LDOnoon

🛏 6P 10acres sheep

FH Mrs E Pain **Park** *(ST745970)* Stancombe Park ☎(0453) 45345

Apr–Sep

Comfortable farmhouse surrounded by beech woods. Off B4060 Wotton-under-Edge to Cam road. Turn at sign marked Millend/Waterly Bottom.

3rm (2hc) (1fb) B&b£12 WB&bfr£84

CTV 4P 130acres arable sheep

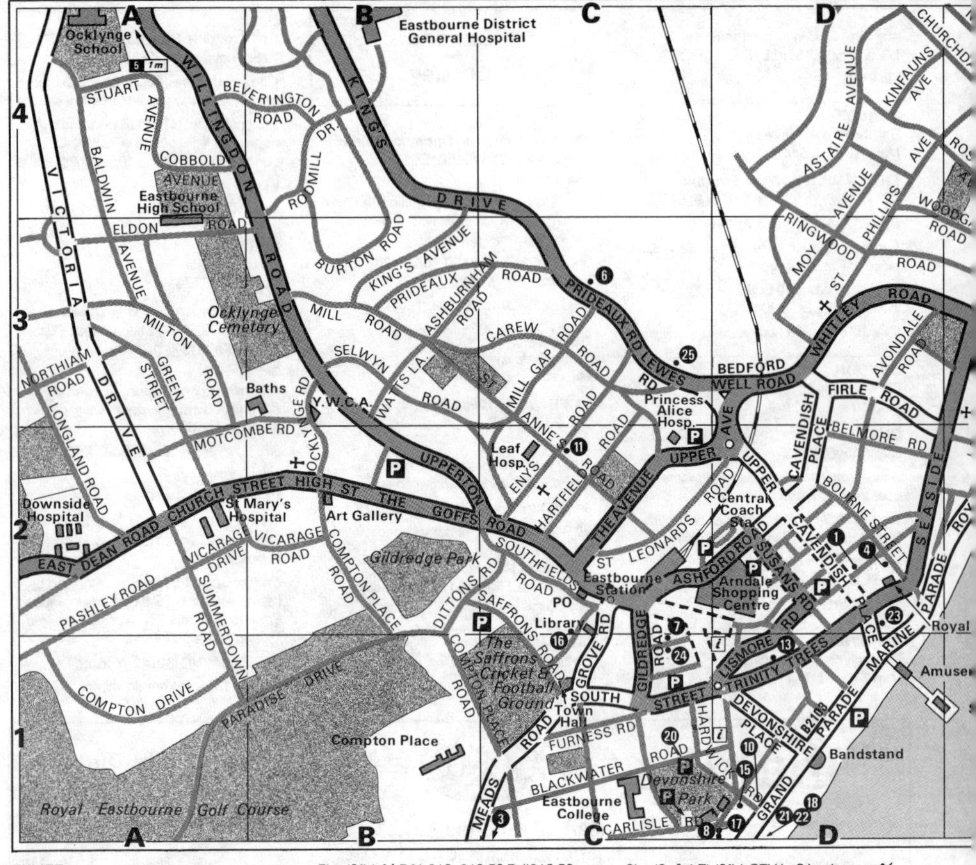

DYLIFE
Powys
Map **6** SN89

INN Star ☎Llanbrynmair (06503) 345

This inn is well-situated for activity holidays. Own pony-trekking centre.

7hc (2⇌) (1fb) B&b£10–£11.50 Bdi£15.95–£17.45 WBdifr£95 Lunch £3.50–£5.95 Dinner 10.30pm £5.95–£7

CTV 30P U

Ⓥ

DYMCHURCH
Kent
Map **5** TR12

GH Chantry Hotel Sycamore Gdns (Guestaccom) ☎(0303) 873137
Mar–Oct

8hc (2⇌ 1fl) (3fb) ✗ B&b£12–£19 Bdi£19–£26 WBdi£98–£115 LDO6pm

Lic CTV 8P

Ⓥ

See advertisement on page 154

GH Waterside 15 Hythe Rd ☎(0303) 872253

7hc (3fb) ✗ B&b£10–£10.50 Bdi£16.50–£17.50 WBdi£107.50–£114 LDO3pm

Lic CTV 9P

Ⓥ

EARDISLAND
Hereford & Worcester
Map **3** SO45

FH Mrs F M Johnson **The Elms** *(SO418584)* (Guestaccom) ☎Pembridge (05447) 405

4hc in all bedrooms ✗ B&b£10.50–£11.50 Bdi£15.50–£17.50 WBdifr£105 LDOnoon

6P nc10yrs 32acres stock rearing

Ⓥ

EARLSWOOD
Gwent
Map **3** ST49

FH Mrs G Powell **Parsons Grove** *(ST 452943)* ☎ Shirenewton (02917) 382

A modern farmhouse, complete with swimming pool, situated in quiet countryside. Newly planted vineyard.

3hc (2⇌ 1fl) (3fb) CTV in 2 bedrooms ✗ Ⓡ B&b£10–£12 Bdi£16–£18 WBdi£100–£112 LDO11am

CTV 10P (heated) 17 acres beef vineyards

Ⓥ

EASTBOURNE
East Sussex
Map **5** TV69

GH *Avalon Private Hotel* 64–66 Pevensey Rd ☎(0323) 22695
Plan **1** *D2*

Meals prepared by the chef-patron himself ensure a pleasant stay in this extended terraced house away from the sea front.

14hc (2fb) CTV in all bedrooms Ⓡ LDO6pm

Lic

Ⓥ

GH Bay Lodge Hotel 61 & 62 Royal Pde ☎(0323) 32515 Plan **2** *E2*

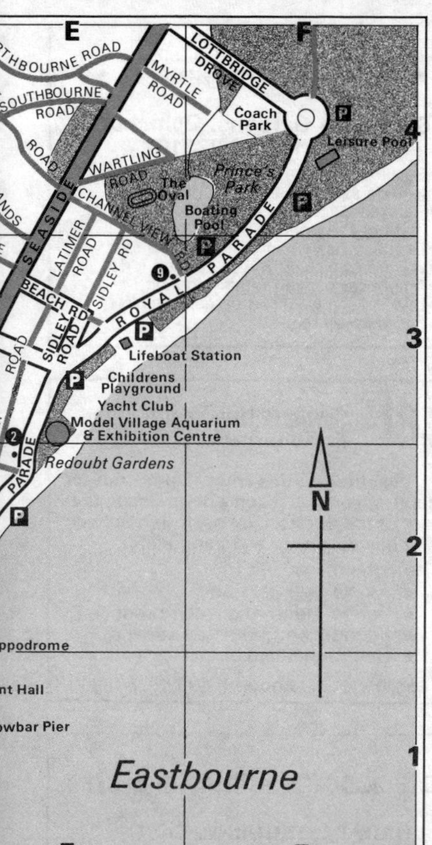

Eastbourne

Located on the seafront next to the bowling green and Redoubt Gardens, this hotel has spacious bedrooms, a small bar and a sun lounge.

11hc (4⇌ 2fl) (1fb) CTV in all bedrooms Ⓡ B&b£11.50–£15 Bdi£15.50–£22 WBdi£89–£135 (W only Jul & Aug) LDO6pm

Lic ♈ CTV 2⌂ (charge) nc7yrs

Credit cards 1 3 Ⓥ

GH Beachy Rise 20 Beachy Head Rd, ☏(0323) 639171 Plan **3** *C1*
Closed Xmas wk

Small but homely and friendly establishment.

6hc (2fb) ✻B&b£9–£11 Bdi£11.50–£13.50 WBdi£69–£77 LDOam

♈ CTV ₽

GH *Bourne House Private Hotel* 16 Bourne St ☏(0323) 21981 Plan **4** *D2*

Charming guesthouse just off the front.

9hc ✕ Ⓡ LDO6pm

Lic ♈ CTV ₽ nc5yrs ♩

Selected

GH Chalk Farm Hotel & Restaurant Coopers Hill, Willingdon (2m NNE) ☏(0323) 503800 Plan **5** *A4*

Guests receive a warm welcome by the proprietors of this charming 17th-century flint farmhouse. Overlooking the Sussex Downs, Chalk farm offers antique-furnished bedrooms and comfortable lounges.

9hc (2⇌ 5fl) (1fb) ✕ ✻B&b£19–£23 Bdi£28.95–£32.95 WBdi£150–£170 LDO9pm

Lic ♈ CTV 30P

Credit card 5

See advertisement on page 154

GH *Delladale Lodge* 35 Lewes Rd ☏(0323) 25207 Plan **6** *C3*
Apr–Oct

Tastefully appointed guesthouse with the accent on comfort and informal atmosphere.

10hc (6fl) (1fb) ✕ Ⓡ

Lic ♈ CTV 10P nc5yrs ⛱(heated)

See advertisement on page 154

GH *Edmar* 30 Hyde Gdns ☏(0323) 33024 Plan **7** *C1*
Apr–Oct

A homely, family-run guesthouse with a bright dining room.

9hc (2⇌ 1fl) (1fb) ✕ Ⓡ LDO6pm

CTV ₽

GH Ellesmere Hotel 11 Wilmington Sq ☏(0323) 31463 Plan **8** *D1*

13hc (2⇌ 8fl) (1fb) CTV in all bedrooms Ⓡ B&b£15–£16.50 Bdi£21–£22.50 WBdi£110–£136 LDO7pm

Lic lift ♈ ₽ nc3yrs

GH *Fairlands Hotel* 15–17 Lascelles Ter ☏(0323) 33287 Plan **10** *D1*
late Mar–mid Oct

Warm, friendly, delightfully modernised guesthouse

25hc (16⇌) (2fb) Ⓡ LDO6.15pm

Lic CTV ₽

GH *Far End Hotel* 139 Royal Pde ☏(0323) 25666 Plan **9** *E3*

Large house with bright and comfortable accommodation, on sea front on eastern outskirts of town.

10hc (2fl) (1fb) ✕ Ⓡ LDO4pm

Lic ♈ CTV 6P 2🚗 nc5yrs

GH Flamingo Private Hotel 20 Enys Rd (Guestaccom) ☏(0323) 21654 Plan **11** *C2*
Closed Jan

Large Victorian house in residential area with comfortable rooms and friendly atmosphere.

12hc (5⇌ 7fl) CTV in all bedrooms ✕ Ⓡ B&b£13.50–£15 Bdi£19–£21.50 WBdi£114–£130 LDO4.30pm

Lic ♈ ₽ nc8yrs

Credit cards 1 3 Ⓥ

See advertisement on page 155

GH Hotel Mandalay 16 Trinity Trees ☏(0323) 29222 Plan **13** *D1*

A comfortable house with a warm and friendly atmosphere.

12fl (1fb) CTV in all bedrooms ✕ Ⓡ B&bfr£20 Bdifr£29 WBdifr£114 LDO10.30pm

Lic ♈ 15P nc5yrs

GH Mowbray Hotel 2 Lascelles Ter ☏(0323) 20012 Plan **15** *D1*
Apr–Dec

Large four-storey Victorian house, adjacent to Devonshire Park and theatres.

16hc (4fl) (1fb) CTV in all bedrooms Ⓡ B&b£12.25–£13.50 Bdi£18.25–£19.50 WBdifr£120 LDO5.30pm

lift CTV ₽ nc6yrs

Credit cards 1 3

GH Orchard House Private Hotel 10 Old Orchard Rd ☏(0323) 23682 Plan **16** *C2*
Feb–Nov

→

The
Chantry
Hotel

AA

Well-appointed semi-detached Victorian house near town centre and railway station. Close to sea and promenade.

7rm (5⇐ 2fiml) (2fb) CTV in all bedrooms ✕ Ⓡ ✱B&b£15.50–£17.50 Bdi£21–£23 WBdi£129.50–£139.50 LDO6pm

Lic ꟾꟾ 3P nc5yrs

Ⓥ

— *Selected* —

GH *Park View Hotel* Wilmington Gdns ☎(0323) 21242 Plan **17** *D1*

Well-appointed family-run hotel with good home-cooking.

13hc (3⇐ 9fiml) CTV in all bedrooms ✕ Ⓡ LDO8pm

Lic lift 10P nc2yrs

Credit cards 1 2 3

GH Saffrons Hotel 30–32 Jevington Gdns ☎(0323) 25539 Plan **18** *D1*

Etr–Oct

Comfortable, large accommodation within this Victorian building, situated in gardens close to town centre.

25hc (7⇐ 6fiml) CTV in all bedrooms Ⓡ B&b£16–£18.50 Bdi£21.50–£24 WBdifr£160 LDO6.15pm

Lic CTV 🅿̸

GH Somerville Private Hotel 6 Blackwater Rd ☎(0323) 29342 Plan **20** *C1*

Eastbourne

Small private hotel convenient for Devonshire Park and the Winter Gardens.

12hc (3fiml) (2fb) Ⓡ ✱B&b£11.50–£14.50 Bdi £17–£20 WBdi£102–120

Lic CTV 🅿̸ nc3yrs

GH South Cliff House 19 South Cliff Av ☎(0323) 21019 Plan **21** *D1*

rs Nov–Mar

Small and cheerful guesthouse in quiet situation short distance from the sea.

7hc ✕ Ⓡ B&b£11–£12 Bdi£15–£16 WBdifr£90

Lic ꟾꟾ CTV 🅿̸ nc9yrs

See advertisement on page 156

GH Southcroft 15 South Cliff Av ☎(0323) 29071 Plan **22** *D1*

Closed 21 Dec–13 Jan

Attractively appointed and well-maintained private hotel.

6hc (4⇐ 2fiml) ✕ Ⓡ B&b£15–£16 Bdi£20–£22 WBdifr£125

Lic ꟾꟾ CTV 🅿̸ nc4yrs

GH *Stirling House Hotel* 5–7 Cavendish Pl ☎(0323) 32263 Plan **23** *D2*

A cosy, personally-run house not far from sea or shops.

21hc (7fiml) (3fb) CTV in 7 bedrooms ✕ Ⓡ LDO9am

Lic CTV 🅿̸

See advertisement on page 156

GH *Traquair Private Hotel* 25 Hyde Gdns ☎(0323) 25198 Plan **24** *C1*

Clean, colourful and comfortable accommodation where cooking is taken seriously.

11hc (6fiml) (3fb) CTV in all bedrooms Ⓡ LDO6.30pm

Lic ꟾꟾ CTV 🅿̸

Credit cards 1 2 3 5

GH Wynstay Private Hotel 13 Lewes Rd ☎(0323) 21550 Plan **25** *C3*

Closed Xmas & New Year rs Winter

Homely hotel about ½ mile from town centre.

7hc (6fiml) (1fb) CTV in all bedrooms ✕ Ⓡ B&b£14.50–£22 Bdi£15.50–£19.50 WBdifr£87.50 LDO2pm

ꟾꟾ 7P nc5yrs

Ⓥ

EAST CALDER
Lothian *Midlothian*
Map **11** NT06

⊢⊣**FH** Mr & Mrs D R Scott **Whitecroft** *(NT095682)* ☎Mid Calder (0506) 881810

Large roadside bungalow attached to smallholding ½m E on B7015.

3hc (1fb) ✖ Ⓡ B&b£9–£11 WB&b£63

▥ CTV 8P ⌂ 5acres beef sheep

ⓥ

EAST CHINNOCK
Somerset
Map **3** ST41

GH Barrows Country House Weston St ☎ West Coker (093586) 2390
Closed 24 Dec–1 Jan

Small, quiet, personally-run house on the edge of this pleasant village.

6hc ✖ Ⓡ B&b£13–£15 Bdi£19–£21 WBdi£126–£140 LDOnoon

Lic ▥ CTV 6P nc5yrs

EAST GRINSTEAD
West Sussex
Map **5** TQ33

GH Cranfield Hotel Maypole Rd ☎(0342) 21251

Homely, comfortable private hotel in quiet residential area.

11hc (4🚿) Annexe 9hc (1🛁 6🚿) (3fb) CTV in all bedrooms Ⓡ B&b£16.10–£20 Bdi£24–£28 LDO8pm

Lic ▥ CTV 11P

Credit cards ①③ ⓥ

EAST MEON
Hampshire
Map **4** SU62

FH Mrs P M Berry ***Giants*** *(SU696207)* Harvesting Ln ☎(073087) 205
Mar–Oct

Modern farmhouse, set in ½acre with views from all rooms of the surrounding countryside. Queen Elizabeth Country Park of 1,400 acres, with facilities for pony-trekking and grass skiing is nearby.

3hc (2🛁) TV in all bedrooms ✖ Ⓡ

▥ CTV 4P 30acres sheep poultry

EAST PRESTON
West Sussex
Map **5** TQ00

INN South Strand ☎ Rustington (0903) 785086

14hc (3🛁) (2fb) B&bfr£20 Bdi£24–£30 WBdifr£210 Lunch£8&alc Dinner7.45pm£8&alc

▥ CTV 30P 🚗 sauna bath solarium gymnasium

Credit cards ①②③⑤

EBBERSTON
North Yorkshire
Map **8** SE88

GH Foxholm Hotel (on B1258) ☎Scarborough (0723) 85550
Mar–Nov & Xmas

Small, family-run country hotel in a peaceful setting. York, the moors, dales and sea all within easy reach.

10hc (1🛁 3🚿) (1fb) Ⓡ B&b£14–£15.50 Bdi£20–£22 WBdi£134–£148 LDO7pm

Lic ▥ CTV 12P 2🚗

ⓥ

REMEMBER

Prices quoted in the gazetteer are minimum double room occupancy to maximum single room occupancy **per person.**

EDINBURGH
Lothian *Midlothian*
Map **11** NT27
See **Central Plan** (pages **158–159**) and **District Plan** (pages **160–161**)

GH Adam Hotel 19 Landsdowne Cres ☎031-337 1148 District Plan **6**
Closed Xmas & 1 & 2 Jan

Comfortable accommodation in quiet, residential area.

9hc (2fb) CTV in all bedrooms ✖ B&b£14–£15

Lic ▥ CTV P̸

ⓥ

See advertisement on page 162

GH Adria Hotel 11–12 Royal Ter ☎031-556 7875 Central plan **1** *F6*
Jan–Oct

Part of a Georgian terrace close to Princes Street. Spacious, well-decorated accommodation.

28hc (2🛁 4🚿) (7fb) ✖ Ⓡ B&b£16.10–£19.55

▥ CTV P̸

ⓥ

GH Allison House 15/17 Mayfield Gdns ☎031-667 8049 District plan **7**
Closed Xmas & New Year

A conversion of two terraced houses to the south of the city centre. Accommodation is comfortable and each bedroom well-equipped.

24hc (21🚿) (10fb) CTV in all bedrooms ✖ Ⓡ B&b£12–£22 WB&bfr£80

Lic ▥ TV 12P

GH Ben Doran 11 Mayfield Gdns ☎031-667 8488 District plan **8**
Closed 20–27 Dec

Situated in a terraced row, with modest bedrooms.

9hc (1🛁 1🚿) (5fb) CTV in all bedrooms Ⓡ B&b£11–£16 WB&b£70–£118

▥ 6P 2🚗

GH Boisdale Hotel 9 Coates Gdns ☎031-337 1134 District plan **9**

Modestly-appointed terraced house situated close to the city's West End. Friendly service and enjoyable breakfasts.

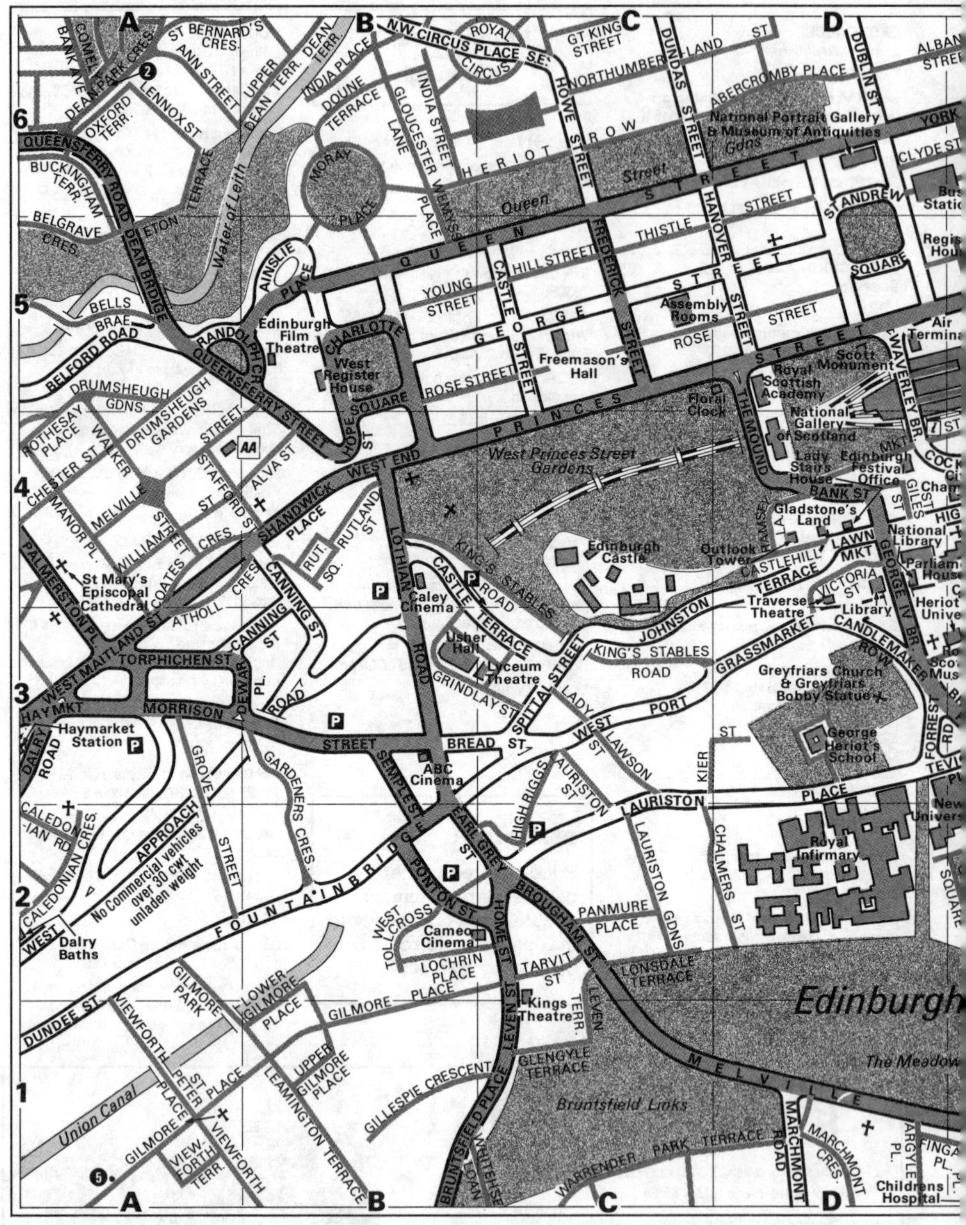

10hc (5⇌ 2🚿) (5fb) TV available in bedrooms Ⓡ B&b£18–£20 Bdi£24–£26 LDO7pm

Lic 🍽 CTV ⚑

See advertisement on page 162

GH *Bonnington* 202 Ferry Rd ☎031-554 7610 District plan **10**

A particularly friendly guesthouse modestly-appointed and with good home cooking.

6hc (3fb) ✗ LDO1pm

🍽 CTV 12P

GH Brunswick 7 Brunswick St ☎031-556 1238 District plan **11**

A newly converted property with spacious bedrooms, convenient for Princes St and city centre.

7hc (5🚿) (2fb) CTV in all bedrooms ✗ ✱B&b£10–£16 WB&b£56–£105

🍽 ⚑ nc2yrs

Ⓥ

See advertisement on page 162

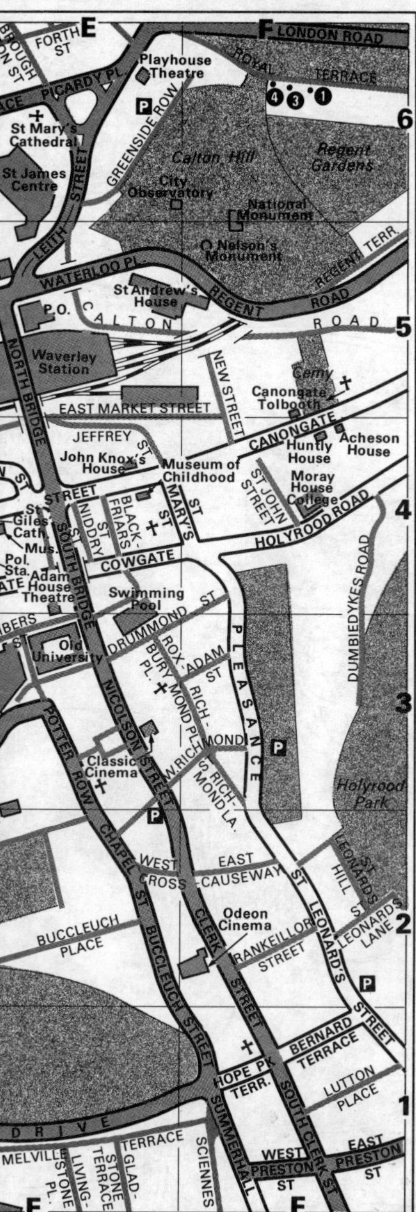

Edinburgh Central
1 Adria
2 Galloway
3 Greenside Hotel
4 Halcyon Hotel
5 Kariba

GH Buchan Hotel 3 Coates Gdns ☎031-337 1045 District plan **12**

Exceptionally well-maintained Victorian guesthouse close to city centre. Spacious public areas are elegantly furnished and the attrtactive bedrooms are comfortable.

10hc (1fl) (6fb) CTV in all bedrooms Ⓡ B&b£14–£16 Bdi£21–£23 WBdifr£147 LDO10am

CTV

Ⓥ

GH Clans Hotel 4 Magdala Cres ☎031-337 6301 District plan **13**

Three-storey house in a terrace row near the city's West End. Spacious but modest accommodation.

7hc (1fl) (2fb) ✗ B&b£12.50–£18

Lic CTV

Selected

GH Dorstan Private Hotel
7 Priestfield Rd ☎031-667 6721
District plan **14**
Closed 23 Dec–9 Jan

A very well-maintained and thoughtfully equipped house that has undergone many improvements recently. Guests can expect a warm and cheerful welcome from owners Mairae and Iain Campbell. Bedrooms are small, modern and well decorated and most have private facilities. Breakfasts are enjoyable and although guests are encouraged to make their choice the previous evening, the system is flexible.

14hc (5→ 4fl) (2fb) CTV in all bedrooms Ⓡ B&b£13–£19 Bdi£20–£26 LDO4pm

CTV 8P

See advertisement on page 162

GH Dunstane House 4 West Coates ☎031-337 6169 District plan **15**
Closed Xmas–4 Jan

Comfortable and spacious accommodation including one bedroom with four-poster bed. All rooms with private shower.

15hc (5fb) CTV in all bedrooms Ⓡ B&b£19.50–£24 WB&b£126–£151.20

Lic CTV 10P

Credit cards 2 3

GH Galloway 22 Dean Park Cres ☎031-332 3672 Telex no 72165 Central plan **2**
A6

This cheerful, informally-run establishment forms part of a handsome Victorian terrace. Most bedrooms are spacious and tastefully appointed; those with private facilities being particularly comfortable. Table-sharing is sometimes unavoidable at breakfast time.

10hc (3→ 2fl) (6fb) CTV in 2 bedrooms Ⓡ B&b£10–£15 Bdi£14–£19 WB&b£60–£90 LDO5pm

CTV

Ⓥ

GH Glendale Hotel 5 Lady Rd ☎031-667 6588 District plan **16**

7hc (1fb) TV in all bedrooms ✗ Ⓡ B&b£10.50–£16 Bdi£16–£21.50 WBdi£90–£120 LDOnoon

CTV 8P

Ⓥ

See advertisement on page 163

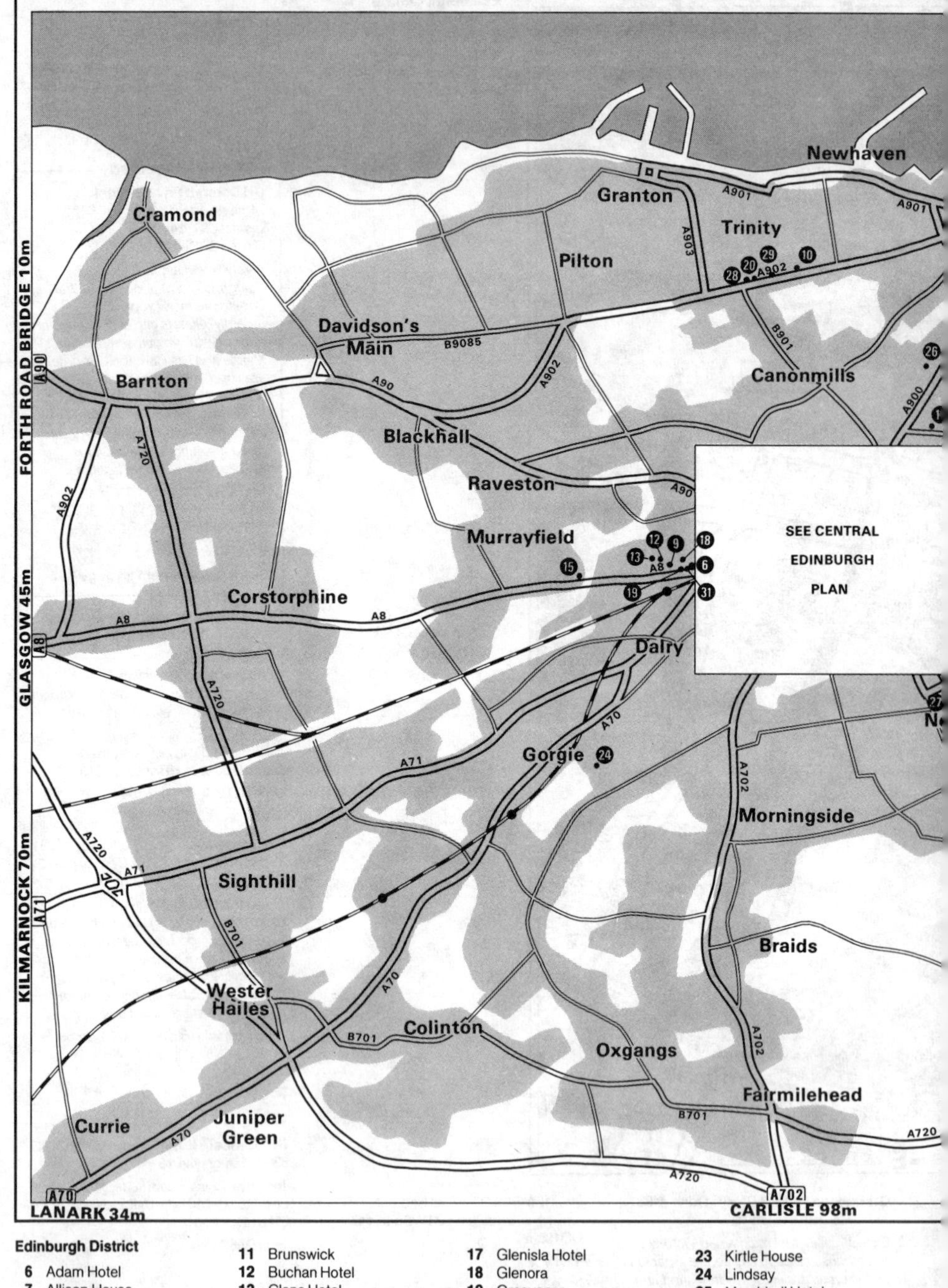

Edinburgh District

6 Adam Hotel
7 Allison House
8 Ben Doran Hotel
9 Boisdale Hotel
10 Bonnington
11 Brunswick
12 Buchan Hotel
13 Clans Hotel
14 Dorstan Private Hotel
15 Dunstane House
16 Glendale
17 Glenisla Hotel
18 Glenora
19 Grosvenor
20 Heriott Park
21 Kildonan Lodge Hotel
22 Kingsley
23 Kirtle House
24 Lindsay
25 Marchhall Hotel
26 Marvin
27 Newington
28 Park View Villa

29 Ravensdown
30 Rockville Hotel
31 Roseberry
32 St Margaret's Hotel
33 Salisbury Hotel
34 Sherwood
35 Southdown
36 Thrums Private Hotel
37 Tiree

GH Glenisla Hotel 12 Lygon Rd ☎031-667 4098 District plan **17**

Most attractive and well-maintained house in a residential area on the south side. The cheerful proprietors have extended the catering facilities and are constantly making improvements throughout.

8hc (2fb) B&b£12–£15 WB&b£105 LDO8.15pm

Lic CTV 6P 1🚗

See advertisement on page 163

GH Glenora 14 Roseberry Cres ☎031-337 1186 District plan **18**

An attractively decorated and furnished compact hotel with well equipped bedrooms.

10fl (2fb) CTV in all bedrooms ®
*B&bfr£17.50

Lic CTV

See advertisement on page 163

GH Greenside Hotel 9 Royal Ter ☎031-557 0022 Central plan **3** *F6*
Feb–Nov

This elegant Regency House is neat and well-maintained with large bedrooms. Service is attentive and friendly, and the hearty breakfasts can be thoroughly recommended.

12hc (2⇌ 3fl) (3fb) B&b£19.55–£25.30

CTV

GH *Grosvenor* 1 Grosvenor Gdns, Haymarket ☎031-337 4143 District plan **19**

A friendly welcome awaits guests at this Victorian town house. Spacious but modest accommodation in a peaceful atmosphere.

7hc (1⇌ 1fl) (3fb) CTV in all bedrooms ®

See advertisement on page 163

GH *Halcyon Hotel* 8 Royal Ter ☎031-556 1033 Central plan **4** *F6*
Closed Feb & New Year

Modestly-appointed house in a fine Regency terraced row.

16hc (4fb)

CTV (hard)

GH Heriott Park 256 Ferry Rd ☎031-552 6628 District plan **20**

Smart, recently converted house on main road in north part of the city.

7hc (3fl) (4fb) CTV in all bedrooms ® B&b£10–£14

CTV P snooker

GH Kariba 10 Granville Ter ☎031-229 3773 Central plan **5** *A1*

Compact and homely guesthouse.

9hc CTV in all bedrooms ® B&b£12–£15

CTV 4P

Ⓥ

See advertisement on page 164

Glendale House Hotel

Mr & Mrs R W Brownlie, Proprietors

5 Lady Road, Edinburgh
EH16 5PA
Tel: 031-667 6588

Glendale House where comfort and cleanliness are our first priority. A warm welcome is extended to everyone by friendly hostess. Enjoy your breakfast in the wood-panelled dining room. Adjacent to bus route, 10 minutes from town centre, buses direct every few minutes. Leave your car in the large private car park. Full central heating. TV in most bedrooms.

Glenisla Hotel

12 Lygon Road, Edinburgh EH16 5QB.
Telephone: 031-667 4098

A small family run hotel situated in quiet area of city, ten minutes from Princes Street and on main bus route. Surrounded by golf courses and within easy reach of Commonwealth Pool and Holyrood Palace. The Hotel is nicely furnished and decorated to a high standard. Full central heating, some bedrooms with shower & toilet. Licensed restaurant for residents and non residents. À la carte and set menu available. Reduced rate for small coach parties. Ample parking. Open all year.

Please send for terms and brochure.

Glenora Hotel

14 ROSEBERY CRESCENT, EDINBURGH EH12 5JY
Reservations: 031-337 1186

Glenora is a small friendly private hotel run under the personal supervision of the resident proprietrix Joy L. Chalmers. Centrally located, Glenora has recently been refurbished throughout, and offers ten superb bedrooms all with their own private en-suite facilities. Tea/coffee making facilities, colour TV, and direct dial telephone in all rooms. Full central heating throughout. Resident drinks licence, full Scottish breakfast, baby listening service, cot available.

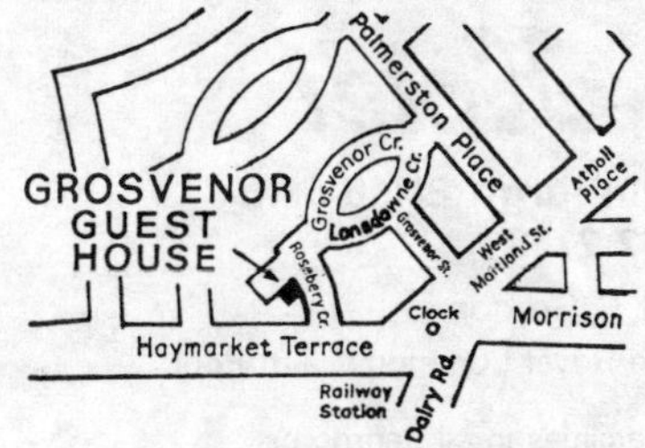

Grosvenor Guest House

Quiet cul-de-sac. Spacious rooms.
All bedrooms with H&C, electric blankets, shaving points and television. Near City centre.
Special off-season rates on weekly basis.
Resident proprietor: John G Gray.

1 Grosvenor Gardens, Haymarket, Edinburgh EH12 5JU. Tel: 031 337 4143

GH Kildonan Lodge Hotel 27 Craigmillar Pk ☎031-667 2793 District plan **21**

A private hotel lying south of the city centre. Modest bedroom accommodation and attractive restaurant and cocktail lounge. Extensive à la carte menu offers value for money.

9hc (5fb) CTV in all bedrooms Ⓡ B&b£10.50–£14.50 LDO9pm

Lic 🏨 20P

Credit card 2 Ⓥ

GH Kingsley 30 Craigmillar Pk, Newington ☎031-667 8439 District plan **22**

A pleasant, homely house on main A7 road to the S of the city.

Edinburgh

7hc (3fb) ✗ Ⓡ B&b£10–£13

🏨 CTV 7P

GH Kirtle House 8 Minto St ☎031-667 2813 District plan **23**

Neat semi-detached house to the south of the city centre.

7hc (4🛁) (4b) CTV in all bedrooms Ⓡ B&b£11.50–£15

🏨 CTV 5P nc4yrs

Credit cards 1 2 3 5

GH Lindsay 108 Polwarth Ter ☎031-337 1580 District plan **24**

Comfortable neatly appointed house with a relaxed and friendly atmosphere.

7rm (6hc) (2fb) CTV in all bedrooms Ⓡ ✱B&b£10–£14 WB&b£70–£98

6P

GH Marchhall Hotel 14–16 Marchhall Cres ☎031-667 2743 District plan **25**

This comfortable guesthouse is situated in a pleasant residential area close to swimming pool and University buildings. The attractive lounge bar is open to non-residents.

13hc (2⋔) (3fb) CTV in all bedrooms Ⓡ
Lic ℳ CTV P̸

Ⓥ

GH Marvin 46 Pilrig St ☏031-554 6605 District plan **26**

A friendly, family-run establishment with homely dining room and lounge. Bedrooms are comfortable and well-appointed. Guests are offered a wide choice of breakfast dishes.

7hc (4⇌) (2fb) CTV in all bedrooms Ⓡ B&b£10–£17 WB&b£65–£109

ℳ 6P ⌂

GH Newington 18 Newington Rd ☏031-667 3356 District plan **27**

A house of character and appeal well-appointed and thoughtfully equipped

8hc (3⋔) (1fb) CTV in all bedrooms Ⓡ B&b£13.50–£17.50

ℳ 3P

GH Park View Villa 254 Ferry Rd ☏031-552 3456 District plan **28**

A comfortable terraced house enjoying good views of Edinburgh Castle. The owner will arrange local tours and sailing on request.

6hc (4fb) Ⓡ B&bfr£10

CTV

GH Ravensdown 248 Ferry Rd ☏031-552 5438 District plan **29**

Edinburgh

Comfortable, well appointed house with views over the city and its imposing castle.

7hc (5fb) CTV in all bedrooms ✖ Ⓡ
✱B&b£10–£14

Lic ℳ CTV 4P

Ⓥ

GH Rockville Hotel 2 Joppa Pans, Joppa (2m E off A1) ☏031-669 5418 District plan **30**
Feb–Nov

5hc (3⇌ ⋔) (2fb) ⚲ in one bedroom ✖ (ex guide dogs) Ⓡ B&b£21 Bdi£30

Lic ℳ CTV 10P
Credit cards 1 2 3 5 Ⓥ

GH Rosebery 13 Rosebery Cres, Haymarket ☏031-337 1085 District plan **31**
Closed 24–31 Dec

Friendly city centre guesthouse conveniently situated for Haymarket Station.

5hc (1fb) CTV in all bedrooms Ⓡ
✱B&b£12–£14.50

ℳ CTV P̸

Ⓥ

GH St Margaret's
18 Craigmillar Pk ☏031-667 2202 District plan **32**
Closed Nov & Feb

Well-appointed Victorian house on main road south of city centre.

8hc (3fb) CTV in all bedrooms Ⓡ
B&b£10.50–£12.50

ℳ CTV 6P

See advertisement on page 166

GH Salisbury Hotel 45 Salisbury Rd ☏031-667 1264 District plan **33**
Closed Xmas & New Year

A neatly decorated combination of two Georgian town houses close to a shopping suburb.

12hc (1⇌ 4⋔) (3fb) CTV in 3 bedrooms Ⓡ B&b£11–£15 WB&b£66–£90

Lic ℳ CTV 12P

Ⓥ

GH Sherwood 42 Minto St ☏031-667 1200 District plan **34**
Closed Xmas & New Year

A friendly, well-maintained terraced house south of the city centre

6hc (3fb) CTV in all bedrooms Ⓡ B&b£10–£13.50

ℳ 3P

Ⓥ

GH Southdown 20 Craigmillar Pk ☎031-667 2410 District plan **35**

Neat terraced guesthouse offering friendly service. Modestly-appointed compact bedrooms and comfortable public areas. Enjoyable breakfasts with home-made preserves a speciality.

8hc (2fb) TV in all bedrooms ✗(except guide dogs) ® B&b£12.50–£15 WB&b£75–£90

Ⅲ CTV 8P

GH Thrums Private Hotel 14 Minto St, Newington ☎031-667 5545 District plan **36**

Closed 10 days Xmas & New Year

Cheerful, compact house with well-equipped bedrooms. Gardens to front and rear and useful parking area.

7hc (3⥮) (2fb) CTV in all bedrooms ® B&b£14.50–£17.50 WB&bfr£91.50 LDO7.45pm

Lic Ⅲ CTV 10P

Ⓥ

GH *Tiree* 26 Craigmillar Pk ☎031-667 7477 District plan **37**

Tidy, well-decorated house with good bedroom facilities.

7hc (3⥮) (2fb) CTV in all bedrooms ®

Ⅲ CTV 7P

EGERTON
Kent
Map **5** TQ94

FH Mrs D Boardman **Link** *(TQ898470)* ☎(023376) 214

Apr–Sep

1m SW off unclass rd.

Modern farmhouse set in secluded and peaceful surroundings, with pretty gardens and extensive views of the Kentish countryside. Nicely appointed bedrooms and spacious, comfortable lounge.

3rm (1⇌) ✗ B&b£10–£12 Bdi15–£17 WBdifr£119 LDO6pm

🝖 CTV 3P 2🚗 nc9yrs 10acres non-working

EGGLESTON
Co Durham
Map **12** NY92

INN Moorcock Hill Top ☎Teesdale (0833) 50395

A charming country inn with comfortable accommodation. Good food served in bar and restaurant.

4hc (1⇌ 1fl) (1fb) CTV in all bedrooms Ⓡ B&b£13.80–£14.50 Bdi£18.30–£19 WBdi£102.50–£119.70 Lunch £4.50–£5.75 High Tea £2.50–£3.75 Dinner 10pm £4.50–£5.75&alc

Lic 🝖 CTV 60P

EGLINGHAM
Northumberland
Map **12** NU11

Selected

FH Mrs A I Easton **West Ditchburn** *(NU131207)* ☎Powburn (066578) 337
Mar–Oct

An impressive stone built farmhouse in a peaceful location. The bedrooms are all attractively furnished and decorated with CTV and other extras. Guests can relax in the cosy lounge and eat good home cooked meals in the dining room. Charm is added throughout the house by interesting ornaments and polished silver.

4hc (2fb) CTV in all bedrooms Ⓡ B&b£12–£13 Bdi£19–£20 WBdi£125–£130 LDO5pm

🝖 14P nc4yrs 1000acres beef sheep

EGREMONT
Cumbria
Map **11** NY01

Egerton — Emsworth

INN Royal Oak Hotel Beckermet (2½m S off A595) ☎ Beckermet (094684) 551

Old inn with low ceilings and open-fires. Bedrooms are modern.

8⇌ CTV in all bedrooms B&b£25 Bdi£35 WBdi£200 Lunch £3–£6&alc Dinner 9.45pm £8–£10&alc

🝖 20P

ELIE
Fife
Map **12** NO40

GH Elms Park Pl ☎(0333) 330404
Feb–Nov

A neatly appointed house with garden to rear.

6hc (1⇌) (2fb) Ⓡ ✻B&b£9.50–£10.50 Bdi£15–£16 WBdi£95–£96

Lic 🝖 CTV 𝙋 ⌂

ELSDON
Northumberland
Map **12** NY99

FH Mrs T M Carruthers **Dunns** *(NY937969)* ☎Rothbury (0669) 40219

Old farmhouse in quiet position amongst the Cheviot Hills and Coquet Valley.

3rm (2hc) (1fb) ✗ ✻B&b£9

CTV P 1000acres beef sheep

Ⓥ

ELSRICKLE
Strathclyde *Lanarkshire*
Map **11** NT04

FH Mr & Mrs Barrie **Howburn** *(NT074439)* ☎Dunsyre (089981) 276
May–Oct

A comfortable farmhouse set back from the A721, ¾ mile N of junction with A702.

2rm (2fb) ✗ Ⓡ B&b£9.50 WBdi£60

🝖 CTV P 850acres arable beef sheep

ELY
Cambridgeshire
Map **5** TL58

GH *Castle Lodge Hotel* 50 New Barns Rd ☎(0353) 2276

10hc (1⇌ 2fl) (1fb) CTV in all bedrooms ✗

Ⓡ LDO7.30pm

Lic 🝖 8P

Credit cards 1 3

GH Nyton 7 Barton Rd ☎(0353) 2459

10hc (1⇌ 9fl) (2fb) CTV in all bedrooms ✗ Ⓡ B&b£14–£20 WBdi£21–£27 Bdifr£133 LDO8pm

Lic 🝖 CTV 12P

Credit cards 1 3 Ⓥ

See advertisement on page 168

EMPINGHAM
Leicestershire
Map **4** SK90

INN White Horse High St ☎(078086) 221

Warm and welcoming village inn whose food enjoys a good local reputation.

3hc Annexe: 8 ⇌ (3fb) CTV in all bedrooms Ⓡ ✻B&b£18.50–£25 Bdi£23.50–£28.50 WBdifr£183 Lunch £6.95–£7.50 High Tea fr£1.50 Dinner 9.45pm £2.50–£5.50&alc

🝖 60P

Credit cards 1 2 3 5 Ⓥ

See advertisement under Oakham

EMSWORTH
Hampshire
Map **4** SU70

GH Chestnuts 55 Horndean Rd ☎(0243) 372233

Quietly situated north west of the town, this lovely house furnished with antiques, offers comfortable, old-fashioned accommodation. There is a cosy lounge and neat garden. Guests can also enjoy the swimming pool.

6hc (2fb) B&b£12–£16 Bdi£18–£22 LDO9am

🝖 CTV 6P ⛵

GH Jingles Hotel 77 Horndean Rd ☎(0243) 373755

Large Victorian house with simple bedroom appointments, run by pleasant and friendly proprietors.

10hc (2⫪) (1fb) Ⓡ ✱B&b£14–£16.50 Bdifr£19 WBdifr£122 LDO6pm

Lic 🍽 CTV 10P

Credit cards 1 3

GH Merry Hall Hotel 73 Horndean Rd ☎(0243) 372424
Closed 25 Dec–3 Jan

An attractive well appointed hotel with large garden. Ideally situated for yachting centres.

10hc (7⇌) (2fb) CTV in all bedrooms ✗ Ⓡ B&b£21–£24 LDO8pm

Lic 🍽 CTV 12P putting

Credit cards 1 3 Ⓥ

ENSTONE
Oxfordshire
Map **4** SP32

INN Crown Church Enstone ☎(060872) 262

Closed 25–26 Dec

Home cooking is the speciality at this charming old Cotswold-stone inn. Attractive bedrooms. Quarter of a mile from the A34.

4⇌ CTV in all bedrooms Ⓡ B&b£18–£20 WB&bfr£125 Lunch £4.65–£13.75&alc Dinner 10pm £4.65–£13.75&alc

🍽 7P

ERLESTOKE
Wiltshire
Map **3** ST95

FH Mrs P Hampton **Longwater Park** *(ST966541)* ☎Bratton (0380) 830095
Closed Xmas & New Year

3⇌⫪ (1fb) TV in all bedrooms Ⓡ B&b£10.50 Bdi£16 WBdifr£108.50 LDO5pm

🍽 CTV 6P ⌂ ✓ 166 acres beef

Ⓥ

ERWOOD
Powys
Map **3** SO04

⊢FH N M Jones **Ty-Isaf** *(SO101425)* ☎(09823) 607

3hc (2fb) Ⓡ B&b£8–£8.50 Bdi£11.50–£12 WBdi£63–£66.50 LDO7.30pm

🍽 CTV P 340acres sheep mixed

Ⓥ

ETON
Berkshire
Map **4** SU97

GH *Christopher Hotel* High St ☎Windsor (0753) 852359
rs Xmas

Well-furnished free-house, with modern, very well-equipped chalets, and complemented by the well-run Peacock Restaurant.

21⫪ (6fb) CTV in all bedrooms Ⓡ LDO10pm

Lic 🍽 16P

Credit cards 1 2 3 5

ETTINGTON
Warwickshire
Map **4** SP24

⊢FH Mrs B J Wakeham **Whitfield** *(SP265506)* Warwick Rd ☎Stratford-upon-Avon (0789) 740260
Closed Dec

Pleasant house set in active farm with a wide variety of animals for interest.

3hc (2fb) ✗ Ⓡ B&b£8–£9 WB&bfr£56

🍽 CTV 3P 220acres mixed

Ⓥ

EVESHAM
Hereford & Worcester
Map **4** SP04

GH Waterside Hotel 56/59 Waterside ☎(0386) 2420

Modernised hotel with a genial atmosphere. Close to the river.

9hc (2⇌ 4⫪) Annexe: 4hc (2⇌ 2⫪) (4fb) CTV in all bedrooms Ⓡ B&b£15–£28 Bdi£22.50–£35.50 LDO9.30pm

Lic 🍽 CTV 30P ✓

Credit cards 1 2 3

EXBOURNE
Devon
Map **2** SS60

FH Mrs S J Allain **Stapleford** *(SS580039)* ☎(083785) 277
Closed Dec & New Year rs Mar

17th-century Devon longhouse, modernised to high standard of comfort. 2m SE unclass rd.

2rm (1hc) ⚞ in all bedrooms ✗ Ⓡ B&b£12.50 Bdi£18.50 WBdifr£115 LDO5pm

CTV 4P 2🚗 nc12yrs ✓ 80acres sheep

Ⓥ

EXETER
Devon
Map **3** SX99
See plan on pages 170–171

GH Braeside 21 New North Rd ☎(0392) 56875 Plan **1** *B4*

9hc CTV in all bedrooms ✗ B&b£10–£15 WB&b£60–£100

🍽 ⱣP nc10yrs

GH Hotel Gledhills 32 Alphington Rd ☎(0392) 71439 Plan **3** *B1*
Closed 2 wks Xmas

Friendly, traditional, small hotel standing in own grounds, close to city and St Thomas' Station.

12hc (8⫪) (3fb) CTV in all bedrooms ✗ Ⓡ B&b£12.50–£15.95 Bdi£16–£20.50 WB&b£87.50–£111.65 LDO6pm

Lic 🍽 CTV 11P 2🚗

Credit cards 1 2 3 5

GH Park View Hotel 8 Howell Rd ☎(0392) 71772 Plan **4** *B4*
Closed Xmas

Attractive Georgian property in quiet position. Friendly service and well equipped bedrooms.

10hc (2⇌ 2⋔) Annexe: 7hc (1⇌ 1⋔) (3fb) CTV in all bedrooms Ⓡ ✱B&b£12.50–£17

𝍔 6P

Credit cards 1 3 Ⓥ

GH Radnor Hotel 79 St Davids Hill ☎(0392) 72004 Plan **5** *A4*
Closed 21 Dec–3 Jan

8hc (2⋔) (4fb) CTV in 4 bedrooms Ⓡ in 4 bedrooms B&b£11–£12 Bdi£17–£18 LDO4pm

𝍔 CTV 7P

GH Sunnymede 24 New North Rd ☎(0392) 73844 Plan **6** *B3*
Closed 24 Dec–1 Jan

Georgian property, recently refurbished, close to shopping area. Comfortable, modern bedrooms and welcoming atmosphere.

8hc (1fb) ✖ B&b£10.50 Bdi£13–£16 LDO9pm

𝍔 CTV ₱

GH Sylvania House Hotel 64 Pennsylvania Rd (Guestaccom) ☎(0392) 75583 Plan **7** *D4*

8hc (1⇌ 4⋔) (3fb) CTV in all bedrooms Ⓡ B&b£10–£19.50

𝍔 CTV 4P

Credit card 3

GH Telstar Hotel 77 St Davids Hill ☎(0392) 72466 Plan **8** *A4*
Closed Xmas & New Year

Exeter — Exmouth

Friendly, family-run guesthouse with cosy bedrooms. Close to colleges and central station.

(8hc) ✖ Ⓡ B&b£9.50–£10.50

𝍔 CTV 5P nc4yrs

Ⓥ

⊢⊣ **GH Trees Mini Hotel** 2 Queen's Cres, York Rd ☎(0392) 59531 Plan **9** *D4*
Closed Xmas

Small, personally run guesthouse in quiet crescent. Convenient for cathedral, university and theatres.

12hc (1fb) ✖ B&b£9–£11 WB&b£63–£70

𝍔 CTV 1P 1🚗 nc3yrs

Ⓥ

GH Trenance House Hotel 1 Queen's Cres, York Rd ☎(0392) 73277 Plan **10** *D4*
Closed Xmas

14hc (1⇌ 1⋔) (2fb) CTV in all bedrooms Ⓡ B&b£10–£14 Bdi£15.50–£19.50 LDOnoon

𝍔 CTV 7P

Credit cards 1 3 Ⓥ

See advertisement on page 170

GH Westholme Hotel 85 Heavitree Rd ☎(0392) 71878 Plan **11** *F2*
Closed mid Dec–mid Jan

7hc (3⋔) (1fb) Ⓡ B&b£10.50–£15 WB&b£66.15–£94.50 LDO7.15pm

CTV 9P

Ⓥ

GH Willowdene Hotel 161 Magdalen Rd ☎(0392) 71925 Plan **12** *F2*

Georgian house with neat garden frontage. Within walking distance of town centre and tourist attractions.

6hc (1fb) B&b£10.50–£11 WB&b£77

𝍔 CTV 6P

Ⓥ

EXFORD
Somerset
Map **3** SS83

GH Exmoor House ☎(064383) 304

13hc (4⋔) (2fb) B&b£10.35–£11.50 Bdi£16.10–£17.50 WBdi fr£112 LDO8.30pm

Lic 𝍔 CTV 14P ⚲

Ⓥ

EXMOUTH
Devon
Map **3** SY08

GH *Blenheim* 39 Morton Rd ☎(0395) 264230
Closed Xmas →

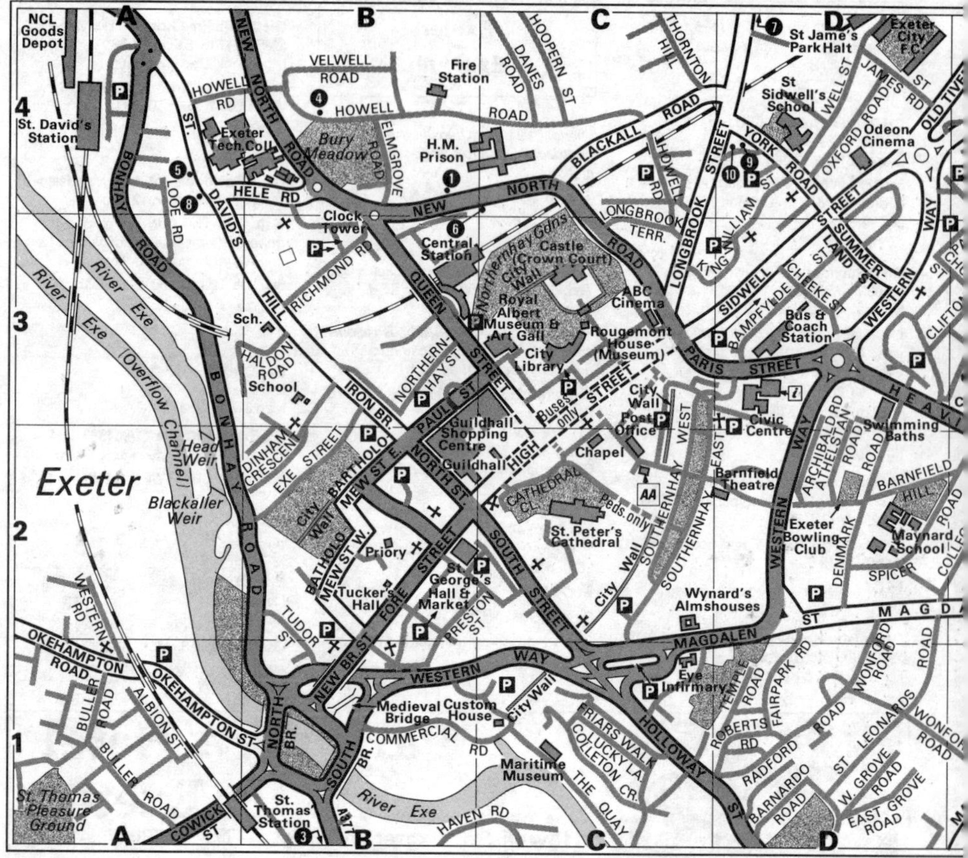

6hc (2fb) CTV in 4 bedrooms ✗ ® LDO5pm

Lic CTV nc4yrs

Credit cards 1 3

GH Carlton Lodge Hotel Carlton Hill
☎(0395) 263314

Pleasant fully-licensed hotel just off sea front. Bedrooms are comfortable and well-maintained and staff are friendly and helpful.

6hc (2⇌ 2fl) (3fb) CTV in all bedrooms ® B&b £15–£18 Bdi£15–£18 WBdifr£125 LDO9pm

Lic 8P nc3yrs

Ⓥ

GH Clinton House 41 Morton Rd
☎(0395) 271969

Semi-detached house with comfortable bedrooms located on the first and second floors. Enjoys convenient location just 200yds from seafront and ½ mile from town.

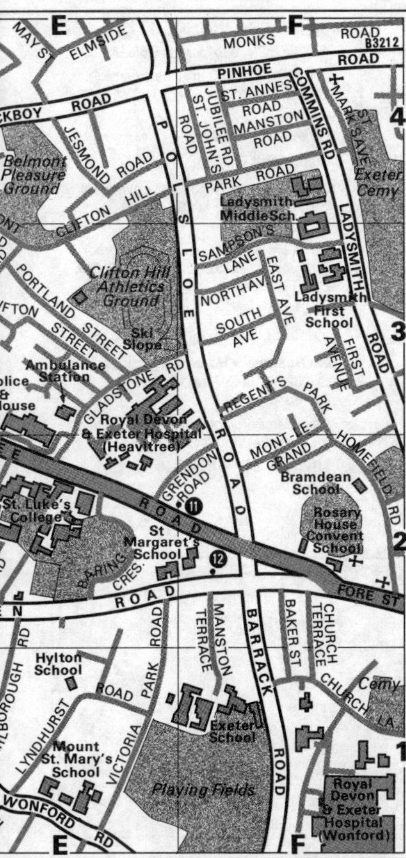

Exeter

1 Braeside
3 Hotel Gledhills
4 Park View Hotel
5 Radnor Hotel
6 Sunnymede
7 Sylvania House Hotel
8 Telstar Hotel
9 Trees Mini Hotel
10 Trenance House Hotel
11 Westholme Hotel
12 Willowdene Hotel

8hc (3fb) CTV in all bedrooms Ⓡ B&b£8–£9 Bdi£11–£12.50 WBdi£70–£80 LDO5pm

Lic 🍴 CTV P

FH Mrs A J Skinner **Maer** *(SY018803)* Maer Ln ☎(0395) 263651

In large garden which has views of sea and Haldon Hills, 5 minutes walk to beach and 20 minutes walk to town.

3rm (1hc) (2fb) ✖ B&b£9–£12 WB&b£63–£84

🍴 CTV 3P 300acres arable beef dairy

FH Mrs J Reddaway ***Quentance*** *(SY037812)* Salterton Rd ☎Budleigh Salterton (03954) 2733

Apr–Oct

Superior-style farmhouse with bedrooms overlooking south-east Devon coastline.

3hc (1fb) ✖ LDO7pm

CTV 3P 2🚗 nc3yrs 260acres arable dairy mixed

FALFIELD
Avon
Map **3** ST69

GH *Green Farm* ☎(0454) 260319

14th-century, former farmhouse, carefully modernised, with tennis court and swimming pool in grounds. Extensive dinner menu.

8hc (1⇌) (1fb) LDO10pm

🍴 CTV 10P ⇌ ♪(hard)

FALMOUTH
Cornwall
Map **2** SW83
See plan on page 172

GH Bedruthan 49 Castle Dr, Sea Front ☎(0326) 311028 Plan **1** *D2*

Occupying a fine seafront position, close to Pendennis Castle and offering panoramic sea views.

8hc (1⇌ 4fl) (2fb) ✖ Ⓡ B&b£9.50–£13.50 Bdi£15–£19 WBdifr£105 LDOnoon

Lic 🍴 CTV 1P nc10yrs

Credit card 3

GH *Cotswold House Private Hotel* 49 Melvill Rd ☎(0326) 312077 Plan **2** *C1*

A small, private hotel pleasantly located close to Gyllyngvase Beach and the town and harbour.

11hc (2⇌ 3fl) (2fb) ✖

Lic CTV 10P

GH *Hotel Dracaena* Dracaena Av ☎(0326) 314470 Plan **3** *B3*

A detached, private hotel, commercially orientated.

10hc (3⇌ 3fl) (6fb) CTV in all bedrooms Ⓡ LDO6.30pm

Lic CTV 18P

Credit cards 1 2 3

GH Gyllyngvase House Hotel Gyllyngvase Rd ☎(0326) 312956 Plan **4** *C1* →

The hotel stands in its own grounds ideally situated for the beaches, town, parks and pavilion.

16hc (2⇌ 7fl) (3fb) CTV in 15 bedrooms B&b£12.50–£15 Bdi£18–£20 WBdi£120–£130 LDO7.30pm

Lic ♛ CTV 15P

ⓥ

⊢⊣**GH Harbour Hotel** 1 Harbour Ter ☎(0326) 311344 Plan **5** *C3*

Small, family-run guesthouse overlooking the harbour.

6hc (2fl) (2fb) Ⓡ B&b£8–£10 Bdi£10.50–£14 WBdi£65–£92 LDO6pm

Lic ♛ CTV Ᵽ

ⓥ

GH Langton Leigh 11 Florence Pl ☎(0326) 313684 Plan **6** *C2*
Mar–Oct

Attractive character terraced property in an elevated position with views of Falmouth Bay.

Falmouth

8hc (3fl) (4fb) Ⓡ in 3 bedrooms ✱B&b£9–£11.50 Bdi£13.25–£15.75 WBdi£78.75–£92 LDO4.30pm

Lic ♛ CTV 6P 1⌂

ⓥ

⊢⊣**GH Milton House** 33 Melvill Rd ☎(0326) 314390 Plan **7** *D1*

Closed Xmas

Small semi-detached residence positioned close to beaches, town and pavilion.

7hc (2fb) B&b£8–£9.50 Bdi£11–£13 WBdi£70–£85 LDO4pm

♛ CTV 6P nc3yrs

⊢⊣**GH Penty Bryn Hotel** 10 Melvill Rd ☎(0326) 314988 Plan **8** *D2*
Feb–Nov

Small, select hotel with high standard of facilities. Close to local amenities.

7hc (5fl) (2fb) CTV in all bedrooms Ⓡ B&b£9–£11 Bdi£14.50–£16.50 WBdifr£85 LDO5pm

Lic ♛ CTV 2P 1⌂ nc6yrs

Credit cards 1 3 ⓥ

GH Rathgowry Hotel Gyllyngvase Hill ☎(0326) 313482 Plan **9** *C1*
Apr–Oct

10hc (2⇌ 8fl) (4fb) CTV in all bedrooms Ⓡ ✱B&b£11–£15 Bdi£13–£18 WBdi£90–£120 LDO5pm

Lic ♛ 10P

ⓥ

GH *Rosemary Hotel* 22 Gyllyngvase Ter ☎(0326) 314669 Plan **10** *C1*
Closed Xmas

Cosy, family-run guesthouse close to town centre and beaches.

11hc (5fb) CTV in 3 bedrooms ✗ LDO6.30pm

♛ CTV 4P

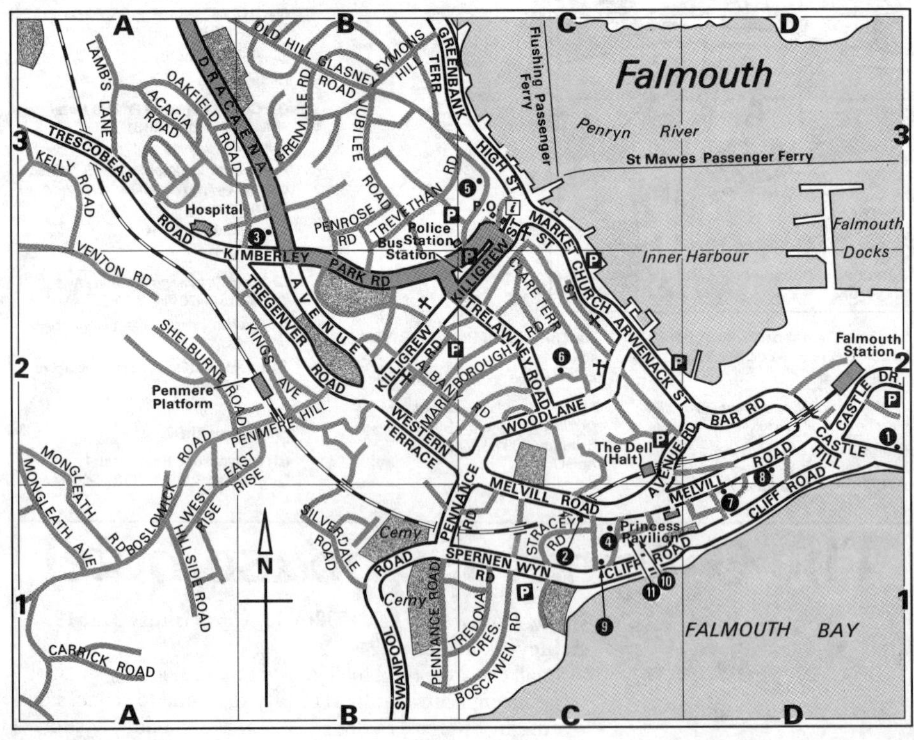

Falmouth

1 Bedruthan
2 Cotswold House Private Hotel
3 Hotel Dracaena
4 Gyllyngvase House Hotel
5 Harbour Hotel
6 Langton Leigh
7 Milton House
8 Penty Bryn House
9 Rathgowry Hotel
10 Rosemary Hotel
11 Wickham

GH Wickham 21 Gyllyngvase Ter ☎(0326) 311140 Plan **11** *C1*
Apr–Oct

Small guesthouse pleasantly situated in a quiet road, close to beaches.

10hc (2⇌ 1fl) (2fb) CTV in 6 bedrooms ✗ Ⓡ B&b£10–£11 Bdi£13–£14 WBdi£83–£88 LDO5pm

CTV 3P nc3yrs

FALSTONE
Northumberland
Map **12** NY78

INN Pheasant Stannersburn ☎Bellingham (0660) 40382

A cosy stone built inn situated at the eastern tip of Keilely Water. The accommodation is attractive and comfortable. Service is friendly and especially recommended are the delicious home cooked evening meals.

Annexe 11hc (2⇌) (1fb) Ⓡ ✽B&bfr£11 Bdifr£18 Lunch £4.50alc Dinner 9.30pm £7alc

CTV 40P snooker

FAREHAM
Hampshire
Map **4** SU50

GH Catisfield Hotel Catisfield (2m W A27) ☎Titchfield (0329) 41851

Modern, well furnished bedrooms on 2 floors above Catisfield Wine Stores in quiet residential area.

20hc (16⇌ 2fl) (7fb) CTV in all bedrooms Ⓡ ✽B&b£10–£16 Bdi£14.50–£20.50 LDO6pm

Lic 🍽 CTV 100P

FARNHAM
Surrey
Map **4** SU84

INN Eldon Hotel 43 Frensham Rd, Lower Bourne ☎Frensham (025125) 2745

Popular, privately-managed hotel with modern, well-equipped bedrooms, good leisure facilities plus restaurant.

14hc (10⇌ 2fl) (2fb) CTV in 12 bedrooms B&b£23–£33 Bdi£27–£48 Lunch £2–£6.50&alc Dinner 9.30pm £5–£14&alc

🍽 CTV 65P ⊭ squash

Credit cards 1 2 3

FARRINGTON GURNEY
Avon
Map **3** ST65

FH Mrs J Candy **Cliff** *(ST633547)* Rush Hill (½m S over county boundary in Somerset) ☎Chewton Mendip (076121) 274
Closed 21–30 Dec

Guest accommodation has been converted from former dairy and cheese room.

2hc (1⇌ 1fl) (1fb) ⊭ in all bedrooms ✗ Ⓡ B&b£10–£12 B&b£130–£150

🍽 CTV 10P nc10yrs 186acres mixed

FAR SAWREY
Cumbria
Map **7** SD39

GH West Vale ☎Windermere (09662) 2817

Pleasant and neat guesthouse set in pretty gardens. The proprietors are friendly and home cooking is a speciality.

8hc (5fl) (3fb) Ⓡ B&b£11–£13 Bdi£18.50–£20.50 WBdi£115.50–£129.50 LDOnoon

Lic 🍽 CTV 8P

Ⓥ

FAZELEY
Staffordshire
Map **4** SK20

GH Buxton Hotel 65 Coleshill St ☎Tamworth (0827) 285805
Closed 25–26 Dec rs 1 Jan

15hc (3⇌ 9fl) (4fb) CTV in all bedrooms Ⓡ B&b£15.50–£19.75 Bdi£20.50–£28 LDO8.30pm

Lic 🍽 CTV 16P

Credit cards 1 3 Ⓥ

FELINDRE (nr Swansea)
West Glamorgan
Map **2** SN60

FH Mr F Jones **Coynant** *(SN648070)* (4m N of Felindre off unclass road linking M4 junc 46 and Ammanford) ☎Ammanford (0269) 2064 & 5640

Secluded house in elevated position at head of valley.

5hc (3fl) (2fb) CTV in all bedrooms ✗ Ⓡ B&b£12 Bdi£15–£16 WBdi£98–£108 (W only Jun–Aug) LDO7pm

Lic 🍽 10P 𝒫(hard) ♩ ∪ 150acres mixed

FENITON
Devon
Map **3** SY19

GH Colestocks House Colestocks (1m N unclass rd) ☎Honiton (0404) 850633

Large 16th-century thatched country house in own gardens. Comfortable accommodation, friendly service, traditional French and English cooking.

7hc (5⇌ 2fl) CTV in all bedrooms ✗ Ⓡ B&b£15.25–£18.50 Bdi£24.75–£29 WBdi£148–£160 LDO9pm

Lic 🍽 9P nc10yrs

Credit card 1 Ⓥ

FENSTANTON
Cambridgeshire
Map **4** TL36

INN *Tudor Hotel* High St ☎Huntingdon (0480) 62532

Mock Tudor inn situated in small village of Fenstanton off busy A604 Hunstanton–Cambridge bypass.

6⇌ (1fb) CTV in all bedrooms Ⓡ LDO9.30pm

Lic 🍽 50P

Credit cards 1 3

FIDDLEFORD
Dorset
Map **3** ST81

INN Fiddleford ☎Sturminster Newton (0258) 72489
Closed Xmas Day

→

Situated near Sturminster Newton on main Blandford to Sherborne road.

4hc (1⇌ 1fl) CTV in 1 bedroom TV in 1 bedroom B&b£12.50–£13.50 WB&bfr£69 Lunch fr£5.25&alc Dinner 9.30pm £5–£7&alc

40P

Ⓥ

FILEY
North Yorkshire
Map **8** TA18

GH Downcliffe Hotel The Beach ☎Scarborough (0723) 513310
Apr–Oct

Detached sea-front hotel offering a special welcome to families.

17hc (1⇌ 6fl) (9fb) CTV in all bedrooms Ⓡ B&b£13.50–£15.50 Bdi£15–£17.50 LDO6pm

Lic 8P 2

GH Seafield Hotel 9–11 Rutland St ☎Scarborough (0723) 513715
Feb–Nov

Spacious accommodation close to sea and town centre.

13hc (1⇌ 2fl) (7fb) CTV in all bedrooms ✖ Ⓡ B&b£10–£12 Bdi£13–£15 WBdifr£90 LDOnoon

Lic CTV 6P

FINTRY
Central *Stirlingshire*
Map **11** NS68

FH Mrs M Mitchell **Nether Glinns** *(NS606883)* ☎(036086) 207
Apr–Sep

Well-maintained farmhouse situated among rolling hills. Signposted drive.

3rm (1fb) B&b£8–£8.50

CTV 3P 150acres beef dairy

FISHGUARD
Dyfed
Map **2** SM93

GH Glanmoy Country House Goodwick (1m NW on A40) ☎(0348) 872844

Spacious, comfortable accommodation on four floors, with friendly and efficient service.

13hc (4fb) ✖ B&b£10.92–£12.65 Bdi£16.09–£17.82 WBdifr£88.55 LDO3pm

Lic CTV 4P(charge)

Ⓥ

Fiddleford — Fordingbridge

Secluded country house with friendly personal service and exceptionally well-appointed bedrooms.

3⇌ CTV in all bedrooms ✖ Ⓡ B&b£17–£22 Bdi£22–£26 WBdifr£147 LDO9pm

Lic 40P nc12yrs

Ⓥ

FLAX BOURTON
Avon
Map **3** ST56

INN Jubilee Farleigh Rd ☎(027583) 2741
Closed 25 Dec evening

4hc B&b£15–£16 Lunch£6–£7alc Dinner10pm£7–£8alc

CTV 51P nc14yrs

FLUSHING
Cornwall
Map **2** SW83

GH Nankersey Hotel St Peters Rd ☎Falmouth (0326) 74471
Closed Nov

Grade II listed building beautifully positioned within character fishing village.

8hc (2fb) Ⓡ B&bfr£12.50 Bdifr£18.50 WBdifr£108.50 (W only Jul & Aug) LDO5pm

Lic CTV

Credit cards 1 2 3

FOLKESTONE
Kent
Map **5** TR23

GH Argos Private Hotel 6 Marine Ter ☎(0303) 54309 Plan **1** *E1*

Homely little house, close to the ferry terminal.

9hc (2fb) ✖ B&bfr£10 Bdifr£15 WBdifr£75 LDO8pm

Lic CTV nc3yrs

GH Arundel Hotel The Leas, 3 Clifton Rd ☎(0303) 52442 Plan **2** *B1*
Mar–Oct

GH Belmonte Private Hotel 30 Castle Hill Av ☎(0303) 54470 Telex no 937400 Plan **4** *B2*

Comfortable family run hotel central and quiet with homely and courteous atmosphere.

9hc (5fl) (1fb) CTV in all bedrooms Ⓡ B&b£16–£20 Bdi£23–£27 WBdi£136–£160 LDO6pm

Lic 4P

Credit cards 1 2 3 5 Ⓥ

GH Westward Ho! 13 Clifton Cres ☎(0303) 52663 Plan **5** *A1*

11hc (1fl) (6fb) B&b£14.50–£16.50 Bdi£17.50–£19.50 WBdifr£99 LDO4pm

Lic lift CTV

Credit cards 1 3 Ⓥ

FONTHILL BISHOP
Wiltshire
Map **3** ST93

INN Kings Arms ☎Hindon (074789) 523

2hc TV in 1 bedroom Ⓡ *B&b£12–£16 Bdi£18–£22 WBdi£119–£126 Lunch £4.50–£8alc Dinner10pm £4.50–£8alc

30P U

FONTMELL MAGNA
Dorset
Map **3** ST81

GH Estyard House ☎(0747) 811460
Closed Nov & Xmas

A warm welcome is assured at this pleasant detached guesthouse.

6hc B&b£11.25–£12.25 Bdi£16.50–£17.50 WBdifr£106 LDO3pm

8P nc8yrs

FORDINGBRIDGE
Hampshire
Map **4** SU11

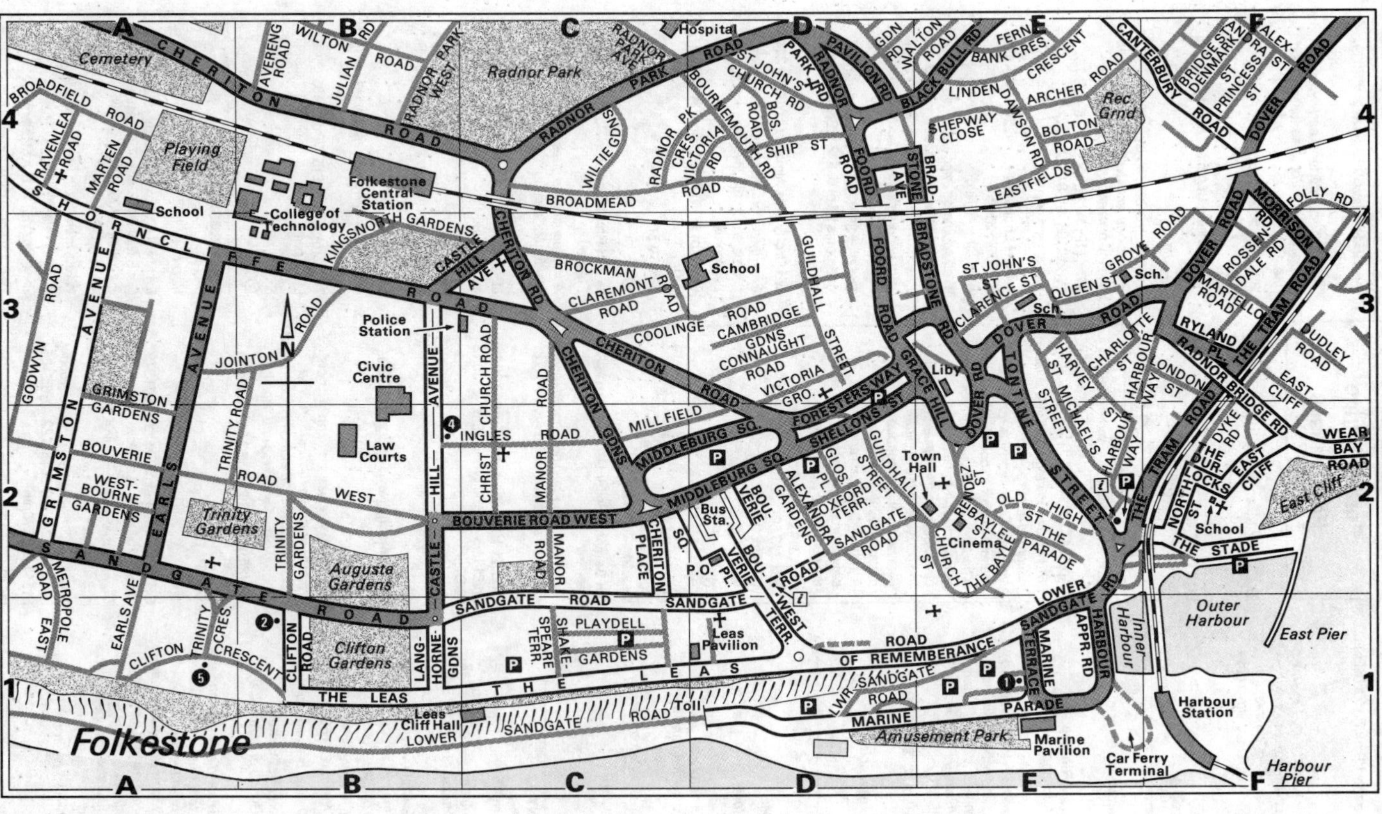

Folkestone

1 Argos Private Hotel
2 Arundel Hotel
4 Belmonte Private Hotel
5 Westwood Ho!

GH ***Oakfield Lodge*** 1 Park Rd ☎(0425) 52789
Closed Xmas

Attractive corner hotel, family-run and offering a warm welcome with a high standard of service. Comfortable, well-maintained accommodation with a cosy lounge.

10hc (1fl) (2fb)

Lic ṁ CTV 8P 2 ⌂

FORDOUN
Grampian *Kincardineshire*
Map **15** NO77

FH Mrs M Anderson **Ringwood** *(NO743774)* ☎Auchenblae (05612) 313
Apr–Oct

Small, modernised villa in open setting amidst farmland and with its own neat garden and outhouse. Very high standard of décor and furnishings. 1½ miles off A94 on B966.

4hc (1fb) ✖ Ⓡ B&b£10–£12 WB&b£63–£77

ṁ CTV 4P 16acres arable

Ⓥ

FORFAR
Tayside *Angus*
Map **15** NO45

INN *Queen's Hotel* 12–14 The Cross ☎(0307) 62533

Small stone-built hotel with good bedrooms, home-cooking and friendly service.

6⇌ (2fb) CTV in all bedrooms ✖ LDO8pm

ṁ ₽

Credit card 2

FORGANDENNY
Tayside *Perthshire*
Map **11** NO01

⊢⊣**FH** Mrs M Fotheringham **Craighall** *(NO081176)* ☎Bridge of Earn (0738) 812415

Large bungalow-type farmhouse tastefully furnished, with friendly atmosphere. ½m W off B935 Bridge of Earn–Forteviot road.

3fl (1fb) ⚟ in all bedrooms ✖ Ⓡ B&b£8.50–£10 WB&bfr£59.50

ṁ CTV 3P 1000acres beef sheep

⊢⊣**FH** Mr T Strong **Netherholm** *(NO069169)* ☎Bridge of Earn (0738) 812289

A small painted harled stone farmhouse with modern extensions set in 150 acres of mixed farmland in the Strathearn Valley. The bedrooms and public rooms are modestly furnished and there is access to the garden from the sitting room. Guests enjoy the secluded location and warm friendly service.

3rm (1hc) (2fb) ⚟ in 1 bedroom Ⓡ B&b£9 WB&b£54

ṁ CTV 6P 140acres sheep

Ⓥ

FORTINGALL
Tayside *Perthshire*
Map **14** NN75

Selected

GH Rose Villa ☎Kenmore (08873) 335
Apr–24 Oct rs 25 Oct–Mar

This charming stone built villa is the delightful home of Michael and Maureen Turner and it is run in the manner of a small country house with a house-party atmosphere. Bedroom decor and soft furnishings correspond to the gardens around the house and the furniture is a pleasant blend of antique and modern. Quality local produce is a feature of breakfast and dinner, served around a large central table in the comfortable dining room.

4hc (2fl) CTV in 2 bedrooms Ⓡ B&b£13.50–£30 Bdi£27.50–£44 WBdifr£165 LDO7pm

ṁ 4P 1⌂

Ⓥ

FORT WILLIAM
Highland *Inverness-shire*
Map **14** NN17

GH Benview Belford Rd ☎(0397) 2966
Mar–Nov

Detached stone-built house with modern extension situated beside A82 just N of town centre.

14hc (2⇌ 1fl) Ⓡ B&b£10.35–£13.80 Bdi£14.95–£18.40 WBdi£96.60–£120.75 LDO7pm

ṁ CTV 20P

Ⓥ

GH Glenlochy Nevis Bridge ☎(0397) 2909
Mar–Nov

An attractive house standing in its own grounds opposite the Distillery. The accommodation is clean and modern and an ideal base for touring and fishing.

8fl (2fb) ✖ B&b£10–£12.60 WB&b£70–£88.20

ṁ CTV 12P

Ⓥ

GH Guisachan Alma Rd ☎(0397) 3797
Closed 20 Dec–4 Jan

Comfortable, well-maintained house in an elevated residential area.

15hc (1⇌ 3fl) (3fb) ✖ Ⓡ in 4 bedrooms B&b£10–£15.50 Bdi£15–£22 WBdi£105–£154 LDO5.30pm

Lic ṁ CTV 15P

⊢⊣**GH Hillview** Achintore Rd ☎(0397) 4349

A friendly, comfortable and nicely appointed guesthouse situated beside the A82 overlooking Loch Linnhe.

8hc (2fb) ✖ Ⓡ B&b£7.50–£10

ṁ 8P

GH Innseagan Achintore Rd ☎(0397) 2452
Apr–Oct

Large stone-built house with modern extensions, situated on the A82 South of the town, overlooking Loch Linnhe.

27hc (12⇌) (2fb) ✖ Bdi£15–£19.75 WBdi£105–£138 LDO7pm

Lic ṁ CTV 30P

⊢⊣**GH Lochview** Heathcroft, Argyll Rd ☎(0397) 3149
Etr–Oct

Well-appointed, modern house offering comfortable accommodation amid peaceful surroundings. Elevated position with panoramic views across Loch Linnher.

6hc (1⇌ 3fl) (2fb) CTV available in bedrooms B&b£9–£12 WB&b£60–£84

ṁ 7P

GH Orchy Villa Alma Rd ☎(0397) 2445

Smartly decorated house, situated on a hillside above the town, with compact bedrooms.

6hc (4fb) ⚟ in all bedrooms ✖ B&b£9.50–£10

ṁ CTV 6P

Ⓥ

⊢⊣**GH Rhu Mhor** Alma Rd ☎(0397) 2213
Etr–Sep

A traditional style guesthouse in a quiet residential area.

7hc (2fb) B&b£9–£9.50 Bdi£14–£15 LDO5pm

ṁ CTV 7P

Ⓥ

GH Stronchreggan View Achintore Rd ☎(0397) 4644
Etr–Oct

Comfortable and well-appointed modern house.

7hc (3fb) ✖ Bdifr£15 WBdifr£105 LDO7pm

ṁ 7P

Ⓥ

FOURCROSSES
Powys
Map **7** SJ21

FH Mrs J E Wigley ***Maerdy*** *(SJ259168)* (½m SW of A483 signed Penrhos) ☎Guilsfield (093875) 202
Apr–Sep

Warm, friendly old farmhouse full of beams and polished floors.

2hc (1fl) (1fb) ✖ LDO2.30pm

TV P 157acres dairy mixed

FOVANT
Wiltshire
Map **4** SU02

INN Cross Keys ☎(072270) 284

4hc (1fb) ✱B&bfr£12.50 Bdifr£17.50 Lunchfr£7alc Dinner 9.30pmfr£8alc

Lic 𝍪 CTV 30p

Credit cards ③ Ⓥ

FOWEY
Cornwall
Map **2** SX15

GH *Ashley House Hotel* 14 Esplanade ☎(072683) 2310
Etr–Oct

8hc (1fl) (4fb) Ⓡ LDO6pm

Lic 𝍪 CTV ⊅

GH Carnethic House Lambs Barn ☎(072683) 3336
Feb–Oct

8hc (5fl) (2fb) ⅄ in 1 bedroom CTV in all bedrooms ⌘ Ⓡ B&b£16–£22 Bdi£21–£29 WBdi£156–£173 LDO6.45pm

Lic 𝍪 20P ⌂ ⩳(heated)

Credit cards ① ② ③ ⑤ Ⓥ

GH Wheelhouse 60 Esplanade ☎(072683) 2452
Closed Xmas

There are magnificent views from this small, family-run guesthouse.

6hc (1fb) ⌘ Ⓡ B&b£11.50–£13.50 Bdi£18.50–£20.50 WBdi£120–£135 LDOnoon

Lic 𝍪 CTV ⊅ nc12yrs

Ⓥ

FH Mrs R. Dunn **Trezare** *(SX112538)* ☎(072683) 3485
Etr–Oct

Conveniently situated 1m from Fowey, pleasant atmosphere and good farmhouse fare.

3hc (1fb) ✱B&b£9 Bdi£14 WBdifr£98 LDO10am

CTV 6P ⌂ 220acres dairy

FOWNHOPE
Hereford & Worcester
Map **3** SO53

GH Bowens Farmhouse ☎(043277) 430
Closed Xmas & New Year

8hc (2⇌ 3fl) (2fb) ⌘ Ⓡ B&b£13.50–£16 Bdi£21–£25 WBdi£120–£140 LDO7.30pm

Lic 𝍪 CTV 15P nc10yrs croquet putting green

Ⓥ

FRADDON
Cornwall
Map **2** SW95

GH St Margaret's Hotel
☎St Austell (0726) 860375

Small family-run hotel on main A30.

11hc (3fb) CTV in 3 bedrooms ⌘ (ex guide dogs) Ⓡ ✱B&b£9.50–£14 Bdi£12.50–£17 WBdifr£81.50 LDO7pm

Lic 𝍪 CTV 15P

Credit card ③ Ⓥ

FRAMLINGHAM
Suffolk
Map **5** TM26

FH Mrs S F Stocker **Broadwater** *(TM289614)* Woodbridge Rd ☎(0728) 723645
Closed Xmas

Fine Georgian house in large garden. Wine produced from 4-acre vineyard here, is available at dinner.

5rm (2hc 1⇌ 1fl) (1fb) ✱B&b£10–£13 Bdi£17–£20 WBdi£108–£120 LDO10am

Lic 𝍪 CTV 6P 28acres non-working

Ⓥ

FRESHWATER
Isle of Wight
See **Wight, Isle of**

FRESSINGFIELD
Suffolk
Map **5** TM27

FH Mrs R Tomson **Hill View** *(TM264771)*
☎(037986) 443
Closed Xmas & New Year

3hc B&bfr£10 Bdifr£15 WBdifr£90

𝍪 CTV 3P nc5yrs 2acres stock

FRINTON-ON-SEA
Essex
Map **5** TM21

GH Forde 18 Queens Rd ☎(02556) 4758
Closed Dec

Traditional-style seaside guesthouse run by friendly proprietors.

6hc (1fb) B&b£11.50 Bdi£16.50 WBdifr£90 LDOnoon.

𝍪 CTV 1P nc5yrs

Ⓥ

GH *Montpellier Private Hotel*
2 Harold Gv ☎(02556) 4462

Situated in residential area and recently renovated, with spacious bedrooms.

6⇌ fl (1fb) CTV in all bedrooms Ⓡ LDO7pm

Lic 𝍪 7P

Credit card ③

FRITH COMMON
Hereford & Worcester
Map **7** SO66

FH Mrs M Keel **Hunt House** *(SO698702)*
☎Clows Top (029922) 277

Guests take delight in the home made cakes available on their arrival at this listed building situated on a hill top commanding magnificent views.

3hc (1fl) ⅄ in all bedrooms ✱B&bfr£9

CTV 4P nc6yrs 180acres

FROGMORE
Devon
Map **3** SX74

INN Globe ☎(054853) 351

17th-century village inn, personally run with relaxed, informal atmosphere.

5hc (1fb) CTV in all bedrooms Ⓡ B&b£14.50–£15 WB&bfr£78 Lunch £6alc Dinner 9.45pm£6alc →

🍽 CTV 20P

Credit cards 1 2 3 5

GAIRLOCH
Highland *Ross & Cromarty*
Map **14** NG87

GH Bain's House Strath ☎(0445) 2472 Closed Xmas Day
A neat and compact guesthouse located on the main street of this small coastal town.
5hc (2fb) Ⓡ B&b£8.50–£9
🍽 CTV no babies

GH Eilean View ☎(0445) 2272
There are fine views over Gairloch Bay from this modern, timber-clad bungalow.
3hc Ⓡ B&b£10.50–£11.50 Bdi£15.50–£17 WBdi£108.50–£119 LDO6.30pm
🍽 CTV 5P

Selected

GH Horisdale House Strath ☎(0445) 2151
May–Sep
Situated just west of Gairloch, this modern guesthouse commands superb views over loch and mountain. The bright bedrooms are tastefully decorated in soft pastel shades. There is a spacious lounge, with open fire. Imaginative evening meals are served in the well-appointed dining room. However, guests are advised to reserve a table in advance to avoid disappointment.
9hc (3fb) in all bedrooms Ⓡ *B&b£10.25–£11.25 Bdi£17–£18 LDO9am
🍽 10P nc7yrs

GH Kerrysdale House ☎(0445) 2292
Family-run country house with pretty bedrooms, lying 1 mile south of Gairloch.
4hc in all bedrooms Ⓡ B&b£9–£11 Bdi£14–£16 LDO5.30pm
🍽 CTV 3P
Ⓥ

GALASHIELS
Borders *Selkirkshire*
Map **12** NT43

GH Buckholmburn Edinburgh Rd ☎(0896) 2697
Closed Nov
Detached house sitting high above the Galawater on the A7 on the northern outskirts of the town.
7hc (3fb) *B&b£12.50–£17 Bdi£20–£22
Lic 🍽 CTV 20P
Credit cards 1 2 3 5

GALSTON
Strathclyde *Ayrshire*
Map **11** NS53

FH Mrs J Bone **Auchencloigh** *(NS535320)* ☎(0563) 820567
Apr–Oct
A comfortable, traditional farmhouse with a friendly atmosphere. 5m S off B7037 – Scorn road.
2rm (1fb) in 1 bedroom B&b£8–£8.50 Bdi £13–£13.50 WBdifr£94 LDO5.30pm
🍽 CTV 4P 4 sauna bath 240acres beef sheep mixed

REMEMBER

Prices quoted in the gazetteer are minimum double room occupancy to maximum single room occupancy **per person.**

GARBOLDISHAM
Norfolk
Map **5** TM08

GH Ingleneuk Hopton Rd (Guestaccom) ☎(095381) 541
rs 1–16 Oct & Xmas
Modern bungalow set in ten acres of quiet wooded countryside.
6hc (5) (1fb) CTV in all bedrooms Ⓡ *B&b£12–£19.50 Bdi£20.50–£28 WBdi£136.50–£189 LDO1pm
Lic 🍽 10P
Credit card 3 Ⓥ

GARGRAVE
North Yorkshire
Map **7** SD95

GH Kirk Syke 19 High St ☎ (075678) 356
Large stone house in village, with pleasant modern bedrooms.
4hc (2 2) Annexe: 6hc (4 2) (1fb) CTV in 8 bedrooms Ⓡ in 8 bedrooms B&b£12 Bdi£18 WBdifr£115 LDOnoon
Lic 🍽 CTV 10P
Ⓥ

GARSTANG
Lancashire
Map **7** SD44

FH Mrs J Higginson **Clay Lane Head** Cabus (2m N on A6) *(SD490474)* ☎(09952) 3132
Mar–23 Dec
A comfortable farmhouse of some character, with fine furniture and log fires.
3hc B&b£9–£10 WB&bfr£60
CTV 4P 1 30acres beef
Ⓥ

FH Mrs J Fowler **Greenhaigh Castle** *(SD501452)* Castle Ln ☎(09952) 2140
Etr–Oct
17th-century character farmhouse, overlooked by ruins of Greenhaigh Castle. ½m E unclass rd.
3hc Ⓡ B&b£8.50–£10 WB&bfr£56
CTV 3P 2 200acres beef dairy sheep

GATEHEAD
Strathclyde *Ayrshire*
Map **10** NS33

INN Old Rome Farmhouse ☎Drybridge (0563) 850265
3hc (1fb) ✗ Ⓡ B&b£12 Bar lunch 60p–£6 LDO9.30pm
▥ CTV 25P ⊞ ⌡
Ⓥ

GATWICK AIRPORT, LONDON
West Sussex
Map **4** TQ24

GH Barnwood Hotel Balcombe Rd, Pound Hill, Crawley ☎Crawley (0293) 882709 Telex no 877005
Closed Xmas & New Year
A small privately-run establishment which has been thoughtfully renovated to offer some very comfortable public rooms. The dining room is particularly attractive and the traditional food offered is of a good standard.
35hc (3⇌ 32fl) (7fb) CTV in all bedrooms ✗(ex guide dogs) Ⓡ B&b£24–£40 Bdi£30–£50 LDO9pm
Lic ▥ 50P ♿
Credit cards 1 2 3 5
See advertisement under Crawley

GH Gainsborough Lodge 39 Massetts Rd, Horley (2m NE of airport adjacent A23) ☎Horley (0293) 783982

Extended Victorian house with comfortable, compact accommodation.
13⇌ fl (3fb) CTV in all bedrooms ✗ Ⓡ B&b£18.25–£22
▥ 16P
Credit cards 1 3 Ⓥ

GH Gatwick Skylodge Motel London Rd, County Oak, Crawley (2m S of airport on A23) ☎Crawley (0293) 544511 Telex no 878307
Closed 24 Dec–2 Jan
45⇌ fl (7fb) CTV in all bedrooms Ⓡ ✱B&b£35–£42 LDO9.45pm
Lic ▥ 60P (charge)
Credit cards 1 2 3

GH Little Foxes Ifield Rd, Crawley ☎Crawley (0293) 552430
This large modern bungalow, conveniently close to the airport, offers comfortable accommodation with particularly good bedrooms. Personally supervised by the owner, a friendly informal atmosphere prevails.
5hc (1fl) (1fb) CTV in all bedrooms ✗ Ⓡ available in bedrooms B&bfr£20
▥ CTV 50P
Credit cards 1 2 3 Ⓥ

GH Woodlands 42 Massetts Rd, Horley ☎Crawley (0293) 782994
Closed 24–26 Dec
Small hotel with friendly atmosphere. Thoughtfully-furnished, comfortable accommodation.
7hc (3fl) (2fb) ⚟ in 7 bedrooms CTV in all bedrooms ✗ Ⓡ ✱B&b£12–£20
▥ CTV 15P (charge) nc5yrs
Credit card 1 Ⓥ

See advertisement on page 180

GAYHURST
Buckinghamshire
Map **4** SP84

FH Mrs K Adams **Mill** *(SP852454)* ☎Newport Pagnell (0908) 611489
17th-century stone-built farmhouse with the River Ouse running through the grounds from which fishing is available. 1m S off B526 unclass road to Haversham.
3hc (1fb) ⚟ in 1 bedroom TV in all bedrooms Ⓡ B&b£10.50–£12.50 Bdi£15.50–£17.50 WBdifr£108.50 LDO4pm
▥ CTV 10P 3🚗 ⌂ ⌡ U 550 acres mixed
Ⓥ

GEDNEY HILL
Lincolnshire
Map **8** TF31

FH Mrs C Cave ***Sycamore*** *(TF336108)* ☎Holbeach (0406) 330445 →

Closed Xmas wk

Situated on the B1166 in the village. The farmhouse is over 100 years old.

3rm (1fb) TV in 1 bedroom Ⓡ LDO4pm

♨ CTV 6P 80acres beef mixed

GIGGLESWICK
North Yorkshire
Map **7** SD86

Selected

GH Woodlands The Mains ☎Settle (07292) 2576

Closed Xmas & New Year

A delightful Georgian-style house in its own well-tended gardens overlooking the River Riddle and the surrounding countryside. Woodlands is superbly furnished throughout and offers every possible comfort. Dinners are cooked to order by Margaret Callan who, together with her husband Roger, ensures that guests are well cared for.

9hc (2⇨ 1⨍) CTV available in bedrooms ✗ B&b£18–£20.50 Bdi£27.25–£29.75 WBdifr£193.50 LDOnoon

Lic ♨ CTV 10P nc12yrs

Ⓥ

Gedney Hill — Gilwern

INN Black Horse Hotel Church St ☎Settle (07292) 2506

A secluded village inn dating back to 1663. Well furnished bedrooms and good home-cooking.

3hc (1⇨ 2⨍) (1fb) ✗ Ⓡ B&b£13–£15 Bdi£15–£21 Bar lunch £1.80–£2.40 Dinner £4.50–£8&alc LDO9pm

♨ CTV 20P ⚑

Credit cards 1 5

Credit Cards

1 Access/Euro/Mastercard

2 American Express

3 Barclaycard/Visa

5 Diners

Selected

FH Mrs B T Hargreaves **Close House** *(SD801634)* ☎Settle (07292) 3540

May–Sep

This charming 17th century farmhouse sits amid 230 acres in the Yorkshire Dales. The elegant interior invites relaxation and the comfortable drawing room has a homely atmosphere. Dinner at Close House is a delightful experience and is freshly cooked to order.

3hc ✗ Ⓡ B&b£18.50–£19.50 Bdi£30–£31 WB&bfr£119 LDOam

Lic 3P nc 230acres dairy sheep

Ⓥ

GILWERN
Gwent
Map **3** SO21

FH Mrs J C Harris **Wenallt** *(SO245138)* ☎(0873) 830694

Carefully restored, 16th-century Welsh longhouse, standing in 50 acres, with magnificent views over the Usk Valley. High standard of catering. Wenallt is situated off the A465 Abergavenny–Merthyr Tydfil road.

7hc (2⇨ 3⨍) (2fb) ✗Ⓡ ✱B&b£10–£13 Bdi£16.50–£19.50 WBdifr£109 LDO7.30pm

Lic 卌 CTV 10P
50acres sheep

GISLINGHAM
Suffolk
Map **5** TM07

Selected

GH Old Guildhall Mill St ☎Mellis (037983) 361

This 15th century Guildhall, in a quiet village location, is a fine example of traditional timber-framed architecture. An attractive two-thirds of an acre landscaped garden at the rear and there is a car park in front of the building. Bedrooms are comfortable and well equipped and there is a small, quiet lounge on the first floor, overlooking the garden. The comfortable ground-floor lounge is dominated by an open brickwork fireplace complete with log fire and an original bread oven. Adjacent to the lounge is a half-size snooker table.

4⇌ CTV in all bedrooms ® ✱B&b£15–£19.50 Bdifr£20–£24.50 WBdifr£130 LDO6pm

Lic 卌 5P

GLAN-YR-AFON (nr Corwen)
Gwynedd
Map **6** SJ04

⊢⊣**FH** Mrs G B Jones **Llawr-Bettws** *(SJO16424)* Bala Rd ☎Maerdy (049081) 224

Rambling, stone-built farmhouse with pleasant, homely atmosphere. At Druid traffic lights on A5 follow A494 Bala road for 2m.

4hc (2fb) ✖ B&bfr£8.50 Bdifr£12.50 LDO7pm

CTV 3P ♧ 18acres beef sheep mixed

Ⓥ

GLASBURY
Powys
Map **3** SO13

FH Mrs B Eckley ***Ffordd-fawr*** *(SO192398)* ☎(04974) 332
Apr–Oct

17th-century farmhouse bordered by the River Wye. 3m from Hay-on-Wye.

2hc ✖ ®

CTV 4P 280acres mixed

GLASFRYN
Clwyd
Map **6** SH95

⊢⊣**FH** Mr C Ellis **Growine** *(SH927502)* ☎Cerrigydrudion (049082) 447
Apr–Oct

Modernised and extended farmhouse at end of drive. N of A5, E of village.

2rm ✖ B&bfr£8.50 Bdifr£12.50 WBdifr£84

卌 CTV 4P 70acres mixed

GLASGOW
Strathclyde *Lanarkshire*
Map **11** NS56
See plan on pages 182–183

GH Dalmeny Hotel 62 St Andrews Dr, Nithsdale Cross ☎041-427 1106 Plan **1**
Closed New Year wk

A friendly, comfortable and nicely appointed private hotel.

10hc (3⇌ 2🚿) (1fb) CTV in all bedrooms ® B&b£22–£32

Lic 卌 CTV 20P

GH Kelvin Private Hotel 15 Buckingham Ter, Hillhead ☎041-339 7143 Plan **2**

A terrace house in West End, close to Botanical Gardens.

14hc (3fb) CTV in 2 bedrooms B&b£13–£16 WB&bfr£91

卌 CTV 5P

Ⓥ

GH Marie Stuart Hotel 46–48 Queen Mary Av, Cathcart ☎041-424 3939 Plan **3**
rs Sun

Private hotel with modern extension.

31hc (8⇌ 1🚿) (3fb) CTV in 8 bedrooms TV in 1 bedroom ® ✱B&b£14.50–£29.30 Bdi£21.70–£36.50 LDO7pm

Lic 卌 CTV 60P

GH Smith's Hotel 963 Sauchiehall St ☎041-339 6363 Plan **4**

A long-established private hotel in the West End.

26hc (4fb) ® B&b£11–£15

卌 CTV Ᵽ

Ⓥ

GLASTONBURY
Somerset
Map **3** ST53

FH Mrs H T Tinney **Cradlebridge** *(ST477385)* ☎(0458) 31827
Closed Xmas

Large, renovated farmhouse with vegetable and fruit garden.

3hc (2⇌ 1🚿) (2fb) ✱B&b£12 Bdi£19 WBdifr£114 LDOnoon

卌 CTV P 200acres dairy

Ⓥ

Selected

FH Mrs J Nurse **Berewall Farm Country Guest House** *(ST516375)* Cinnamon Ln ☎(0458) 31451
Jun–Dec

Attractive property on edge of town, with views of Glastonbury Tor. Tennis court, stables and small outdoor pool. In the winter season, shooting can be arranged. Good home cooking.

9⇌ (3fb) CTV in all bedrooms ✖ B&b£13.50–£16.50 Bdi£20–£23 WBdi£120–£135 LDO9.30pm

Lic 卌 CTV 12P ⛆ 🎾(hard) U

120acres dairy

Credit cards 1 3

FH Mr & Mrs Staines **Laverley House** *(ST564394)* West Pennard ☎Pilton (074989) 696

Detached stone built Georgian property offering very comfortable accommodation throughout. Fine countryside views. →

3hc (1⇌) (1fb) CTV in all bedrooms Ⓡ
✱B&bfr£12 LDO7.30pm

12P 🏠 5acres fruit

GLENCOE
Highland *Argyllshire*
Map **14** NN15

GH Scorrybreac ☎Ballachulish (08552) 354

A modern guesthouse, comfortable and well-appointed.

5hc (1fb) Ⓡ B&b£9.50–£10.50 Bdi£16–£17 WBdifr£105 LDO10am

🚫 CTV 8P nc8yrs

Ⓥ

GLENFARG
Tayside
Map **11** NO11

FH Mrs W E A Lawrie **Candy** *(NO118098)* ☎(05773) 217
Apr–Oct

Built of local stone, this Victorian farmhouse sits at the east end of the Ochil Hills in a secluded position. Accommodation includes well-appointed bedrooms with a blend of traditional and modern facilities.

3hc ⚡ in 3 bedrooms ✈ Ⓡ B&b£10–£12 Bdi£16–£18 WBdifr£110 LDO10am

🚫 CTV 6P nc5yrs ♪ 520acres dairy sheep

Ⓥ

GLENMAVIS
Strathclyde *Lanarkshire*
Map **11** NS76

FH Mrs M Dunbar ***Braidenhill*** *(NS742673)* ☎Glenboig (0236) 872319

300-year-old farmhouse on the outskirts of Coatbridge. About ½m from town boundary, N off B803.

3hc (1fb)

🚫 CTV 4P 50acres arable sheep mixed

GLENRIDDING
Cumbria
Map **11** NY31

GH *Bridge House* ☎(08532) 236
Mar–Oct

Friendly little guesthouse overlooking the lake.

6hc (5fb) Ⓡ

🚫 CTV 7P

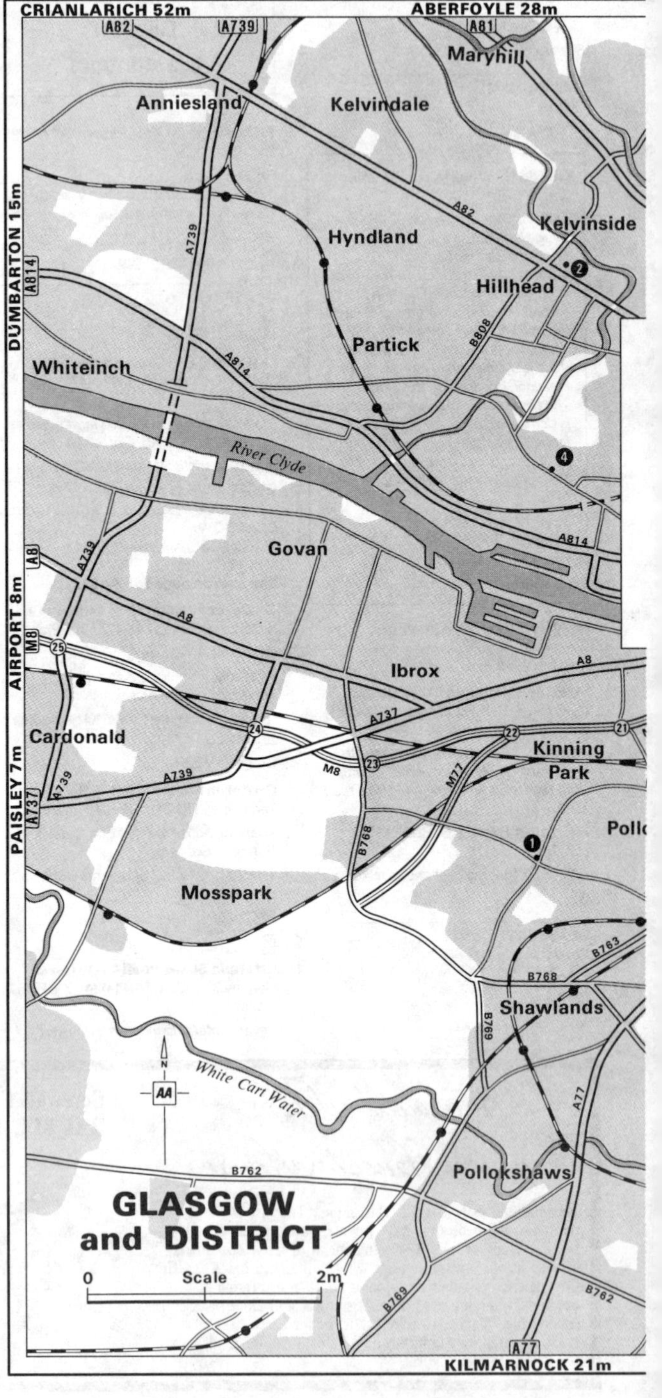

Glasgow

1 Dalmeny Hotel
2 Kelvin Private Hotel
3 Marie Stuart Hotel
4 Smith's Hotel

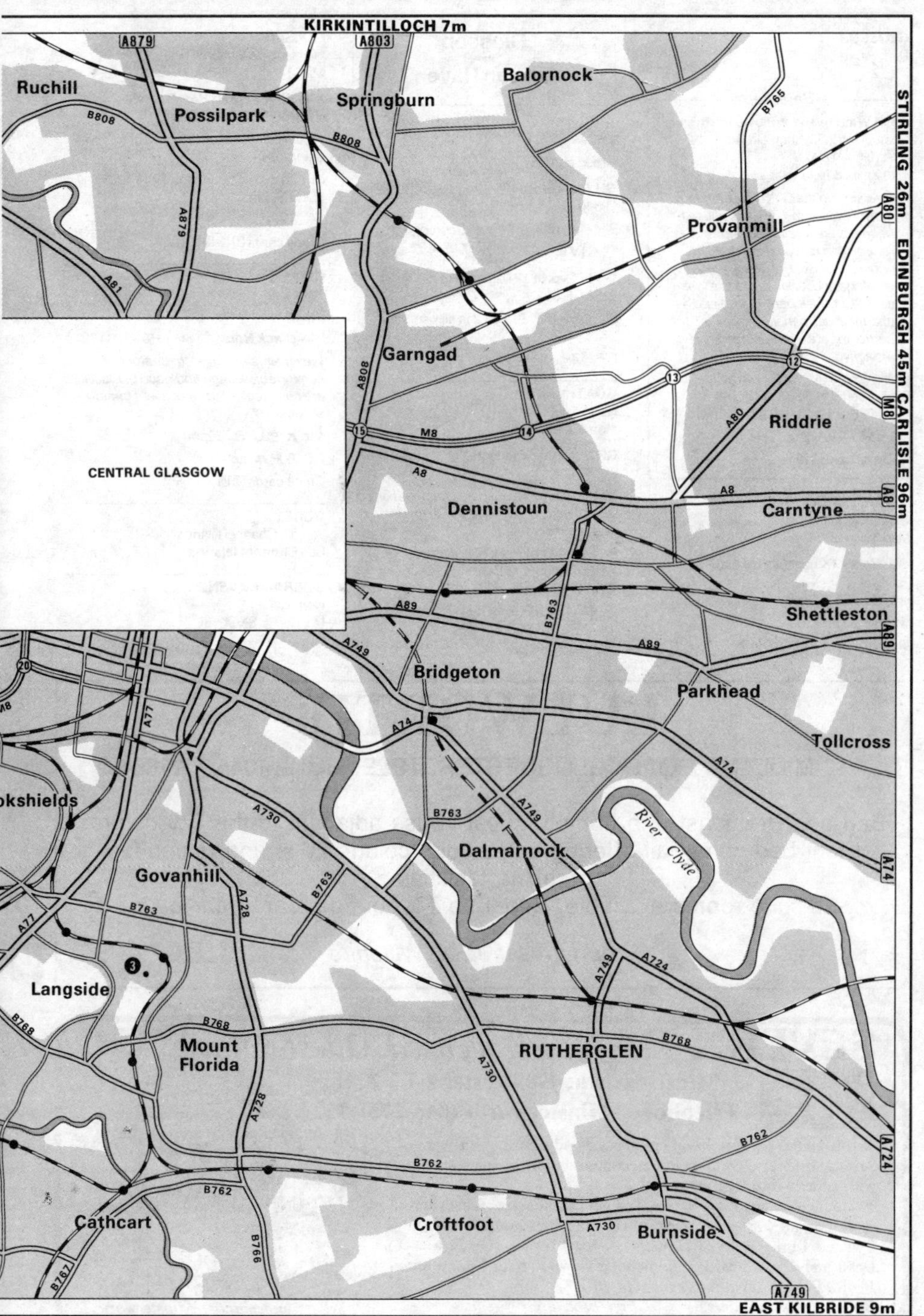
KIRKINTILLOCH 7m
A879
A803
Ruchill
Possilpark
Springburn
Balornock
B808
B808
B765
STIRLING 26m
A80
EDINBURGH 45m
M8
CARLISLE 96m
A8
A879
A81
Provanmill
Garngad
A808
13
12
CENTRAL GLASGOW
15
M8
14
A80
Riddrie
A8
A8
Dennistoun
Carntyne
B763
A89
Shettleston
A89
A749
A89
20
Bridgeton
Parkhead
A77
M8
A74
Tollcross
A74
okshields
A730
B763
A749
River Clyde
A74
Dalmarnock
Govanhill
B763
A728
B763
A77
3
Langside
A749
A724
B768
B768
B768
Mount Florida
RUTHERGLEN
A730
A728
B762
A724
B762
B762
Cathcart
Croftfoot
A730
Burnside
B766
B767
A749
EAST KILBRIDE 9m

GLOSSOP
Derbyshire
Map **7** SK09

Selected

GH Wind In The Willows Derbyshire Level (off A57) Sheffield Rd ☎(04574) 68001
rs Xmas & New Year
Overlooking the Golf Course, this early Victorian mill owner's house has been tastefully restored and refurbished retaining much of the original atmosphere. Many modern comforts and facilities are available as well as an elegant lounge and a charming oak panelled study. All the bedrooms are well-equipped and attractive.
8hc (2⇌ 6fl) (1fb) CTV in all bedrooms ✗ Ⓡ B&b£18–£48 Bdi£28–£58 WBdifr£196 LDO4pm
Lic ꟾꟾꟾ CTV 12P nc10yrs
Credit card ② ③

GLOUCESTER
Gloucestershire
Map **3** SO81

GH *Alma* 49 Kingsholm Rd ☎(0452) 20940
A well-maintained guesthouse offering a warm welcome.
8hc (2fb) TV in 1 bedroom ✗
ꟾꟾꟾ CTV 6P 1🚗
Credit card ③

GH *Claremont* 135 Stroud Rd ☎(0452) 29540
7hc (1fl) (2fb) CTV in all bedrooms ✗
ꟾꟾꟾ CTV 6P

GH Lulworth 12 Midland Rd ☎(0452) 21881
8hc (1⇌ 1fl) (2fb) CTV in all bedrooms Ⓡ B&b£11–£13
CTV 14P

GOATHLAND
North Yorkshire
Map **8** NZ80

GH Heatherdene Hotel ☎Whitby (0947) 86334
Comfortably furnished accommodation on the outskirts of the village with fine views over the moors.
6hc (2⇌) (3fb) ⚟ in 1 bedroom Ⓡ
✱B&b£12.50–£19 Bdi£17.50–£25 WBdi£116–£168 LDO4pm
Lic ꟾꟾꟾ CTV 10P solarium
Ⓥ

GOLSPIE
Highland *Sutherland*
Map **14** NH89

INN *Stag's Head Hotel* Main St ☎(04083) 3245
A comfortable and well-appointed, town-centre inn.
5⇌ CTV in all bedrooms ✗ Ⓡ LDO7.30pm
ꟾꟾꟾ CTV ₱
Credit cards ① ② ③ ④ ⑤

GOMSHALL
Surrey
Map **4** TQ04

INN *Black Horse* ☎Shere (048641) 2242
Well-maintained modern bedrooms, comfortable lounge and good bar facilities are complemented by efficient friendly service.
4hc ✗ Ⓡ LDO9.30pm
CTV 60P 🚗 nc12yrs
Credit cards ③ ⑤

GOREY
Jersey, Channel Islands
See **Channel Islands**

GORRAN HAVEN
Cornwall
Map **2** SX04

GH *Perhaver* ☎Mevagissey (0726) 842471
Apr–early Oct
Situated on top of cliffs, 500 yds from village.
5hc ✖ ® LDO5pm
Lic CTV 5P nc18yrs

INN Llawnroc Hotel ☎Mevagissey (0726) 843461
Closed Xmas Day & Boxing Day
Pleasant inn with large garden and modern bedrooms in new extension.
6hc (3⇌ 3fl) (2fb) CTV in all bedrooms ® B&b£12–£22 WB&b£70–£140 Lunch £4–£6 Dinner 9pm £5–£10
fff CTV 40P ⇌ ⌂
Credit cards 1 2 3 5 Ⓥ

GOUDHURST
Kent
Map **5** TQ73

INN *Vine* High St ☎(0580) 211261
Small country inn of character with interesting restaurant.
5hc (2⇌) ✖ LDO10pm
CTV 15P
Credit cards 1 3

GOUROCK
Strathclyde *Renfrewshire*
Map **10** NS27

GH Claremont 34 Victoria Rd ☎(0475) 31687
Stone-house on hillside overlooking the Clyde Estuary.
6hc (2fb) TV in all bedrooms ✱B&b£11 WB&b£77
fff CTV 4P

GRAMPOUND
Cornwall
Map **2** SW94

GH Perran House Fore St ☎St Austell (0726) 882066
Friendly service is offered at this semi-detached residence beside A390.
6hc ✖ ✱B&bfr£8 Bdifr£12 LDO7pm
Lic CTV P

FH Mrs S M Wade **Tregidgeo** *(SW960473)* ☎St Austell (0726) 882450
Mar–Oct
Comfortably furnished farmhouse in a beautiful, secluded and peaceful setting.
5hc (2fb) ✖ ® in 4 bedrooms ✱B&b£7.50–£8 Bdi£12–£13 WBdifr£79.50 LDO10am
CTV 4P 216acres dairy mixed

GRAMPOUND ROAD VILLAGE
Cornwall
Map **2** SW95

GH Midway Country House ☎St Austell (0726) 882343
4hc (1fb) CTV in all bedrooms ✖ ® B&b£12.45–£14.30 Bdi£18.75–£20.70 WBdifr£138.25 LDO6pm
Lic fff CTV 4P

GRANDES ROCQUES
Guernsey, Channel Islands
See **Channel Islands**

GRANGE (in Borrowdale)
Cumbria
Map **11** NY21

GH Grange ☎Borrowdale (059684) 251
19 Mar–Oct
Attractive house of lakeland slate set in its own gardens.
7hc (1⇌ 1fl) (1fb) ® B&b£10.50 WB&b£65
fff 8P
See advertisement under Borrowdale

GRANGE-OVER-SANDS
Cumbria
Map **7** SD47

GH Clare House Park Rd ☎(04484) 3026
Apr–Oct
A charming hotel with well-appointed bedrooms and pleasant lounges set in its own gardens with magnificent views of the bay.
17hc (14⇌ 1fl) (1fb) CTV in all bedrooms ✖ ® B&b£17–£21.50 Bdi£21–£25 WBdi£129–£160
Lic fff CTV 20P
Ⓥ

GH Corner Beech Methven Ter, Kents Bank Rd ☎(04484) 3088
Bright and cheerful guesthouse with a pleasant front garden.
9hc (2fb) CTV in 2 bedrooms TV in 4 bedrooms B&b£9–£10.50 Bdi£12.50–£14.50 WBdi£82–£92 LDO4.30pm
fff CTV ⁄P
Ⓥ

GH Elton Private Hotel Windermere Rd ☎(04484) 2838
Mar–Oct
A stone-built, traditional-style guesthouse offering good-value accommodation.
7hc (2fb) ✖ B&b£10.50–£12 Bdi£15.78–£17.25 WBdi£99–£103 LDO4pm
Lic CTV ⁄P nc8yrs
Ⓥ

GH *Grayrigge Private Hotel* Kents Bank Rd ☎(04484) 2345
Large family owned hotel with spacious rooms.
27hc (3⇌) Annexe: 9hc (13fb) CTV in 14 bedrooms
Lic fff CTV 60P 6🚗

⊢⊣**GH Thornfield House** Kents Bank Rd ☎(04484) 2512
Etr–Oct
A pleasant and comfortable guesthouse with good views over Morecambe Bay.
6hc TV in all bedrooms ✖ ® B&b£9–£9.50 Bdi£13–£13.50 WBdifr£85 LDO5pm
fff 6P nc5yrs

GRANTOWN-ON-SPEY
Highland *Morayshire*
Map **14** NJ02

GH Dar-Il-Hena Grant Rd ☎(0479) 2929
Etr–Oct
This well appointed property has a friendly atmosphere, elegant lounge and comfortable bedrooms. →

7hc (3fb) Ⓡ ✱B&bfr£8.50 Bdifr£14 WBdifr£92.50 LDO6pm

Ⲯ CTV 10P

GH Dunachton Coppice Court (off Grant Rd) ☎(0479) 2098
Closed Nov

Comfortable, well appointed house in a quiet residential area.

8hc (1⇌) (2fb) Ⓡ ✱B&b£9.25–£10.25 Bdi£16.75–£17.75 WBdifr£115.75 LDO7pm

Lic Ⲯ CTV 10P

GH *Dunallan* Woodside Av ☎(0479) 2140
May–Nov

Late Victorian house in quiet, residential location with several family bedrooms.

5hc (2fb) LDO4pm

Ⲯ CTV 5P

⊢⊣**GH Firhall** ☎(0479) 3097

A secluded, residential location for this house of character with fine woodwork and elaborate ceilings. Comfortable bedrooms and spacious public rooms.

6hc (3fb) ✖ Ⓡ B&b£8.75 Bdi£14 WBdifr£92 LDO7pm

Ⲯ CTV 10P

GH Kinross House Woodside Av ☎(0479) 2042
Closed Xmas

Stone-built house in quiet residential part of town.

6hc (2fb) ⊁ in 6 bedrooms Ⓡ B&b£8.50–£10.50 Bdi£13.50–£16 WBdifr£99.50 LDO7pm

Lic Ⲯ CTV 6P

Ⓥ

⊢⊣**GH Pines Hotel** Woodside Av ☎(0479) 2092
Etr–Sep

Traditional style house with spacious rooms, conveniently situated for shops.

10hc (2fb) B&bfr£9 Bdifr£15 WBdifr£98 LDO5pm

CTV 4P

Ⓥ

Grantown-on-Spey — Grassington

GH *Ravenscourt* Seafield Av ☎(0479) 2286
Jan–Oct

Offers comfortable and spacious accommodation.

6hc (2fb) LDO7pm

Lic Ⲯ CTV 15P

⊢⊣**GH Riversdale** Grant Rd ☎(0479) 2648

Detached house with small garden at front and lawn at rear.

7hc (2fb) Ⓡ B&b£8.25–£8.50 Bdi£13–£13.50 WBdifr£87.50 LDO6pm

Ⲯ CTV 8P ♿

Ⓥ

⊢⊣**GH Umaria** Woodlands Ter ☎(0479) 2104
Closed Nov & Dec

Situated on main road at the south end of town.

8hc (3fb) Ⓡ B&bfr£9 Bdifr£14.50 WBdifr£95 LDO5.30pm

Lic CTV 9P

Ⓥ

GRASMERE

Cumbria
Map **11** NY30

GH Beck Steps College St ☎(09665) 348
Mar–Nov

Friendly, family-run guesthouse overlooking green specialising in home-cooked English food.

10hc (4⇌ 3⫪) (1fb) ✖ Ⓡ Bdi£20.50–£22.50 WBdifr£136.50 LDO5pm

Lic Ⲯ CTV 8P nc4yrs

GH Bridge House Hotel Stock Ln ☎(09665) 425
mid Mar–mid Nov

Lovely village centre house standing within its own gardens beside the river.

12hc (7⇌ 3⫪) (1fb) CTV available in bedrooms ✖ Ⓡ B&b£19–£21.50 Bdi£24–£29.50 WBdi£161–£190 LDO7pm

Lic Ⲯ CTV 20P nc6months

Credit cards 1 3 Ⓥ

See advertisement under Ambleside

GH Lake View Lake View Dr ☎(09665) 384
Mar–Nov

A comfortable, detached house with lovely gardens with private footpath leading down to the lake.

6hc (2⫪) Ⓡ B&b£12 Bdi£19.50 WBdi£126 LDOnoon

CTV 11P nc10yrs

GH Raise View Whitebridge ☎(09665) 215
Apr–Oct

A very pleasant house with lovely views. The lounge is comfortable and the bedrooms are tastefully decorated and arranged.

6hc (3⫪) (1fb) ✖ Ⓡ B&bfr£9.25

CTV 6P nc5yrs

GH Titteringdales Pye Ln ☎(09665) 439
Apr–1 Nov

A pleasant house in 2½ acres of gardens with good views over the surrounding fells.

7hc (1⇌ 2⫪) Ⓡ B&b£12.50–£17.50 Bdi£20–£25 WBdifr£130 LDO4pm

Lic Ⲯ CTV 8P

GRASSINGTON

North Yorkshire
Map **7** SE06

GH Ashfield House Hotel ☎(0756) 752584
Apr–Oct

Secluded, comfortable 17th century house, offering splendid food.

7hc (2⫪) (2fb) ✖ Ⓡ ✱B&b£12.70–£17.90 Bdi£19–£26.70 WBdifr£135.30 LDO5.30pm

Lic Ⲯ CTV 7P

Ⓥ

GH Lodge 3 Wood Ln ☎(0756) 752518
Closed 5 Jan–Feb

Family run house with good furnishings, in village centre.

7hc (1fb) Ⓡ B&b£11–£15 Bdi£18–£22 WBdifr£115

CTV 7P

Ⓥ

GRAVESEND
Kent
Map **5** TQ67

GH *Cromer* 194 Parrock St ☎(0474) 61935
Closed 24 Dec–2Jan

Victorian corner house with well-furnished bedrooms and tastefully-appointed restaurant.

11hc (1⇌) (3fb) CTV in all bedrooms

CTV 15P nc12yrs

Credit card ③

GH Overcliffe Hotel 15–16 The Overcliffe ☎(0474) 322131

Tastefully decorated hotel with very well-equipped bedrooms and a separate restaurant.

19fl (1fb) CTV in all bedrooms Ⓡ ✱B&b£35–£40 Bdi£45–£50 WBdifr£315 LDO9.30pm

Lic 20P

Credit cards ① ② ③ ⑤

GREAT
Placenames incorporating the word 'Great', such as Gt Malvern and Gt Yarmouth, will be found under the actual placename, *ie* Malvern, Yarmouth.

GREENHEAD
Northumberland
Map **12** NY66

FH Mrs P Staff **Holmhead** *(NY659661)* ☎Gilsland (06972) 402
Closed Xmas & New Year

A traditional Northumbrian farmhouse offering warmth and comfort and an excellent selection of breakfast dishes. The Roman wall runs beneath the house and Thirlwall Castle is behind.

4hc (1fb) in 4 bedrooms B&b£10–£11 Bdi£17–£17.50 WBdi£109–£112 LDO5pm

Lic CTV 6P 300acres beef & sheep breeding non-working

Ⓥ

GRETNA
Dumfries & Galloway *Dumfriesshire*
Map **11** NY36

GH *Surrone House* Annan Rd ☎(0461) 38341

Converted from a farmhouse some years ago, this beautifully-maintained establishment offers modern and spacious accommodation, each bedroom has a bathroom and is well-equipped.

6hc (5⇌ fl) (4fb) CTV in all bedrooms Ⓡ LDO8pm

Lic CTV 16P

INN Crossways Annan Rd ☎(0461) 37465

This attractive roadside inn is popular with newly-weds. Featuring a well-appointed honeymoon suite.

6fl (1fb) CTV in all bedrooms Ⓡ ✱B&b£15 Lunch fr£1.80&alc Dinner 9.30pm fr£3.50&alc

30P

Credit cards ① ③

GRETNA GREEN
Dumfries & Galloway *Dumfriesshire*
Map **11** NY36

GH Greenlaw ☎Gretna (0461) 38361

A cosy house situated on the edge of the village with fresh, compact bedrooms.

8hc (1fb) ✱B&b£8.50–£9 Bdi£12.50–£14 W£84–£93.50 LDO6pm

CTV 8P 1

Ⓥ

GUERNSEY
See **Channel Islands**

GUILDFORD
Surrey
Map **4** SU94

GH Blanes Court Hotel Albury Rd ☎(0483) 573171
Closed Xmas wk

Quietly situated, elegant accommodation, with well equipped bedrooms and homely atmosphere.

21hc (1⇌ 11fl) (3fb) CTV in all bedrooms Ⓡ B&b£17–£33 WB&bfr£102

Lic CTV 22P

Credit cards ① ② ③ Ⓥ

GH *Quinns Hotel* 78 Epsom Rd (Guestaccom) ☎(0483) 60422

A fine Victorian house, close to all main routes through the busy town centre. Personally run establishment, offering well-equipped and stylishly-decorated bedrooms.

10hc (3⇌ 4fl) (2fb) CTV in all bedrooms Ⓡ

Lic 14P

Credit cards ① ② ③ ⑤ Ⓥ

GUNNISLAKE
Cornwall
Map **2** SX47

GH Hingston House St Anns Chapel ☎Tavistock (0822) 832468

A country house built originally for the captain of the local tin mines, now providing comfortable accommodation and friendly service.

9hc (4fl) (1fb) TV in 2 bedrooms Ⓡ B&b£12.75–£17.50 Bdi£21.25–£26 WBdifr£143.75 LDO7pm

Lic CTV 10P

Credit cards ① ③ Ⓥ

See advertisement on page 188

HADDINGTON
Lothian
Map **12** NT57

FH Mrs K Kerr **Barney Mains** *(NT523764)* Barney Mains ☎Athelstaneford (062088) 310
Mar–Oct →

3hc ⅟ in all bedrooms ✱B&b£8.50–£10 Bdi£14.50–£16 LDO8.30pm

Lic CTV 6P 580acres arable beef sheep

HALFORD
Warwickshire
Map **4** SP24

INN Halford Bridge Fosse Way☏Stratford-upon-Avon (0789) 740382

Cheerful, character-inn, built of local Cotswold stone, on Fosse Way. 16th-century coaching inn built of Cotswold stone. Family run with a friendly atmosphere.

5hc (2fb) CTV in all bedrooms ✗ B&bfr£18.50 Bdifr£23 WBdifr£165 Lunch £3.95–£4.95&alcDinner 9.45pm£2.95–£4.50alc

100P

HALFWAY HOUSE
Shropshire
Map **7** SJ31

FH Mrs E Morgan **Willows** *(SJ342115)* ☏Shrewsbury (0743) 884233
Mar–Oct

Farm house in pretty garden, well situated for those travelling to Wales. It is surrounded by Long Mountain and Middlebar Hills.

3rm (1hc) (1fb) ✗ ✱B&b£7.50–£9 Bdi£10.50–£12 WBdi£70–£90 LDO2pm

TV 10P 35acres beef sheep

HALIFAX
West Yorkshire
Map **7** SE02

INN Stump Cross Stump Cross ☏(0422) 66004

Large period building beside the A58 1m from Halifax in the attractive Shibden Valley. 1m E A58/A6036 junction.

12hc (6⇌) (1fb) CTV in 6 bedrooms TV in 3 bedrooms Ⓡ ✱B&b£16–£26 Bdi£21–£34 Lunch £5&alc Dinner 9.45pm £7alc

40P nc5yrs

HALSTOCK
Dorset
Map **3** ST50

Haddington — Halwell

Selected

FH Mr W Budd **Old Mill** *(ST530086)* (Guestaccom)☏Corscombe (093589) 278
Mar–Oct

Comfortable 17th-century mill with friendly atmosphere and interesting food, in peaceful rural setting. 2m W unclass rd.

3⇌ (1fb) CTV in all bedrooms Ⓡ ✱B&b£15–£26 Bdi£23.50–£34.50 WBdi£154–£179 LDO9pm

Lic CTV 10P nc5yrs 10acres non-working

Credit cards 1 3 Ⓥ

HALTWHISTLE
Northumberland
Map **12** NY76

GH Ashcroft ☏(0498) 20213
Closed 22 Dec–3 Jan

Carefully modernised former Victorian vicarage with spacious rooms and tranquil atmosphere.

8hc (3fb) ⅟ in 1 bedroom ✗ B&bfr£10 Bdifr£15 WBdifr£90 LDO3pm

CTV 10P

Ⓥ

Credit Cards

1 Access/Euro/Mastercard
2 American Express
3 Barclaycard/Visa
5 Diners

Selected

FH Mrs J Brown **Broomshaw Hill** *(NY706654)* Willia Rd ☏(0498) 20866
Apr–Oct

Although close to the town centre, this 18th-century, stone-built farmhouse is in an attractive rural setting just 1 mile from Hadrian's Wall. It has been enlarged and modernised over the years but still retains much of its original character. Comfortable accommodation includes an impressive sitting room, elegant dining room and spacious bedrooms.

3hc (1fb) TV in 1 bedroom Ⓡ B&b£9–£10 Bdi£15–£16 WBdifr£95 LDO10am

CTV 4P 2🚗 7acres livestock horses

Ⓥ

FH Mrs M Dawson **Park Burnfoot** *(NY 687619)* Featherstone Pk ☏(0498) 20378
Apr–Oct

Attractive stone-built farmhouse of 1740 situated on the banks of the South Tyne.

2hc (1fb) CTV in 2 bedrooms ✗ Ⓡ ✱B&b£8–£9 Bdi£12.50–£13

3P nc3yrs 220acres dairy beef

Ⓥ

FH Mrs J I Laidlow **Ald White Craig** *(NY713649)* Shield Hill ☏(0498) 20565
Apr–Sep & Etr

Modernised, croft-style farmhouse, with well appointed bedrooms but retaining an olde worlde atmosphere in the comfortable lounge.

3hc (1⇌ 2fl) CTV in all bedrooms ✗ Ⓡ B&b£12–£15 Bdifr£18.50 WBdifr£126.50 LDOnoon

nc7yrs 60acres mixed

Ⓥ

HALWELL
Devon
Map **3** SX75

GH Stanborough Hundred Hotel
☎East Allington (054852) 236
Mar–5 Jan

Much of historic interest surrounds this charming small hotel. The sheltered gardens were originally laid out c1840 and nearby is a Bronze Age campsite. There are extensive views of Dartmoor and the coast. A friendly welcome awaits the visitor.

6hc (2⇌) Annexe: 1⇌ (3fb) ✗ Ⓡ in 3 bedrooms B&b£15–£16 Bdi£24–£25 WBdi£90–£125 LDO6.50pm

Lic ♨ CTV 10P

Ⓥ

HAMBLEDEN
Buckinghamshire
Map **4** SU78

INN *Stag & Huntsman* ☎Henley-on-Thames (0491) 571227

Small country inn offering simple but comfortable accommodation and warm, informal atmosphere.

3hc ✗ Ⓡ

♨ P ⛟ nc18yrs

Credit cards ① ③

HAMBLETON
Lancashire
Map **7** SD34

FH Mrs B Jenkinson **White Lodge** (*SD382435*) Sower Carr Ln ☎(0253) 700342

An attractive modern farmhouse with accommodation of a very high standard ideally located betweeen Blackpool and Lancaster.

3rm (1fb) ⊁ in all bedrooms ✗ ✱B&b£12 WB&b£77

♨ CTV 6P nc5yrs ↲ 220acres arable dairy pig sheep

HAMILTON
Strathclyde *Lanarkshire*
Map **11** NS75

FH Mr R Hamilton **East Drumloch** (*NS678521*) Chapelton (3m SW off A723) ☎Chapelton (03573) 236
Closed Xmas Day & New Years Day

Large stone-built farmhouse with a modern, well-furnished interior. Signposted from A723 and A726.

3rm (1hc) (2fb) ✱B&bfr£7 Bdifr£10 WBdifr£70 LDO6pm

♨ CTV 10P 260acres beef mixed

HANLEY CASTLE
Hereford & Worcester
Map **3** SO84

Selected

GH Old Parsonage
☎Hanley Swan (0684) 310124
Closed 11 Dec–2 Jan

If you want the comfort and amenities of a hotel, combined with personal service, then this Georgian house should fit the bill. Mr and Mrs Addison offer three extremely comfortable bedrooms with private facilities, interesting and varied meals and a good wine list. Fly fishing and shooting can be arranged or just relax in the 1½ acres of grounds.

3hc (2⇌) (1fb) TV in 1 bedroom B&b£15–£19 Bdi£25.50–£29.50 WBdi£192.50

Lic ♨ CTV 6P 1🚗 nc6yrs 1½acres non-working

Credit card ② Ⓥ

HANMER
Clwyd
Map **7** SJ44

FH C Sumner & F Williams-Lee **Buck** (*SJ435424*) ☎(094874) 339

On A525 Whitchurch (7m) to Wrexham (9m) road this accommodation, for non-smokers, is an ideal touring base. Good country cooking. →

4hc 🚭 in all bedrooms B&b£10–£11 Bdi£17–£18.50 WBdi£112–£121

🏛 CTV 12P 8acres non-working

Ⓥ

HARBERTON
Devon
Map **3** SX75

FH Mrs I P Steer **Preston** *(SX777587)* ☎Totnes (0803) 862235
Apr–Oct

Old farmhouse on outskirts of quaint and attractive village. Totnes about 2½m.

3hc (1fb) ✗ Ⓡ B&b£10–£11 Bdi£15–£16 WBdifr£100 LDO6.45pm

CTV 3P nc3yrs 250acres dairy mixed

Ⓥ

FH Mr R Rose **Tristford** *(SX775587)* ☎Totnes (0803) 862418

Charming house with 'olde worlde' atmosphere. Good centre for touring the coast between Plymouth and Torbay.

3hc ✗ B&b£10

🏛 CTV 5🚗 150acres arable beef mixed sheep

HARDSTOFT
Derbyshire
Map **8** SK46

INN *Shoulder of Mutton* ☎Chesterfield (0246) 850276

Hanmer — Harrogate

A much-extended inn, originally a farmhouse with a tap room, dating from 1660. Well-equipped accommodation and extensive facilities for functions.

7rm (6hc 2🚿) (1fb) CTV in all bedrooms Ⓡ LDO9.30pm

🏛 150P

HARLECH
Gwynedd
Map **6** SH53

Selected

GH Castle Cottage Hotel Pen Llech ☎(0766) 780479

6hc (4🛁) Ⓡ ✱B&bfr£13.50 Bdifr£23.50 LDO9.30pm

🏛 CTV 🐕

Credit cards 1 3

GH Gwrach Ynys Country Guest House Ynys, Talsarnau ☎(0766) 780742

Beautifully restored Edwardian country-house situated in own grounds, close to Harlech.

7hc (1🛁 5🚿) (2fb) Ⓡ ✱B&b£10–£12 Bdi£15–£17.50 WBdi£105–£120

🏛 CTV 10P

⊢⊣**FH** Mrs E A Jones **Tyddyn Gwynt** *(SH601302)* ☎(0766) 780298

2½m off B4573 (A496).

4rm (3hc) (1fb) B&bfr£9 Bdifr£13

CTV 6P 3acres smallholding

Ⓥ

INN Rum Hole Hotel ☎(0766) 780477

Two-storey inn at lower end of village.

8hc (3🚿) (6fb) CTV in 3 bedrooms Ⓡ B&b£11–£12.50 WB&b£65–£75 Bar lunch 75p–£4 LDO 9pm

CTV 25P

Ⓥ

HARROGATE
North Yorkshire
Map **8** SE35

GH Abbey Lodge 31 Ripon Rd ☎(0423) 69712

Smart, stylish house with very comfortable bedrooms and pleasant public areas.

15hc (2🛁 6🚿) (3fb) CTV in all bedrooms ✗ Ⓡ B&b£13.50–£15.50 Bdi£21–£23 WBdifr£142 LDO4pm

Lic 🏛 16P 2🚗

Credit cards 1 3 Ⓥ

GH Alexa House & Stable Cottages 26 Ripon Rd ☎(0423) 501988
Closed Xmas wk

Guesthouse of distinction with bedrooms of a very high quality.

8hc (3⇌ 4⋒) Annexe: 4⋒ (2fb) CTV in all bedrooms ✗ Ⓡ B&bfr£17 Bdi£25.50 WBdifr£153 LDOnoon

Lic ⌂ CTV 14P

Ⓥ

GH Alphen Lodge 2 Esplanade ☎(0423) 502882
Closed Xmas

An early-Victorian guesthouse of some style and character. Accommodation comprises well-fitted, spacious bedrooms, comfortable lounge and an elegant breakfast room. Outside, there is an attractive small terraced garden.

11hc (6⇌ 1⋒) (2fb) ⊁ in all bedrooms CTV in all bedrooms ✗ Ⓡ ✱B&b£17.50–£23

Lic ⌂ 12P

Credit cards 1 2 3 Ⓥ

GH Ashley House Hotel 36–40 Franklin Rd ☎(0423) 507474

Nicely appointed combination of three town houses with spacious public rooms.

18hc (3⋒) (2fb) TV in all bedrooms Ⓡ B&b£13–£16 Bdi£20–£24 WBdi£133–£157.50 LDO4pm

Lic ⌂ CTV 9P

Credit card 1 Ⓥ

Harrogate

GH *Aston Hotel* Franklin Mount ☎(0423) 64262

A pair of stone-built townhouses, with small lawned gardens to front situated close to the conference centre. Bedrooms are well-appointed and nicely furnished.

16hc (12⋒) (1fb) ⊁ in 4 bedrooms CTV in 6 bedrooms TV in 10 bedrooms Ⓡ LDO4pm

Lic ⌂ CTV 10P 1🚗

GH Aygarth 11 Harlow Moor Dr ☎(0423) 68705

Simple and homely accommodation overlooking Valley Gardens.

7hc (3fb) CTV in 5 bedrooms TV in 2 bedrooms Ⓡ B&b£12–£15 Bdi£18.50–£21.50 WBdifr£126 LDO4pm

⌂ CTV

Ⓥ

GH Cavendish Hotel 3 Valley Dr ☎(0423) 509637
Closed Xmas

Conveniently placed guesthouse with nicely equipped bedrooms.

11hc (1⇌ 9⋒) (5fb) CTV in all bedrooms Ⓡ B&b£14.50–£21.50 Bdi£20–£27 WBdifr£176 LDO6.30pm

Lic ⌂ CTV P̸

Credit cards 1 2 3 5 Ⓥ

GH Coppice Hotel 9 Studley Rd ☎(0423) 69626

A stone-built town house in a quiet area close to local facilities and Conference Centre.

6hc (1⇌) (3fb) TV in 3 bedrooms Ⓡ B&b£12–£14 Bdi£19–£21 WBdifr£140 LDO4.30pm

⌂ CTV P̸ nc8yrs

Credit cards 1 3 5 Ⓥ

GH Craigleigh 6 West Grove Rd ☎(0423) 64064
rs Xmas & New Year

Charming and cosy Victorian town house close to the Conference Centre.

6hc (1fb) CTV in 1 bedroom TV in 1 bedroom Ⓡ B&b£9.50–£11.50 Bdi£16.50–£17.50 WBdi£112–£125 LDOnoon

⌂ CTV 2P

Ⓥ

GH Croft Hotel 42–46 Franklin Rd ☎(0423) 63326

Situated close to the town centre and conference centre, these two converted town houses have attractive public rooms and a small bar. →

17hc (7⥂) (4fb) CTV in all bedrooms ✈ (ex guide dogs) Ⓡ ✱B&b£13.50–£19 Bdifr£18.50 WBdifr£126 LDO8.30pm

Lic 🍴 CTV 8P

Credit card ⊡ Ⓥ

GH Dales Hotel 101 Valley Dr ☎(0423) 507248

Four-storey town house run by friendly, helpful proprietors. Accommodation is clean and comfortable. Situated close to the town centre overlooking Valley Gardens.

8hc (3⥂) (3fb) CTV in all bedrooms Ⓡ B&b£14–£28 Bdi£21–£35 WBdi£140–£160 LDO9am

Lic 🍴 CTV

Ⓥ

GH Gillmore Hotel 98 Kings Rd ☎(0423) 503699

An imaginative and well-organised conversion of two terraced houses.

22hc (2⇌ 4⥂) (8fb) CTV in 9 bedrooms B&b£14–£15 Bdi£19.25–£20.25 WBdi£115–£133

Lic 🍴 CTV P snooker solarium

GH Grafton Hotel 1–3 Franklin Mount ☎(0423) 508491

Stone town houses, restored and providing comfortable modern accommodation.

Harrogate

17hc (1⇌ 10⥂) (1fb) CTV in 12 bedrooms ✈ Ⓡ B&b£14–£17.50 Bdi£20–£23.50 WBdifr£148

Lic 🍴 CTV 3P

Credit cards ⊡ ② ③ ⑤

GH *Kingsway* 36 Kings Rd ☎(0423) 62179

Three-storey town house offering modest, comfortable accommodation opposite Conference Centre.

7hc (1⇌ 6⥂) (1fb) LDO11.55am

Lic 🍴 CTV 2P 1🚘

GH Lamont House 12 St Mary's Walk ☎(0423) 67143

Closed Xmas

Late Victorian town house near town centre and Spa Baths.

8hc (2fb) B&b£11.50–£12.75 Bdi£19–£20.25 LDO6pm

Lic 🍴 CTV ⌿

Ⓥ

GH Mowbray House 18 Harlow Moor Dr ☎(0423) 63350

A sturdy Victorian town house, overlooking Valley Gardens, with simply furnished bedrooms.

8hc (2fb) ⚔ in 2 bedrooms TV in 1 bedroom ✱B&b£11–£15 Bdi£17–£21 WBdi£161–£189 LDO5pm

Lic 🍴 CTV 20P

Ⓥ

GH Norman Hotel 41 Valley Dr ☎(0423) 502171

Tall town house overlooking Valley Gardens with small comfortable lounge bar and attractive dining room.

18hc (5⥂) (7fb) CTV in 1 bedroom TV in 1 bedroom ✱B&b£14–£16 Bdi£15.50–£23 WBdi£135–£140 LDO6pm

Lic CTV ⌿

Ⓥ

GH Oakbrae 3 Springfield Av ☎(0423) 67682

Closed Xmas

Small, picturesque semi, near Conference Centre, with well-proportioned lounge and breakfast room, and pleasant bedrooms.

6hc (1⇌ 4⥂) (1fb) CTV in all bedrooms ✈ Ⓡ B&b£11–£12.50 Bdi£18–£19.50 WBdifr£120 LDO4pm

🍴 CTV 4P nc2yrs

GH Prince's Hotel 7 Granby Rd ☎(0423) 883469

Victorian house of style and character offering comfortable accommodation.

8hc (2⇆ 2fl) (1fb) ⅟ in 1 bedroom CTV in all bedrooms ✕ Ⓡ B&b£11–£18 Bdi£17.50–£24.50 WBdifr£125 LDO9am

Lic 🅿 CTV ⅟P nc3yrs

Ⓥ

GH Roan 90 Kings Rd ☎(0423) 503087 Closed Xmas

Town house near Conference Centre with charming bedrooms and spacious public areas.

7hc (3fl) (1fb) ✕ Ⓡ B&bfr£10.50 Bdifr£16.50 LDO4.30pm

🅿 CTV ⅟P nc7yrs

Ⓥ

GH Rosedale Hotel 86 Kings Rd ☎(0423) 66630 Closed Xmas

Three-storey Victorian house with good bedrooms, a cosy bar and separate lounge; near Conference Centre.

8hc (1⇆ 4fl) (1fb) CTV in all bedrooms ✕ Ⓡ B&b£13–£15 Bdi£20.50–£22.50 WBdifr£150 LDO1pm

Lic 🅿 6P nc5yrs

GH Shelbourne 78 Kings Rd ☎(0423) 504390 Closed Xmas wk

Harrogate

Good, clean, comfortable, town centre guesthouse.

7hc (2fb) Ⓡ LDO10am

Lic 🅿 CTV 1P

Credit card 3

GH Spring Lodge 22 Spring Mount ☎(0423) 506036

Three-storey town house near to the conference centre.

8hc (2⇆) (2fb) TV in 2 bedrooms Ⓡ B&b£11–£13 Bdi£15–£17.50 WBdi£94.50–£110.25 LDO3pm

Lic 🅿 CTV 6P

Ⓥ

REMEMBER

Prices quoted in the gazetteer are minimum double room occupancy to maximum single room occupancy per person.

GH Strayend 56 Dragon View, Skipton Rd ☎(0423) 61700

An interesting house with bright, cheerful bedrooms and welcoming staff.

6hc (4 fl) (1fb) TV in 2 bedrooms B&b£12.50–£13.50 Bdi£16.50 WBdifr£112.50 LDO9am

🅿 CTV 4P nc5yrs

GH Wharfedale House 28 Harlow Moor Dr ☎(0423) 522233 Closed Dec rs Nov

Large town house overlooking Valley Gardens. Wholefood dishes and vegetarian breakfasts are available.

8hc (1⇆ 7fl) (2fb) CTV in all bedrooms Ⓡ *B&b£15–£16 Bdi£20.25–£21.25 WBdifr£121.50 LDOam

Lic 🅿 3P

Ⓥ

GH Woodhouse 7 Spring Grove ☎(0423) 60081

Closed 24 Dec–1 Jan

Stylish Victorian house with lovely dining room featuring co-ordinated crockery and deçor.

9hc (3⇆ 3fl) (2fb) CTV in all bedrooms ✕ Ⓡ B&b£14–£16 Bdi£22–£24 WBdi£136–£149 LDOnoon

Lic 🅿 CTV nc14yrs

See advertisement on page 194

HARROP FOLD
Lancashire
Map **7** SD74

Selected

FH Mr & Mrs P Wood **Harrop Fold Country Farmhouse Hotel** *(SD746492)* (Guestaccom) ☎Bolton-by-Bowland (02007) 600 Telex No 635562

A 17th century Lancashire longhouse, situated in peaceful surroundings, lovingly furnished with antiques by Peter and Victoria Wood. Good home cooking makes the most of local produce and recipes. The lounge and dining room are quite delightful and the bedrooms are provided with thoughtful extras.

5⇌ Annexe: 2⇌ CTV in all bedrooms Ⓡ B&b£21.50–£30 Bdi£31.50–£42.50 WBdi£210–£259 LDO8.45pm

Lic ♛ 16P nc 280acres sheep

Credit cards 1 3

HARROW
Gt London
London plan **4** B5 *(pages 258–259)*

GH Central Hotel 6 Hindes Rd ☎01-427 0893

Edwardian house in residential area of town centre.

9hc (2fl) (3fb) CTV in all bedrooms ✗ Ⓡ ✱B&b£20 WB&b£140

♛ CTV 9P

Credit cards 1 2 3 5

GH Hindes Hotel 8 Hindes Rd ☎01-427 7468

Homely and nicely appointed hotel under personal supervision of the owners.

13hc (1fl) (2fb) CTV in all bedrooms ✗ Ⓡ B&b£19.50

♛ CTV 5P

Credit cards 1 3

GH Kempsford House Hotel 21–23 St Johns Rd ☎01-427 4983
Closed 2 wks Xmas

Family-run private hotel offering basic but comfortable accommodation.

30hc (9fl) (6fb) CTV in all bedrooms ✗ B&b£24.15–£45

Lic ♛ CTV 30P

Credit cards 1 3

GH *Lindal Hotel* 2 Hindes Rd ☎01-863 3164

Small and welcoming family-run guesthouse with simple accommodation.

9hc (1fl) Annexe: 4hc (2⇌ 2fl) (3fb) CTV in all bedrooms ✗ LDO8.30pm

Lic ♛ CTV 20P

Credit card 3

HARTFIELD
East Sussex
Map **5** TQ44

FH Mrs C Cooper **Bolebrook Mill** *(TQ481373)* Perry Hill, Edenbridge Rd ☎(089277) 425
Closed Xmas

Interesting and unusual accommodation is offered at this watermill dating back to 1086. The steep narrow stairs make it unsuitable for small children, the elderly or disabled.

Annexe 2⇌ CTV in all bedrooms ✗ Ⓡ ✱B&bfr£15 Bdifr£25 LDO7pm

Lic 2P nc7yrs 6½acres smallholding

HARTLAND
Devon
Map **2** SS22

GH Fosfelle ☎(02374) 273

Former manor house dating from the 17th century amidst open countryside.

7hc (2fb) ✗ Ⓡ B&b£11.50–£12.50 Bdi£17–£19 WBdi£92.50–£119 LDO9pm

Lic CTV 20P ⌂ fishing snooker

Ⓥ

Central Hotel

6 Hindes Road, Harrow, Middlesex, HA1 1SJ.
Telephone: 01-427 0893

Friendly family run hotel. Full English breakfast served.
En suite rooms available. Colour TV and tea and coffee in all rooms. TV lounge.
Car Park. 15 minutes London's West End. 6 minutes by train to
Wembley Stadium and Conference Centre. 15 minutes M1 and M25 motorway.
Buses direct to Heathrow Airport. Tourist Board Approved!

Hindes hotel

8 Hindes Road, Harrow,
Middlesex HA1 1SJ
Telephone: 01-427 7468

* Bed & Breakfast
* Colour TV & tea & coffee in all rooms
* Full central heating
* Car park
* 5 mins Harrow on the Hill Underground Station
* 6 mins (by train) Wembley Conference Centre and Stadium
* 15 mins M1 motorway & London's West End

KEMPSFORD HOUSE HOTEL

21/23 St. John's Road, Harrow, Middlesex HA1 2EE.
Telephone: 01-427 4983/01-427 0390

The Hotel is a superior Bed and Breakfast Hotel with many of the comforts of more expensive establishments. Our rooms are comfortable, centrally heated, and with the benefit of television and radio.

We serve a traditional hearty English breakfast each morning and for those wishing to eat locally there are an excellent variety of restaurants within walking distance of the Hotel.

Lindal Hotel

21 bedroom hotel in central Harrow, five minutes from rail and tube stations. Extensive car park. ★ Colour TV, telephone and tea & coffee making facilities in all rooms ★ En suite rooms ★ Bar & lounge ★ Restaurant ★ Conference room ★ Wembley Complex Centre — 6 mins by tube, Baker Street — 12 mins by tube.

2 Hindes Road, Harrow HA1 1SJ.
Telephone: 01-863 3164

HARWICH
Essex
Map **5** TM23

GH Hotel Continental 28/29 Marine Pde, Dovercourt Bay ☎(0255) 503454

Small private hotel run by friendly and hospitable owners.

15hc (5fl) (5fb) CTV in all bedrooms Ⓡ ✱B&b£16–£21 Bdi£22–£30 LDO8.30pm

Lic 🍽 4P

Credit cards 1 2 3

HASTINGS & ST LEONARDS
East Sussex
Map **5** TQ80

GH Argyle 32 Cambridge Gdns ☎(0424) 421294
Closed Xmas

Homely and well situated guesthouse near the sea front and local amenities.

8hc (2fl) (3fb) ✗ Ⓡ ✱B&bfr£9 WB&bfr£56

🍽 CTV P nc5yrs

GH *Chimes Hotel* 1 St Matthews Gdns, Silverhill, St Leonards (Guestaccom) ☎(0424) 434041

Relaxing Edwardian house with good home cooking and friendly proprietors.

9hc (2⇌ 2fl) (2fb) CTV in 9 bedrooms ✗ Ⓡ LDO2pm

Lic 🍽 CTV P

GH Eagle House 12 Pevensey Rd, St Leonards ☎(0424) 430535

Situated in residential area, offering comfortable modern accommodation and period bar-lounge.

15hc (2⇌ 9fl) CTV in all bedrooms Ⓡ B&b£19–£23 Bdi£29–£33 WBdifr£231 LDO7.30pm

Lic 🍽 13P nc

Credit cards 1 2 3 5

GH Gainsborough Hotel 5 Carlisle Pde ☎(0424) 434010

Well-maintained sea-front house with modern well-equipped bedrooms and comfortable public rooms.

14hc (3⇌ 5fl) (3fb) CTV in all bedrooms Ⓡ ✱B&b£11.50–£14 Bdi£16.50–£19 WBdifr£132 LDO4.30pm

Lic 🍽 P

Ⓥ

GH Harbour Lights 20 Cambridge Gdns ☎(0424) 423424
Closed 4 days Xmas

Small, conveniently situated town centre guesthouse.

8hc (1fb) CTV in all bedrooms ✗ Ⓡ B&b£8.50–£10.50 WB&bfr£60

🍽 CTV P

GH Tower Hotel 28 Tower Rd West, St Leonards ☎(0424) 427217

A quiet and very comfortable house well away from the sea front. Unrestricted street parking.

8hc (1⇌) (2fb) CTV in all bedrooms Ⓡ B&bfr£9.50 Bdifr£14.50 WBdifr£92

Lic 🍽 CTV P

GH Waldorf Hotel 4 Carlisle Pde ☎(0424) 422185

Homely, friendly accommodation with nicely appointed restaurant and lounge.

12hc (3⇌ 1fl) (3fb) CTV in all bedrooms ✗ Ⓡ B&b£11.50–£17.50 Bdi£16.50–£23.50 WBdi£110–£140 LDO11.30am

Lic CTV P

HASWELL PLOUGH
Co Durham
Map **12** NZ34

GH The Gables Front St ☎091-526 2982

A comfortable house with very friendly proprietors. Dinner, in the public restaurant, can be especially recommended.

5hc (3fb) CTV in all bedrooms ✗ B&b£11.50–£15 LDO9.30pm

Lic 🍽 20P

Ⓥ

See advertisement under Durham

HATHERLEIGH
Devon
Map **2** SS50

INN Bridge Bridge St ☎Okehampton (0837) 810357

4hc (1fb) Ⓡ B&b£10.50–£13.50 Bar lunch £2.80–£5 Dinner 9.30pm £7.90–£14.95 &alc

🍽 CTV 20P nc5yrs

Ⓥ

HATHERSAGE
Derbyshire
Map **8** SK28

FH Mrs T C Wain **Highlow Hall** *(SK219802)* ☎Hope Valley (0433) 50393
mid Mar–Oct

16th-century house of character with well-furnished interior in isolated position south of Hathersage.

6hc (2fb) Ⓡ ✱B&bfr£13 WB&bfr£84

Lic CTV 12P 900acres sheep

HATTON
Warwickshire
Map **4** SP26

Selected

FH Mrs S M Fenwick **Northleigh** *(SP225693)* Five Ways Rd ☎Haseley Knob (092687) 203

Credit must be given to Sylvia Fenwick who runs this super hotel with great charm and skill. Accommodation is of a high standard with many thoughtful extras in the individually designed bedrooms. Breakfasts are wholesome and filling, prepared by this most hospitable hostess.

4hc (2⇌ 4fl) CTV in all bedrooms Ⓡ B&b£14–£22 Bdi£22.50–£30.50

🍽 CTV 6P 16acres sheep

Ⓥ

See advertisement under Warwick

HAUGH OF URR
Dumfries & Galloway *Kirkcudbrightshire*
Map **11** NX86

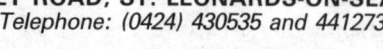

⊢⊣**FH** Mrs G J MacFarlane **Markfast** *(NX817682)* ☎(055666) 220

A comfortable house offering a nice mix of traditional and modern, spacious bedrooms. 1m E of village.

3hc ✗ Ⓡ B&bfr£8.50 Bdifr£13 WBdifr£91 LDO4pm

CTV 3P 140acres mixed

Ⓥ

HAWKSHEAD
Cumbria
Map **7** SD39

GH Greenbank Hotel ☎(09666) 497

Charming and friendly little hotel in 17th century former farmhouse.

10hc (2fl) Ⓡ B&b£13–£15 Bdi£18–£22 WBdi£125–£140 LDO5pm

Lic 🍽 CTV 12P

Ⓥ

GH *Highfield House Hotel* Hawkshead Hill ☎(09666) 344

Delightful lakeland house with spacious rooms.

12hc (3⇌) (3fb) CTV in 3 bedrooms LDO6.30pm

Lic 🍽 CTV 15P

GH Ivy House ☎(09666) 204
Mar–Oct

Attractive, well furnished Georgian house.

6hc (2⇌ 3fl) Annexe: 5hc (3fb) Ⓡ B&b£13–£14.50 Bdi£19.25–£20.75 WBdi£113.75–£124.25 LDO6pm

Lic 🍽 CTV 14P

Ⓥ

GH Rough Close Country House ☎(09666) 370
Apr–Oct rs Mar

A fine country house overlooking the Esthwaite Water and set in lovely gardens. Guests are assured of a friendly welcome and very comfortable accommodation. Excellent, home-cooked dinner of five courses.

6hc (2fb) ✗ Ⓡ B&b£13.50 Bdi£19–£21 WBdifr£133 LDO7pm

Haugh of Urr — Hayfield

Lic 🍽 CTV 10P nc5yrs

Ⓥ

GH Summer Hill Cottage Country House Hotel Hawkshead Hill ☎(09666) 311
Mar–Nov rs Jan, Feb & Dec

17th-century country residence transformed into comfortable and friendly little hotel, serving good home cooking.

7hc (1⇌ 4fl) (1fb) CTV in all bedrooms ✗ Ⓡ ✱B&b£12.50–£17 Bdi£21–£25.50 WBdi£131.50–£161.50 LDO7pm

Lic 🍽 10P nc8yrs

Ⓥ

FH Mr & Mrs Chandler **Walker Ground Manor** *(SD349981)* ☎(09666) 219

A charming 400-year-old stone house, set in lovely gardens, embellished by oak beams and antiques, including Jacobean and Regency four-poster beds. Good home cooking is served by the affable proprietors.

3hc (2⇌ 1fl) ⊁ in all bedrooms ✗ Ⓡ B&b£15–£25 Bdi£23–£35 WBdi£161–£245 LDO6pm

🍽 CTV 6P nc12yrs 17½acres sheep cattle

Ⓥ

INN King's Arms Hotel ☎(09666) 372

16th-century inn with oak beams and open fire, overlooking the village square.

6hc (3fl) (2fb) CTV in all bedrooms Ⓡ B&b£13–£16.50 Bdi£17–£26.50 WBdi£126–£185.50 Lunch £4.85–£8.60 Dinner 9pm£4.85–£8.40&alc

🍽 ⇼

⊢⊣**INN Red Lion** The Square ☎(09666) 213
Closed Xmas Day

This delightful village inn featuring log stoves and oak beams offers comfortable accommodation and good food.

8fl (2fb) ✗ ✱B&bfr£16.50 Bdifr£24 WBdifr£160 Lunch £1.95–£6.50 Dinner 9pm£4.95–£7.95&alc

🍽 CTV 8P

Credit cards 1 3

HAWNBY
North Yorkshire
Map **8** SE58

INN Hawnby Hotel ☎Bilsdale (04396) 202

A stone-built country inn of some age and character standing on a hillside position in the centre of an unspoilt village in the North York Moors.

4⇌ CTV in all bedrooms ✗ Ⓡ ✱B&b£19–£23 Bdi£25–£29 Bar lunch 80p–£3.50 Dinner 8pm £8.50

🍽 8P ⌡

HAWORTH
West Yorkshire
Map **7** SE03

GH Ferncliffe Hebden Rd ☎(0535) 43405

Modern style house/restaurant situated in elevated position overlooking the Worth valley.

6fl (1fb) CTV in all bedrooms Ⓡ ✱B&b£14.50–£18.50 Bdi£19.75–£23.75 WBdifr£138.25 LDO9pm

Lic 🍽 CTV 12P

Credit card 3

HAYFIELD
Derbyshire
Map **7** SK08

INN *Sportsman* Kinder Rd ☎New Mills (0663) 42118

Traditional country inn, with well-furnished, modern bedrooms, in valley of the River Set on the approach to Kinder Scout.

7hc (5fl) (1fb) CTV in all bedrooms Ⓡ LDO10.30pm

🍽

Credit cards 1 3

HAY-ON-WYE
Powys
Map **3** SO24

GH York House Hardwick Rd, Cusop ☎(0497) 820705
rs Xmas
Comfortable, reasonably priced accommodation in large Victorian house in extensive gardens with views of Black Mountains.
6hc (1fb) ⊬ in 6 bedrooms B&b£10–£11 Bdi£16.50–£17.50 WBdifr£103.95 LDO5pm
CTV 8P
Ⓥ

HEASLEY MILL
Devon
Map **3** SS73

GH Heasley House ☎North Molton (05984) 213
Closed Feb
Georgian style building, full of atmosphere and antiques, overlooking mill stream.
8hc (2⇌ 3fl) B&b£10.50–£12.50 Bdi£16.20–£18.20 WBdifr£105
Lic CTV 11P
Ⓥ

HEATHROW AIRPORT
Greater London
London plan **4** A3

GH Shepiston Lodge 31 Shepiston Ln, Hayes ☎01-573 0266
Closed Xmas & New Year
An attractive house offering comfortable accommodation and pleasant public rooms situated near to Heathrow.
13hc (3fb) CTV in all bedrooms
*B&b£14.50–£19.50
CTV 12P nc8yrs

HELSBY
Cheshire
Map **7** SJ47

GH Poplars 130 Chester Rd ☎(09282) 3433
Closed 25–31 Dec
Large detached house in own grounds.
6hc (2fb) TV in all bedrooms B&b£12–£15 WB&bfr£84
CTV 10P

HELSTON
Cornwall
Map **2** SW62

Within a short radius of this town there are AA-listed farmhouses at the following locations: (see appropriate gazetteer entry for full details) **Coverack Bridges & Trenear**

GH Hillside Godolphin Rd ☎(0326) 574788
Small stone-built residence, a few minutes walk from town centre.
7hc (4fb) Ⓡ B&b£8–£9 Bdi£11–£12 WBdifr£77 LDO10am
Lic CTV 6P

GH Strathallan Monument Rd ☎(0326) 573683
On the edge of town, a recently extended, Georgian house, with friendly atmosphere.
7hc (3fl) (1fb) CTV in all bedrooms Ⓡ B&b£8.50–£13.50 Bdi£14.50–£19.50 WBdifr£101.50 LDO6pm
Lic CTV 7P 1

GH *Wheal Tor Hotel* 29 Godolphin Rd ☎(0326) 561211
Situated on a main road, two minutes walk from the town centre.
8hc (1fl) (2fb) CTV in 5 bedrooms LDO7pm
Lic CTV snooker

HEMEL HEMPSTEAD
Hertfordshire
Map **4** TL00

GH Southville Private Hotel 9 Charles St ☎(0442) 51387
Comfortable family hotel in residential road.
14hc (2fb) TV in all bedrooms Ⓡ B&b£15–£19
CTV 8P
Ⓥ

HENFIELD
West Sussex
Map **4** TQ21

FH Mrs M Wilkin **Great Wapses** *(TQ243192)* Wineham (Guestaccom) ☎(0273) 492544
Part 16th-century and part Georgian farmhouse set in rural surroundings, with horses, calves and chickens. 3m NE off B2116.
3hc (2⇌ 1fl) (2fb) CTV in all bedrooms Ⓡ
*B&b£10–£15
7P 1 33acres mixed

HENLEY-IN-ARDEN
Warwickshire
Map **7** SP16

GH Ashleigh House Whitley Hill ☎(05642) 2315
Comfortable and welcoming hotel in peaceful area. Interesting gardens.
6hc (1⇌ 5fl) TV in all bedrooms Ⓡ B&b16.50–£35 WB&b£105–£140
CTV 11P nc5yrs
Credit cards 1 3 Ⓥ

HENLEY ON THAMES
Oxfordshire
Map **4** SU78

GH Flohr's Hotel & Restaurant Northfield End ☎(0491) 573412
Simply furnished modern bedrooms together with a high quality formal restaurant.
9hc (1⇌ 2fl) (4fb) CTV in all bedrooms Ⓡ B&b£22–£24.50 LDO10pm
Lic 6P
Credit cards 1 2 3 5 Ⓥ

HENSTRIDGE
Somerset
Map **3** ST71

FH Mrs P J Doggrell **Toomer** *(ST708192)*
Templecombe ☎Milborne Port (0963) 250237
200-year-old stone-built farmhouse with large walled garden with an Elizabethan dovecote. 1½m W then S off A30.
3rm (2hc) (2fb) CTV in 1 bedroom TV in 1 bedroom ✱ Ⓡ
CTV 6P 400acres arable dairy
Ⓥ

HEREFORD
Hereford & Worcester
Map **3** SO54
See also **Kingstone** & **Little Dewchurch**

GH *Breinton Court* Lower Breinton (2m W unclass on N side of River Wye)
☎(0432) 268156
Apr–Oct
Peaceful and relaxing accommodation on the banks of the River Wye.
6hc (1fb) TV in all bedrooms ✱ Ⓡ
CTV 8P grass

GH Ferncroft Hotel 144 Ledbury Rd
☎(0432) 265538
Closed mid Dec–1st Jan
11hc (4) (2fb) CTV in all bedrooms ✱
B&b£15–£20 Bdi£22–£27 WBdifr£137
LDO7.30pm
Lic CTV 8P
Credit cards 1 3

Selected

GH Hermitage Manor Canon Pynon ($3\frac{1}{2}$m W off A4110 towards Canon Pynon) ☎(0432) 760317
Mar–Dec

Set in eleven acres of grounds overlooking rural Herefordshire, this elegant manor house combines an air of luxury with a warm friendly atmosphere. Mrs Hickling has refitted the bedrooms to a high standard, all with private facilities and thoughtful extras. Guests can relax in the oak panelled hall lounge which features an open log fire, or the smaller yet elegant non-smoking lounge. A substantial English breakfast is served each morning.

3hc (2⇌ 1fl) CTV available in bedrooms ✗ ® available in bedrooms B&b£12.50–£17.50 WB&b£87.50–£105

CTV 12P 2 nc10yrs

GH White Lodge Hotel 50 Ledbury Rd ☎(0432) 273382

Modest, competitive hotel offering personal service.

7hc (1⇌ 2fl) CTV in all bedrooms ✗ ✱B&b£12.50–£17 Bdi£20–£24.50 LDO5.30pm

Lic 12P nc12yrs

Credit card 3

FH Mrs R A Price **Dinedor Court** *(SO545368)* Dinedor (3m SE B4399) ☎Holme Lacy (043273) 481
Mar–Nov

A long drive leads to this peacefully located 16th-century farmhouse that has attractive well-kept gardens and access to the Rive Wye.

3rm (2hc) (1fb) ® ✱B&bfr£9.50 Bdifr£15 LDO4pm

CTV 6P nc10yrs (grass) 220acres arable beef

FH Mrs M J Barrell **Orchard** *(SO575384)* (Mordiford 3m E off B4224) ☎Holme Lacy (043273) 253
Closed Xmas

3hc in all bedrooms ® B&b£9–£10 Bdi£14.50 WBdifr£90 LDO7pm

Lic CTV P 57acres sheep mixed

Ⓥ

HERNE BAY
Kent
Map **5** TR16

GH Northdown Hotel 14 Cecil Park (Guestaccom) ☎(0227) 372051

Friendly small hotel with good bedrooms and quite spacious ground floor facilities.

5hc (1fl) (2fb) CTV in all bedrooms ✗ ® ✱B&b£12–£15

Lic CTV 10P

Ⓥ

Hereford — Higham

HERSTMONCEUX
East Sussex
Map **5** TQ61

GH Cleavers Lyng Country Hotel Church Rd (Guestaccom) ☎(0323) 833131
Closed Xmas & New Year rs Jan

Comfortable rooms and restaurant are features of this 16th-century house in rural setting near the Royal Greenwich Observatory.

8hc ® B&b£12–£12.75 Bdi£16.95–£18.50 WBdi£108.50–£120 LDO6pm

Lic CTV 15P

HESKET NEWMARKET
Cumbria
Map **11** NY33

GH *Denton House* ☎Caldbeck (06998) 415

Large 17th century house with new restaurant extension.

6hc (2fb) LDO8pm

Lic CTV 6P

HETHERSGILL
Cumbria
Map **12** NY46

FH Mr & Mrs Elwen **New Pallyards** *(NY469713)* (3m N unclass) ☎Nicholforest (022877) 308

A modern farmhouse situated $5\frac{1}{2}$ miles east of Longtown on the Stapleton Rd affording pretty bedrooms and comfortable lounges in a friendly atmosphere.

3hc (2⇌) (1fb) ® B&bfr£10 Bdifr£15.50 LDO8pm

CTV 8P 65acres beef sheep mixed

Ⓥ

HEWISH
Avon
Map **3** ST46

GH Kara ☎Yatton (0934) 834442

Small, personally run, period house with an attractive garden. 3m from Weston-Super-Mare & 1m from M5 junction 21..

5hc (2fb) TV in 1 bedroom ® B&b£9–£9.50 Bdi£14–£14.50 WBdifr£91 LDO3pm

Lic CTV 5P

See advertisement under Weston-Super-Mare

HEXHAM
Northumberland
Map **12** NY96

GH Westbrooke Hotel Allendale Rd ☎(0434) 603818

Detached Victorian house with a pretty little garden. Well-appointed and comfortable bedrooms.

7hc (1fl) (1fb) in 2 bedrooms CTV in 1 bedroom ® B&b£13–£13.50

Lic CTV 3P snooker

Credit cards 1 3 Ⓥ

HEYSHAM
Lancashire
Map **7** SD46

GH *Carr-Garth* Bailey Ln ☎(0524) 51175
Etr–Oct

A family-owned house of character with small walled garden.

10hc (3fb) LDO4pm

CTV 8P

HICKLING
Norfolk
Map **9** TG42

GH *Jenter House* Town St ☎(069261) 372
Mar–Nov

10hc (1fb) in 1 bedroom TV in 1 bedroom LDO4pm

CTV 10P

HIGHAM
Lancashire
Map **7** SD83

FH Mrs G Taylor **Cappers** *(SD814388)* Wellhead Lane Sabdenford (2m N unclass off A6068) ☎(0282) 602092
Etr–Oct

3hc (2⇌) (1fb) CTV in all bedrooms ✗ ® B&bfr£16.50

CTV P (heated) 18acres sheep

HIGHAM
Suffolk
Map **5** TM03

Selected

GH Old Vicarage ☎(020637) 248

Featured as one of the best newcomers in 1985, this timber-framed 16th-century house is located just 1 mile from the A12. Bedrooms in both the house and its adjoining barn annexe have excellent private facilities, most are en-suite. Breakfast is a feature here with a 'help-yourself' farmhouse family-style platter. Evening meals are not served.

3hc (2⇌) Annexe: 2hc (1⇌) (1fb) CTV in all bedrooms ® B&b£16–£25

CTV 10P (hard)

Ⓥ

HIGH CATTON
North Yorkshire
Map **8** SE75

FH Mrs S Foster **High Catton Grange** *(SE128541)* ☎Stamford Bridge (0759) 71374
mid Jan–Nov
Substantial, well-kept farmhouse with an attractive garden.

3rm (1hc) (1fb)

🏠 TV 6P 300acres mixed

HIGHER BURWARDSLEY
Cheshire
Map **7** SJ45

INN Pheasant Inn
☎Tattenhall (0829) 70434

6⇌ fl CTV in all bedrooms ✗ Ⓡ B&b£22–£24 Bdi£30–£32 WBdifr£200 Bar lunch 80p–£4.30 Dinner 9.30pm£8–£10&alc

🏠 CTV 60P ⛟ nc14yrs

Credit cards 1 2 3 5 Ⓥ

See advertisement under Chester

HIGH WYCOMBE
Buckinghamshire
Map **4** SU89

GH Amersham Hill 52 Amersham Hill
☎(0494) 20635
Closed Xmas & New Year
Small, friendly place to stay.

7hc CTV in all bedrooms ✗ Ⓡ ✱B&b£23–£25 WB&b£161–£175

🏠 9P

GH Clifton Lodge Private Hotel
210 West Wycombe Rd ☎(0494) 40095
Closed 10 days Xmas
Comfortable guesthouse that has recently undergone major refurbishment of its bedrooms. Friendly and enthusiastic proprietress.

20hc (5⇌ 5fl) (2fb) CTV in all bedrooms ✗ Ⓡ B&b£19.55–£32.20 Bdi£30–£42.20 WBdifr£210 LDO8.45pm

Lic 🏠 CTV 17P

Credit cards 1 2 5

GH Drake Court Hotel London Rd
☎(0494) 23639
Closed Xmas wk
A friendly, family-style hotel, ½m from town centre, with separate lounge and bar.

19hc (2⇌ 1fl) (3fb) CTV in all bedrooms ✗ Ⓡ B&b£22.43–£29.90 Bdi£32.43–£39.90 WBdifr£227.01 LDO8.30pm

Lic 🏠 CTV 18P ⛍

Credit cards 1 2 3 5

HIMBLETON
Hereford & Worcester
Map **3** SO95

FH Mrs P Harvard **Phepson** *(SO941599)*
☎(090569) 205
Closed Xmas & New Year
Children are especially welcome at this peaceful, family-run stock farm in the heart of the English countryside.

3hc (1fb) Ⓡ ✱B&b£9.50–£10 Bdi£15.50–£16 WBdifr£105 LDOnoon

CTV 6P ♨

170acres beef sheep

Ⓥ

HITCHAM
Suffolk
Map **5** TL95

⊢⊣**FH** Mrs B Elsden **Wetherden Hall** *(TL971509)* ☎Bildeston (0449) 740412
Closed Jan & Dec
Part Tudor style farmhouse close to the ruins of a former hall offering friendly accommodation. 1m W of unclass road to Kettlebaston.

3rm (1fb) ✗ B&b£9–£10.50 WB&b£55–£60

🏠 CTV 6P nc10yrs 300acres mixed

Ⓥ

HOARWITHY
Hereford & Worcester
Map **3** SO52

FH Mrs C Probert **Old Mill** *(SO546294)* ☎Carey (043270) 602

Small, white, cottage-style farmhouse in village centre with traditional English country front garden.

4rm (3hc) in 1 bedroom B&b£9–£10 Bdi£14–£15 WBdifr£75 LDO7pm

CTV 4P

6acres calf rearing

HOCKHAM, GREAT
Norfolk
Map **5** TL99

FH Mrs E M Morfoot **Church Cottage** *(TL957946)* Breckles (1m N A1075) ☎(095382) 286
Closed 20 Dec–4 Jan

Farmhouse-style accommodation set in two acres of smallholding, gardens and paddock with an outdoor heated swimming pool. There is access to a two-acre coarse fishing lake one mile from the cottage.

4rm (3hc) B&b£10.50–£11 Bdi£16.50–£17 LDOnoon

CTV 10P nc10yrs (heated)

2acres smallholding

HOLBETON
Devon
Map **2** SX65

FH Mrs J A Baskerville **Keaton** *(SX595480)* ☎(075530) 255
Apr–Sep

Large, stone-built and well-maintained farmhouse in isolated rural position. Yachting at Newton Ferrers 3m away.

3rm (1fb) in all bedrooms B&b£9–£10 WB&bfr£53

CTV 3P nc5yrs 117acres beef

Ⓥ

HOLLYBUSH
Strathclyde *Ayrshire*
Map **10** NS31

Hoarwithy — Holsworthy

FH Mrs A Woodburn **Boreland** *(NS400139)* ☎Patna (0292) 531228
Jun–Sep

Two-storey farmhouse with roughcast exterior, situated on the banks of the River Doon. West off A713 south of village.

3rm (2fb) Ⓡ B&b£9–£10

CTV 6P 126acres dairy

HOLMFIRTH
West Yorkshire
Map **7** SE10

INN White Horse Scholes Rd, Jackson Bridge ☎(0484) 683940
Closed Xmas Eve, Xmas Day & New Years Eve rs 26–30 Dec

Warm and welcoming inn of traditional Pennine stone, close to a stream. 3m E A616 towards Sheffield.

5hc (3fb) CTV in 1 bedroom TV in 4 bedrooms Ⓡ B&b£11.50–£14 Bdi£16.50–£19 WBdifr£115 Lunch £1.10–£4.85&alc High tea £1.45–£3.20 Dinner 10pm £1.65–£4.88

12P 1

Credit card 3 Ⓥ

HOLMROOK
Cumbria
Map **6** SD09

GH Carleton Green Saltcoats Rd ☎(09404) 608
Mar–Oct

A delightful house in rural setting, run by a local couple.

7hc (2 1) (2fb) Ⓡ B&b£10–£11 Bdi£16–£17 WBdifr£96 LDOam

Lic CTV 7P

HOLNE
Devon
Map **3** SX76

Selected

FH S Townsend **Wellpritton** *(SX716704)* ☎Poundsgate (03643) 273
Closed Xmas day & Boxing day

Tastefully modernised farmhouse in Dartmoor National Park. There are panoramic views and the farm has its own swimming pool.

5hc (1 3) Ⓡ *B&b£10–£11 Bdi£15–£17 WBdifr£98 (W only Jul & Aug) LDO6pm

CTV 6P 15acres goats pigs sheep mixed

Ⓥ

INN *Church House* ☎Poundsgate (03643) 208

6hc CTV in 5 bedrooms TV in 1 bedroom Ⓡ Dinner 9.30pm

7P nc5yrs

Credit cards 1 3

HOLNEST
Dorset
Map **3** ST60

FH Mrs J Mayo **Almhouse** *(ST651082)* (S off A352 on unclass road towards Hermitage) ☎(096321) 296
Mar–Oct

3hc Ⓡ *B&b£8.50–£10 Bdi£13–£14 LDO2pm

CTV 4P

140acres dairy sheep

HOLSWORTHY
Devon
Map **2** SS30

GH Coles Mill ☎(0409) 253313
Etr–Oct

Comfortable and well equipped converted mill house.

5 TV in all bedrooms Ⓡ B&b£10–£13 Bdi£16.50–£19.50 WBdi£91–£107 LDO5pm

Lic CTV 12P nc6yrs

FH Mr & Mrs E Cornish **Leworthy** *(SS323012)* ☎(0409) 253488

Low, white-fronted farmhouse with attractive garden facing open country.

10hc (3⫛) (5fb) ✖ Ⓡ B&b£11.50–£13.50 Bdi£17–£20 WBdi£100–£125

Lic CTV 20P 2🚗 ⩠ ⚲ ⤶ Ư 235acres mixed

Ⓥ

HOLT
Clwyd
Map **7** SJ35

↦**FH** Mrs G M Evans **New** *(SJ394538)* Commonwood ☎Farndon (0829) 270358
Closed 21–31 Dec

Small, comfortable and cosy farm.

2rm ✖ B&bfr£9 WB&bfr£60

♛ CTV 4P 92acres dairy sheep

HOLT
Norfolk
Map **9** TG03

GH Lawns Hotel Station Rd ☎(0263) 713390

This Georgian house, previously part of Gresham Public School, offers fresh home cooking.

11hc (2⇔) (2fb) Ⓡ ✱B&b£14–£17 Bdi£21–£24 WBdifr£125 LDO5pm

Lic ♛ CTV 12P

Ⓥ

Holsworthy — Honiton

HOLYHEAD
Gwynedd
Map **6** SH28

↦**GH Witchingham** 20 Walthew Av ☎(0407) 2426

Large, personally run house close to town centre and port. Bright, comfortable rooms.

5hc (1⫛) (2fb) ✖ B&b£8.50–£9 Bdi£13–£14 WBdifr£55 LDO3pm

♛ CTV 3P (charge)

HOLYWELL
Clwyd
Map **7** SJ17

FH Mrs D E Masterman ***Garreg Ganol*** *(SJ157771)* Lloc ☎Mostyn (0745) 560488
Etr–Sep

19th-century farmhouse with well-planned extension, providing good, comfortable accommodation. 3m west of Holywell.

2hc CTV in 1 bedroom TV in 1 bedroom LDO6.45pm

♛ P nc8yrs

10acres beef smallholding

↦**FH** Mrs M D Jones **Green Hill** *(SJ188769)* ☎(0352) 713270
Mar–Nov

15th-century farmhouse completely modernised to provide comfortable accommodation, overlooking the Dee estuary.

5hc (1⇔) (3fb) ✖ B&bfr£9 Bdifr£14 WBdifr£94 LDO9am

CTV 6P ⩠ 120acres dairy mixed

Ⓥ

HONITON
Devon
Map **3** ST10
See also **Feniton** & **Upottery**

GH Old Rectory Northleigh, Colyton (3m SE) ☎Farway (040487) 300

Originally a rectory, dating back to the 1820's, this neat hotel stands in 4½ acres of gardens and paddocks and enjoys fine country views.

3hc (1⇔) CTV in 1 bedroom TV in 2 bedrooms ✖ Ⓡ B&b£12–£15 WB&b£84–£105

♛ 6P 2🚗 nc8yrs

Ⓥ

↦**FH** Mrs I J Underdown **Roebuck** *(ST147001)* (western end of Honiton-by-pass) ☎(0404) 2225

Modern farm 8 miles from the coast.

4hc (1fb) B&b£8.50–£9 Bdi£13 WBdifr£91

♛ CTV P 180acres dairy

INN Monkton Court Monkton (2m E A30) ☎(0404) 2309

8hc (3⇌) (2fb) TV in 4 bedrooms Ⓡ B&b£15–£22 Bdi£20–£27 WBdifr£125 Lunch £5alc Dinner 10pm£9alc

🅿 100P

Ⓥ

HOOK
Hampshire
Map **4** SU75

GH Oaklea London Rd (Guestaccom) ☎(025672) 2673

Detached Victorian house with large walled garden and good home cooking.

10hc (3fl) (1fb) ⊁ in 3 bedrooms Ⓡ in 3 bedrooms B&b£12.50–£26.50 Bdi£21.10–£35 WBdifr£185 LDOnoon

Lic CTV 11P

HOPE COVE
Devon
Map **3** SX63

GH Fern Lodge ☎Kingsbridge (0548) 561326
Apr–Oct rs Mar

Small, friendly house in elevated position overlooking Hope Cove and surrounding countryside. Two bedroom, self-catering flat also available.

5hc (3fl) Annexe: 3hc (2fb) Ⓡ B&b£9.50–£10.50 Bdi£16–£17 WBdi£91–£105 LDO5pm

Lic 🅿 CTV 8P 1🚘 nc3yrs ⛫

GH Sand Pebbles Hotel ☎Kingsbridge (0548) 561673
Mar–Nov

Small, private hotel overlooking Hope Cove, with compact, modern bedrooms.

6hc (3⇌ fl) (2fb) TV available in bedrooms Ⓡ B&b£12–£17 Bdi£20–£23.50 WBdi£154–£180 LDO8.15pm

Lic CTV 14P nc5yrs sauna bath

Ⓥ

HOPTON
Derbyshire
Map **8** SK25

GH Henmore Grange ☎Carsington (062985) 420
rs Xmas Day

Tastefully and cleverly converted farm buildings provide high quality accommodation.

10hc (6⇌ 2fl) (4fb) Ⓡ B&b£18–£20 Bdi£26.50–£28.50 WBdifr£185.50 LDO7.30pm

CTV 14P ♿

Ⓥ

HORLEY
Surrey
For accommodation details see under **Gatwick Airport**

HORNS CROSS
Devon
Map **2** SS32

⊢⊣**FH** Mrs B Furse **Swanton** *(SS355227)* ☎Clovelly (02373) 241
Closed Dec

Modern dormer-style bungalow pleasantly situated overlooking the Bristol Channel.

3rm (2hc) (2fb) ✖ B&bfr£7.50 Bdifr£11 WBdifr£72 LDO2pm

🅿 CTV P 60acres dairy

HORNSEA
Humberside
Map **8** TA24

GH Hotel Seaforth Esplanade ☎(04012) 2616

A large house overlooking the bowling green with sea views from the front. Cosy atmosphere.

7hc (3fb) CTV in 4 bedrooms Ⓡ B&b£9.50 Bdi£14.75 WBdifr£98 LDO4pm

Lic 🅿 CTV 4P

HORSHAM
West Sussex
Map **4** TQ13

GH Blatchford House 52 Kings Rd ☎(0403) 65317
rs 2 wks Xmas

A converted Georgian house under the personal supervision of the owners who offer comfortable accommodation and a warm, homely atmosphere.

9hc (2⇌ 7fl) (2fb) CTV in all bedrooms Ⓡ ✱B&bfr£20.25–£28.50

🅿 12P

GH Wimblehurst Hotel 6 Wimblehurst Rd ☎(0403) 62319

Detached house with modern bedrooms, also catering for non smokers.

14hc (4⇌ 4fl) (2fb) ⊁ in all bedrooms CTV in all bedrooms ✖ Ⓡ B&b£16.99–£39.99 Bdi£25.99–£48.99 LDO6.45pm

🅿 CTV 14P ⛫

Credit card 3

GH Winterpick Corner Winterpit Ln, Manning's Heath ☎(0403) 53882

This small country house enjoys a delightfully peaceful setting. Tastefully-appointed accommodation with comfortable lounge. Situated 2½m S off A281.

4hc (1fb) ✖ Ⓡ B&b£15–£18

🅿 CTV 6P ⛆(heated)

HORSHAM ST FAITH
Norfolk
Map **9** TG21

GH Elm Farm Chalet Hotel Norwich Rd ☎Norwich (0603) 898366
rs Xmas

4hc (1⇌ 1fl) Annexe: 15fl (1fb) CTV in all bedrooms ✖ (ex guide dogs) Ⓡ B&b£15–£22 Bdi£22–£29 WBdi£147–£193 LDO6.30pm

Lic 🅿 CTV 20P

Credit cards 1 3 Ⓥ

HORSMONDEN
Kent
Map **5** TQ74

FH Mrs S M Russell **Pullens** *(TQ689389)* Lamberhurst Rd ☎Brenchley(089272) 2241
Mar–Nov

Black and white farmhouse with warm atmosphere.

3hc (1fb) ✗ Ⓡ B&b£10.50–£13.50 Bdi£16–£17 WBdifr£110

ꟿ CTV 3P 200acres arable hops

HORTON
Dorset
Map **4** SU00

Selected

GH Northill House ☎Witchampton (0258) 840407
Closed 20 Dec–Feb

A converted farmhouse standing in 1½ acres of its own grounds overlooking open farmland. The bedrooms and public rooms are all attractive and good home cooking is served.

5hc (4⇌ 1ꟻ) (1fb) CTV in all bedrooms ✗ Ⓡ ✱B&b£18.50–£32 Bdifr£26 LDO7pm

Lic 9P nc8yrs

Credit cards ⊡1 ⊡3

INN Horton Cranborne Rd ☎Witchampton (0258) 840252

Large detached inn on crossroads. Good food and very well-equipped bedrooms.

5hc (2⇌) CTV in all bedrooms ✗ Ⓡ ✱B&b£17.50–£28 WB&b£105–£168 Lunch fr£6.95 Dinner 10pm£10.95&alc

ꟿ 100P ⇎

Credit cards ⊡1 ⊡3

HORTON-IN-RIBBLESDALE
North Yorkshire
Map **7** SD87

INN Crown Hotel ☎(07296) 209

An attractive Dales pub offering warm and comfortable accommodation

10hc (4fb) ✱B&b£12.60 Bdi£19 WBdifr£120.75 Bar lunch 50p–£2.50 Dinner 6pm£6.33

ꟿ CTV 15P

Credit card ⊡5 Ⓥ

HOUNSLOW
Gt London
London plan **4** B3
(page 258)

GH Shalimar Hotel 219–221 Staines Rd ☎01-572 2816

Modest and informal guesthouse offering friendly personal service.

14hc (4ꟻ) (4fb) CTV in all bedrooms ✗ Ⓡ B&b£20–£25

ꟿ CTV 6P

Credit cards ⊡1 ⊡2 ⊡3 ⊡5 Ⓥ

HOUSESTEADS
Northumberland
Map **12** NY87

Selected

FH Mrs B Haddleston **Beggar Bog** *(NY797686)* ☎Haydon Bridge (04984) 320

4hc (1ꟻ) (1fb) ✗ ✱B&bfr£12 Bdifr£17 LDO8pm

Lic CTV 6P 2⌂ 38acres stock

HOVE
East Sussex
Map **4** TQ20
See **Brighton & Hove**

HOYLAKE
Merseyside
Map **7** SJ28

GH Sandtoft Hotel 70 Alderley Rd ☎051-632 2204

Small guesthouse in a quiet side road close to the Dee estuary.

9hc (1ꟻ) (1fb) CTV available in bedrooms Ⓡ B&b£11.50–£15 Bdi£16.50–£20 WBdi£125 LDO8pm

Lic ꟿ CTV 6P 3⌂

HUBBERHOLME
North Yorkshire
Map **7** SD97

INN George Kirk Gill ☎Kettlewell (075676) 223
Closed Christmas Day evening

Old Dales hostelry in attractive rural surroundings, offering home produced food.

3hc Ⓡ B&b£12.50 WB&bfr£73.50 Bar lunch £3–£4 Dinner 9pm£10alc

ꟿ 20P ⇎ nc8yrs ↲

Ⓥ

HUGHLEY
Shropshire
Map **7** SO59

FH Mrs E Bosworth ***Mill*** *(SO565978)* ☎Brockton (074636) 645

Lovely old house in pleasant rural area beneath Wenlock Edge.

2hc (1ꟻ) (1fb) CTV in 1 bedroom ✗

CTV 4P ↲ U 250acres arable beef

HULL
Humberside
Map **8** TA02

GH Ashford 125 Park Av ☎(0482) 492849
Closed Xmas

Well furnished, comfortable bedrooms are a feature of this end of terrace building in a tree lined street.

6hc (1fb) ✗ Ⓡ B&b£11–£12 Bdi£15.50–£16.50 WBdifr£102 LDO11am

ꟿ CTV 4P

GH Earlesmere Hotel 76–78 Sunny Bank, Spring Bank West ☎(0482) 41977
Closed Xmas rs wknds

15hc (7ꟻ) (4fb) CTV in all bedrooms Ⓡ ✱B&b£16.67–£17.25 Bdi£24.72–£26.45 LDO7pm

Lic ꟿ CTV ⱣP

GH Parkwood Hotel 113 Princes Av ☎(0482) 445610

Terraced town house on bus route with well fitted comfortable bedrooms.

8hc (1fb) CTV in all bedrooms Ⓡ ✱B&b£12.95–£16.68 Bdi£16.65–£24.65 WBdifr£130 LDO8pm

Lic ꟿ CTV ⱣP

Ⓥ

HUNA
Highland *Caithness*
Map **15** ND37

GH Haven Gore ☎John O'Groats (095581) 314

Modernised cottage with matching extension and sea views to Stroma and Orkney Isles.

5hc (3fb) ✱B&b£7.50–£8 WB&bfr£52.50

卌 CTV 8P

Ⓥ

HUNNINGHAM
Warwickshire
Map **4** SP36

FH Mrs R Hancock **Snowford Hall** *(SP386666)* ☎Marton (0926) 632297
Jan–Oct rs Jul–Sep & Xmas

3hc (1fb) ✘ 🚭 in 3 bedrooms ✱B&b£10–£12 Bdi£17.50–£19.50

卌 CTV 4P

250acres arable beef

HUNSTANTON
Norfolk
Map **9** TF64

GH Caley Hall Motel ☎(04853) 33486

20⇌ ⋔ (4fb) CTV in all bedrooms ✱B&bfr£19.50 Bdifr£28 WBdifr£174 LDO9.30pm

Lic 卌 CTV 40P

Credit card [3]

GH Claremont 35 Greevegate ☎(04853) 33171

7hc (3fb) ✘ Ⓡ B&b£10 Bdi£14 WBdifr£87.50

Lic 卌 CTV 2P

Ⓥ

GH Deepdene Hotel 29 Avenue Rd ☎(04853) 2460

Victorian building constructed from local Carstone stone.

9hc (1⇌) (3fb) ✘ Ⓡ B&b£15 Bdi£22.50 WBdifr£150 LDO8pm

Lic 卌 CTV 12P ⊡(heated) sauna bath solarium gymnasium

GH Sunningdale Hotel 3 Avenue Rd ☎(04853) 2562

Small comfortable establishment in a residential road close to the town centre.

11hc (5⇌ 6⋔) CTV in all bedrooms Ⓡ B&b£14–£15 Bdi£20–£21 WBdi£135–£142 LDO6pm

Lic 卌 CTV 3P nc10yrs

Credit cards [1] [3] Ⓥ

GH Sutton House Hotel 24 Northgate ☎(04853) 2552

Family-run house in a quiet residential road close to town.

9hc (1⋔) (3fb) Ⓡ B&b£12–£17 Bdi£18–£23 WBdi£120 LDO7.30pm

Lic CTV 5P

Credit cards [1] [3] Ⓥ

HUNTINGDON
Cambridgeshire
Map **4** TL27

INN Black Bull Post St, Godmanchester ☎(0480) 53310
1m S B1043.

10hc (2fb) CTV in 3 bedrooms Ⓡ B&b£16 Bdi£22 WBdi£138 Lunch £9.50alc Dinner 10pm£1.78–£10&alc

卌 CTV 60P

Credit card [1]

HUNTON
North Yorkshire
Map **7** SE19

INN Countryman's ☎Bedale (0677) 50554

A lovely renovated stone-built inn full of charm and character offering pleasant accommodation.

4hc (1⇌ 3⋔) (1fb) 🚭 in all bedrooms CTV in all bedrooms ✘ Ⓡ B&b£15–£30 WB&bfr£100 Bar lunch £7alc LDO9.30pm

卌 20P ⛟ nc5yrs

Ⓥ

HURSLEY
Hampshire
Map **4** SU42

INN *Kings Head Hotel* ☎Winchester (0962) 75208
Closed Xmas Day
Popular roadside Charrington's house with good-size bedrooms and cosy lounge. Bar serves bistro-type food.
5hc (1fb) ✗ Ⓡ LDO9.30pm
CTV 25P
Credit cards [1] [3]

HUSTHWAITE
North Yorkshire
Map **8** SE57

FH Mrs E Smith **Baxby Manor** *(SE512753)* ☎Coxwold (03476) 572
Closed Xmas
Unspoilt stone-built 13th-century manor with old beams, exposed stone walls and feature fireplace.
3hc (1fb) ✗ Ⓡ ✱B&b£9.50–£14 WBdifr£65
Lift ⊞ CTV 4P nc5yrs ↯ 110acres mixed

HUTTON-LE-HOLE
North Yorkshire
Map **8** SE79

Selected

GH Barn ☎Lastingham (07515) 311
Etr–Oct
A quaint hotel and tea room situated in the centre of this charming village. The bedrooms are prettily decorated and the cosy lounge features a large stone fireplace. In addition the charming tea shop offers an extensive range of light meals, served by the helpful and attentive proprietors.
9hc (2fl) CTV in 2 bedrooms ✗ Ⓡ B&b£12.50–£17
Lic ⊞ CTV 20P nc12yrs

IDOLE
Dyfed
Map **2** SN41

↦**FH** Mr & Mrs A Bowen **Pantgwyn** *(SN419157)* ☎Carmarthen (0267) 235859
Apr–Oct
Spacious rebuilt farmhouse, 3m S of Carmarthen.
2rm (1fb) ✗ B&bfr£8.50
CTV 4P 35acres dairy sheep

ILAM
Staffordshire
Map **7** SK15

FH Mrs S Prince ***Beechenhill*** *(SK129525)* ☎Alstonefield (033527) 274
Closed Xmas
Two-storey, stone-built farmhouse with exposed beams, built around 1720. Situated in unspoilt rural area with panoramic views.
2hc (1fb) ✗ Ⓡ
⊞ CTV 3P 92acres dairy sheep

ILFORD
Gt London
London plan **4** F4
(page 259)

GH Cranbrook Hotel 24 Coventry Rd ☎01-554 6544
Detached corner house in quiet residential area close to main shopping centre. Good comfortable accommodation with extra facilities and a lounge bar.
16hc (13fl) (7fb) CTV in all bedrooms Ⓡ B&b£18.11–£27.97 Bdi£23.61–£33.47 LDO8.30pm
Lic ⊞ CTV 11P 2⛍
Credit cards [1] [2] [3] ⓥ

GH Park Hotel 327 Cranbrook Rd ☎01-554 9616
Modern, family accommodation overlooking Valentines Park.
21hc (5⇌ 6fl) (3fb) CTV in all bedrooms Ⓡ B&b£22.50–£29.75 Bdi£29.50–£36.75 LDO8pm
Lic ⊞ CTV 23P
Credit cards [1] [2] [3]
See advertisement on page 208

ILFRACOMBE
Devon
Map **2** SS54
See plan
For additional accommodation see **West Down**

GH *Avenue Private Hotel* Greenclose Rd ☎(0271) 63767 Plan **1** *B2*
Apr–6 Nov
24hc (3⇌ 3fl) (7fb) ✗ LDO7pm
Lic ⊞ CTV 15P
Credit cards [1] [3]

GH Avoncourt Hotel 6 Torrs Walk Avenue ☎(0271) 62543 Plan **2** *A2*
A purpose-built, modern hotel situated in an elevated position with views over the town.
13hc (6⇌) ✗ ✱B&b£8–£10 Bdifr£12.50 LDO6pm
Lic CTV 10P
Credit card [3]
See advertisement on page 209

GH Briercliffe Hotel 9 Montpelier Ter ☎(0271) 63274 Plan **3** *C2*
Closed Nov
A small personally-run guesthouse with friendly, informal atmosphere. Situated in a quiet elevated position within easy reach of all facilities.
10hc (5fb) B&b£10 Bdi£14 WBdi£84–£94.50 (W only last 2 wks Jul, first 2 wks Aug)
Lic ⊞ CTV 5P

GH Cavendish Hotel 9–10 Larkstone Ter ☎(0271) 63994 Plan **5** *D2*
Etr–Oct
Family-owned private hotel close to town centre. Well-equipped bedrooms with CTV in all rooms.
23hc (15fl) (5fb) CTV in all bedrooms Ⓡ ✱B&b£6.50–£14.50 Bdi£12–£20 WBdifr£75 LDO5pm
Lic ⊞ CTV 20P snooker
See advertisement on page 209

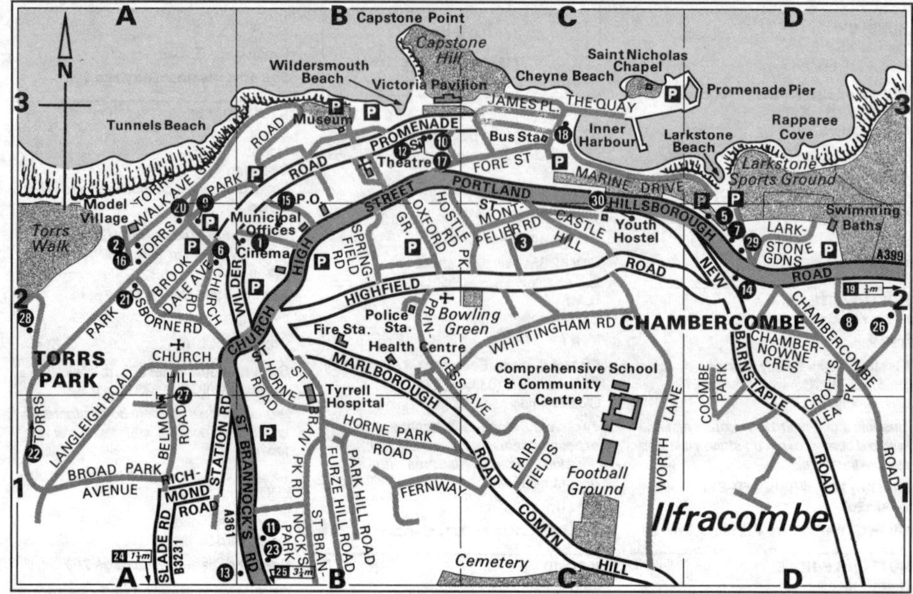

Ilfracombe

1 Avenue Private Hotel
2 Avoncourt Hotel
3 Briercliffe Hotel
5 Cavendish Hotel
6 Chalfont Private Hotel
7 Collingdale Hotel
8 Combe Lodge Hotel
9 Cresta Private Hotel
10 Dèdés Hotel
11 Earlsdale Hotel
12 Glendower
13 Lantern House Hotel
14 Laston House Private Hotel
15 Lympstone Private Hotel
16 Merlin Court Hotel
17 Queens Court Hotel
18 Royal Britannia *(Inn)*
19 Rosebank Hotel
20 Seven Hills Hotel
21 Southcliffe Hotel
22 South Tor Hotel
23 Strathmore Private Hotel
24 Sunny Hill
25 Sunnymeade Country House Hotel (listed under West Down)
26 Varley House
27 Wentworth House Private Hotel
28 Westwell Hall Hotel
29 Wilson
30 Wychbury Hotel

GH Chalfont Private Hotel 21 Church Rd
☎(0271) 62224 Plan **6** *A2*
Mar–Oct
Small well-maintained guesthouse in residential area close to beach and shops. Friendly atmosphere and neat bright accommodation. Traditional home cooking is the order of the day using fresh local produce whenever possible.
13hc (2fl) (6fb) Ⓡ B&b£10.50–£11.50
Bdi£15–£16 WBdifr£95 LDO5pm
Lic ♛ CTV P
Credit cards 1 3 V

GH *Collingdale Hotel* Larkstone Ter
☎(0271) 63770 Plan **7** *D2*
Jan–Oct
9hc (3fb) ✕ Ⓡ
Lic ♛ CTV P
Credit cards 1 3

GH Combe Lodge Hotel
Chambercombe Park Rd ☎(0271) 64518
Plan **8** *D2*
Closed Xmas

9hc (1fl) (3fb) CTV available in bedrooms Ⓡ ✱B&b£9–£10.50 Bdi£13.50–£15 WBdifr£93–£103 LDO3.30pm

Lic 🍽 CTV 8P

Ⓥ

GH *Cresta Private Hotel* Torrs Park ☎(0271) 63742 Plan **9** *A2*
mid May–Sep (rs first half May & first half Oct)

24hc (2fl) (10fb) Ⓡ LDO6.30pm

Lic lift 🍽 CTV 30P

⊢⊣**GH Dèdés Hotel** 1–3 The Promenade ☎(0271) 62545 Plan **10** *B3*
Etr–Oct rs Nov–Etr

Ilfracombe

17hc (7⇌) (6fb) CTV available in 5 bedrooms Ⓡ B&b£8.50–£12 Bdi£13.50–£17 WBdifr£94.50 LDO10pm

Lic CTV 6P

Credit cards 1 2 3 5 Ⓥ

See advertisement on page 210

⊢⊣**GH Earlsdale Hotel** 51 St Brannocks Rd ☎(0271) 62496 Plan **11** *B1*

10hc (4fl) (4fb) CTV in 5 bedrooms ✱ B&b£8.50–£9.50 Bdi£13–£14 WBdi£85–£95 LDO6.30pm

Lic 🍽 CTV 10P

Ⓥ

⊢⊣**GH Glendower** Wilder Rd ☎(0271) 66788 Plan **12** *B3*

Three-storey balconied guesthouse overlooking Jubilee gardens.

9hc (3fb) TV in 2 bedrooms Ⓡ in 4 bedrooms B&b£8.50–£10.50 WB&b£56–£70

Lic CTV 9P

The Avoncourt Hotel

6 TORRS WALK AVENUE, ILFRACOMBE, N. DEVON EX34 8AU. TEL. (0271) 62543.

Avoncourt is a friendly family run hotel situated in a quiet private road adjacent to National Trust land. The hotel enjoys a sunny position facing south with panoramic views of town and countryside. A footpath from the hotel leads to cliff walks and Lee Downs, yet only a few minutes walk from the hotel to the town centre, promenade and harbour. Avoncourt is a modern hotel offering a high level of comfort and service. 13 bedrooms, some ensuite with bath and toilet and some with balconies, TV lounge, cosy licensed bar and ample parking. The excellent food and relaxed atmosphere will help you to enjoy your holiday. Avoncourt is ideally situated for all types of holiday whether exploring the beautiful unspoilt coast, touring Exmoor, walking or relaxing on the beach. Write or phone for brochure to:
David and Gill Ruffle, Torrs Walk Avenue, Ilfracombe, North Devon (0271) 62543.

The Cavendish Hotel

Larkstone Terrace, Ilfracombe, North Devon. Telephone: (0271) 63994

Family owned and managed Hotel offers you Home from Home accommodation. We are situated in the loveliest part of Ilfracombe. Breathtaking Coastal Views can be enjoyed from our Public rooms, and most of our bedrooms, which are tastefully furnished. Tea Making facilities. All bedrooms with Colour TV and most with shower and toilet en suite. Well stocked Bar. Lounge. Games Room. Free Parking. Full English breakfast. Four course evening dinner. (No Hidden Extras).
A real friendly welcome and a Pot of Tea on arrival from your hosts John and Angela Davies.

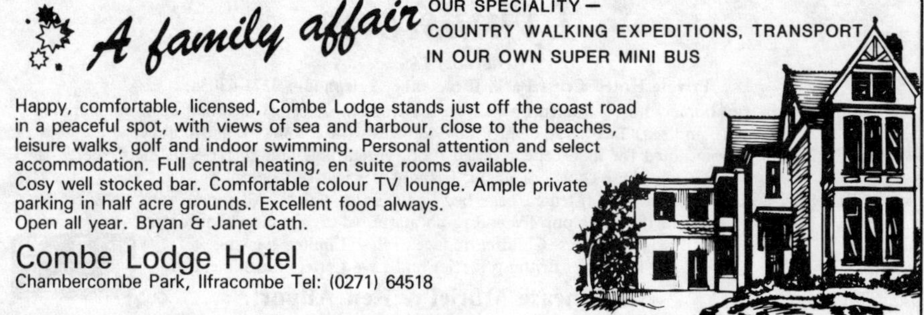

GH Lantern House Hotel
62 St Brannocks Rd ☎(0271) 64401
Plan **13** *B1*

10hc (3fb) B&b£12–£15.50 Bdi£16–£19 WBdifr£98 LDO5.30pm

Lic CTV 8P

Credit card 3 Ⓥ

GH Laston House Private Hotel
Hillsborough Rd ☎(0271) 62627 Plan **14** *D2*

Elegant Georgian house with country house atmosphere set in 2½ acres of wooded grounds and lawned gardens in elevated position overlooking sea and within easy reach of the town centre. Personally-run by the Alexander family who offer friendly services and a good standard of accommodation.

11hc (5⇌ 1fl) (4fb) CTV in all bedrooms Ⓡ *B&b£10–£15 Bdi£15–£19 WBdifr£119 LDO7pm

Lic CTV 20P

Credit cards 1 3

GH Lympstone Private Hotel
14 Cross Park ☎(0271) 63038
Plan **15** *B2*
Mar–Oct

15hc (10fl) (5fb) CTV in all bedrooms Ⓡ B&b£10–£12.50 Bdi£14–£16.50 WBdi£87–£117 LDO5pm

Lic CTV P

Ilfracombe

GH *Merlin Court Hotel* Torrs Park
☎(0271) 62697 Plan **16** *A2*
Apr–Oct

14hc (1⇌) (4fb) Ⓡ LDO6.45pm

Lic CTV 12P

GH Queens Court Hotel Sea Front, Wilder Rd ☎(0271) 63789 Plan **17** *B3*

This centrally located house facing the sea and gardens offers clean, bright bedrooms, comfortable public areas and helpful service.

14rm (1⇌ 3fl) (7fb) CTV in 4 bedrooms *B&b£11.65–£11.95 Bdi£15.70–£17 LDO7pm

Lic CTV 14P

Credit card 3

GH *Rosebank Hotel* 26 Watermouth Rd, Hele Bay ☎(0271) 66488 Plan **19** *D2*
Closed Oct

7hc (2⇌) (2fb) LDO8.30pm

Lic CTV billiards

GH Seven Hills Hotel Torrs Park
☎(0271) 62207 Plan **20** *A2*
Apr–Oct

15hc (5⇌) (4fb) Ⓡ in 5 bedrooms B&b£9.50–£10.50 Bdi£13.50–£14.50 WBdifr£82.50 LDO7pm

Lift CTV 10P nc3yrs

GH Southcliffe Hotel Torrs Park
☎(0271) 62958 Plan **21** *A2*
Spring Bank Hol–Sep

A small family-run hotel offering friendly service and attractive bedrooms.

15fl (10fb) B&b£12.65–£13.80 Bdi£17.25–£18.40 WBdi£101–£109 (W only last 2 wks Jun–Aug) LDO6pm

Lic CTV 11P

Ⓥ

GH South Tor Hotel Torrs Park ☎(0271) 63750 Plan **22** *A1*
Etr–Oct & Xmas

13hc (11fl) (3fb) Ⓡ *B&b£10–£12.50 Bdi£11.50–£16 WBdifr£70 LDO6pm

Lic CTV 12P nc4yrs

GH Strathmore Private Hotel
57 St Brannocks Rd ☎(0271) 62248
Plan **23** *B1*

Modest guesthouse run by friendly owners.

9hc (2⇌ 5fl) (3fb) CTV in all bedrooms Ⓡ *B&b£9–£10 Bdi£14–£15 WBdi£93–£99.75 LDO5pm

Lic CTV 7P

Credit cards 1 2 3 5 Ⓥ

GH Sunny Hill Lincombe ☎(0271) 62953 Plan **24** *A1*
Closed Dec

2m SW off B3231.

6hc (2🚿) (1fb) B&b£14–£16 WB&b£88–£100 LDO8.30pm

Lic 🍽 CTV 6P nc10yrs

GH Varley House 13 Chambercombe Ter, Chambercombe Pk ☎(0271) 63927 Plan **26** *D2*

Well-maintained establishment in residential area within easy reach of sea and shops. Friendly proprietors offer helpful service with a house party atmosphere. Menu offers a limited choice of well-cooked English dishes. Bright bedrooms and attractive, comfortable public rooms.

9hc (3🛁 2🚿) (3fb) CTV in 8 bedrooms TV in 1 bedroom Ⓡ B&b£9.50–£12 Bdi£15–£17.50 WBdi£95–£115 LDO5.30pm

Lic CTV 7P

Credit cards ① ③ Ⓥ

GH *Wentworth House Private Hotel* Belmont Road ☎(0271) 63048 Plan **27** *A1*
Closed Xmas

11hc (1🚿) (4fb)

Lic CTV 11P

GH Westwell Hall Hotel Torrs Park ☎(0271) 62792 Plan **28** *A2*
Mar–Dec

Ilfracombe — Ingham

An attractive detached house in own grounds with car park. Offers well-equipped bedrooms and comfortable public areas.

14hc (7🛁 7🚿) (2fb) CTV in all bedrooms Ⓡ B&b£13–£18 Bdi£21–£24 WBdi£133–£147 LDO8.30pm

Lic 🍽 CTV 14P nc6yrs snooker

Ⓥ

⊢⊣**GH Wilson** 16 Larkstone Ter ☎(0271) 63921 Plan **29** *D2*

Victorian terrace with glorious views over the harbour.

9hc (5fb) ✗ Ⓡ B&b£8–£10 Bdi£12–£14 WBdi£95 LDO5pm

Lic CTV 🅿̸

Ⓥ

GH Wychbury Hotel (formerly Bristol Merchant) 10 Hillsborough Ter ☎(0271) 62141 Plan **30** *C2*

11rm (3fb) CTV in all bedrooms Ⓡ ✱B&b£10–£11.50 Bdi£14.50–£16 LDO7pm

Lic 4P 4🏠

INN *Royal Britannia* The Quay ☎(0271) 62939 Plan **18** *C3*

12hc (2fb) CTV in all bedrooms LDO10pm

CTV 🅿̸ 🏠

Credit cards ① ③

ILKLEY
West Yorkshire
Map **7** SE14

GH Moorview House Hotel 104 Skipton Rd (Guestaccom) ☎(0943) 600156
Closed Xmas

Large Victorian house overlooking valley of the River Wharfe. Lounge furnished with antiques and paintings; good-sized bedrooms.

11hc (1🛁 5🚿) (6fb) CTV in 8 bedrooms TV in 3 bedrooms ✗ Ⓡ B&b£12–£25 Bdi£20.50–£33.50 WB&b£75.60–£156.60 LDO5pm

Lic 🍽 12P 🏠

Ⓥ

See advertisement on page 212

INGHAM
Suffolk
Map **5** TL87

INN *Cadogan Arms* The Street ☎Culford (028484) 226

Fairly modern village pub situated on the A134. →

4hc (2fb) CTV in 3 bedrooms TV in 1 bedroom ✖ Ⓡ LDO9.30pm

ꟿ 80P

Credit cards ☐1 ☐2 ☐3 ☐5

See advertisement under Bury St Edmunds

INGLEBY GREENHOW
North Yorkshire
Map **8** NZ50

FH Mrs M Bloom **Manor House** *(NZ586056)* ☎Great Ayton (0642) 722384
Closed 24–31 Dec

Comfortable accommodation in historic surroundings in National Park at the foot of the Cleveland Hills. Good farmhouse fayre. Ideal for walking and relaxation.

3rm (1fb) ✖ Ⓡ B&bfr£13 Bdifr£21 WBdifr£147 LDO5pm

Lic ꟿ CTV 40P 10🚗 nc12yrs ♩ 164acres mixed

ⓥ

INGLETON
North Yorkshire
Map **7** SD67

GH Langber Country ☎(0468) 41587
Closed Xmas

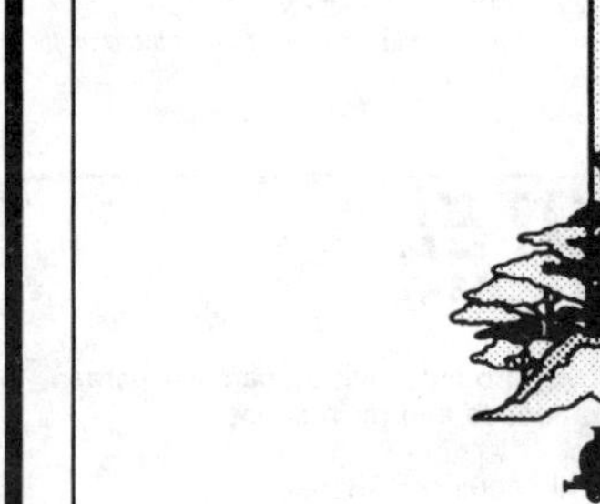

A large detached property in open countryside in an elevated position situated in a quiet country lane about 1m south of Ingleton village. Turn off A65 at 'Masons Arms'.

6hc (4fb) ✱B&b£8.95–£10 Bdi£11.75–£13.75 WBdi£79–£93 LDO5.15pm

ꟿ CTV 6P ⌂

GH Oakroyd Private Hotel Main St ☎(0468) 41258

Formerly the Vicarage, now a small family run hotel with comfortable accommodation and a friendly atmosphere.

8hc (6fb) ✗ Ⓡ B&b£10.50 Bdi£16.50 WBdifr£108.50

Lic 🍽 CTV 9P

Ⓥ

GH Pines Country House Hotel ☎(0468) 41252

Set in ¾ acre of gardens this neat hotel provides attractive accommodation and good food.

4hc (3⇌) (1fb) CTV in all bedrooms ✗ Ⓡ B&b£13.50–£18 Bdi£20–£24.50 LDO6.30pm

Lic 10P 3🏠

GH Springfield Private Hotel Main St ☎(0468) 41280

Jan–Oct

Large Victorian villa. Family-run hotel with homely atmosphere and panoramic views at rear.

6hc (4fl) (4fb) CTV in all bedrooms B&b£9.50–£10.50 Bdi£14.50–£15.50 WBdi£100–£107 LDO5pm

Lic 🍽 CTV 12P

Ⓥ

INGLEWHITE
Lancashire
Map **7** SD54

FH Mrs R Rhodes **Park Head** *(SD542395)* ☎Brock (0995) 40352

A well-furnished farmhouse with old oak beams and offering true Lancashire hospitality.

2rm (1fb) ✗ B&b£10 Bdi£14 WBdifr£90 LDO7pm

🍽 CTV 4P

214acres dairy sheep

INKBERROW
Hereford & Worcester
Map **4** SP05

INN Bulls Head Hotel High St ☎(0386) 792233

8hc (1⇌) ✗Ⓡ ✱B&bfr£15 Bdifr£16.60 Lunch £1.60–£4.95&alc Dinner 9.30pm£1.60–£4.95&alc

🍽 60P ⇄ 🏠

Credit card ③

INSTOW
Devon
Map **2** SS43

GH Anchorage Hotel The Quay ☎(0271) 860655

Mar–Dec

Private hotel on quay, facing river and beach. Excellent views.

11hc (10fl) (2fb) Ⓡ B&b£14–£16 Bdi£19–£22 WBdi£111–£145

Lic CTV 9P

Credit cards ① ③

INVERGARRY
Highland *Inverness-shire*
Map **14** NH30

GH *Craigard* ☎(08093) 258

Mar–Nov

Detached house with spacious bedrooms and comfortable lounges.

7hc Ⓡ LDO7pm

Lic CTV 6P

Ⓥ

⊢GH **Forest Lodge** South Laggan (3m SW A82) ☎(08093) 219

Apr–Oct

7hc (2fb) Ⓡ B&b£9–£12 Bdi£14.25–£19 WBdifr£95 LDO6.30pm

🍽 CTV 10P

⊢GH **Lundie View** Aberchalder ☎(08093) 291

Closed Xmas & New Year

Modernised roadside cottage with extension overlooking pleasant hill and woodland scenery. 3m NE A82. →

5hc (3fb) Ⓡ B&b£8.50–£9 WB&bfr£57

CTV 8P ♿

Ⓥ

FH Mr & Mrs R Wilson **Ardgarry** *(NH286015)* Faichem (Guestaccom) ☎(08093) 226

A comfortable and homely traditional farmhouse, now operating as a small holding. Located about 1m from Invergarry off the A87—signed Faichem.

1hc Annexe: 3hc (1fb) Ⓡ ✱B&b£10 Bdi£14 WBdi£98 (W only Jul & Aug) LDO4pm

CTV 10P nc5yrs 10acres mixed

FH Mr & Mrs O'Connell **Faichem Lodge** *(NH286014)* ☎(08093) 314

Mar–Oct

Beautiful, modernised old stone house with cosy bedrooms and lounge. Although not a working farm the house is set in 1½ acres of farmland and owners keep ducks and hens in the garden. A non-working farm but has access to one.

4hc (1fb) in all bedrooms Ⓡ ✱B&b£9–£9.50 Bdifr£15

CTV 5P 1½acres non-working

INVERKEITHING

Fife

Map **11** NT18

GH *Forth Craig Private Hotel* 90 Hope St ☎(0383) 418440

A smart, modern hotel with comfortable well-equipped bedrooms, popular with businessmen.

5fl CTV in all bedrooms Ⓡ LDO7pm

Lic 8P

INVERNESS

Highland *Inverness-shire*

Map **14** NH64

See plan on page 215

GH Ardnacoille House 1A Annfield Rd ☎(0463) 233451 Plan **2** *D1*

Apr–Oct

Semi-detached house with lovely lounge, in own gardens. Nicely appointed and very well maintained.

6hc (2fb) B&b£10–£10.50 WB&b£67–£70

CTV 8P nc7yrs

GH Arran 42 Union St ☎(0463) 232115 Plan **3** *B2*

Set in upper floors of tenement building in central location between shops.

7hc (2fb) B&b£9–£9.50 WB&bfr£63

TV

GH Brae Ness Hotel 16–17 Ness Bank ☎(0463) 231732 Plan **4** *B1*

Apr–Oct rs, Feb, Mar & Nov

Family run accommodation, situated beside the River Ness and close to town centre.

8hc (7fl) (2fb) CTV in all bedrooms Ⓡ B&b£12–£17 Bdi£18.50–£24 WBdi£115–£147 LDO7.30pm

Lic 6P

Ⓥ

Selected

GH Craigside House 4 Gordon Ter (Guestaccom) ☎(0463) 231576 Plan **5** *C2*

May–Oct rs Nov, Mar & Apr

Isa MacLeod's welcoming Victorian house stands in a quiet residential area overlooking the castle and only a short distance from the main shopping area. The bright, cheerful bedrooms, four which have en suite facilities, are tastefully furnished and thoughtfully equipped. Well-filled bookshelves and magazines are provided for guests seeking relaxation in the comfortable lounge. Good home cooking with fresh local produce is guaranteed, as is the genuine Highland hospitality.

6hc (1⇌ 3fl) CTV in all bedrooms Ⓡ B&b£12–£16 Bdi£18–£22 WBdi£130–£140 LDO5pm

4P nc14yrs

GH Four Winds 42 Old Edinburgh Rd ☎(0463) 230397 Plan **6** *C1*

Closed Xmas & New Year

Detached lodge set in own grounds in residential suburb.

7hc (3fl) (2fb) Ⓡ B&b£10–£11 WB&bfr£70

CTV 15P

Ⓥ

GH Glencairn 19 Ardross St ☎(0463) 232965 Plan **7** *B2*

Closed 2 wks Xmas/New Year

Nicely appointed house in residential street.

11hc (2fb) B&b£9 WB&bfr£63

CTV 4P

GH Leinster Lodge 27 Southside Rd ☎(0463) 233311 Plan **8** *C1*

Closed Xmas & New Year

Large town house with gardens, in a residential area.

6hc (2fb) ✱B&b£9.50–£10 WB&bfr£66.50

CTV 8P

GH Moray Park Hotel Island Bank Rd ☎(0463) 233528 Plan **9** *B1*

Apr–Oct

A stone villa pleasantly situated close to the River Ness. This family-run establishment offers well-equipped bedrooms and a comfortable lounge and bar.

7hc (2⇌ 4fl) (2fb) CTV in all bedrooms Ⓡ B&b£11.50–£14.50 Bdi£19.50–£22.50 WBdi£126–£147 LDO6pm

Lic 7P nc9yrs solarium

Credit card 1

GH Riverside House Hotel 8 Ness Bank ☎(0463) 231052 Plan **10** *B1*

Pleasantly situated beside river. Friendly service and comfortable accommodation.

11hc (5⇌ 5fl) (3fb) CTV in all bedrooms B&b£15–£18 Bdi£22–£24 LDO7pm

Lic CTV

Ⓥ

See advertisement on page 216

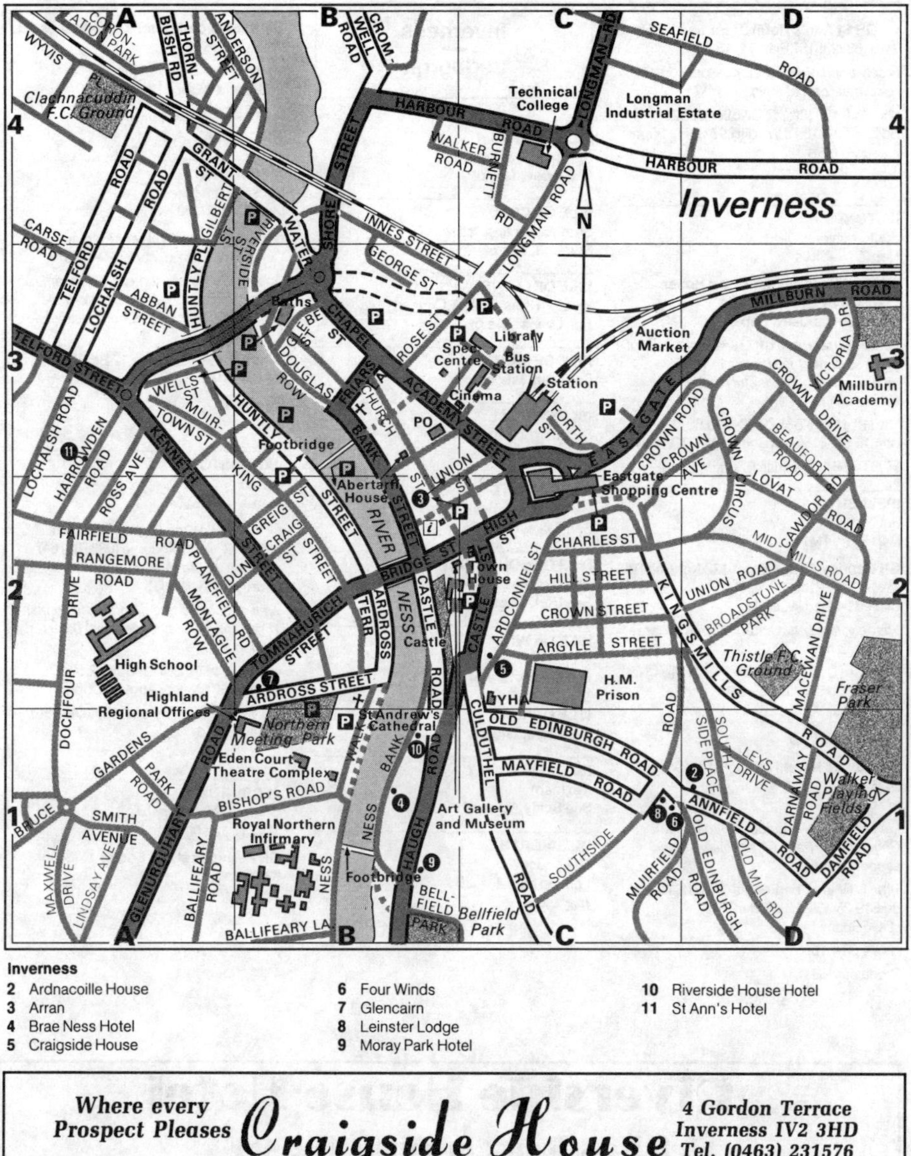

Inverness

2 Ardnacoille House
3 Arran
4 Brae Ness Hotel
5 Craigside House
6 Four Winds
7 Glencairn
8 Leinster Lodge
9 Moray Park Hotel
10 Riverside House Hotel
11 St Ann's Hotel

⊢⊣**GH St Ann's Hotel** 37 Harrowden Rd ☎(0463) 236157 Plan **11** *A3*

Nicely appointed guesthouse in a quiet, residential part of town.

6hc (1⇌ 4⋒) (2fb) Ⓡ B&b£9–£12.25 Bdi£15.50–£18.75 WBdifr£97 LDO3.30pm

Lic 🅼 CTV 3P

Ⓥ

IPSTONES
Staffordshire
Map **7** SK04

FH Mrs J Brindley **Glenwood House** *(SK006488)* ☎(053871) 294
Closed Xmas, Jan & Feb

Large house approx 100 years old, built of dressed sandstone blocks in very picturesque and peaceful rural surroundings.

3hc (1fb) ✖ Ⓡ B&b£9.50–£10.50 Bdi£15.50–£16.50 WBdifr£105 LDOnoon

🅼 CTV 6P 1🏠 ⁂(hard) 58acres beef

IPSWICH
Suffolk
Map **5** TM14

GH Bentley Tower Hotel 172 Norwich Rd ☎(0473) 212142
Closed 24 Dec–4 Jan

Friendly, family-run establishment in large detached house.

11⋒ (2fb) CTV in all bedrooms ✖ Ⓡ B&b£28 Bdi£37 LDO8.45pm

Lic 🅼 12P

Credit cards 1 3

GH Gables Hotel 17 Park Rd ☎(0473) 54252
rs Xmas wk

Large house in a residential road near Christchurch Park. Offers clean, basic accommodation.

14hc CTV in 12 bedrooms Ⓡ B&b£14–£18 Bdi£19.25–£23.25 WBdifr£147 LDO6.30pm

Lic 🅼 CTV 10P

Credit card 3

ISLE OF ARRAN
Strathclyde *Buteshire*
See **Arran, Isle of**

ISLE OF COLL
Strathclyde *Argyllshire*
See **Coll, Isle of**

ISLE OF LEWIS
Western Isles, Ross & Cromarty
See **Lewis, Isle of**

ISLE OF MAN
See **Man, Isle of**

ISLE OF MULL
Strathclyde *Argyllshire*
See **Mull, Isle of**

ISLE OF SKYE
Highland *Inverness-shire*
See **Skye, Isle of**

ISLE OF SOUTH UIST
Western Isles *Inverness-shire*
See **Uist, South, Isle of**

ISLE OF WIGHT
Hampshire
See **Wight, Isle of**

ISLE ORNSAY
See **Skye, Isle of**

ISLES OF SCILLY
(No map)
See **Scilly, Isles of**

ISLEWORTH
Gt London
London plan **4** B3
(page 258)

GH Kingswood Hotel 33 Woodlands Rd ☎01-560 5614

10hc CTV in all bedrooms ✖ Ⓡ in 5 bedrooms ✱B&b£18.40–£36.80

Lic 🅼 CTV 5P nc8yrs

Ⓥ

IVER HEATH
Buckinghamshire
Map **4** TQ08

GH Bridgettine Convent Fulmer Common Rd ☎Fulmer (02816) 2073

An unusual establishment, a convent run by nuns, offering simple, comfortable accommodation in a friendly, peaceful atmosphere.

13hc (3fb) ✖ B&b£10–£12 Bdi£13–£15 WBdifr£91 LDO2pm

🅼 CTV 🅿

Ⓥ

JACOBSTOWE
Devon
Map **2** SS50

⊢⊣**FH** Mrs J King **Higher Cadham** *(SS585026)* ☎Exbourne (083785) 647
Apr–Oct (rs Mar & Nov, only two bedrooms available)

Well-decorated and comfortably furnished 16th-century farmhouse. Ideal base for touring.

4hc (1fb) ✖ Ⓡ B&b£8 Bdi£12.50 WBdifr£80 (W only Aug) LDO5pm

Lic 🅼 CTV 6P nc3yrs ⌐ 139acres beef sheep mixed

Ⓥ

JEDBURGH
Borders *Roxburghshire*
Map **12** NT62

GH Ferniehirst Mill Lodge ☎(0835) 63279
Apr–Oct

Modern, purpose-built lodge in secluded position beside the River Jed. 3m S of Jedburgh off A68. Horse-riding holidays are a speciality.

11hc (5⇌ 3⋒) Ⓡ B&b£18.50 Bdi£30 WBdi£199.50 LDO8.30pm

Lic ₩ 16P nc12yrs ♪ ∪

Credit card ③

GH Kenmore Bank Oxnam Rd ☎(0835) 62369

Compact house perched high above the Jed Water and looking across to the town.

6hc (2⋒) (2fb) CTV in all bedrooms ✗ (ex guide dogs) Ⓡ B&b£10.50–£16 Bdi£16.50–£22 WBdifr£112 LDO8pm

Lic ₩ 6P

Credit cards ① ③ Ⓥ

GH The Spinney Langlee (2m S on A68) ☎(0835) 63525
mid Apr–Oct

Converted country cottages, now modernised and tastefully furnished. 2m S of Jedburgh on the A68.

3rm (2⇌) (1fb) Ⓡ B&bfr£13

₩ CTV P

Ⓥ

JERSEY
Channel Islands
Map **16**
See **Channel Islands**

KEITH
Grampian *Banffshire*
Map **15** NJ45

⊢FH Mrs J Jackson **The Haughs** *(NJ416515)* ☎(05422) 2238
Apr–1 Nov

Traditional stone-built farmhouse, with pleasant views, 1m from Keith off A96.

5hc (1⋒) (1fb) ⚟ in 2 bedrooms CTV in 1 bedroom ✗ Ⓡ B&b£8.50–£9.50 Bdi£14–£16.50 WBdi£105–£110 LDO3pm

CTV 10P 2🚗 ⌂ 165acres beef mixed sheep

Ⓥ

⊢FH Mrs E C Leith **Montgrew** *(NJ453517)* ☎(05422) 2852
Apr–Oct

Neat, well-maintained house with a homely atmosphere. Conveniently situated for beaches and Cairngorms. 1½m E off A95.

4rm (1hc) (1fb) B&bfr£9 Bdifr£14 WBdifr£98 LDO7pm

₩ CTV 5P 211acres arable beef

⊢FH Mrs G Murphy **Tarnash House** *(NJ442490)* ☎(05422) 2728
May–Oct

Two-storey, stone farmhouse with well maintained garden to the front. 1m S off A96.

4hc (1fb) B&b£9–£10

₩ CTV 10P 100acres arable

Credit cards ① ② ③ ⑤ Ⓥ

KELMSCOTT
Oxfordshire
Map **4** SU29

FH Mrs A Amor **Manor Farm** *(SU253995)* ☎Faringdon (0367) 52620

An attractive Cotswold Farm (National Trust property) on edge of peaceful village of Kelmscott.

2hc (2fb) ⚟ in all bedrooms ✗ Ⓡ B&b£11–£15 WB&b£77–£110

₩ CTV 4P 315acres arable dairy

Ⓥ

KELSO
Borders *Roxburghshire*
Map **12** NT73

GH Bellevue House Bowmont St ☎(0573) 24588

Attractive house with good standard throughout. Ten minutes walk from the town centre.

8hc (3⋒) (2fb) ✗ Ⓡ B&b£11.50–£12.50 Bdi£18–£19 WBdifr£120.75 LDO8.30pm

Lic ₩ CTV 8P

Credit cards ① ② ③ Ⓥ

KENDAL
Cumbria
Map **7** SD59
See also **Brigsteer** & **Crook**

GH Lane Head Country House Hotel Helsington (½m S off A6) ☎(0539) 31283
Closed Nov

South of Kendal on a lane off the A6, this peacefully located 17th-century house offers spacious and tastefully appointed accommodation.

7hc ✗ ✱B&b£12.50–£15 Bdi£21–£23.50 LDO7pm

Lic CTV 10P

See advertisement on page 218

FH Mrs S Beaty **Garnett House** *(SD500959)* Burneside ☎(0539) 24542
Closed Xmas & New Year

15th-century stone-built farmhouse situated in an elevated position overlooking Howgill Fells, close to Windermere and Kendal.

5hc (2fb) ✗ Ⓡ ✱B&b£8.50–£9.50 Bdi£12.50–£13.50 LDO5pm

CTV 6P 600acres dairy sheep

Ⓥ

⊢FH Mrs J Ellis **Gateside** *(NY494955)* Windermere Rd ☎(0539) 22036

16th-century farmhouse of great charm and character.

4hc (1fb) CTV in all bedrooms B&b£9–£9.50 Bdi£13.75–£14.25 WBdifr£95 LDO4.30pm

₩ 6P 280acres dairy sheep

Ⓥ

See advertisement on page 218

FH Mrs E M Gardner **Natland Mill Beck** *(SD520907)* (1m from Kendal on A65) ☎(0539) 21122
Mar–Oct
→

17th-century, local stone-built farmhouse with original beams, doors and cupboards. Large well-furnished rooms. Attractive walled garden.

3rm (2hc) ✗ Ⓡ ✱B&bfr£9

CTV 3P 100acres dairy

Ⓥ

FH Mrs S K Bell **Oxenholme** *(SD529905)* Oxenholme Rd ☎(0539) 27226

A delightfully furnished farmhouse dating back to 1540. Many natural beams and features an inglenook fireplace. 2m SE B6254.

3hc (1fb) ✗ B&b£8.50–£9.50 WB&b£55–£60

CTV 3P nc3yrs 180acres dairy sheep soft fruit

Ⓥ

KENILWORTH
Warwickshire
Map **4** SP27

GH Castle Laurels 22 Castle Rd ☎(0926) 56179

6hc (2⥮) (1fb) CTV in all bedrooms Ⓡ ✱B&bfr£11.50

CTV 10P

GH Enderley 20 Queens Rd ☎(0926) 55388

5hc (4⥮) (1fb) CTV in all bedrooms ✗ (ex guide dogs) Ⓡ B&b£11.50–£15 WB&bfr£70

Lic CTV 2P

Ⓥ

GH Ferndale 45 Priory Rd ☎(0926) 53214
Closed Xmas & New Year

9hc (2fb) ✗ B&b£11–£13

CTV 6P

Ⓥ

GH Hollyhurst 47 Priory Rd ☎(0926) 53882
Closed Xmas Day

Large semi-detached house with well-decorated bedrooms and comfortable lounge.

9hc (3fb) Ⓡ B&b£10–£12 Bdi£15–£17 WBdifr£100 LDOnoon

Lic CTV 10P

GH Nightingales Hotel & Restaurant 95–97 Warwick Rd ☎(0926) 53594

Modest hotel with interesting menus which include fresh seasonal fare and selected wines.

10hc (1fb) ✗ B&b£14–£16 Bdi£22–£24 WBdifr£136 LDO9pm

Lic CTV P nc6yrs

Credit cards 1 3 Ⓥ

KENNFORD
Devon
Map **3** SX98

FH Mrs R Weeks ***Holloway Barton*** *(SX893855)* ☎Exeter (0392) 832302
Closed Xmas

Well appointed house retaining its old charm and offering panoramic views. Situated just off the M5 & A38. Central for two racecourses, coast and moors.

4hc (1fb) Ⓡ in 2 bedrooms LDO4pm

CTV 4P 1🚗 billiards 360acres arable beef dairy

KENTALLEN
Highland *Argyllshire*
Map **14** NN05

FH Mrs D A MacArthur ***Ardsheal Home*** *(NN996574)* ☎Duror (063174) 229
Apr–Oct

Tastefully decorated house with a tidy garden, standing in sheltered position.

3rm (1hc 1⇌) (1fb) ✗ Ⓡ

CTV 5P 1000acres beef dairy sheep mixed

KESWICK
Cumbria
Map **11** NY22
See plan on page 220

GH Acorn House Hotel Ambleside Rd
☎(07687) 72553
Plan **1** *C2*
Large detached house with pleasant garden in quiet part of town.
10hc (4⫶fl) (3fb) Ⓡ B&b£10–£12.50 Bdi£15.50–£18 WBdi£102.50–£120 LDO4.30pm
Lic 🍽 CTV 9P
Ⓥ

Keswick

GH Allerdale House 1 Eskin St
☎(07687) 73891 Plan **2** *C1*
Closed Nov
Spacious lakeland slate house in quiet location. The friendly resident proprietors are constantly improving facilities including en suite in most bedrooms. The comfortable lounge features an attractive wooden fireplace.
6hc (2⇨ 4⫶fl) (2fb) CTV in all bedrooms Ⓡ B&b£11–£12.50 Bdi£16–£17.50 WBdi£112–£122.50
Lic 🍽 3P nc3yrs
Ⓥ

GH Charnwood 6 Eskin St ☎(07687) 74111 Plan **3** *C2*
A personally run guest house with spacious bedrooms and a lounge featuring a living flame fire set in an unusual carved wooden fireplace.
6hc (4fb) ✗ Ⓡ B&bfr£9.50 Bdifr£15 LDO4pm
Lic CTV ₽̸

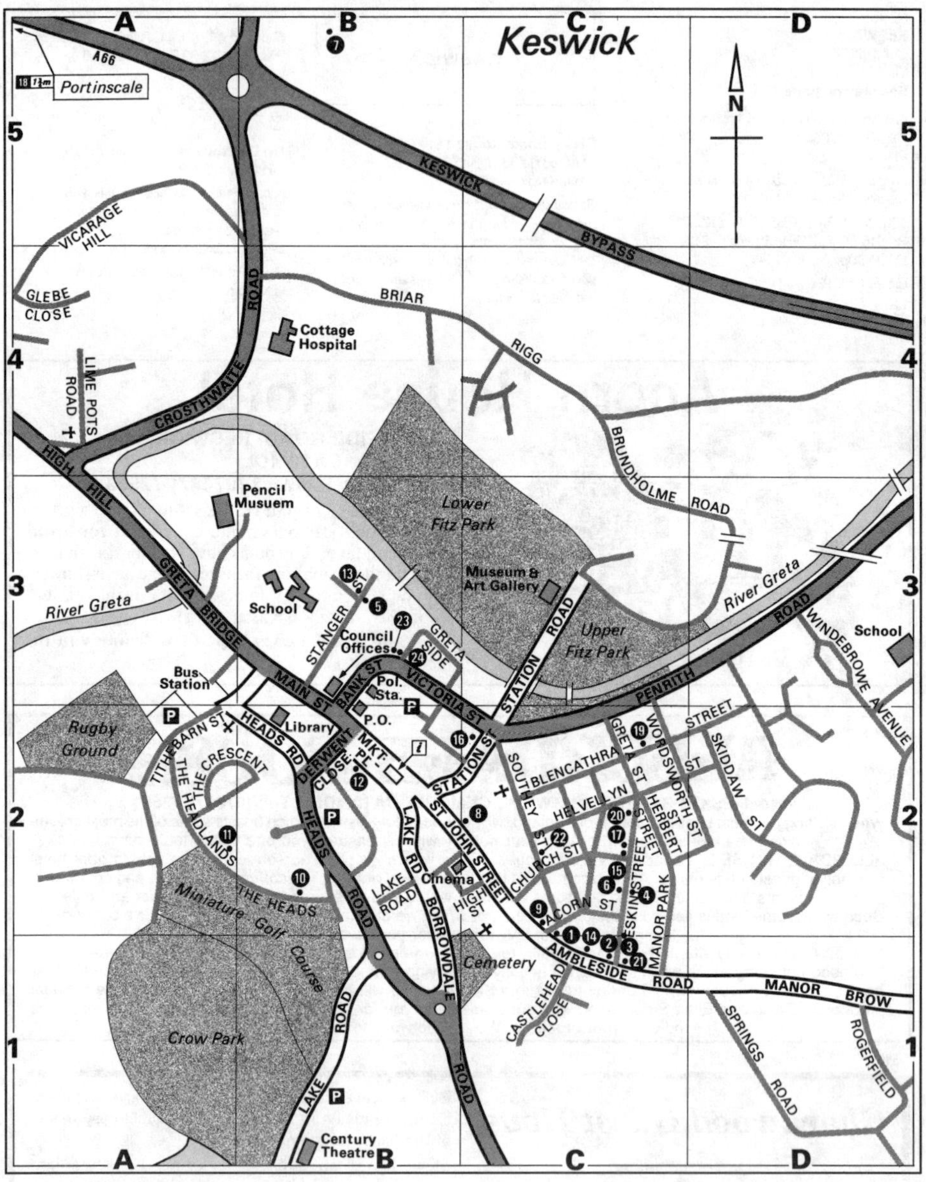

Keswick

1 Acorn House Private Hotel
2 Allerdale House
3 Charnwood
4 Clarence House
5 Fell House
6 Foye House
7 Gale Hotel
8 George Hotel *(Inn)*
9 Greystones
10 Hazeldene Hotel
11 Holmwood House
12 Kings Arms Hotel *(Inn)*
13 Lincoln House
14 Lynwood Private Hotel
15 Melbreak House
16 Ravensworth Private Hotel
17 Richmond House
18 Rickerby Grange
19 Silverdale Hotel
20 Squirrel Lodge
21 Stonegarth
22 Sunnyside
23 Swiss Court
24 Thornleigh

GH Clarence House 14 Eskin St ☎(07687) 73186 Plan **4** *C2*
Closed 25 & 26 Dec

A very comfortable Lakeland residence renowned for its good food and hospitality. Most bedrooms have en-suite facilities.

8hc (6fl) (2fb) ⅟ in 2 bedrooms Ⓡ B&b£11.50–£12.50 Bdi£17–£18 WBdifr£118 LDO6pm

Lic 𝍎 CTV ⁄P

Ⓥ

⊢⊣**GH Fell House** 28 Stranger St ☎(07687) 72669 Plan **5** *B3*

Warm and welcoming guesthouse with spacious and comfortable bedrooms.

6hc (2fb) CTV in all bedrooms ✕ Ⓡ B&b£9–£10 Bdi£13.50–£15 WBdi£93–£100 LDO3.30pm

𝍎 CTV 4P

GH Foye House 23 Eskin St ☎(07687) 73288 Plan **6** *C2*

Pleasant guesthouse with a friendly atmosphere. Dinner is a hearty five course meal.

6hc (1fb) Ⓡ B&b£9.50 Bdi£14.50 WBdifr£98 LDO5pm

Lic 𝍎 CTV ⁄P

GH Gale Hotel Underskiddaw ☎(07687) 72413 Plan **7** *B5*
Mar–Nov

Keswick

A lovely, spacious, comfortable house set in large attractive gardens with good views of Borrowdale.

13hc (6⇌ 5fl) (2fb) ✕ Ⓡ B&b£14–£17 Bdi£22–£25 WBdi£140–£158 LDO6pm

Lic 𝍎 CTV 10P

Credit cards 1 3 Ⓥ

GH Greystones Ambleside Rd ☎(07687) 73108 Plan **9** *C1*
Closed 1–27 Dec

An attractive and spacious end-terrace house serving good home-cooking.

9hc (1⇌ 5fl) (2fb) ✕ Ⓡ B&b£10–£14 Bdi£16.50–£20.50 WBdifr£110 LDO2pm

Lic 𝍎 CTV 5P 2🚗 nc8yrs

GH Hazeldene Hotel The Heads ☎(07687) 72106 Plan **10** *B2*
Mar–Nov

Large guesthouse with some lovely views of lake and surrounding fells.

23hc (16fl) (5fb) CTV in all bedrooms Ⓡ B&b£11.80–£15.90 Bdi£18.80–£22.90 WBdi£125–£153 LDO7pm

Lic 𝍎 CTV 18P

Ⓥ

See advertisement on page 222

GH Holmwood House The Heads ☎(07687) 73301 Plan **11** *A2*
mid Mar–mid Nov

A well-appointed, comfortable house with fine views across Derwent Water.

7hc (1fb) ✕ ✱B&b£12–£13 Bdi£17.50–£18.50 WBdifr£119.50 LDO2pm

Lic 𝍎 CTV ⁄P nc5yrs

Ⓥ

GH Lincoln House Stanger St ☎(07687) 72597 Plan **13** *B3*
Closed Dec

Terraced house in an elevated position close to centre of town.

6hc (1fb) ✕ ✱B&b£9.50–£10.50 Bdi£14–£14.50 WBdifr£101.50 LDO3pm

Lic 𝍎 CTV 5P

Ⓥ

See advertisement on page 222

GH Lynwood Private Hotel 12 Ambleside Rd ☎(07687) 72081 Plan **14** *C1*
rs Jan

150-year-old semi-detached house built of Lakeland stone, with pretty front garden in a residential area.

7hc (2fb) ✕ Ⓡ ✱B&b£9.50–£10.50 Bdi£15.50–£16.50 WBdi£108.50–£115.50 LDO4.30pm

→

Lic 🍽 CTV P̸ nc5yrs

ⓥ

GH Melbreak House 29 Church St ☎(07687) 73398 Plan **15** *C2*

Spacious and cheerful guesthouse with attractive lounge and dining room.

12hc (2⇌ 1🚿) (5fb) CTV in all bedrooms Ⓡ ✱B&b£10–£12 Bdi£15–£17 WBdifr£100 LDO5pm

Lic CTV P̸

ⓥ

GH Ravensworth Private Hotel 29 Station St ☎(07687) 72476 Plan **16** *C2*
rs Jan

Comfortable slate built private hotel offering personal service.

9hc (1⇌ 3🚿) (1fb) ✈ Ⓡ B&b£11–£15 Bdi£17.25–£22 WBdi£110–£145 LDO6pm

Lic 🍽 CTV 5P

Credit cards 1 2 3 5 ⓥ

GH Richmond House 37–39 Eskin St ☎(07687) 73965 Plan **17** *C2*

A comfortable guesthouse set in a residential area close to town centre.

12hc (5🚿) (1fb) 🚭 in all bedrooms ✈ Ⓡ ✱B&b£10–£12 Bdi£15–£18 WBdi£100–£120 LDO5pm

Lic 🍽 CTV P̸ nc10yrs

Credit cards 1 2 3 5 ⓥ

Keswick

Selected

GH Rickerby Grange Portinscale (Guestaccom) ☎(07687) 72344 Plan **18** *A5*
Closed 23–28 Dec

An appealing guesthouse surrounded by attractive gardens situated in this picturesque village. There are two comfortable lounges one with CTV and the other full of books and games, as well as a cosy lounge bar. Excellent four-course meals are served in the delightfully refurbished dining room and all the bedrooms are attractively decorated.

14hc (2⇌ 9🚿) (3fb) CTV available in bedrooms Ⓡ in 3 bedrooms ✱B&b£13.50–£18 Bdi£21–£26 WBdi£140–£168 LDO5pm

Lic 🍽 20P

ⓥ

See advertisement on page 224

GH Silverdale Hotel Blencathra St ☎(07687) 72294 Plan **19** *C2*

Large detached house in residential area.

12hc (1⇌ 1🚿) (1fb) Ⓡ B&bfr£11 Bdifr£16 WBdifr£102 LDO5pm

Lic 🍽 CTV 6P

Credit card 1 ⓥ

GH Squirrel Lodge 43 Eskin St ☎(07687) 73091 Plan **20** *C2*

Lovely little family-run guesthouse with well-appointed bedrooms and good food.

7hc 🚭 in all bedrooms CTV in all bedrooms Ⓡ ✱B&b£9.75–£10 Bdi£15–£15.50 WBdifr£98 LDO5pm

Lic 🍽 CTV P̸ nc10yrs

Credit card 1

GH Stonegarth 2 Eskin St ☎(07687) 72436 Plan **21** *C1*
Mar–Oct

This large Victorian house has been extended recently to provide several en-suite rooms. Accommodation is comfortable and spacious. Resident proprietors ensure a warm welcome.

9hc (3⇌ 1🚿) (3fb) CTV in all bedrooms Ⓡ B&b£11–£13 Bdi£16–£18 WBdi£110–£124 LDO6pm

Lic 🍽 9P nc3yrs

ⓥ

See advertisement on page 224

GH *Sunnyside* 25 Southey St ☎(07687) 72446 Plan **22** *C2*

A bright and comfortable family-run guesthouse. →

Lynwood Guest House

12 Ambleside Road, Keswick-on-Derwentwater, Cumbria CA12 4DL Telephone: Keswick (07687) 72081

Quietly and pleasantly situated 800 yards from Derwentwater and 350 yards from the town, is a small guesthouse with a residential licence where a high standard of comfort, cuisine and personal attention are ensured. All the bedrooms are centrally heated, tastefully furnished, have hot and cold water, shaver points and facilities for making hot drinks. Good home cooked food can be enjoyed in the friendly, relaxed atmosphere of the spacious dining room. Wholesome packed lunches can be provided & special diets catered for. Drying facilities and a lock up cycle store are available and ample street parking is close-by. Open all year. Special 3 day Christmas break.

ravenstone hotel

Near Keswick, Cumbria CA12 4QG
Telephone: (059681) 240

A well-appointed comfortable Country House Hotel on slopes of Skiddaw, with fine views over Bassenthwaite Valley and Lake, ideally situated for touring the Lake District and Cumbrian coast. Reductions for children sharing family rooms. Extensive grounds, Residential Licence, Games and Billiards Room, TV Lounge, Spacious Parking, Full Central Heating. Situated on the A591 road, Keswick to Scotland. *Personally managed by the Proprietors.*

Ravensworth

29 Station Street
Keswick-on-Derwentwater
Cumbria CA12 5HH
Tel: Keswick (07687) 72476

CONVENIENT AND QUIET RELAXATION

Close to the centre of Keswick and all its amenities, but overlooking the peaceful Fitz Park Gardens. The lake shore is only a short walk away. Some bedrooms with en-suite bath or shower. All have tea & coffee trays. Views over the Park or surrounding fells. Open all year. Central heating. Residential licence. Car parking. Brochure on Request.

Richmond House

37/39 Eskin Street
Keswick-on-Derwentwater
Cumbria CA12 4DG

Tel: Keswick (07687) 73965

A comfortable guesthouse in traditional Lakeland slate, only a few minutes' level walk from town centre, parks and lake. All bedrooms have CH, H&C, shaver points, tea/coffee makers and some have en suite shower and WC. Our high standard of cuisine offers a choice of dishes at all meals and we are happy to cater for special diets. Two lounges, well-stocked bar and colour TV. Brochure on request.

8hc (2fb) CTV in all bedrooms ✖ Ⓡ

🍽 8P

Credit card 1

GH *Swiss Court* 25 Bank St ☎(07687) 72637 Plan **23** *B3*

Victorian terraced house in town centre.

7hc ✖

🍽 CTV 3P nc6yrs

GH Thornleigh 23 Bank St ☎(07687) 72863 Plan **24** *B3*

A well-appointed and comfortable house set in a residential area close to town centre. All bedrooms are en suite. First-class home cooking and a friendly welcome are assured.

Keswick

6⫶ CTV in all bedrooms ✖ Ⓡ B&b£13.95–£15.95 Bdi£21.90–£24.90 LDO3pm

🍽 3P nc16yrs

Credit cards 1 3 Ⓥ

INN George Hotel St Johns Street (Mount Charlotte) ☎(07687) 72076 Plan **8** *C2*

16th-century coaching inn full of charm and character, with restaurant and bar meals.

17hc (3fb) Ⓡ B&b£14–£15 Bdi£18–£19 WBdifr£133 Lunch £2.50–£5.50&alc High tea £2.25–£5 Dinner8.30pm £6.50–£8.50&alc

CTV 12P

Credit cards 1 2 3 5 Ⓥ

INN Kings Arms Hotel Main St ☎(07687) 72083 Plan **12** *B3*

An 18th-century coaching inn with attractively decorated and furnished bedrooms. Good food served in restaurant, pizzeria and bar.

20hc (2⇌ 11⫶) (1fb) CTV in all bedrooms ✖ Ⓡ B&b£19 Bdi£23 Bar lunch fr£2.75 Dinner9.30pm fr£8.50

🍽 🚫

Ⓥ

KETTLEBURGH
Suffolk
Map **5** TM26

FH Mrs I A Pearce **Rookery** *(TM273606)* Framlingham ☎Framlingham (0728) 723248
Closed Dec & Jan

Georgian farmhouse standing in 1½ acres of well kept gardens. Situated ¾m N of Kettleburgh.

3hc (1fb) ⚡ in all bedrooms 🐕 Ⓡ B&b£10–£10.50 Bdi£16–£16.50 WBdifr£112 LDO6pm

🍽 CTV 4P nc8yrs 350acres arable

Ⓥ

KETTLEWELL
North Yorkshire
Map **7** SD97

GH Dale House ☎(075676) 836

Charming stone built village house close to the River Wharfe.

6hc (1⇌ 4fl) CTV in all bedrooms Ⓡ B&b£16–£20.60 Bdi£22.50–£27.20 WBdifr£154 LDO8.30pm

Lic 🍽 5P nc8yrs

Ⓥ

GH Langcliffe House ☎(075676) 243
Mar–4 Jan

Charming, relaxed house on the edge of the village.

6hc (2⇌ 4fl) (1fb) CTV in all bedrooms Ⓡ B&b£14–£15 Bdi£21–£22 WBdifr£135 LDO7pm

Lic 🍽 4P 2🚗

Credit cards 1 3 Ⓥ

KEXBY
North Yorkshire
Map **8** SE75

FH Mrs K R Daniel **Ivy House** *(SE691511)* ☎York(0904) 489368

Brick-built farmhouse adjacent to A1079 York–Pocklington road. Snug accommodation of neat and modest proportions.

3rm (1fb) 🐕 B&b£8.50–£9

🍽 CTV 5P 132acres mixed

KEYNSHAM
Avon
Map **3** ST66

FH Mrs L Sparkes **Uplands** *(ST663664)* Wellsway ☎(0272) 865764
Closed Dec

9hc (2fl) (4fb) Ⓡ ✱B&b£15–£17.50 Bdi£19.50–£21.50 LDOnoon

🍽 CTV 20P 200acres dairy

Ⓥ

INN Grange Hotel 42 Bath Rd ☎Bristol (0272) 869181

A large detached former farmhouse situated just outside the town centre. The bedrooms are very well equipped and an informal atmosphere prevails.

11hc (8⇌ 3fl) (4fb) ⚡ in all bedrooms CTV in all bedrooms 🐕 Ⓡ ✱B&b£22–£50 Bdi£31–£59 Bar lunch £1.75–£3.50 Dinner 8.45pm£9alc

CTV 29P 🚗

Credit cards 1 3

KIDDERMINSTER
Hereford & Worcester
Map **7** SO87

GH Cedars Hotel Mason Rd ☎(0562) 745869

Set in a residential area easily accessible to town centre and ring road: A Georgian house well equipped with modern facilities.

18fl (5fb) ⚡ in 4 bedrooms CTV in all bedrooms Ⓡ B&b£17–£32 Bdi£22–£37 LDO10pm

Lic 🍽 20P

Credit cards 1 2 3 5

KIDLINGTON
Oxfordshire
Map **4** SP41

Selected

GH Bowood House 238 Oxford Rd ☎(08675) 70244
rs 25 & 26 Dec

Well-kept family house with modern bedroom facilities.

10hc (3⇌ 3fl) (3fb) CTV in all bedrooms 🐕 Ⓡ B&b£17.50–£28 Bdi£27–£37.50 LDO4pm

Lic 🍽 CTV 18P ⛆(heated)

Credit cards 1 3

See advertisement under Oxford

KILBURN
North Yorkshire
Map **8** SE57

INN Foresters Arms Hotel ☎Coxwold (03476) 386

Attractive village inn nestling beneath the slopes of the North Yorkshire Moors. Parts of the building are believed to be around 800 years old, but there is nothing old-fashioned about the present accommodation. The proprietors are friendly and delicious meals are served in the comfortable dining room.

8⇌ (2fb) CTV in all bedrooms Ⓡ B&b£15–£20 Bdi£17.50–£25 WBdifr£130 Lunch £6alc Dinner 9.30pm£8alc

🍽 40P

Credit cards 1 2 3 Ⓥ

See advertisement under York

KILGETTY
Dyfed
Map **2** SN10

GH Manian Lodge Begelly ☎Saundersfoot (0834) 813273
May–Sep

→

Family hotel beautifully situated near Tenby and Saundersfoot

7fl (4fb) Ⓡ B&b£10–£12 Bdi£15–£17 WBdi£90–£110

Lic CTV 16P ⌂

Ⓥ

FH Mrs S A James ***Little Newton*** *(SN122073)* ☎Saundersfoot (0834) 812306

May–Sep

Small farm with modern house of character.

9hc (6fb) ✗

𝍪 CTV 10P ⌂ 10acres non-working

KILLIECRANKIE
Tayside *Perthshire*
Map **14** NN96

GH Dalnasgadh House ☎Pitlochry (0796) 3237

Etr–Oct

Attractive house standing on the outskirts of this village.

6hc ⚟ in all bedrooms ✗ B&b£10–£10.50

𝍪 CTV 10P nc

KILMARTIN
Strathclyde *Argyllshire*
Map **10** NR89

INN *Kilmartin Hotel* ☎(05465) 250

A white painted inn with attractive hanging baskets, on the main A816, it is a popular eating place.

5hc (1fb) Ⓡ LDO9pm

CTV 13P ⌗

KILPECK
Hereford & Worcester
Map **3** SO43

FH Mrs I J Pike **Priory** *(SO446302)* ☎Wormbridge (098121) 366

Apr–Oct

2hc ✗ Ⓡ B&b£10 WB&b£70

𝍪 P 2🚗 9acres small-holding mixed

KILVE
Somerset
Map **3** ST14

Selected

INN Hood Arms ☎Holford (027874) 210

Closed Xmas Day

5hc (3⇌ 2fl) CTV in all bedrooms Ⓡ B&b£20–£23 Bdi£25–£33 WBdifr£161 Lunch £2.75–£5&alc Dinner 10pm£2.75–£5&alc

𝍪 12P ⌗ nc7yrs

Credit cards 1 3

KINCRAIG
Highland *Inverness-shire*
Map **14** NH80

GH March House Lagganlia ☎(05404) 388

Closed Nov

Modern guesthouse with well-appointed rooms and magnificent views.

6hc (3⇌) (1fb) ⚟ in 4 bedrooms Ⓡ ✱B&b£9.50–£12 Bdi£14.50–£17 WBdi£99–£105 LDO6pm

𝍪 8P

Ⓥ

KINGHAM
Oxfordshire
Map **4** SP22

GH *Conygree Gate* Church St (Guestaccom) ☎(060871) 389

Mar–Oct

Attractive Cotswold-stone house situated in charming, peaceful village, with modern amenities. Kept spotlessly clean and run by two very English ladies providing good home cooking.

6rm (5hc) (1fb) ✗ LDO5pm

Lic 𝍪 CTV 2P 5🚗 nc7yrs

KINGHORN
Fife
Map **11** NT28

INN Long Boat 107 Pettycur Rd ☎(0592) 890625

Large modern villa looking out across the Firth of Forth decorated and furnished to the highest standards.

6⇌ fl CTV in all bedrooms Ⓡ ✱B&b£19.50–£25 Bdi£26–£31.50 Lunch £4.50–£5.50 High Tea £4–£5.95 Dinner 9.30pm£7.95–£9.95&alc

𝍪 CTV 10P

Credit cards 1 2 3 5

KINGSBRIDGE
Devon
Map **3** SX74

Selected

GH Ashleigh House Ashleigh Rd, Westville ☎(0548) 2893

Apr–Oct rs Dec–Nov

Friendly, personally-run guesthouse offering first-class accommodation amid a tranquil atmosphere. Charming bedrooms are bright and spotless as are the delightful public rooms. Attractive small garden.

8hc (1fb) ⚟ in all bedrooms Ⓡ B&b£11–£12 Bdi£17.50–£18.50 WBdifr£122.50

Lic 𝍪 CTV 5P nc5yrs

GH Harbour Lights Hotel Ebrington St ☎(0548) 2418

Friendly, personal service at this converted 18th-century property in the heart of Kingsbridge.

5hc (2fb) ✱B&b£10.50–£12.50 Bdi£18.50–£20.50 WBdi£115–£125

Lic CTV 6P

Ⓥ

KINGSDOWN
Kent
Map **5** TR34

GH Blencathra Country Kingsdown Hill ☎Deal (0304) 373725

Friendly, modern, country guesthouse with use of a croquet lawn.

7hc (3fb) CTV in 4 bedrooms Ⓡ B&b£10–£12 Bdi£16–£18 WBdi£112–£126 LDO5pm

Lic CTV 7P

KINGSEY
Buckinghamshire
Map **4** SP70

FH Mr N M D Hooper **Foxhill** *(SP748066)* ☎Haddenham (0844) 291650
Feb–Nov

17th-century farmhouse with spacious, comfortable bedrooms. Delightful garden with pool and pond.

3hc (2🚿) 🚭 in 3 bedrooms ✖ *B&b£13 WB&bfr£91

🍽 CTV 40P nc5yrs ⩮(heated) 4acres non-working

Ⓥ

KINGSGATE
Kent
Map **5** TR37

GH Marylands Hotel Marine Dr ☎Thanet (0843) 61259
Apr–Oct

Friendly hotel overlooking the sea with direct access to the beach.

9rm (8hc 1🛁) (3fb) Ⓡ B&b£11–£12 Bdi£16–£17 WBdi£95–£105 LDOnoon

Lic CTV 9P

Ⓥ

KINGSLAND
Hereford & Worcester
Map **3** SO46

FH Mrs F M Hughes ***Tremayne*** *(SO447613)* ☎(056881) 233
Apr–Nov

Deceptively large, two-storey building on one of the main roads to Leominster.

3hc (1fb)

🍽 CTV 3P 40acres sheep mixed

KING'S LYNN
Norfolk
Map **9** TF62

GH Havana 117 Gaywood Rd ☎(0553) 772331

Family run guesthouse offering simple, good- value accommodation.

7hc (1🚿) (2fb) CTV in 5 bedrooms TV in 2 bedrooms ✖ Ⓡ B&b£10–£11 Bdi£16.50–£17.50 WBdifr£115.50 LDO1pm

🍽 CTV 8P

Ⓥ

See advertisement on page 228

⊢⊣**GH Maranatha** 115 Gaywood Rd ☎(0553) 774596

Large semi-detached house on busy town road.

6hc (2fb) CTV in 3 bedrooms B&b£9 Bdi £12 WBdi£84 LDO6pm

Lic 🍽 CTV 4P

Ⓥ

GH Russet House Hotel 53 Goodwins Rd ☎(0553) 773098
Closed Xmas–New Year

12hc (4🛁 4🚿) (1fb) CTV in 11 bedrooms TV in 1 bedroom Ⓡ B&b£13.25–£26.50 Bdi£20.75–£34 LDO7.30pm

Lic 🍽 12P

Credit cards 1 3 5

See advertisement on page 228

FH Mr N Olsen **Lodge** *(TF824172)* Castle Acre ☎(07605) 206

3hc (2🛁) (1fb) ✖ Ⓡ *B&bfr£10 Bdifr£16 LDO5pm

20P 2000acres arable mixed

KINGSTON
Devon
Map **2** SX64

GH Trebles Cottage Private Hotel (Guestaccom) ☎Bigbury-on-Sea (0548) 810268
Mar–Oct

This comfortable small hotel enjoys an unspoilt village setting and stands in its own attractively wooded grounds of 1½ acres. Personally-managed, its proprietors offer a good standard of service and traditional home-cooking. All bedrooms are spotless and well-equipped and there are cosy public rooms. →

5⇌ ✗ Ⓡ ✱B&b£14–£16 Bdi£21.50–£23.50 WBdi£136.50–£143.50 LDO6pm

Lic 🍴 CTV 10P nc12yrs

Ⓥ

KINGSTON BAGPUIZE
Oxfordshire
Map **4** SU49

Selected

FH Mrs A Y Crowther **Fallowfields** (Guestaccom) *(SU393979)* Fallow Field, Southmoor ☎Longworth (0865) 820416 Telex 83388
Apr–Sep

This manorial farmhouse, standing in 112 acres, is situated 10m SW of Oxford. Bedrooms are tastefully furnished with many extras thoughtfully provided. Mrs Crowther's personal service and attention is complemented by her high standard of cuisine based on her own recipes and home grown produce. No dinners on Wednesdays.

4hc (3⇌ 1🚿) Ⓡ B&bfr£20 Bdifr£32.50 WBdifr£215 LDO6.30pm

Lic 🍴 CTV 15P nc10years ⛆(heated) 🎾(hard) 12 acres sheep

Credit card ① Ⓥ

Kingston — Kington

INN Hinds Head Witney Rd
☎Longworth (0865) 820204
Closed Xmas

Small roadside inn with comfortable, modern bedrooms.

3hc ✗ B&b£11–£15 Lunch£1.85–£6 Dinner9.30pm£2.40–£10

🍴 60 P nc12yrs snooker

Credit card ③

KINGSTONE
Hereford & Worcester
Map **3** SO43

⊢⊣**FH** Mrs G C Andrews **Webton Court** *(SO421365)* ☎Golden Valley (0981) 250220

Georgian farmhouse amidst large farm buildings. Located off B4348.

6hc (2fb) Ⓡ B&b£9–£10 Bdi£14–£15 WBdifr£98 LDO8pm

Lic CTV 10P snooker 300acres arable beef horse

Ⓥ

KINGSTON UPON THAMES
Gt London
London plan **4** B2
(page 248)

GH *Hotel Antoinette* 26 Beaufort Rd
☎01-546 1044

A friendly family run commercial hotel with most bedrooms en-suite and attractive garden. Situated in quiet residential area.

115hc (50⇌ 50🚿) (20fb) CTV in 30 bedrooms TV in 85 bedrooms Ⓡ in 20 bedrooms LDO9.30pm

Lic 🍴 CTV 70P

Credit cards ① ③

KINGSWELLS
Grampian *Aberdeenshire*
Map **15** NJ80

FH Mrs M Mann ***Bellfield*** *(NJ868055)*
☎Aberdeen (0224) 740239
Closed Dec

Modern, nicely-furnished farmhouse on quiet road set amid farmlands. 4m W of Aberdeen city centre off A944.

3hc (2fb) CTV in 1 bedroom

🍴 CTV P 🏠 200acres arable dairy

KINGTON
Hereford & Worcester
Map **3** SO25

⊢⊣**FH** Mrs E E Protheroe **Bucks Head** *(SO265550)* Upper Hergest ☎(0544) 231063

2m SW on unclass Gladestry rd.

5hc (2fb) ✗ B&b£8.50–£9 Bdi£13.50–£14 WBdi£92 LDO8pm

🍽 CTV 6P 290acres arable beef sheep

Ⓥ

FH Mrs M Eckley ***Holme*** *(SO339553)*
Lyonshall ☎ Lyonshall (05448) 216
Etr–Oct

Fully-modernised farmhouse standing on outskirts of village, 2m E of Kington.

4rm (3hc) (1fb) ✈ LDOam

🍽 CTV P nc 270acres arable dairy sheep mixed

FH J A Layton ***Park Gate*** *(SO332575)*
Lyonshall ☎Lyonshall (05448) 243
Closed Xmas

Two-storey, stone-built farmhouse with land overlooking Wales. Offa's Dyke runs through part of the farm. 2m E of Kington

2hc (1fb) ✈

🍽 CTV P ⌂ 230acres sheep mixed

KINGUSSIE
Highland *Inverness-shire*
Map **14** NH70

GH Homewood Lodge Newtonmore Rd
☎(05402) 507

Victorian house amidst tree-studded grounds with splendid views.

5hc (4⌂) (2fb) Ⓡ B&b£12–£14 Bdi£21–£23 WBdi£140–£155 LDO9pm

Lic 🍽 CTV 10P

Ⓥ

⊢⊣**GH Sonnhalde** East Ter ☎(05402) 266
Closed Nov

Attractive grey stone detached house located in terrace in elevated position behind main street.

7hc (2fb) B&b£9–£9.50 Bdi£13.50–£14 WBdifr£90

🍽 CTV 8P ⌂

KINVER
Staffordshire
Map **7** SO88

INN Kinfayre Restaurant 41 High St
☎(0384) 872565

12⌂ CTV in 7 bedrooms ✈ Ⓡ B&bfr£17 WB&b£100–£150 Lunch£5.30&alc Dinner 10pm

🍽 CTV P ⛆(heated)

KIPPEN
Central *Stirlingshire*
Map **11** NS69

FH Mrs J Paterson **Powblack** *(NS670970)*
☎(078687) 260
Apr–Oct

Pleasant farmhouse near the River Forth on the Kippen to Doune road.

2hc (1fb) B&b£10 WB&b£65

🍽 CTV P 300acres arable sheep

KIRKBEAN
Dumfries & Galloway *Dumfriesshire*
Map **11** NX95

GH *Cavens House* ☎(038788) 234

Charming guesthouse in 10 acres of grounds; good hospitality and excellent home cooking. Ideally constructed to suit disabled persons.

6hc (4⇌ 2⌂) (1fb) Ⓡ LDO6.45pm

Lic 🍽 CTV 20P ♿ ⌂

KIRKBY LONSDALE
Cumbria
Map **7** SD67

GH Abbot Hall ☎(0468) 71406
Mar–Oct

A charming, 17th-century farmhouse with character, warmth and comfort.

6hc (1⇌ 4⌂) (1fb) ⊁ in all bedrooms ✈ B&b£13.50–£17.50 Bdi£20.50–£24.50 WBdifr£143.50 LDO6pm

🍽 CTV 10P 2🚗 ⛳9 🎾(hard) ⚲ solarium

Ⓥ

KIRKBYMOORSIDE
North Yorkshire
Map **8** SE68

— *Selected* —

GH Appletree Court Town Farm,
9 High St ☎(0751) 31536

Standing at the end of a stone-built terrace in the tiny market place, Appletree Court was once a working farm and still has attractive walled gardens to side and rear. The interior has been converted and fitted to retain much of the original character including beamed ceilings and old fireplaces in the charming lounge and cosy sitting room. Pretty bedrooms boast many thoughtful extras. Traditional farmhouse meals served by helpful hosts who obviously enjoy caring for their guests.

6rm (3hc 3⇌) (2fb) CTV in all bedrooms ✈ ✱B&b£12–£14 Bdi£20–£22 WBdi£190–£205 LDOnoon

🍽 2P nc8yrs

KIRKCAMBECK
Cumbria
Map **12** NY56

FH Mrs M Stobart ***Cracrop*** *(NY521697)*
☎Roadhead (06978) 245
Closed Dec & Jan

Delightful farmhouse with very spacious and comfortable bedrooms.

2hc (2fb) ✈ Ⓡ

🍽 CTV 3P 425acres mixed

KIRKCONNEL
Dumfries & Galloway *Dumfriesshire*
Map **11** NS71

⊢⊣**FH** Mrs E A McGarvie **Niviston** *(NS691135)* ☎(06593) 346
mid May–Oct

Pleasant, well maintained farm delightfully set overlooking River Nith. (NB washing facilities are on ground floor).

2rm (1fb) B&b£9 WB&bfr£60

🍽 TV 4P 1🚗 ⚲ 345acres sheep stock

KIRKHILL
Highland *Inverness-shire*
Map **14** NH54

⟼**FH** Mrs C Munro **Wester Moniack** *(NH551438)* ☎Drumchardine (046383) 237

Follow signs 'Highland Vineries' from A862 and watch for farm sign.

2hc (1fb) B&b£8.50–£9 Bdi£13–£13.50 WBdifr£90 LDO8pm

CTV 4P 600acres arable beef Ⓥ

KIRKMUIRHILL
Strathclyde, *Lanarkshire*
Map **11** NS74

FH Mrs I H McInalby **Dyecroft** *(NS776419)* ☎Lesmahagow (0555) 892226

Compact and homely accommodation can be found at this cheerful, modern bungalow situated 1½ miles west of Kirkmuirhill on an unclassified road to Strathaven.

3rm ✱B&bfr£8

CTV 4P 60acres sheep

KIRKOSWALD
Cumbria
Map **12** NY54

Selected

GH Prospect Hill Hotel (Guestaccom) ☎Lazonby (076883) 500
Closed Feb

An 18th-century farm complex tastefully converted, full of charm and character. Bedrooms are individually styled and all enjoy fine views. The excellent à la carte dinner menu offers a wide range of home-cooked dishes and is served in an attractive stone-walled restaurant.

9hc (2⇌ 1fl) (1fb) Ⓡ ✱B&b£16–£25 WB&b£100.80–£157.50 LDO8.45pm

Lic CTV 20P 4

Credit cards 1 2 3 5

KIRKWHELPINGTON
Northumberland
Map **12** NY98

Selected

FH Mrs J B White ***Horncastle*** *(NY986847)* (1m W of village off A696) ☎Otterburn (0830) 40247
Apr–Oct

A comfortable farmhouse offering friendly service and interesting home cooked food. There is an attractive lounge and the bedrooms are very comfortable.

3hc (2⇌ 1fl) (1fb) Ⓡ LDO9am

CTV 6P squash snooker 310acres arable beef sheep mixed

Selected

FH Mrs C Robinson-Gay **Shieldhall** *(NZ026827)* (½m E of crossroads B6342/A694) ☎Otterburn (0830) 40387
Mar–Oct rs Nov–Feb

A meticulously modernised farmhouse built around a pretty courtyard dating back to 1705. The house has some magnificent furniture made or restored by Mr Gay, notably a carved 17th-century sideboard situated in the oak beamed dining room. The bedrooms are interesting and comfortable, one of which has an impressive four poster bed. Evening meals are home cooked and very enjoyable.

6hc (1⇌ 4fl) (1fb) Ⓡ in 5 bedrooms ✱B&bfr£12 Bdifr£18 WBdifr£119 LDO10am

CTV 10P 10acres beef

KIRTLING
Cambridgeshire
Map **5** TL65

INN Queens Head ☎Newmarket (0638) 730253

3hc Ⓡ ✱B&b£12.50–£14 WB&bfr£87.50 Lunch90p–£10&alc Dinner9.30pm£1.25–£15&alc

20P nc

Ⓥ

KIRTON
Nottinghamshire
Map **8** SK66

GH Old Rectory Main St ☎Mansfield (0623) 861540
Closed Dec

Lovely old Georgian house with spacious gardens in village centre.

10hc (1fl) B&bfr£13.75 Bdifr£19.75 WBdifr£125 LDO5pm

Lic CTV 18P

Ⓥ

KNARESBOROUGH
North Yorkshire
Map **8** SE35

GH Newton House 5–7 York Pl. ☎Harrogate (0423) 863539

A converted Georgian town house with archway access to inner courtyard car park. Dining room usually has à la carte menu available.

11hc (1⇌ 6fl) (3fb) CTV in all bedrooms Ⓡ B&b£11.50–£17.50 Bdi£18.45–£24.45 WBdifr£110 LDOnoon

Lic CTV 7P 2

Credit card 3 Ⓥ

KNIGHTON
Powys
Map **7** SO27

Selected

GH Milebrook House Mile Brook ☎(0547) 528631

This attractive 18th century building was the former Dower House to Swanage Castle. It is situated in the tiny village of Milebrook just 1½m from Knighton. Cleverly converted by owners Rodney and Beryl Marsden, it is now a country hotel of quality offering high standards in furnishings, food and hospitality.

6⇌ Ⓡ ✱B&b£17.50–£19.25 Bdi£26–£27.75 WBdi£150–£160 LDO9pm

Lic CTV 20P nc10yrs

Credit card 1 Ⓥ

FH R Watkins ***Heartsease*** *(SO343725)* ☎Bucknell (05474) 220
Apr–Oct

Georgian, mellow-stone farmhouse with country house atmosphere and large garden.

3rm (1hc 1⇌) (1fb) LDO9pm

CTV 6P 3 snooker 800acres mixed

Credit card 3

KNOWSTONE
Devon
Map **3** SS82

INN Masons Arms ☎Anstey Mills (03984) 231
Closed 24–26 Dec

An historic thatched inn on the edge of Exmoor.

4hc (1fl) Annexe: 1fl CTV in all bedrooms Ⓡ ✱B&b£12.50–£28.50 Bdi£20–£26 WBdi£140–£161 Bar lunch 75p–£5.75 Dinner 9.30pm £8.95&alc

10P

Ⓥ

KNUTSFORD
Cheshire
Map **7** SJ77

GH Longview Private Hotel 55 Manchester Rd ☎(0565) 2119
Closed Xmas & New Year

Personal service is assured at this small family run hotel overlooking the common. A small menu of good home cooking is offered in the pleasant dining room.

14hc (2fl) (1fb) CTV in all bedrooms Ⓡ ✱B&b£14.25–£30 Bdi£21.75–£37.50 LDO8.45pm

Lic CTV 22P

LADYBANK
Fife
Map **11** NO31

GH Redlands Country Lodge ☎(0337) 31091
Closed Mar & Apr
A splendid pine-clad lodge with smart, well appointed bedrooms and lounge. Meals are taken in the attractive stone built house surrounded by a pretty garden and patio.
Annexe 4⇋ CTV in all bedrooms ✗ Ⓡ
✱B&Bfr£12 Bdifr£21 LDO8pm
6P

LAIRG
Highland *Sutherland*
Map **14** NC50

⊢GH Carnbren ☎(0549) 2259
Apr–Sep
Modern detached house in roadside location overlooking Loch Shin.
3hc B&bfr£8.50
CTV 3P

LAMBERHURST
Kent
Map **5** TQ63

INN *Chequers* School Hill ☎(0892) 890260
4⇋ (1fb) CTV in all bedrooms Ⓡ
LDO10pm
60P
Credit cards 1 2 3 5

LAMLASH
Isle of Arran
See **Arran, Isle of**

LANCING
West Sussex
Map **4** TQ10

GH Beach House Hotel 81 Brighton Rd ☎(0903) 753368 →

Homely, comfortable seafront guesthouse.

6hc (2fb) ✕ Ⓡ B&b£9.50–£10 WB&bfr£63

🎹 CTV 6P

INN Sussex Pad Hotel Old Shoreham Rd ☎Shoreham (0273) 454647

A modern, well-appointed inn with elegant restaurant.

6⇌ (1fb) CTV in all bedrooms Ⓡ ✱B&b£31 Lunch £10alc Dinner 10pm £10alc

🎹 150P

Credit cards 1 2 3 5

L'ANCRESSE VALE
Guernsey
See **Channel Islands**

LANERCOST
Cumbria
Map **12** NY56

INN Newbridge Hotel ☎Brampton (06977) 2224
Closed Xmas Day & New Year's Day

An attractive listed building, comfortable and well decorated. Excellent meals are served in the Blacksmiths, a bar which dates from 1691 and features oak beams and open fires.

4hc (1⇌) ✱B&b£14–£16.50 Lunch £6.50–£14alc Dinner 9pm £6.50–£14alc

🎹 CTV 30P 🍺

Ⓥ

LANGDALE, GREAT
Cumbria
Map **11** NY30

GH Long House ☎(09667) 222
Closed Xmas Day & New Year's Eve

A peacefully situated 17th-century cottage with oak beams, open fires and stained glass windows.

3⇌ ✕ B&b£13–£14.50 Bdi£19.50–£21 WBdi£130–£140 LDO5pm

🎹 CTV 5P nc8yrs

INN Three Shires Little Langdale ☎(09667) 215
rs mid Nov–mid Feb

Small, friendly, family run inn with bright, attractive bedrooms, set in peaceful lakeland valley.

11hc (3⇌ 2fl) (1fb) ✕ Ⓡ in 5 bedrooms B&b£17.50–£20 Bdi£27–£29.50 WBdifr£175 Lunch £1–£9 Dinner 9pm £11.25

🎹 CTV 20P 🍺

See advertisement under Ambleside

LANGLAND BAY
West Glamorgan
Map **2** SS68

See also **Bishopston** and **Mumbles**

GH Brynteg Hotel 1 Higher Ln ☎Swansea (0792) 366820
Closed Xmas

11hc (2⇌) (4fb) Ⓡ B&b£12–£14 Bdi£18–£20 WBdifr£110 LDO8pm

Lic 🎹 CTV 10P

Ⓥ

GH Wittemberg Hotel 2 Rotherslade Rd ☎Swansea (0792) 369696
Closed Xmas

Small family-run hotel within walking distance of sea.

11hc (9fl) (2fb) ⚟ in 5 bedrooms CTV in all bedrooms ✕ Ⓡ B&b£14–£21 Bdi£21–£28 WBdifr£145

Lic 🎹 CTV 11P nc5yrs

Ⓥ

LANHYDROCK
Cornwall
Map **2** SX06

FH Mrs P A Smith **Treffry** *(SW073637)* ☎Bodmin (0208) 4405
19 Mar–Sep Closed Xmas & New Year rs Oct–18 Mar

Large, 18th-century farmhouse with garden in quiet location on working farm, 7 miles from coast.

3hc (1fl) (1fb) ⚟ in all bedrooms ✕ Ⓡ B&b£9.50–£10.50 Bdi£14–£15 WBdi£94–£101 (W only Jul & Aug) LDOnoon

🎹 CTV 4P 🐄 170acres dairy

LANLIVERY
Cornwall
Map **2** SX05

⊢⊣ **FH** Mr & Mrs J Linfoot **Treganoon** *(SX065589)* ☎Bodmin (0208) 872205
Etr–15 Oct

Farmhouse with small garden in fairly isolated position and beautiful countryside.

7rm (6hc) (2fb) Ⓡ B&b£8–£10 Bdi£14–£16 WBdi£75–£90 LDO7pm

Lic CTV 8P 🐄 70acres beef

LAPWORTH
West Midlands
Map **4** SP17

FH Mr & Mrs Smart **Mountford** *(SO164714)* Church Ln ☎(05643) 3283

Tudor house with outdoor swimming pool and duck pond.

4rm (1hc) TV in 1 bedroom ✕ Ⓡ in 1 bedroom B&b£12–£17

🎹 CTV 4P 1🚗 nc10yrs ⛱(heated) 30acres arable mixed water fowl Ⓥ

LARGS
Strathclyde *Ayrshire*
Map **10** NS25

⊢⊣ **GH Avondale** 8 Aubrey Cres ☎(0475) 672773
Mar–Sep

6hc (2fb) Ⓡ B&bfr£8.50

🎹 CTV 6P

Credit cards 1 2 3

⊢⊣ **GH Carlton** 10 Aubery Cres ☎(0475) 672313
Apr–Oct

Friendly, family-run guesthouse on the sea front.

6hc (2fb) Ⓡ B&b£8.50–£9 Bdi£12.50–£13.50 WBdifr£87.50

🎹 CTV 6P Ⓥ

LATHERON
Highland *Caithness*
Map **15** ND13

⊢⊣ **FH** Mrs C B Sinclair **Latheron** *(ND195352)* ☎(05934) 224
May–Oct

Two-storey farmhouse in elevated position with fine views across the North sea. The farm runs its own Ponies of Britain Pony Trekking Centre.

3rm (1fb) ⚟ in 2 bedrooms ✕ B&b£8–£9 Bdi£11–£12 WBdi£85

CTV 6P U 200acres stock rearing mixed

Ⓥ

LAUNCESTON
Cornwall
Map **2** SX38

GH Eagle House Hotel ☎(0566) 2036
Closed Xmas

18hc (6⇌ 3fl) (2fb) B&b£12–£14 Bdi£17–£20 WBdifr£115 LDO9pm

Lic CTV 50P ♿

Credit cards 3 5 Ⓥ

LAVERTON
Gloucestershire
Map **4** SP03

GH Leasow House Laverton Meadows (2m SW of Broadway off A46) ☎Stanton (038673) 526

Converted 17th-century Cotswold stone farmhouse with attractive garden in peaceful countryside 2½m SSW of Broadway.

5hc (2⇌ 3fl) (2fb) CTV in all bedrooms Ⓡ B&b£15–£20

🎹 10P

Credit cards 1 3 Ⓥ

See advertisement under Broadway

LAXTON
Nottinghamshire
Map **8** SK76

⊢⊣ **FH** Mrs L S Rose **Moorgate** *(SK726665)* ☎Tuxford (0777) 870274
Closed Xmas Day

¾m S unclass rd.

3rm (1fb) ✕ B&b£8.50–£10 Bdi£12–£14 WBdifr£78 LDO8.30pm

CTV 6P 145acres mixed

Ⓥ

See advertisement under Newark on Trent

LEAMINGTON SPA (ROYAL)
Warwickshire
Map **4** SP36
See plan on page 234

GH Buckland Lodge Hotel 35 Avenue Rd ☎(0926) 23843 Plan **1** *C2*

11hc (4⇌) (2fb) CTV in all bedrooms Ⓡ ✱B&b£13–£20 Bdi£20–£27 WBdifr£119 LDOnoon

Lic 🍽 16P

Credit cards ① ② ③ Ⓥ

Laxton — Leamington Spa

GH Coverdale Private Hotel 8 Portland St ☎(0926) 30400 Plan **2** *C3*

During the summer this fine Georgian house can be recognised by a colourful display of window boxes and hanging baskets. Mr & Mrs Selby run their establishment in a truly professional manner, and hospitality is shown towards every guest.

8hc (2⇌) (2fb) CTV in all bedrooms Ⓡ B&b£12.50–£20

🍽 3P

Ⓥ

GH Glendower 8 Warwick Pl ☎(0926) 22784 Plan **3** *B3*

End terrace Victorian house offering comfortable bed-and-breakfast accommodation. Evening meals by prior arrangement.

9hc (1⇌) (4fb) Ⓡ B&b£10–£12 WB&b£70–£84

🍽 CTV ⊘

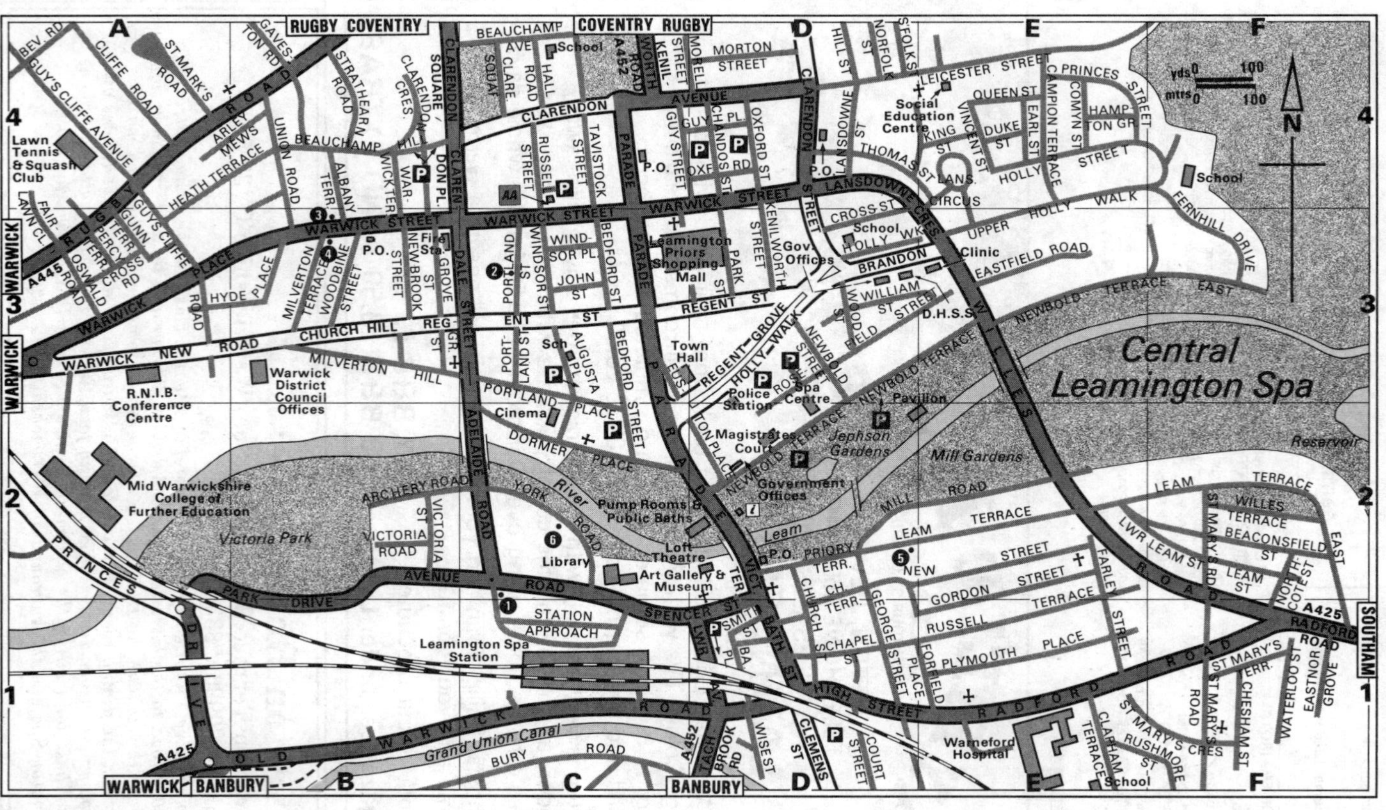

Leamington Spa (Royal)

1 Buckland Lodge Hotel
2 Coverdale Private Hotel
3 Glendower
4 Milverton House Hotel
5 Westella Hotel
6 York House Hotel

GH Milverton House Hotel 1 Milverton Ter (Guestaccom) ☎(0926) 28335 Plan **4** *B3*

12hc (3⇨ 5fl) (2fb) CTV in all bedrooms ✈ Ⓡ B&b£14.50–£20 Bdi£21–£27 WBdi£140–£182

Lic 🍽 5P

Credit card ① Ⓥ

GH *Westella Hotel* 26 Leam Ter ☎(0926) 22710 Plan **5** *D2*

Large, brightly painted Georgian terraced house near town centre.

10hc (3fb) LDO7pm

🍽 CTV 10P

Credit cards ① ③

GH York House Hotel 9 York Rd ☎(0926) 24671 Plan **6** *C2*
Closed Xmas–New Year

Impressive Victorian house overlooking the River Leam and Royal Pump room gardens. Proprietors, Mr and Mrs Davis, offer a warm welcome and friendly service. Accommodation is tastefully furnished throughout.

8hc (2⇨ 2fl) (2fb) CTV in all bedrooms Ⓡ B&b£12–£18 Bdi£20–£26 WBdifr£135 LDO7.30pm

Lic 🍽 3P

FH Mrs R Gibbs **Hill** *(SP343637)* Lewis Rd, Radford Semele ☎(0926) 37571
Closed Xmas

Farmhouse situated in large attractive garden. 2½m SE off A425.

3hc (1fb) ✈ Ⓡ B&b£10–£12 Bdi£18–£20 WBdi£126–£140 LDO5.30pm

🍽 CTV 4P ⌂ 350acres arable beef sheep mixed

Ⓥ

FH Mrs N Ellis **Sharmer** *(SP359624)* Fosse Way, Radford Semele (3m E A425 then ½m S on Fosse Way) ☎Harbury (0926) 612448
Apr–Nov

2hc (1fb) ✈ ✱B&b£10–£12 WBdifr£98

🍽 CTV 3P 120acres arable beef

LEEDS
West Yorkshire
Map **8** SE33

GH Aragon Hotel 250 Stainbeck Ln, Meanwood ☎(0532) 759306
Closed Xmas

Detached stone building with pleasant garden in suburban area.

13hc (7⇨ 2fl) (1fb) CTV in all bedrooms B&b£12.53–£24.38 Bdi£19.54–£31.39 LDO6.30pm

Lic 🍽 23P

Credit cards ① ② ③ ⑤ Ⓥ

GH *Ash Mount Hotel* 22 Wetherby Rd, Roundhay ☎(0532) 658164
Closed Xmas wk

Large detached Victorian house in quiet residential area.

14hc (1fl) (1fb) ✈ Ⓡ

🍽 CTV 11P

GH Clock Hotel 317 Roundhay Rd, Gipton Wood ☎(0532) 490304

Practical accommodation in convenient position for business people.

22hc (3⇨ 2fl) (4fb) Ⓡ B&b£14.50–£18 Bdi£19.68–£25 WBdi£137.76–£175 LDO8pm

Lic 🍽 CTV 16P

GH *Highfield Hotel* 79 Cardigan Rd, Headingley ☎(0532) 752193

Modest three-storey house with nicely fitted bedrooms.

10hc (1fb)

🍽 CTV 7P

GH Oak Villa Hotel 57 Cardigan Rd, Headingley ☎(0532) 758439
rs Xmas

Large Victorian semi-detached house with walled garden.

13hc (4fb) CTV in all bedrooms Ⓡ B&b£12.50–£15 Bdi£19–£21.50 WB&bfr£90 LDO10.30am

🍽 CTV 12P

Ⓥ

GH Trafford House Hotel 18 Cardigan Rd, Headingley ☎(0532) 752034
Closed Xmas

Pair of Victorian town houses with spacious dining room, lounge bar and good bedrooms. Near Headingley cricket ground.

18hc (4fl) (4fb) CTV in 10 bedrooms ✈ ✱B&b£14.95–£34.50 Bdi£21.85–£40 WB&bfr£85 LDOnoon

Lic 🍽 CTV 30P

Ⓥ

LEEK
Staffordshire
Map **7** SJ95

GH Peak Weavers Hotel King St ☎(0538) 383729

Built in 1828, this former convent provides comfortable accommodation close to town centre.

11hc (3⇨ 1fl) (2fb) TV in all bedrooms ✈ (ex guide dogs) Ⓡ B&b£12–£20 Bdi£19.50–£27.50 WBdifr£137.50 LDO8.30pm

Lic 🍽 CTV 8P 4🚗

Credit cards ① ③ Ⓥ

⊢ **FH** Mrs D Needham **Holly Dale** *(SK019556)* Bradnop ☎(0538) 383022
Apr–Oct

Two-storey, stone-built farmhouse typical of the area. 2m SE on unclass road off A523.

2hc ✈ B&b£7.50–£8 WB&bfr£50

🍽 CTV 3P 72acres dairy

LEE-ON-THE-SOLENT
Hampshire
Map **4** SU50

GH Ash House 35 Marine Parade West ☎(0705) 550240

Quiet house overlooking the Solent with many antique items of interest in all rooms.

6hc (2fb) B&b£9.50–£11

CTV 6P nc6yrs

LEICESTER
Leicestershire
Map **4** SK50

GH Alexandra Hotel 342 London Rd, Stoneygate ☎(0533) 703056
Closed Xmas & New Year rs Etr

Recently modernised guesthouse popular with business people.

18hc (3⇌ 6fl) (3fb) CTV in 9 bedrooms ✗ Ⓡ in 8 bedrooms B&b£16.50–£24 Bdi£24–£31.50 LDO6pm

Lic Ⴡ CTV 16P

Credit cards [1] [3]

GH Burlington Hotel Elmfield Av
☎(0533) 705112
Closed Xmas

16hc (4⇌ 5fl) (1fb) CTV in all bedrooms ✗ Ⓡ B&b£15–£24 Bdi£21–£32 WBdi£145–£220 LDO7.30pm

Lic Ⴡ CTV 23P

Credit cards [1] [3]

GH Daval Hotel 292 London Rd ☎(0533) 708234

Predominantly commercial hotel in large Victorian building.

14hc (2fb) CTV in all bedrooms B&b£12–£21.50 Bdi£18.50–£28 WBdifr£135 LDO7pm

Lic Ⴡ CTV 20P

Ⓥ

Leicester — Leominster

GH Old Tudor Rectory Main St, Glenfield
☎(0533) 320220
Closed 24 Dec–2 Jan

3m W A50.

16hc (4⇌ 3fl) (3fb) CTV in all bedrooms Ⓡ ✱B&b£20.70–£24.15 Bdi£27.20–£30.65 LDO8.45pm

Lic Ⴡ 35P

Credit cards [1] [3]

GH Scotia Hotel 10 Westcotes Dr
☎(0533) 549200
Closed Xmas & New Year

Pleasant, predominantly commercial hotel in side street.

10hc Annexe: 6hc (2fb) CTV in all bedrooms Ⓡ B&b£15–£16 Bdi£21–£28 LDO5pm

Lic Ⴡ 5P

GH Stanfre House Hotel 265 London Rd
☎(0533) 704294
Closed 24 Dec–2 Jan

12hc (1fb) ✱B&b£10.75–£13 WB&bfr£75.25

Lic Ⴡ CTV 6P

GH Stoneycroft Hotel 5/7 Elmfield Av
☎(0533) 707605

In a residential area just a few minutes from city centre, large hotel with high proportion of single rooms.

49hc (2fb) CTV in all bedrooms Ⓡ B&b£16–£18 Bdi£23–£25 LDO9pm

Lic Ⴡ CTV 20P

Credit cards [1] [3] Ⓥ

LEIGH
Hereford & Worcester
Map **3** SO75

FH Mrs F S Stewart **Leigh Court** *(SO784535)* ☎Leigh Sinton (0886) 32275
11 Mar–9 Oct

3hc (1fb) ✗ Ⓡ B&b£11–£15 Bdi£19–£23 WBdi£128–£146

Ⴡ CTV 6P ♪ 270acres arable sheep

Ⓥ

LEOMINSTER
Hereford & Worcester
Map **3** SO45

GH Broadward Lodge Guesthouse & Restaurant Hereford Rd ☎(0568) 2914

A Georgian lodge on the outskirts of the town offering reasonably priced accommodation.

6hc (3fb) TV in 3 bedrooms Ⓡ in 4 bedrooms B&b£10–£12 WB&bfr£70 LDO9.15pm

Lic Ⴡ CTV 12P

Credit card [1] Ⓥ

FH Mrs Y Conad ***Eye Court*** *(SO495638)* Eye (3m N between B4361 & A49) ☎(0568) 5718
end Mar–Oct

Part 14th-century farmhouse, now fully modernised, situated in peaceful hamlet; friendly atmosphere.

2hc (2fb) TV in 2 bedrooms ✗ Ⓡ

Lic CTV P 🚗 ⌂ 210acres arable dairy sheep mixed

Credit cards 1 2 3

⊢⊣**FH** M J & S W Lloyd **Menalls** *(SO528611)* Kimbolton (3m NE A4112) ☎(0568) 2605
Apr–Oct

2hc (2fb) ✗ Ⓡ B&bfr£8.50

CTV P 40acres mixed

Ⓥ

⊢⊣**FH** Mrs E M Morris **Park Lodge** Eye (3m N between B4361 & A49) *(SO502643)* ☎Leominster (0568) 5711

2hc (1fb) ✗ Ⓡ B&b£9–£10 Bdi£13.50–£14.15 WBdi£80–£90 LDO6pm

꙰ CTV 6P 2🚗 snooker 200acres mixed

Ⓥ

⊢⊣**FH** Mrs S J Davenport **Stagbatch** *(SO465584)* ☎(0568) 2673
Closed Xmas

A large listed, half-timbered farmhouse with a large stableyard.

3⇌ (1fb) ✗ B&b£9–£10 WB&bfr£60

꙰ CTV 6P nc10yrs ⩰(heated) ℛ(hard) 20acres racing stables sheep

FH A P Black ***Wharton Bank*** Wharton Bank *(SO508556)* ☎(0568) 2575

Stone built hill-top farmhouse of 18th century date, surrounded by attractive Herefordshire countryside.

4hc (1⇌) ✗ Ⓡ

꙰ CTV 5P ⩰ ℛ(grass) 174acres dairy

LERWICK
Shetland
See **Shetland**

LEW
Oxfordshire
Map **4** SP30

Leominster — Lifton

Selected

FH Mrs M J Rouse **The Farmhouse & Restaurant** University Farm *(SP322059)* ☎Bampton Castle (0993) 850297
Closed Xmas & New Year

Picturesque Cotswold farmhouse with comfortable bedrooms, good food and hospitality.

6hc (2⇌ 4⫪) (2fb) CTV in all bedrooms ✗ B&b£15–£17 Bdi£25.50–£27.50 WBdifr£178.50 LDO6pm

Lic ꙰ 25P ♿ nc5yrs 216acres dairy

See advertisement on page 238

LEWDOWN
Devon
Map **2** SX48

GH Stowford House Hotel ☎(056683) 415
Mar–Oct

Spacious and friendly former rectory in an acre of gardens.

6hc (2⇌ 2⫪) ✗ Ⓡ ✱B&b£16.50–£22.50 Bdi£22.50–£25.50 WBdi£155.50–£170 LDO8.30pm

Lic ꙰ CTV 8P nc5yrs

Ⓥ

See advertisement under Okehampton

FH Mrs M E Horn ***Venn Mill*** *(SX484885)* ☎Bridestowe (083786) 288
Etr–Oct

Large modern bungalow set in peaceful surroundings with river fishing and private trout lake. 400 yards from the A30.

4rm (3hc) (1fb) ✗ LDO4pm

CTV 4P 4🚗 ⌂ ⹁ 160acres beef sheep

LEWIS, ISLE OF
Western Isles *Ross & Cromarty*
Map **13**

STORNOWAY
Map **13** NB43

⊢⊣**GH Ardlonan** 29 St Francis Street ☎(0851) 3482
Closed Xmas & New Year

A pleasantly appointed house just off town centre. Communal breakfast tables.

5hc (1fb) ✗ B&b£9–£10

꙰ CTV ⁋

Ⓥ

LEYBURN
North Yorkshire
Map **7** SE19

GH Eastfield Lodge St Matthews Ter ☎Wensleydale (0969) 23196

Comfortable house with spacious accommodation and jovial proprietors.

8hc Annexe: 2⫪ (2fb) CTV in 9 bedrooms TV in 1 bedroom Ⓡ B&b£11–£12.50 WB&bfr£175 (W Feb–early Jun) LDO8.30pm

Lic ꙰ 10P snooker

Credit card 3

LICHFIELD
Staffordshire
Map **7** SK10

GH Oakleigh House Hotel 25 St Chads Rd (Guestaccom) ☎(0543) 262688

10hc (4⇌ 4⫪) CTV in all bedrooms ✗ (ex guide dogs) Ⓡ ✱B&b£17.50–£30 LDO9.30pm

Lic ꙰ 30P nc5yrs

Credit cards 1 3 Ⓥ

LIFTON
Devon
Map **2** SX38

GH Mayfield House Tinhay ☎(0566) 84401

Detached house in good-sized gardens off main A30. Personally run with friendly, informal atmosphere, and good food.

6hc (1⫪) (2fb) ⚟ in all bedrooms CTV in all bedrooms Ⓡ ✱B&b£9.50 Bdi£12–£17.50 WB&b£66.50 LDO5pm

Lic CTV 9P 1🚗 ⌂

Ⓥ

See advertisement under Launceston

LINCOLN
Lincolnshire
Map **8** SK97

GH Brierley House Hotel 54 South Park ☎(0522) 26945
Closed 2½ wks Xmas

Large house with good quality accommodation in quiet cul de sac overlooking park. Large family run hotel.

11hc (2⇌ 4fl) CTV in 8 bedrooms TV in 3 bedrooms ✗ B&b£11.75–£16.95 Bdi£17.25–£22.45 LDOam

Lic 🍽 CTV 🚫

Ⓥ

GH D'Isney Place Hotel Eastgate ☎(0522) 38881

This small luxury hotel in the older part of the city has individually designed bedrooms, some with four-poster beds; substantial breakfasts served to the rooms.

16hc (14⇌ 2fl) (2fb) CTV in all bedrooms Ⓡ B&bfr£34

🍽 7P

Credit cards 1 2 3 5 Ⓥ

GH Ferncliffe House Hotel 2 St Catherines ☎(0522) 22618
Closed Xmas & New Year

An appealing restored Victorian house situated on the A1434 Lincoln to Newark road. The bedrooms are well appointed and overlook the South Common, Golf Course and the magnificent Cathedral.

5hc (2fl) (2fb) CTV in all bedrooms Ⓡ ✱B&bfr£14.25 Bdifr£20.75 LDO7.30pm

Lic 6P

Credit cards 1 5

GH Tennyson Hotel 7 South Park ☎(0522) 21624

Pair of Victorian houses, extensively modernised to provide good accommodation.

8hc (2⇌ 6fl) (1fb) CTV in all bedrooms ✗ Ⓡ B&b£17.50–£19.50 Bdi£25–£27.50 WBdi£175 LDO7.45pm

Lic 🍽 8P

Credit cards 1 3 Ⓥ

LINDRIDGE
Hereford & Worcester
Map **7** SO66

FH Mrs J M May **Middle Woodston** *(SO673696)* ☎Eardiston (058470) 244
Etr–Oct

A comfortable farmhouse with extensive views across the beautiful Teme Valley. Home-made bread a speciality.

3hc (1fb) ✗ Ⓡ B&b£9–£10 Bdi£15–£16 WBdifr£100 LDO5pm

🍽 CTV 6P nc5yrs 10acres fruit mixed stock

Ⓥ

LINLITHGOW
Lothian *West Lothian*
Map **11** NS97

FH Mrs A Hay **Belsyde House** *(NS976755)* Lanark Rd ☎(0506) 842098
Closed Xmas

Well maintained Georgian farmhouse in tree studded grounds above town. 1½m SW A706.

4hc (1fb) ✗ Ⓡ B&b£9–£10 Bdi£15–£16 WBdifr£105 LDOnoon

🍽 CTV 10P 🏠 106acres beef sheep

FH Mrs W Erskine **Woodcockdale** *(NS973760)* Lanark Rd ☎(0506) 842088

Modern, comfortable two-storey house lying adjacent to farmyard and outbuildings. Shared table for meals. 1½m SW on A706.

4rm (2fb) ✗ B&b£9–£10 Bdi£14 WB&bfr£60

🍽 CTV 12P 🏠 700acres dairy sheep mixed

Ⓥ

LISKEARD
Cornwall
Map **2** SX26

↦**GH Elnor** 1 Russell St ☎(0579) 42472
Closed Xmas

6hc (1🚿) (1fb) ✗ Ⓡ B&b£9–£11 Bdi£13.50–£15.50 WBdi£88–£101.50

Lic 🅼 CTV 6P

Ⓥ

↦**FH** S A Kendall **Tencreek** *(SX265637)* ☎(0579) 43379

A well-kept 16th-century listed farmhouse set in beautiful countryside, 1m from Liskeard.

2hc ✗ Ⓡ B&b£9–£10.50 WB&bfr£59

CTV 2P 250acres mixed

LITTLE BREDY
Dorset
Map **3** SY58

FH Mrs D M Fry ***Foxholes*** *(SY582882)* ☎Long Bredy (03083) 395
Closed 20–27 Dec

2m E of village.

6rm (5hc) (6fb) Ⓡ in 4 bedrooms LDO4.15pm

Lic 🅼 CTV 8P ⌂ 390acres dairy mixed

LITTLE DEWCHURCH
Hereford & Worcester
Map **3** SO53

↦**FH** Mrs G Lee **Cwm Craig** *(SO535322)* ☎Carey (043270) 250

Spacious Georgian farmhouse in quiet wooded surroundings. Hereford 6 miles, Ross-on-Wye 7 miles. Few minutes drive from the Wye Valley.

3hc (1fb) ✗ Ⓡ B&b£7.50–£9 WB&bfr£50

🅼 CTV 5P 190acres arable beef

Ⓥ

See advertisement under Hereford

LITTLEHAMPTON
West Sussex
Map **4** TQ00

GH Old Windmill House 83 South Ter ☎(0903) 724939

Comfortable seafront house with friendly atmosphere. A non-smoking establishment.

9hc (2fb) ⊘ in all bedrooms CTV in all bedrooms ✗ Ⓡ B&bfr£10.50 WB&bfr£70 LDO9pm

Lic 🅼 CTV ⊘

Credit cards 1 2 3 5 Ⓥ

GH Regency Hotel 85 South Ter ☎(0903) 717707
Closed Xmas

Small, neatly-furnished house on seafront with a friendly atmosphere.

8hc (3fb) CTV in all bedrooms Ⓡ B&b£11.75–£15 Bdi£14–£17.25 WBdifr£95.75 LDO9pm

Lic 🅼 CTV ⊘

Credit cards 1 3 Ⓥ

LITTLE HAVEN
Dyfed
Map **2** SM81

GH Pendyffryn Private Hotel ☎Broad Haven (043783) 337 (due to change to Broadhaven (0437) 781337)
mid May–Sep

Pleasant detached house in elevated position.

7hc (6fb) TV in all bedrooms ✗ Ⓡ B&b£11.50 Bdi£16.75 WBdifr£98.90 LDO6.45pm

Lic 🅼 CTV 6P nc4yrs

LITTLEHEMPSTON
Devon
Map **3** SX86

FH Mrs E P Miller **Buckyette** *(SX812638)* ☎Staverton (080426) 638
May–Sep

7rm (6hc) (4fb) ✗ ✱B&b£9.75–£9.77 Bdi£14.50 WBdi£87.50–£94.50 LDO6.30pm

CTV 8P 51acres grassland

Ⓥ

LITTLE HEREFORD
Hereford & Worcester
Map **7** SO56

↦**FH** Mrs H Williams **Lower Upton** *(SO547663)* Lower Upton (1½m S of A456) ☎Brimfield (058472) 322
Closed Xmas & New Year

Impressive Victorian farmhouse set in peaceful, picturesque surroundings; offering friendly service and choice of meals.

3hc (1fb) ✗ B&bfr£8.50 Bdifr£12.50 WBdifr£87.50 LDO6.30pm

🅼 CTV 4P 167acres mixed

LITTLE MILL
Gwent
Map **3** SO30

FH Mrs A Bradley **Pentwyn** *(SO325035)* ☎(049528) 249
rs Dec & Jan

A 16th-century, traditional Welsh long house set in ½acre garden with swimming pool situated off A472, ½m E of junction with A4042.

4hc (1fb) ✗ Ⓡ ✱B&b£10 Bdi£15.50 WBdi£96 LDO6pm

Lic 🅼 CTV P nc4yrs ⌒(heated) 120acres arable

Ⓥ

LITTLE PETHERICK
Cornwall
Map **2** SW97

GH The Old Mill ☎Rumford (0841) 540388

6hc (2⇌ 2🚿) (1fb) ⊘ in 1 bedroom B&b£9.50–£13.50 Bdi£16.50–£20.50 WBdi£109.05–£118.80

Lic CTV 10P

Ⓥ

LITTON
Derbyshire
Map **7** SK17

↦**FH** Mrs A Barnsley **Dale House** *(SK160750)* ☎Tideswell (0298) 871309
Closed Xmas →

Large, stone-built Edwardian farmhouse situated on edge of picturesque village off B6049.

3rm (1hc) (1fb) ✗ B&bfr£8.50

₪ CTV 6P nc5yrs 100acres sheep

LITTON
North Yorkshire
Map **7** SD97

GH Park Bottom ☎Arncliffe (075677) 235

Stone-built house in beautiful scenery offering modern accommodation and good service.

8rm (7hc 5⥲) (1fb) Ⓡ ✱B&b£12.50–£15 Bdi£17–£22 WBdifr£122 LDO6pm

Lic ₪ CTV 16P nc5yrs

Ⓥ

LIVERPOOL
Merseyside
Map **7** SJ39

GH Aachen Hotel 91 Mount Pleasant ☎051-709 3477
rs 20 Dec–7 Jan

Cosy little hotel with well equipped rooms and competitive prices.

17hc (3⇌) (6fb) CTV in all bedrooms ✗ Ⓡ B&b£14–£17 Bdi£20–£23 WBdi£140 LDO8.30pm

Lic ₪ CTV 2P 3🚗

Credit cards 1 2 3 5 Ⓥ

GH New Manx Hotel 39 Catherine St ☎051-708 6171

Listed Victorian building with modern facilities.

15hc (3fb) CTV in all bedrooms Ⓡ B&b£11.50–£13 WB&bfr£50

₪ CTV ℙ̸

Credit cards 1 2 3 5 Ⓥ

LIZARD
Cornwall
Map **3** SW71

GH Parc Brawse House ☎(0326) 290466

Comfortable character house, friendly attention from family. Property overlooks sea across farmland.

6hc Ⓡ B&b£9.90–£11.50 Bdi£13.95–£16.50 WBdifr£94.50 LDO7pm

Lic CTV 6P

Credit card 1 Ⓥ

GH Penmenner House Hotel
Penmenner Rd ☎(0326) 290370
Apr–Oct

Friendly family hotel. Home cooking including local produce, fresh fish, Cornish cream.

8hc (5⥲) (2fb) Ⓡ ✱B&b£11.50–£12.50 Bdi£17.50–£18.50 WBdifr£119 LDO6pm

Lic ₪ CTV 10P

LLANBERIS
Gwynedd
Map **6** SH56

GH *Lake View Hotel* Tan-y-Pant ☎(0286) 870422

Cottage-style guesthouse alongside A4086 overlooking Llyn Padarn. 1m NW of town.

10hc (7⥲) (3fb) CTV in 7 bedrooms ✗ Ⓡ in 7 bedrooms LDO9.30pm

Lic ₪ CTV 10P

LLANBOIDY
Dyfed
Map **2** SN22

⊢⊣**FH** Mrs B Worthing **Maencochyrwyn** *(SN181243)* Login ☎Hebron (09947) 283
Apr–Oct

Small isolated farmhouse in elevated position overlooking its own farmland and hills. 3½m WNW of Llanboidy on unclass road to East Login/Llanglydwen road.

3rm (1fb) ⚟ in 2 bedrooms ✗ B&b£9–£10 Bdi£14–£15 WBdi£90–£100 LDO4pm

CTV P 80acres dairy

Ⓥ

⊢⊣**FH** Mrs M A E Lewis **Maesgwyn Isaf** *(SS203229)* ☎(09946) 385
Apr–Oct

A bright, modern farmhouse neatly tucked away in a secluded valley.

3rm ⚟ in 1 bedroom ✗ B&b£8.50–£9 Bdi£13.50–£14 WBdifr£90 LDO11am

₪ CTV

180acres beef dairy

Ⓥ

LLANDDEINIOLEN
Gwynedd
Map **6** SH56

Selected

FH Mrs Kettle ***Ty'n-Rhos*** *(SH548672)* Seion (Guestaccom) ☎Port Dinorwic (0248) 670489
Closed Xmas & New Year

Farm has been extended to provide modern hotel comforts while retaining farm atmosphere. Imaginative country cooking using fresh produce. ½m N unclass rd.

Winner for Wales of the 1987/8 AA Farmhouse of the Year Award.

9⇌ (3fb) CTV in all bedrooms ✗ Ⓡ B&b£13–£16.50 Bdi£19.50–£23 WBdi£120–£150 (W only 18 Jul–4 Sep) LDO6.30pm

Lic ₪ 10P 72acres mixed

Ⓥ

LLANDEILO
Dyfed
Map **2** SN62

FH N & J Card **Llwyndewl Farm Guesthouse** *(SN658177)* Trapp (3m SE off A483) ☎Llandybie (0269) 850362
Closed Jan

A warm welcome and good home cooking are assured at this delightful old farmhouse.

4rm (1hc) (1fb) ✗ ✱B&b£8.75–£9.25 Bdi£12.75–£13.25 WBdifr£92.75 LDO4.30pm

Lic ₪ 12P nc6yrs 6acres small holding

Ⓥ

LLANDELOY
Dyfed
Map **2** SM82

FH Mrs M Jones **Upper Vanley** *(SM862245)* ☎Croesgoch (03483) 418

Friendly Welsh farmhouse where good home cooking is a speciality. Vegetarians are well-catered for. Useful play area for children.

8hc (4⇌) (5fb) CTV in all bedrooms Ⓡ ✱B&b£8–£10 Bdi£12–£16 WBdi£84–£112 (W only Whit–Aug) LDO6pm

₪ CTV P 150acres dairy

Ⓥ

LLANDINAM
Powys
Map **6** SO08

⊢⊣**FH** Mrs M C Davies **Trewythen** *(SJ003901)* ☎Caersws (068684) 444
May–Sep

Farmhouse dating from 1820 situated 2m SW of Caersws, on unclass road off B4569.

2hc (1fb) B&b£9–£10 Bdifr£13–£14 WBdifr£90

₪ CTV P arable beef sheep mixed

Ⓥ

LLANDOGO
Gwent
Map **3** SO50

GH *Brown's Hotel & Restaurant* ☎Dean (0594) 530262
Feb–Nov

Proprietor-run tea rooms and guesthouse. Walking distance of the river.

7hc (1⇌) LDO7.30pm

Lic CTV 20P

Selected

INN Sloop ☎Dean (0594) 530291

Former mill overlooking Wye Valley with modern extension providing charming, beautifully furnished bedrooms of character.

4hc (3⇌ 1⥲) CTV in 3 bedrooms TV in 1 bedroom Ⓡ B&b£15.50–£21 Lunch £4.50–£9&alc Dinner10pm £4.50–£9&alc

₪ 40P ⌧ nc12yrs

Credit cards 1 2 3 5 Ⓥ

LLANDOVERY
Dyfed
Map **3** SN73

GH Llwyncelyn ☎(0550) 20566
Closed Xmas
Proprietor-run comfortable guesthouse with grounds running down to river.
6hc (3fb) ✖ B&b£11–£13 Bdi£18.75–£20.75 WBdi£119.70–£131.25 LDO7.30pm
Lic ▥ CTV 12P 🎣
ⓥ

LLANDRINDOD WELLS
Powys
Map **3** SO06
See also **Crossgates** & **Penybont**

GH Corven Hall Country (Howey 2m S A483) ☎(0597) 3368
Closed Xmas
7hc (5⫪) (5fb) Ⓡ B&b£9.50–£11.50 Bdi£15–£17 WBdi£92–£108 LDO7pm
Lic ▥ CTV 10P 2🏠 🏠
ⓥ

GH Griffin Lodge Hotel Temple St (Guestaccom) ☎(0597) 2432
Attractive Victorian house with cosy modern bedrooms and intimate restaurant.
8hc (4⫪) Ⓡ B&b£13–£17.50 Bdi£19–£24 WBdi£134–£165 LDO9pm
Lic ▥ CTV 8P
Credit cards 1 2 3 5 ⓥ

⊢⊣**FH** Mrs P Lewis **Bailey Einon** *(SO078616)* Cefnllys ☎(0597) 2449
May–Sep
Stone-built Georgian farmhouse, part of which dates back to the 17th-century. 2m E of town off A483.
3hc ✖ B&b£8.50–£9.50 Bdi£13–£14 LDO4pm
CTV 3P nc14yrs 280acres beef sheep mixed

⊢⊣**FH** Mrs C Nixon **Brynhir** *(SJ067586)* (Howey 2m S A483, unclass rd E 1m) ☎(0597) 2425
Mar–Nov
Remote 17th-century hill farm, traditionally furnished. Pony for children to ride. 1m E on unclass road.
7hc (2⫪) (2fb) 🚭 in 2 bedrooms Ⓡ B&b£9–£9.50 Bdi£13–£14 WBdi£87–£94 (W only Jun, Jul & Aug) LDO5pm
10P 🎣 150acres mixed working hill farm
ⓥ

⊢⊣**FH** Mrs D Evans **Dolberthog** *(SO048602)* Dolberthog Ln ☎(0597) 2255
Apr–Oct
Victorian stone farmhouse on outskirts of town.
3hc (2fb) ✖ B&b£8.50–£9 Bdi£12.50–£13 WBdifr£90
▥ CTV 3P 🎣 250acres mixed

⊢⊣**FH** Mrs S A Evans **Highbury** *(SO044628)* Llanyre (1m W off A4081) ☎(0597) 2716
Apr–Oct
3rm (2hc) (1fb) ✖ B&b£8–£9 Bdi£12.50–£13.50 WBdi£85–£90 LDO3pm
▥ CTV 3P 1🚗
20acres sheep
ⓥ

⊢⊣**FH** Mrs R Jones **Holly** *(SJ045593)* (Howey 2m S A483) ☎(0597) 2402
Apr–Nov
18th century building close to the A483, on the edge of the village, surrounded by open country.
3hc (1⫪) (1fb) ✖ B&b£9–£10 Bdi£13–£14 WBdifr£86 LDO5pm
▥ CTV P 70acres beef sheep

FH Mr & Mrs R Bufton **Three Wells** *(SO062586)* (Howey 2m S A483, unclass rd E 1m) ☎(0597) 2484
Set in beautiful countryside overlooking lake. Detached farmhouse with modern bedrooms and cosy bar. Good food. Fishing available. →

12hc (6⇌ 6fl) (3fb) CTV in all bedrooms ® *B&b£10–£12.50 Bdi£15–£17.50 WBdi£98–£119 LDO5pm

Lic lift ꟾ CTV 20P ✓ U 50acres beef sheep mixed

Ⓥ

LLANDRINIO
Powys
Map **7** SJ21

FH Mrs G M Wigley **New Hall** *(SJ296171)*
☎Llanymynech (0691) 830384
Apr–Sep

Modernised farmhouse, partly dating from 16th century.

2hc (1⇌ 1fl) (2fb) ✗ B&b£10 Bdi£15 WBdifr£105 LDO5pm

CTV P snooker 265acres arable beef dairy sheep mixed

FH Mrs S M Pritchard ***Rhos*** *(SO276174)*
☎Llanymynech (0691) 830785

3rm (1hc 1⇌) (1fb) ⅟ in 2 bedrooms CTV in 1 bedroom LDO5.30pm

ꟾ CTV 8P 265acres arable beef

LLANDUDNO
Gwynedd
Map **6** SH78
See plan on pages 246–247

GH Braemar Hotel 5 St Davids Rd
☎(0492) 76257 Plan **1** *B3*

Edwardian house in residential area 5 minutes from beach and shops.

9hc (2fb) ⅟ in 2 bedrooms CTV in 1 bedroom *B&b£8–£8.50 Bdi£10.50–£11.50 WBdifr£75 (W only Jun–Aug)

ꟾ CTV ℙ̸ nc7yrs

Ⓥ

⊢→**GH Brannock Private Hotel**
36 St Davids Rd ☎(0492) 77483
Plan **2** *B3*
Closed Xmas & New Year

Edwardian house in residential area 5 minutes from beach and shops.

7hc (3fl) (2fb) CTV in all bedrooms ® B&b£9–£10 Bdi£12–£13 WBdifr£77 LDO5pm

ꟾ 5P nc

Credit cards 1 3 Ⓥ

GH Brigstock Private Hotel 1 St David's Pl ☎(0492) 76416 Plan **3** *B3*
Mar–Oct

In corner position in quiet residential area 5 minutes to shops and beach.

10hc (2⇌) (2fb) CTV in all bedrooms ✗ ® *B&b£9.50–£10.50 Bdi£13.50–£14.50 WBdi£78–£90

Lic ꟾ CTV 7P nc3yrs

GH *Britannia Hotel* 15 Craig-y-Don Pde
☎(0492) 77185 Plan **4** *E3*
Closed Xmas

Single-fronted Victorian terraced house on Promenade, ¾ mile from main shopping area.

9hc (4fl) (5fb) CTV in all bedrooms ® LDO5pm

ꟾ CTV ℙ̸

⊢→**GH Bryn Rosa** 16 Abbey Rd ☎(0492) 78215 Plan **5** *B4*
Closed Xmas

Listed Victorian semi-detached house with friendly atmosphere. Short walk to sea and town centre.

7hc (2fl) (2fb) CTV in all bedrooms ® B&b£8–£9.50 Bdi£12–£13.50 WBdifr£80 LDO4.30pm

ꟾ CTV 4P nc2yrs

Credit cards 1 3 Ⓥ

REMEMBER

Prices quoted in the gazetteer are minimum double room occupancy to maximum single room occupancy per person.

GH Bryn-y-Mor Private Hotel North Pde
☎(0492) 76790 Plan **6** *C4*
Mar–Nov

Semi-detached Victorian house on Promenade 2 minutes from shops.

15hc (3⇌) (5fb) ⅟ in 3 bedrooms CTV in all bedrooms ✗ ® B&b£10–£12.50 Bdi£14–£16 WBdifr£99 LDO6pm

ꟾ CTV 1P ⌂

Ⓥ

Selected

GH Buile Hill Private Hotel 46 St Mary's Rd ☎(0492) 76972 Plan **7** *B3*
Etr–mid Oct

A large detached house in a corner position within easy walking distance of the shops and the seafront. The bedrooms and public rooms are attractive and comfortable and good food is served by friendly staff.

13hc (3⇌ 4fl) ✗ ® B&b£12–£18 Bdi£15–£22 WBdi£100–£130 LDO4pm

Lic ꟾ CTV 6P

⊢→**GH Capri Hotel** 70 Church Walks
☎(0492) 79177 Plan **8** *B4*

Victorian terraced house offering a warm welcome and bright comfortable bedrooms. Situated within easy reach of shops, pier and gardens.

8hc (6fb) B&b£8.50–£11.50 Bdi£11–£14 WBdi£74–£95 LDO4.30pm

Lic ꟾ CTV 6P nc3yrs

Ⓥ

GH Carmel Private Hotel 17 Craig-y-Don Pde, Promenade ☎(0492) 77643 Plan **9** *E3*
Etr–Oct

Terraced Victorian house on Promenade, ¾m from main shopping area.

10hc (5fl) (4fb) ® *B&b£9–£11 Bdi£12.50–£15.50 WBdifr£91 LDO4pm

ꟾ CTV 7P nc4yrs

GH *Hotel Carmen* Carmen Sylva Rd, Craig-y-Don ☎(0492) 76361 Plan **10** *E3*

Spacious house in quiet location close to the promenade. Attractive and comfortable public rooms.

15hc (1⇋) (4fb) CTV in 7 bedrooms LDO6.45pm

Lic ₩ CTV ₱

↦ **GH Cliffbury Private Hotel** 34 St Davids Rd ☎(0492) 77224 Plan **11** *B3*
Closed Xmas

Semi-detached house in quiet residential area, a short walk to shops and beach.

6hc (1⇋) (2fb) CTV in all bedrooms Ⓡ B&b£8.50–£9.25 Bdi£11–£12.50 WBdi£79–£87.50 LDO6pm

₩ 6P nc5yrs

Ⓥ

Llandudno

GH Craig Ard Private Hotel Arvon Av ☎(0492) 77318 Plan **12** *B4*
Mar–Dec

Semi-detached Victorian house in quiet residential street adjacent to beaches and shops.

17hc (5fb) Ⓡ ✱B&b£8.50–£10 Bdi£12.50–£14 LDO4pm

Lic ₩ CTV 12P

Ⓥ

Selected

GH Craiglands Private Hotel 7 Carmen Sylva Rd, Craig Y Don ☎(0492) 75090 Plan **13** *E2*
Mar–Nov

Situated in a quiet part of town, but close to the Promenade.

6fl (1fb) CTV in all bedrooms Ⓡ ✱B&b£10.25–£12.50 Bdi£13.50–£15.95 WBdi£95–£125 LDO4pm

₩ CTV ₱ nc4yrs

GH Cranberry House 12 Abbey Rd ☎(0492) 79760 Plan **32** *B4*
Etr–mid Oct →

Close to the promenade and beach, this well maintained hotel offers attractive accommodation and a varied menu using fresh local produce.

5hc ✗ in all bedrooms ✗ Ⓡ ✱B&b£9–£11 Bdi£14–£16 WBdi£93 LDOnoon

卌 CTV 3P nc12yrs

GH Cumberland Hotel North Pde ☏(0492) 76379 Plan **14** *C4*

Victorian mid-terrace by Central Promenade and adjacent shops.

18hc (1fl) (10fb) CTV in all bedrooms ✗ B&b£9.50–£10.50 Bdi£13–£14 WBdi£90–£97 LDO6.30pm

Lic 卌 CTV 3P

Ⓥ

GH Grafton Hotel 13 Craig-y-Don Pde ☏(0492) 76814 Plan **15** *E3*
Mar–Nov

Double-fronted Victorian mid-terrace on Promenade. ¾m from main shopping area.

20hc (5⇌ 13fl) (4fb) CTV in all bedrooms Ⓡ ✱B&b£15 Bdi£22 WBdifr£146.30 LDO5.30pm

Lic 卌 15P pool table

Credit cards 1 3 Ⓥ

GH Granby Deganwy Av ☏(0492) 76095 Plan **16** *B3*
Apr–Oct

Llandudno

Bright, well appointed guesthouse in quiet residential area.

8hc (3fl) (4fb) CTV in all bedrooms ✗ Ⓡ ✱B&b£9–£9.50 Bdi£12–£12.50 WBdi£84–£87.50 LDO4.30pm

Lic CTV 6P

Credit card 3 Ⓥ

GH Heath House Hotel Central Prom ☏(0492) 76538 Plan **17** *D3*

Restored and extended Victorian building with sea and mountain views.

22hc (12⇌) (14fb) CTV in 12 bedrooms ✗ Ⓡ in 4 bedrooms B&b£12–£24 Bdi£18–£30 WBdi£126–£210 LDO4pm

Lic 卌 CTV 2P

Ⓥ

See advertisement on page 246

GH Hên Dy Hotel 10 North Pde ☏(0492) 76184 Plan **18** *B4*
Closed Jan–Feb

A well appointed seaside hotel with friendly and helpful owners.

14hc (2fl) (2fb) Ⓡ ✱B&bfr£12 Bdifr£15 LDO7pm

Lic 卌 CTV P

GH Hilary Hotel 32 St Davids Rd ☏(0492) 75623 Plan **19** *B3*
Apr–Oct

A bright, modern hotel with well-equipped bedrooms and public rooms in a quiet position between the two sea fronts.

8hc (1⇌ 1fl) (3fb) ✗ Ⓡ ✱B&bfr£8.50 Bdifr£12 LDO6.30pm

CTV 3P

GH *Lynwood Private Hotel* Clonmel St ☏(0492) 76613 Plan **20** *C3*
Mar–Nov & Xmas

Four-storey single-fronted mid-Victorian terrace just off Promenade near shops.

12hc (1fl) (8fb) Ⓡ

Lic 卌 CTV P

GH Mayfair Private Hotel 4 Abbey Rd ☏(0492) 76170 Plan **21** *B4*
Mar–Oct

13hc (5⇌ 2fl) (6fb) CTV in all bedrooms Ⓡ B&b£10–£12 Bdi£14–£16 WBdifr£105 LDO6pm

Lic 卌 CTV 3P

Ⓥ

GH *Minion Private Hotel* 21–23 Carmen Sylva Rd, Craig-y-Don ☏(0492) 77740 Plan **22** *E2*
Etr–mid Oct

Detached Edwardian house in quiet residential area adjacent to beach.

16hc (6⥂) (4fb) LDO5pm

Lic CTV 8P

GH Montclare Hotel North Pde ☎(0492) 77061 Plan **23** *B4*
Mar–Oct

Victorian mid-terrace overlooking bay adjacent to shops & pier.

16hc (1⥂) (8fb) CTV in all bedrooms B&b£10.50–£12 Bdi£14–£15.50 WBdifr£90 LDO6pm

Lic 4P

Ⓥ

GH *Nant-y-Glyn* 59 Church Walks ☎(0492) 75915 Plan **24** *B4*
Closed Dec & Jan

Semi-detached house on high ground just a short distance from the sea and town centre.

10hc (3fb) ✖ LDO5.30pm

💬 CTV ⨳ nc5yrs

GH Orotava Private Hotel 105 Glan-y-Mor Rd, Penrhyn Bay ☎(0492) 49780 Plan **25** *E3*
Etr–Oct

Detached Edwardian house, 2 miles from town below Little Orme.

6hc ✖ B&bfr£11 Bdifr£16 WBdifr£112 LDO6.30pm

CTV 6P nc6yrs

Ⓥ

Llandudno

GH *Plas Madoc Private Hotel* 60 Church Walks ☎(0492) 76514 Plan **26** *B4*

Semi-detached Victorian house, close to shops and Promenade.

9hc (2fb) ✖ Ⓡ LDO4pm

Lic 💬 CTV 6P nc3yrs

⊢⊣**GH Rosaire Private Hotel** 2 St Seiriol's Rd ☎(0492) 77677 Plan **28** *B2*
Feb–Nov

Edwardian house in quiet corner position of residential area.

10hc (3fb) Ⓡ B&b£8–£9.50 Bdi£11–£12.50 WBdifr£76 LDO4pm

Lic CTV 6P nc3yrs

GH Rose-Tor Mostyn St ☎(0492) 70433 Plan **29** *B4*

Well-run family guesthouse with good facilities.

9hc (1⇌ 8⥂) (2fb) CTV in all bedrooms Ⓡ B&b£11.50–£13.80 Bdi£16.67–£18.97 WBdifr£115 LDO7.30pm

Lic 💬 ⨳

Credit cards 1 2 3 Ⓥ

See advertisement on page 248

⊢⊣**GH St Davids** 32 Clifton Rd ☎(0492) 79216 Plan **30** *B3*

Semi-detached building in central position just off sea front.

6hc (3fb) B&b£8.50–£10 Bdi£11–£12.50 WBdifr£77

Lic 💬 CTV ⨳

⊢⊣**GH St Hilary Hotel** 16 Promenade, Craig-y-Don Pde ☎(0492) 75551 Plan **31** *E3*

Single-fronted Victorian terraced house ¾ mile from main shopping area.

11hc (6⥂) (6fb) CTV in all bedrooms Ⓡ B&b£9–£11.50 Bdi£12.50–£15 WBdi£87.50–£105 LDO5pm

💬 CTV ⨳

Ⓥ

GH *Stratford Hotel* Promenade, Craig-y-Don ☎(0492) 77962 Plan **33** *E3*

10hc (6⥂) (3fb) ✖ Ⓡ

Lic 💬 CTV ⨳

⊢⊣**GH Tan-y-Marian Private Hotel** 87 Abbey Rd, West Shore ☎(0492) 77727 Plan **34** *A3*
Mar–Oct

Family-run private hotel near the town's West Shore.

8hc (2⥂) (2fb) Ⓡ B&b£9–£11 Bdi£13–£16 WBdi£85–£100 LDO7pm

Lic 💬 CTV 4P 2🚗 nc2yrs

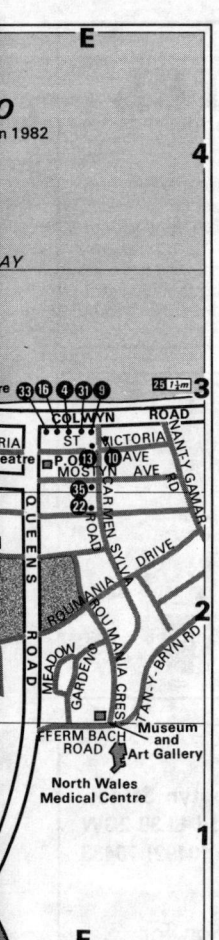

Ⓥ

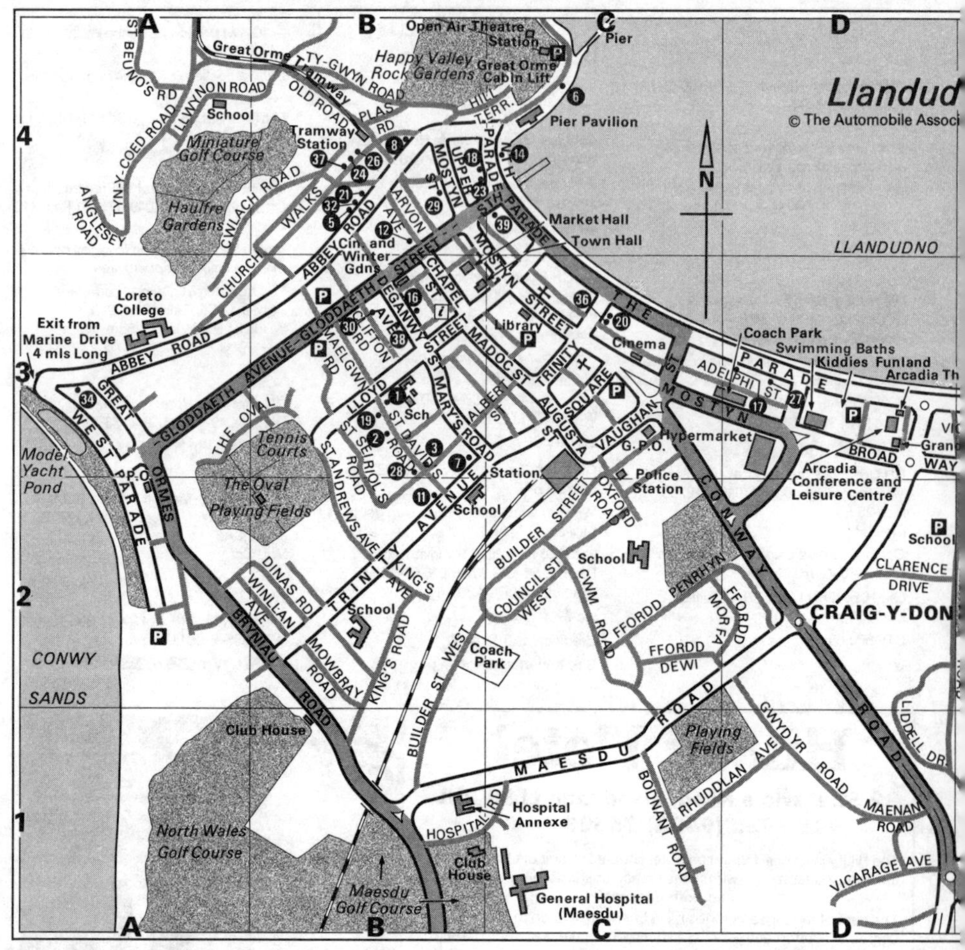
A
B
C
D
4
3
2
1
Llandud
© The Automobile Associ
N
Open Air Theatre
Station
Pier
Happy Valley
Rock Gardens
Great Orme
Cabin Lift
Great Orme Tramway
TY-GWYN ROAD
OLD ROAD
ST BEUNO'S RD
LLWYNON ROAD
School
TYN-Y-COED ROAD
ANGLESEY ROAD
Miniature
Golf Course
Haulfre
Gardens
CWLACH ROAD
Tramway
Station
PLAS RD
HILL TERR.
Pier Pavilion
MOSTYN ST
UPPER
N'TH PARADE
STH PARADE
Market Hall
Town Hall
LLANDUDNO
WALKS
ABBEY ROAD
ARVON AVE
Cin. and
Winter
Gdns
CHURCH
CHAPEL ST
MOSTYN ST
Loreto
College
Exit from
Marine Drive
4 mls Long
ABBEY ROAD
GLODDAETH AVENUE
GLODDAETH STREET
DEGANWY AVE
CLIFTON RD
MAELGWYN RD
STREET
Library
MADOC ST
TRINITY SQUARE
THE PARADE
Cinema
Coach Park
Swimming Baths
Kiddies Funland
Arcadia Th
ADELPHI ST
PARADE
MOSTYN ST
GREAT
WEST PARADE
Model
Yacht
Pond
P.O.
ORMES
THE OVAL
Tennis
Courts
The Oval
Playing Fields
LLOYD ST
Sch
ST DAVID'S ROAD
ST SEIRIOL'S ROAD
ST ANDREWS AVE
ST MARY'S ROAD
ALBERT ST
AUGUSTA ST
VAUGHAN ST
G.P.O.
Hypermarket
BROAD
WAY
Grand
Arcadia
Conference and
Leisure Centre
Station
School
TRINITY AVENUE
Police
Station
OXFORD ROAD
BUILDER STREET
School
School
CLARENCE
DRIVE
CONWAY ROAD
CRAIG-Y-DON
DINAS RD
WINLLAN AVE
KING'S AVE
School
COUNCIL ST WEST
CWM ROAD
FFORDD PENRHYN
FFORDD MORFA
FFORDD DEWI
BRYNIAU ROAD
MOWBRAY ROAD
KING'S ROAD
BUILDER ST WEST
Coach
Park
CONWY
SANDS
Club House
MAESDU ROAD
Playing
Fields
GWYDYR ROAD
RHUDDLAN AVE
BODNANT ROAD
LIDDELL DR
MAENAN ROAD
VICARAGE AVE
Hospital
Annexe
HOSPITAL RD
North Wales
Golf Course
Club
House
General Hospital
(Maesdu)
Maesdu
Golf Course

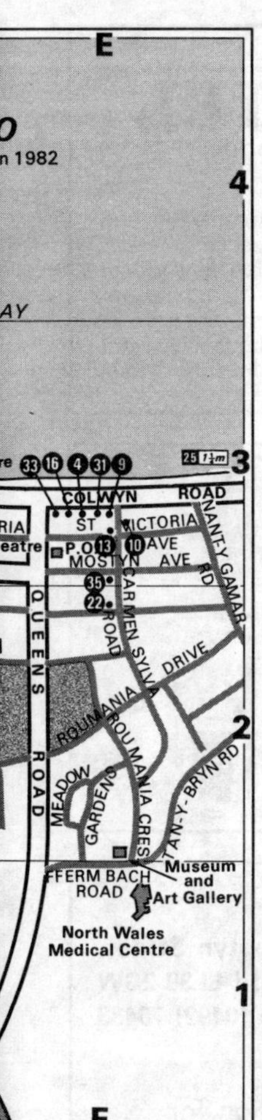

Llandudno

Llandudno

1 Braemar Hotel
2 Brannock Private Hotel
3 Brigstock Private Hotel
4 Britannia Hotel
5 Bryn Rosa
6 Bryn-y-Mor Private Hotel
7 Buile Hill Private Hotel
8 Capri Hotel
9 Carmel Private Hotel
10 Hotel Carmen
11 Cliffbury Private Hotel
12 Craig Ard Private Hotel
13 Craiglands Private Hotel
14 Cumberland Hotel
15 Grafton Hotel
16 Granby
17 Heath House Hotel
18 Hen Dy Hotel
19 Hilary Hotel
20 Lynwood Private Hotel
21 Mayfair Private Hotel
22 Minion Private Hotel
23 Montclare Hotel
24 Nant-y-Glyn
25 Orotava Private Hotel
26 Plas Madoc Private Hotel
27 White Lodge Hotel
28 Rosaire Private Hotel
29 Rose Tor
30 St Davids
31 St Hilary Hotel
32 Cranberry House
33 Stratford Hotel
34 Tan-y-Marian Private Hotel
35 Tilstone Private Hotel
36 Uxbridge Hotel
37 Warwick Hotel
38 Wedgewood Hotel
39 Wilton Hotel

⊢⊣**GH Tilstone Private Hotel** Carmen Sylva Rd, Craig-y-Don ☎(0492) 75588 Plan **35** *E3*

On corner position in quiet secondary shopping area; short walk to beach.

7hc ✗ B&b£8.50–£9 Bdi£14–£16 WBdifr£90 LDO4.30pm

Lic 🍴 CTV P̸ nc14yrs

GH Uxbridge Hotel Clonmel St ☎(0492) 77383 Plan **36** *C3*
Closed Xmas

This comfortable hotel is conveniently situated not far from the shops and the promenade.

12hc (5⇌) (6fb) CTV in all bedrooms ✗ Ⓡ
✱B&bfr£10.50 Bdifr£14.50 LDO6.30pm

Lic 🍴 CTV P̸

Credit card 3

GH Warwick Hotel 56 Church Walks ☎(0492) 76823 Plan **37** *B4*
mid Apr–mid Oct

Semi-detached Victorian house with good views over the town.

17hc (6⇌) (9fb) CTV in all bedrooms Ⓡ B&b£10.50–£12 Bdi£15–£16.50 WBdi£97–£107 LDO6.45pm

Lic 🍴 CTV P̸ ⌂

Ⓥ

See advertisement on page 248

Credit Cards

1 Access/Euro/ Mastercard
2 American Express
3 Barclaycard/Visa
5 Diners

Welcome to the

WARWICK HOTEL

Church Walks, Llandudno, Gwynedd
Telephone: (0492) 76823

Situated a few minutes walk from the main shopping centre, the Pier and Promenade, and ideally sited for many of Llandudno's attractions. Guests are sure of comfortable and relaxed surroundings to enable them to take full advantage of Llandudno's invigorating climate. The bedrooms are attractively styled, some bedrooms have bathrooms en suite, all have an abundance of hot water, shaver points, tea/coffee making facilities and colour TV with central heating throughout. Restaurant and residential licence.

WEDGWOOD

Private Hotel
6 Deganwy Avenue, Llandudno, North Wales
Telephone: (0492) 78016

A small, comfortable hotel, with friendly, family atmosphere. The Hotel is ideally situated within easy walking distance of Llandudno's two beaches, pier, children's amusements, sports centre, swimming pool and excellent shopping centre. Large comfortable lounge, colour TV. Licensed bar. Children welcome. Private car park. Fire certificate.

Rose Tor

124 Mostyn Street,
Llandudno Gwynedd LL30 2SW
Luxury Guest House Tel: Llandudno (0492) 70433

Rose-Tor is situated in an ideal position for shops, theatres, pier, promenade and all the attractions of Llandudno and the Great Orme.

Rose-Tor is decorated throughout with great flair and creates a calm, relaxing atmosphere.

All the bedrooms are beautifully furnished and very well equipped with colour T.V., D.D. Telephone, clock/radio, tea/coffee unit, hair dryer, and of course are all en-suite.

The restaurant offers a wide choice of menu also fine beers and wine.

Bar snacks and meals are served all day until midnight.

GH Wedgewood Hotel 6 Deganwy Av ☎(0492) 78016 Plan **38** *B3*

Conveniently situated for the beach and shops, this neat little hotel is run by enthusiastic owners.

11hc (4fb) Ⓡ ✱B&b£8.50–£9.50 Bdifr£12 LDO6pm

🍽 CTV 8P

GH White Lodge Hotel 9 Neville Cres, Central Prom ☎(0492) 77713 Plan **27** *D3*
Apr–Oct

Single-fronted Victorian mid-terrace on Central Promenade within a short walk of shops.

12hc (8⇌) (7fb) CTV in all bedrooms ✈ Ⓡ B&b£12–£12.50 Bdi£16–£16.50 WBdifr£112 LDO5pm

Lic 🍽 CTV 12P nc5yrs

GH Wilton Hotel South Pde ☎(0492) 76086 Plan **39** *C4*
Mar–mid Nov

15hc (4⇌ 5⫿) (6fb) CTV in all bedrooms Ⓡ ✱B&b£12 Bdi£17 WBdi£98 LDO4.30pm

Lic CTV ℙ

Ⓥ

LLANFAIR CLYDOGAU

Dyfed
Map **2** SN65

Selected

FH Mrs M Eleri-Davies **Pentre** *(SN625506)* ☎Llangybi (057045) 313
Mar–Oct

Hospitable and comfortable stone-built farmhouse overlooking the Vale of Teifi. Spacious lounge with oak beams and inglenook fireplace. Fishing available. Ideal for country walks.

3hc (1⇌ 1⫿) (2fb) ✈ Ⓡ B&b£11–£12 Bdi£15–£17 WBdi£105–£115 LDO6pm

🍽 CTV P ⌂ ⸙

300acres dairy sheep

Llandudno — Llangollen

LLANFAIR DYFFRYN CLWYD

Clwyd
Map **6** SJ15

Selected

GH Eyarth Station ☎Ruthin (08242) 3643
Closed Xmas

As the name suggests, this attractive guesthouse was originally a railway station. It has been carefully converted and extended to provide exceptionally comfortable accommodation. The Spencer family extend a friendly welcome and genuine hospitality to all guests.

3hc (1⇌ 2⫿) (1fb) Ⓡ B&b£12–£20 Bdi£19–£27 WBdifr£124

🍽 CTV 6P 2🚗 ⩤(heated) sauna bath

Ⓥ

⊢⊣**FH** Mrs E Jones **Llanbenwch** *(SJ137533)* ☎Ruthin (08242) 2340
Feb–Nov

17th-century farmhouse, 3 miles S of Ruthin on A525.

3hc (1fb) TV in all bedrooms ✈ Ⓡ B&b£8–£9 Bdi£12–£13 WBdifr£75 LDO5pm

🍽 CTV P nc5yrs 40acres mixed

Ⓥ

LLANFAIR WATERDINE

Shropshire
Map **7** SO27

FH Mrs J Williams **Monaughty Poeth** *(SO255748)* ☎Knighton (0547) 528348
Etr–Nov

2hc (1fb) Ⓡ ✱B&b£9.50

CTV 4P ⸙ 640acres arable stock mixed

INN *Red Lion* ☎Knighton (0547) 528214
Closed Xmas Day

3hc (1⇌) ✈ LDO9pm

🍽 20P ⛟ nc14yrs

LLANFIHANGEL-YNG-NGWYNFA

Powys
Map **6** SJ01

FH Mrs E Jenkins **Cyfie** *(SJ085147)* ☎Llanfyllin (069184) 451

17th-century beamed farmhouse set in peaceful undulating countryside. 2m S on unclass rd off B4382.

2hc (1fb) CTV in 1 bedroom ✈ Ⓡ ✱B&b£11.50–£12.50 Bdi£16.50–£17.50 WBdi£95–£105 LDO7.30pm

🍽 CTV 6P ⌂ 178acres beef sheep mixed

LLANFIHANGEL-Y-PENNANT

Gwynedd
Map **6** SH60

⊢⊣**FH** Mrs M Jones **Tynybryn** *(SH659080)* ☎Abergynolwyn (065477) 277

1½m SW unclass rd.

3hc (1⇌) (2fb) ⚔ in 1 bedroom ✈ Ⓡ B&b£8–£11 Bdi£12.50–£15 WBdi£80–£100 LDO6.30pm

🍽 CTV 10P 300acres mixed

Ⓥ

See advertisement under Tywyn

LLANGATTOCK

Powys
Map **3** SO21

GH Ty-Croeso Hotel & Restaurant The Dardy ☎Crickhowell (0873) 810573

6⫿ (1fb) CTV in all bedrooms Ⓡ ✱B&b£14–£23.50 WB&b£88.20–£148.05 LDO9.45pm

Lic 🍽 35P

Credit card 3

See advertisement on page 250

LLANGOLLEN

Clwyd
Map **7** SJ24

FH Mrs A Kenrick ***Rhydonnen Ucha Rhewl*** *(SJ174429)* ☎(0978) 860153
Etr–Nov

Large, stone-built, three-storey farmhouse, pleasantly situated with shooting on farm and trout fishing on River Dee (permit).

→

4hc (2fb) LDO5pm

♨ CTV 6P 125acres dairy

LLANGRANOG
Dyfed
Map **2** SN35

FH Mrs B Williams **Hendre** *(SN344538)* Hendre (2m E B4321) ☎(023978) 342
Apr–Oct

Conveniently positioned 2 miles from the sandy beach, offering good home cooking.

3hc (1fb) ✖ Ⓡ B&b£9.50–£12 Bdi£14–£16 WBdifr£98 LDOnoon

♨ CTV 6P 100acres arable beef

Ⓥ

INN Pentre Arms Hotel ☎(023978) 345

Simply-appointed inn situated in friendly seaside town.

8hc (3fb) CTV in 4 bedrooms B&b£10–£13.50 Bdi£15.50–£18.50 WB&b£70–£91 Bar lunch £1.50–£6.75 Dinner 9pm£5.50

♨ 5P ⇉ snooker

LLANGURIG
Powys
Map **6** SN98

GH Old Vicarage ☎(05515) 280

5hc (2fb) ⅟ in 1 bedroom CTV in 2 bedrooms TV in 1 bedroom Ⓡ ✱B&b£10.50–£11.50 Bdi£16.95–£17.95 WBdi£106.50–£113.50 LDO8.30pm

Lic ♨ CTV 8P ⌂

Ⓥ

INN *Blue Bell* ☎(05515) 254

10hc (1⇌)

♨ CTV 40P ⇉

LLANRHAEADR
Clwyd
Map **6** SJ06

⊢⊣**FH** Mrs S Evans **Tan-yr-Accar** *(SJ078614)* ☎Llanynys (074578) 232
Apr–Oct

Good family accommodation in 18th century farmhouse within the lovely Vale of Clwyd.

2rm (1fb) ✖ B&b£8.50–£9 WBdifr£60

♨ TV 6P 80acres dairy sheep

LLANSANTFFRAID-YM-MECHAIN
Powys
Map **7** SJ22

FH Mrs M E Jones **Glanvyrnwy** *(SJ229202)* ☎Llansantffraid (069181) 258

200-year-old stone-built farmhouse, set back from main road, with pleasant lawns and orchard.

2hc ✖ B&b£9.50–£10.50 Bdi£13.50–£15 WBdifr£100 LDO6pm

CTV 3P nc3yrs 42acres dairy

LLANTILIO CROSSENY
Gwent
Map **3** SO31

FH Mrs B A Ford **Little Treadam** *(SO376159)* ☎(0600 85) 326

This delightful 16th-century farmhouse is set amid beautiful open countryside overlooking the Black Mountains, 5m from Abergavenny on the B4233. Charming beamed interior with comfortable accommodation and good home cooking from fresh produce.

3hc (1fb) ✖ B&b£10–£12 Bdi£16–£18 WBdifr£100 LDO6pm

Lic ♨ CTV 12P 35acres mixed

Ⓥ

LLANTRITHYD
South Glamorgan
Map **3** ST07

FH Mrs T Lougher ***Treguff*** *(SS032711)* ☎St Athan (0446) 750210
Closed Xmas wk

Traditionally furnished Elizabethan farmhouse amid 525 acres.

3rm ✖ LDOnoon

CTV 6P 2🚗 no babies

525acres beef sheep mixed

LLANTWIT MAJOR
South Glamorgan
Map **3** SS96

FH Mrs Penny **Downs** *(SS952702)* Wick Rd ☎(04465) 4252

Dating back to the 1700's this light stone listed building is peacefully situated off the B4265 and offers tasteful, modern accommodation with views towards the Somerset coastline.

3rm (2hc) CTV in all bedrooms ✖ Ⓡ ✱B&bfr£10 LDO4pm

CTV 6P nc10yrs 4acres poultry sheep

LLANUWCHLLYN
Gwynedd
Map **6** SH83

⊢⊣**FH** Mrs D Bugby **Bryncaled** *(SH866314)* ☎(06784) 270
Closed Xmas day

Small farmhouse with oak-beamed dining room, overlooking Aran mountains. A fishing river runs through the grounds. Approximately 6 miles from Bala.

3rm (2hc) ✖ Ⓡ B&bfr£8.50 Bdifr£13 WBdifr£88 LDOam

Lic ♨ CTV 6P ⤴ 500acres beef sheep mixed

LLANVAIR-DISCOED
Gwent
Map **3** ST49

FH Mrs A Barnfather **Cribau** *(ST454941)* The Cwm ☎Shirenewton (02917) 528
Closed Xmas

16th-century farmhouse at the head of the "cwm". (Off unclass road joining Llanvair-Discoed & Shirenewton).

2⋔ ✖ Ⓡ B&b£10 WB&bfr£70

♨ 2P nc12yrs 33acres smallholding

FH Mr & Mrs S Price **Great Llanmellyn** *(SO456923)* ☎Shirenewton (02917) 210
Apr–Oct

Family farmhouse full of character with flag-stone floors and cosy accommodation.

2hc (2fb) ✖ Ⓡ B&b£10 WB&bfr£60

♨ CTV 3P 250acres dairy mixed

Ⓥ

LLANWARNE
Hereford & Worcester
Map **3** SO52

FH Mrs I E Williams **Llanwarne Court** *(SO503275)* ☎Golden Valley (0981) 540385
Closed 15 Dec–15 Jan
Farmhouse, set away from the main road with large walled garden.
3hc (1🚿) ✗ Ⓡ B&b£10–£12
▥ CTV P 260acres mixed

LLANWDDYN
Powys
Map **6** SJ01

FH R B & H A Parry **Tynymaes** *(SJ048183)* ☎(069173) 216
May–Sep
The farmhouse is situated near the nature reserve at Lake Vyrnwy.
3hc (1fb) ✗ ✱B&b£9–£9.50 Bdi£13–£13.50 WBdifr£90 LDO5pm
▥ CTV 4P 420acres beef sheep
ⓥ

LLANWRIN
Powys
Map **6** SH70

FH Mrs R J Hughes ***Mathafarn*** *(SN812055)* Cemmaes Rd ☎Cemmaes Road (06502) 226
Apr–Oct
Comfortable, ivy-clad farmhouse dating back to 1628 in the beautiful Dovey Valley.
2hc (1🛁) ✗
CTV 3P 600acres sheep mixed

LLANWRTYD WELLS
Powys
Map **3** SN84

GH Carlton Court Hotel Dolecoed Rd ☎(05913) 248
9hc (1🛁) (1fb) CTV in all bedrooms Ⓡ ✱B&b£10.95–£13.95 Bdi£16.90–£19.90 WBdifr£110 LDO9pm
Lic ▥ P̶ sauna bath
ⓥ

GH Lasswade House (Guestaccom) ☎(05913) 515
Handsome Edwardian house with high quality rooms, very enjoyable meals, and charming country house atmosphere. Outdoor swimming pool.
8hc (2🛁 4🚿) (1fb) CTV in all bedrooms Ⓡ B&bfr£20 Bdifr£30 WBdifr£195 LDO8.30pm
Lic ▥ 12P 🚗
Credit cards [1] [3]

LOCHEYNORT' (NORTH)
Isle of South Uist, Western Isles *Inverness-shire*
See **Uist (South), Isle of**

LOCHGOILHEAD
Strathclyde *Argyllshire*
Map **10** NN10

⊢⊣**FH** Mrs J H Jackson **Pole** *(NN192044)* ☎(03013) 221
Etr–Sep rs Apr
Pleasant well-kept farmhouse, 2 miles from Lochgoilhead.
3hc (1🚿) (1fb) Ⓡ in 1 bedroom B&b£9–£10 Bdi£13.50–£15 WBdi£80–£100 (W only Etr–Oct) LDO7pm
▥ CTV 4P snooker 7,550acres sheep
ⓥ

LOCHINVER
Highland *Sutherland*
Map **14** NC02

⊢⋆**GH Ardglas** ☎(05714) 257
Feb–Nov
Modern villa on elevated site overlooking the village.
8hc (3fb) B&b£9–£10 WB&b£63–£70
ꟷ CTV 12P

GH *Hillcrest* Badnaban ☎(05714) 391
Apr–Oct
Modern bungalow set in unspoilt environment, 2 miles S of the village on unclass rd.
4hc LDO5pm
ꟷ CTV 7P

LOCHRANZA
Isle of Arran, Strathclyde *Buteshire*
See **Arran, Isle of**

LOCHWINNOCH
Strathclyde *Renfrewshire*
Map **10** NS35

FH Mrs A Mackie **High Belltrees** *(NS377584)* ☎(0505) 842376
Situated 1m off the A737, Paisley to Largs road. Overlooks Castle Semple Loch which has an R.S.P.B. Bird Sanctuary and yachting facilities.
4rm (3hc) (2fb) CTV in 1 bedroom TV in 1 bedroom ✗ Ⓡ B&b£10–£11
ꟷ CTV 6P 220acres dairy mixed.

LOCKERBIE
Dumfries & Galloway *Dumfriesshire*
Map **11** NY18

GH Rosehill Carlisle Rd ☎(05762) 2378
Victorian, two-storey, sandstone house with attractive garden.
5hc (3fb) Ⓡ B&b£9.50
ꟷ CTV 5P

LODDON
Norfolk
Map **5** TM39

FH Mrs J Rackham **Stubbs House** *(TM358977)* ☎(0508) 20231
Mar–Oct
Fine, old Georgian farmhouse with excellent kitchen producing delicious, professional meals.
9hc (3⫪) ✗ B&bfr£15 Bdifr£23 WBdifr£110
Lic ꟷ CTV 18P nc10yrs 206acres arable

LONDON
Greater London
Map **4** & **5**
See plans 1–4 pages 255–259
A map of the London postal area appears on pages 260–261
Places within the London postal area are listed below in postal district order commencing East then North, South and West, with a brief indication of the area covered. Detailed plans **1–3** show the locations of AA-listed hotels within the Central London postal districts which are indicated by a number. Plan **4** highlights the districts covered within the outer area keyed by a grid reference eg A5
Other places within the county of London are listed under their respective placenames and are also keyed to this plan or the main map section.

E18
South Woodford
London plan **4** F5

Grove Hill Hotel 38 Grove Hill, South Woodford ☎01-989 3344
Comfortably appointed small hotel offering good standard of service.
21hc (10⇌ 2fl) (2fb) CTV in all bedrooms Ⓡ B&b£19
Lic CTV (charge)
Credit cards [1] [2] [3] Ⓥ

N8
Hornsey
London plan **4** D5

Aber Hotel 89 Crouch Hill ☎01-340 2847
Occupying an elevated roadside position in a busy residential area, this comfortable hotel offers good accommodation and friendly service.
8hc (4fb)
CTV

NW2
Cricklewood
London plan **4** C4

Clearview House 161 Fordwych Rd, Cricklewood ☎01-452 9773

London

A friendly family run establishment in a residential area offering clean, simple accommodation in a relaxed atmosphere.
6hc (1fb) TV in 4 bedrooms
CTV nc5yrs

Garth Hotel 70–76 Hendon Way, Cricklewood ☎01-455 4742 Telex no 914360
A commercial hotel with functional modern bedrooms and generous public rooms. Combined bar and dining room. Situated on the busy Hendon Way with good access to central London.
61hc (48⇌ fl) (10fb) CTV in all bedrooms
Ⓡ B&b£29.50–£42 LDO10pm
Lic CTV 30P

NW3
Hampstead and Swiss Cottage
London plan **4** D4

Frognal Lodge Hotel 14 Frognal Gdns, off Church Row, Hampstead ☎01-435 8238 Telex no 8812714
A friendly and well-managed hotel, quietly situated in Hampstead village. Five-minutes walk from underground station. Comfortable bedrooms all with telephones. Lift to all floors.
17hc (7⇌) (5fb) CTV in 10 bedrooms
Lic lift CTV
Credit cards [1] [2] [3] [5]

NW4
Hendon
London plan **4** C5

Peacehaven Hotel 94 Audley Rd, Hendon ☎01-202 9758
Modern, bright bedrooms, all with colour TV. Bathroom facilities well above average.
12hc (4⇌) (2fb) CTV in all bedrooms
B&bfr£25
2P
Credit cards [1] [3]

SE3
Blackheath
London Plan **4** E3

Selected

Bardon Lodge Hotel 15 Stratheden Rd, Blackheath ☎01-853 4051
Warm, friendly private hotel, tastefully decorated and offering good standard of accommodation.
41hc (28fl) (7fb) CTV in all bedrooms
Ⓡ B&b£25–£36 LDO9.30pm
Lic CTV 16P
Credit cards [1] [3]

Stonehall House 35–37 Westcombe Park Rd, Blackheath ☎01-858 8706
Old fashioned and comfortable guesthouse with pleasant TV lounge and garden.
23hc (1fl) (9fb) CTV in all bedrooms
CTV

SE9
Eltham
London plan **4** F2

Selected

Yardley Court Private Hotel 18 Court Rd, Eltham ☎01-850 1850
Small private hotel with very comfortable and generous accommodation. Extensive service is available.
10hc (6fl) (1fb) CTV in all bedrooms
B&b£22–£48
10P

REMEMBER
Prices quoted in the gazetteer are minimum double room occupancy to maximum single room occupancy **per person.**

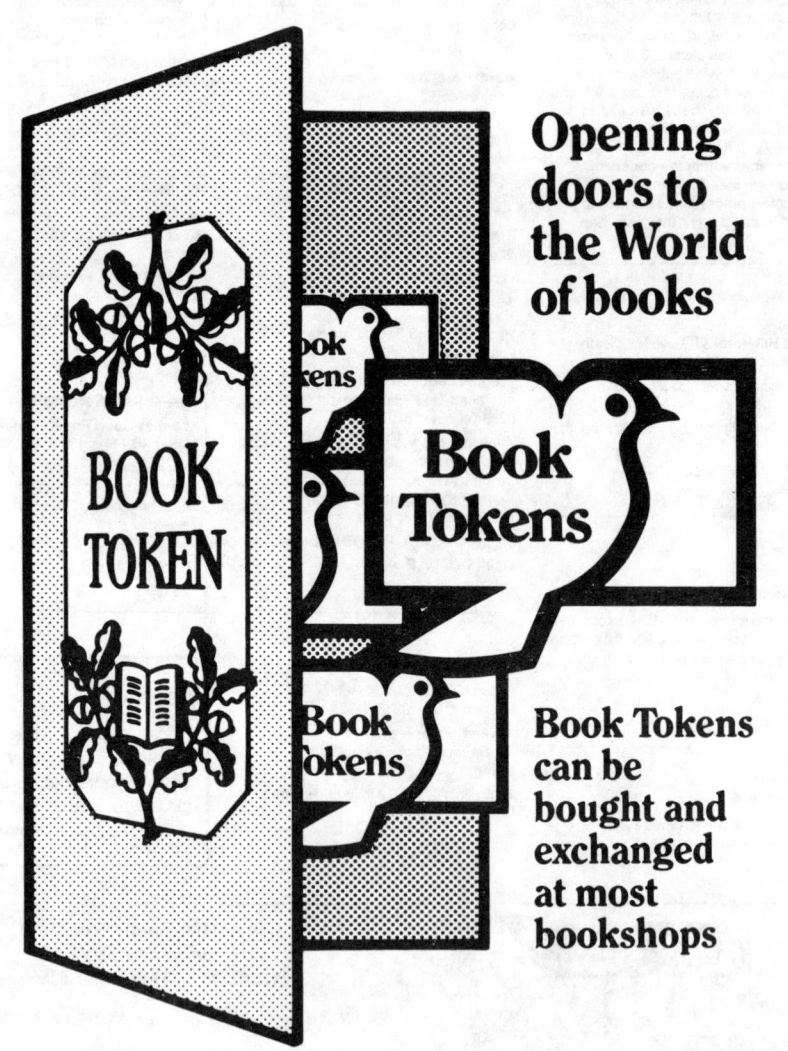

Details of the establishments shown on this map can be found under the *London Postal District* which follows the establishment name.

London Plan 1

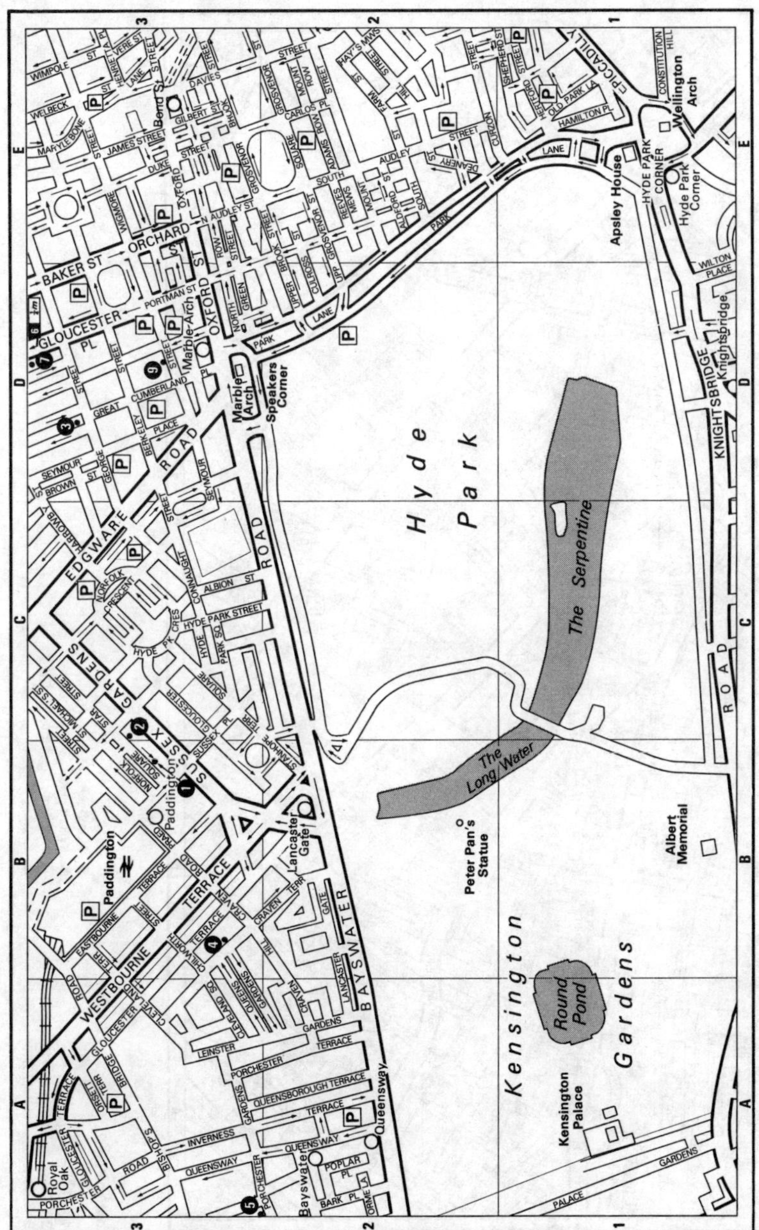

London Plan 1

1 Ashley Hotel (*W2*)
2 Camelot Hotel (*W2*)
3 Hotel Concorde (*W1*)
4 Dylan Hotel (*W2*)
5 Garden Court Hotel (*W2*)
6 Georgian House Hotel (*W1*)
7 Hart House Hotel (*W1*)
9 Edward Lear Hotel

London Plan 2

Details of the establishments shown on this map can be found under the *London Postal District* which follows the establishment name.

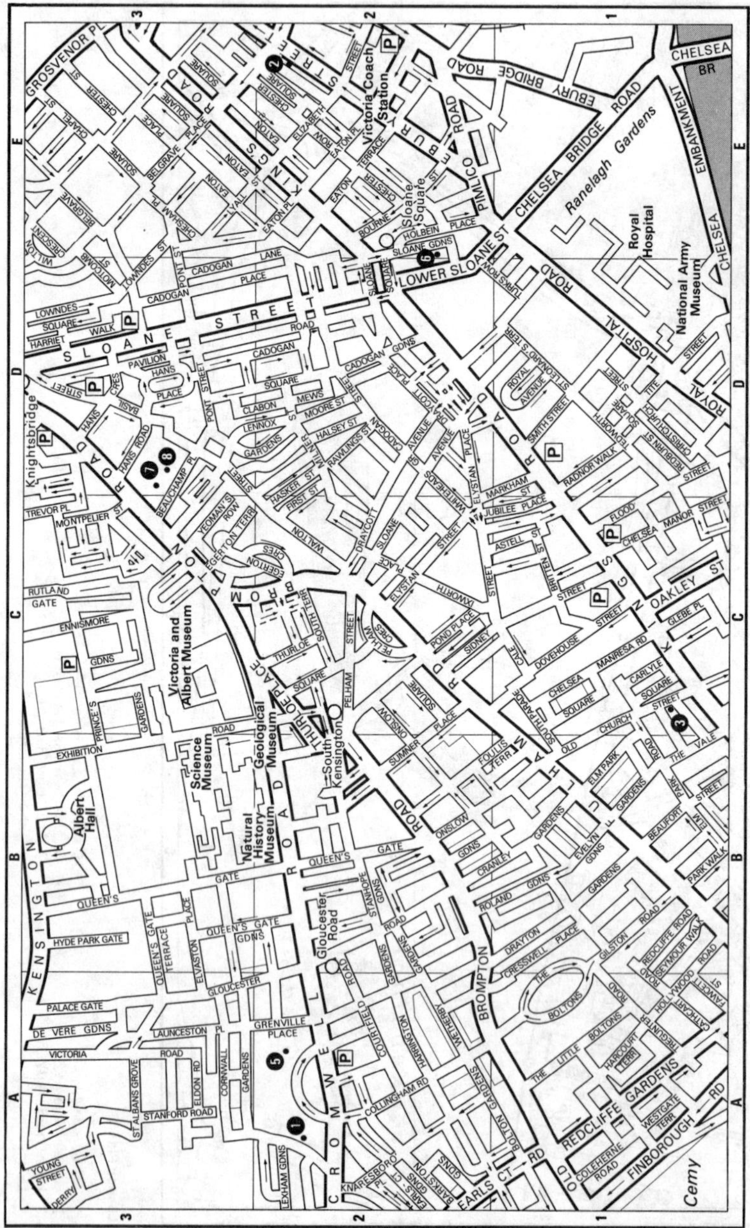

London Plan 2

1 Atlas Hotel *(W8)*
2 Chesham House *(SW1)*
3 Eden House Hotel *(SW3)*
5 Number Eight Hotel *(SW7)*
6 Willett Hotel *(SW1)*
7 Knightsbridge Hotel *(SW3)*
8 Claverley Hotel

Details of the establishments shown on this map can be found under the *London Postal District* which follows the establishment name.

London Plan 3

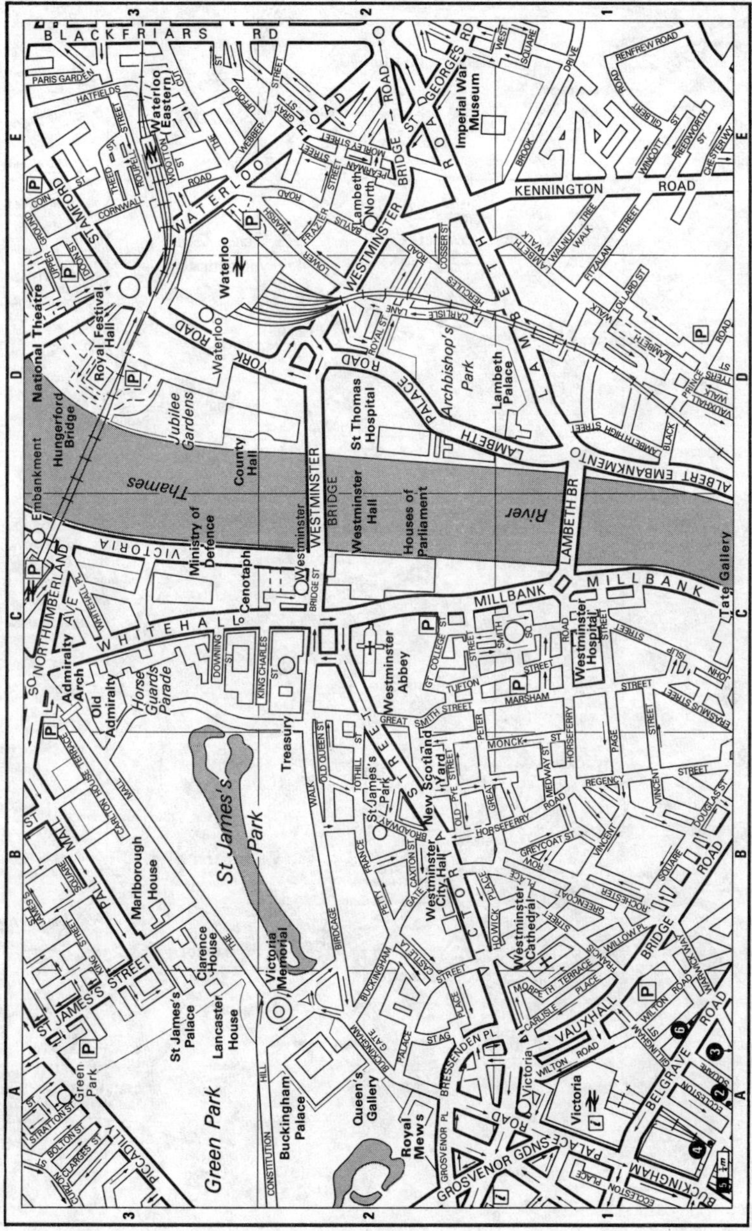

London Plan 3

1 Arden House *(SW1)*
2 Elizabeth Hotel *(SW1)*
3 Windermere Hotel *(SW1)*
4 Hanover Hotel *(SW1)*
6 Winchester Hotel

London Plan 4

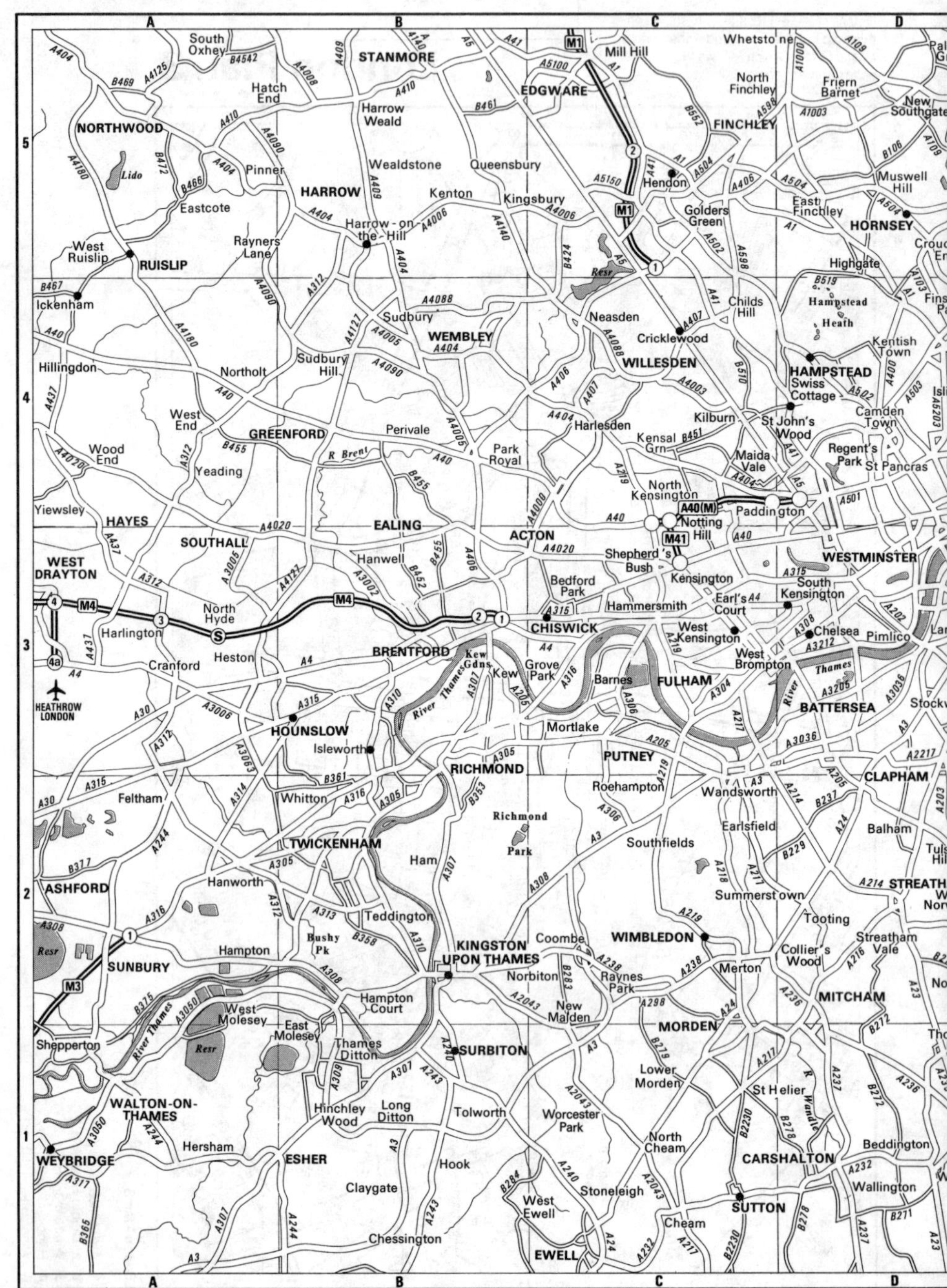

London Plan 4

The placenames highlighted by a **dot** are locations of AA listed establishments outside the Central London Plan area (Plans 1–3). Some of these fall within the London Postal District area and can therefore be found in the gazetteer under **London** in postal district order (see London Postal District map on following page). Others outside the London Postal District area can therefore be found under their respective placenames in the main gazetteer.

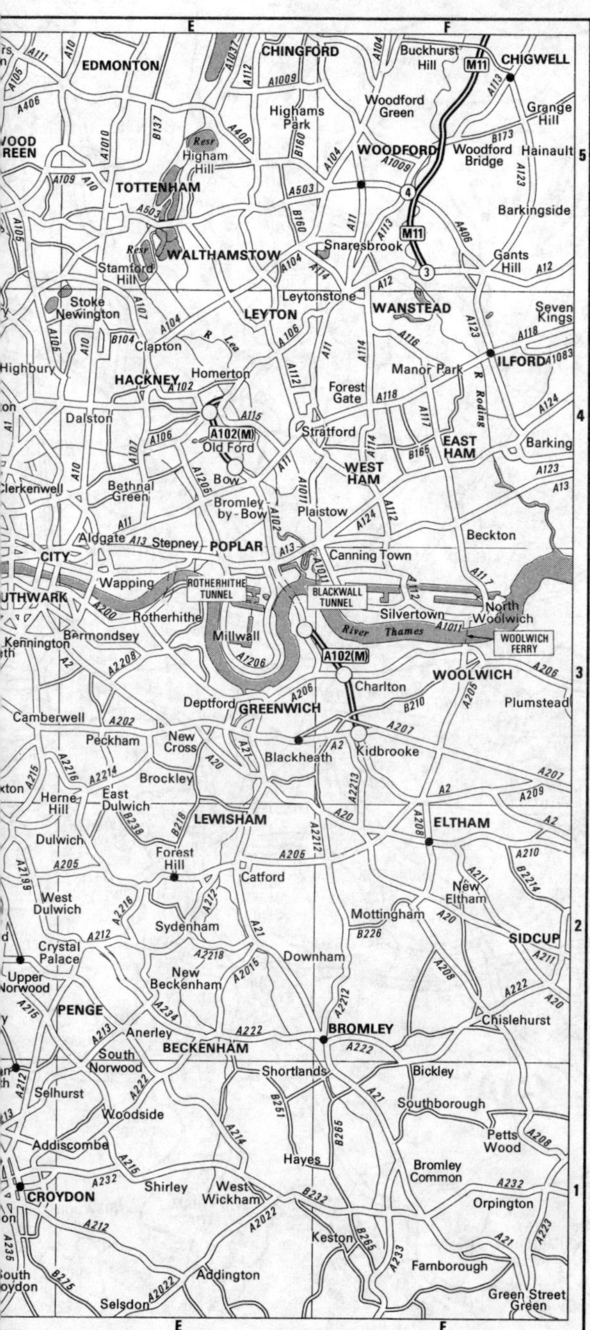

London Postal Districts and ways in and out of London

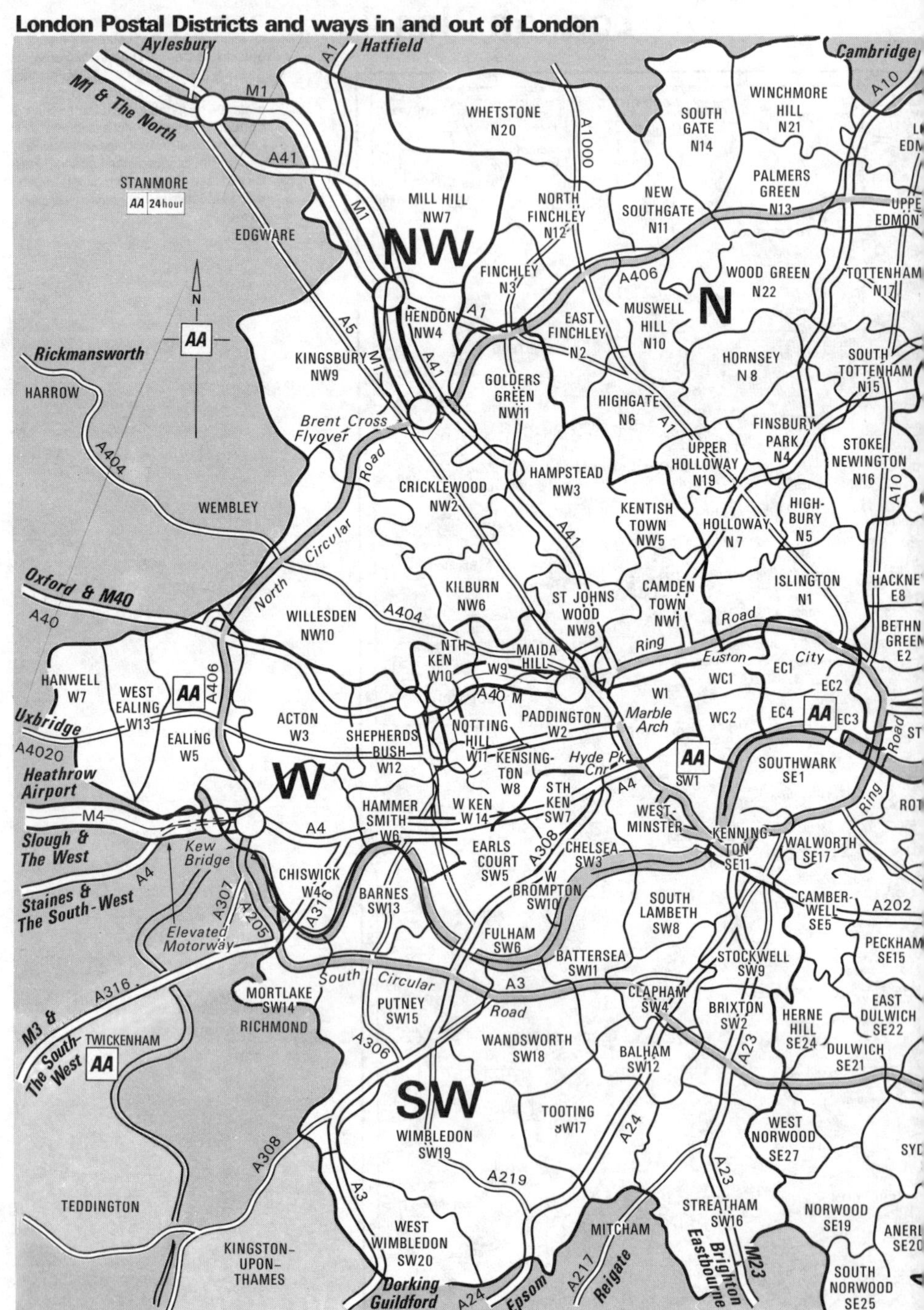

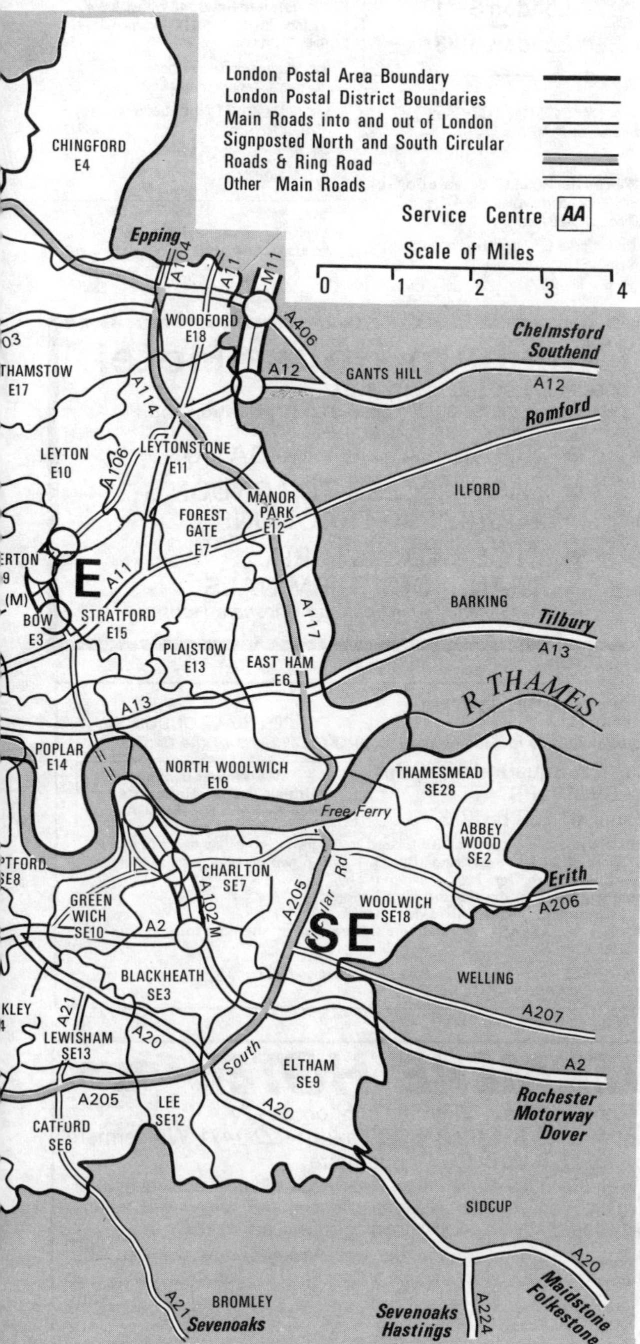

SE19
Norwood
London plan **4** D2

Crystal Palace Tower Hotel 114 Church Rd ☎01-653 0176

Large Victorian house, close to all amenities and with easy access to central London. Spacious, comfortable bedrooms and compact lounge and basement dining room. Car parking on hotel forecourt.

11hc (2⇌ 2⊪) (4fb) TV in all bedrooms Ⓡ in 4 bedrooms ✱B&b£11–£15

ꟿ CTV 10P

Ⓥ

SE23
Forest Hill
London plan **4** E2

Rutz 16 Vancouver Rd, Forest Hill ☎01-699 3071
Closed mid Dec–mid Jan

6hc (1⇌ 2⊪) (1fb) ✗ Ⓡ B&b£15–£17 WB&bfr£105

ꟿ CTV ₱

SW1
West End–Westminster, St James's Park, Victoria Station
London plan **4** D3

Arden House 12 St Georges Dr ☎01-834 2988 Telex no 22650 Plan 3:**1** *A1*

Simply furnished hotel with easy access to Victoria Station.

35hc (10⇌ 4⊪) (10fb) CTV in all bedrooms ✗

ꟿ CTV ₱

Chesham House 64–66 Ebury St, Belgravia ☎01-730 8513 Telex no 912881 (ESP) Plan 2:**2** *E2*

23hc (3fb) CTV in all bedrooms ✗ ✱B&b£18–£22

ꟿ ₱

Credit cards 2 3 5

See advertisement on page 262

Elizabeth Hotel 37 Eccleston Sq, Victoria ☎01-828 6812 Plan 3:**2** *A1*

Simply furnished hotel situated near Victoria Station.

24hc (1⇌ 2⊪) (6fb) CTV in 4 bedrooms ✗ B&b£18.50–£25

ꟿ CTV 🎾(hard)

See advertisement on page 262

REMEMBER

Prices quoted in the gazetteer are minimum double room occupancy to maximum single room occupancy **per person.**

GH *Hanover Hotel* 30 St Georges Dr ☎01-834 0134 Plan 3:**4** *A1*

An early 19th-century terrace house with comfortable accommodation.

34hc (8⇌ 18⫪) (4fb) CTV in all bedrooms

Ⓜ CTV Ᵽ

Credit cards 1 2 3

Willett Hotel 32 Sloane Gdns, Sloane Sq ☎01-824 8415 Telex no 9413498 Plan 2:**6** *E2*

Terraced house with spacious comfortably furnished bedrooms.

London SW1 — London SW3

18hc (14⇌ 4⫪) (11fb) CTV in all bedrooms Ⓡ ✱B&bfr£30

Ⓜ Ᵽ

Winchester Hotel 17, Belgrave Rd ☎01-828 2972 London plan 3:**5** *A1*
Closed 23–29 Dec

18⇌ ⫪ (2fb) CTV in all bedrooms ✗
✱B&bfr£58

Ⓜ Ᵽ

Windermere Hotel 142 Warwick Way, Victoria ☎01-834 5163 Telex no 931770 Plan 3:**4** *A1*

Well-maintained, small hotel, with comfortable bedrooms.

8hc (5⫪) (4fb) CTV in all bedrooms ✗
✱B&b£15–£25

Ⓜ Ᵽ

Credit card 3

SW3
Chelsea
London plan **4** D3

Selected

Claverley Hotel 13–14 Beaufort Gdns Knightsbridge ☎01-589 8541 London plan 2: **8** *D3*

36hc (25⇨ ﬁ) (2fb) CTV in all bedrooms ✗ ✱B&bfr£36

lift ꟿ Ᵽ

Credit card ③

Eden House Hotel 111 Old Church St ☎01-352 3403 Plan 2: **3** *C1*

Homely Edwardian house with a comprehensive room service but lacking any public rooms.

14hc (4⇨ 5ﬁ) (2fb) CTV in all bedrooms ✱B&b£18–£26 WB&bfr£230

ꟿ CTV Ᵽ

Credit cards ① ② ③ ⑤ Ⓥ

Knightsbridge Hotel 10 Beaufort Gdns ☎01-589 9271 Plan 2: **7** *D3*

Comfortable, well-equipped bedrooms, limited lounge accommodation and small basement dining room. Ideally located close to Harrods.

20hc (4⇨ 5ﬁ) (4fb) CTV in 3 bedrooms ✗ ✱B&b£13.50–£29.50Bdi£15.75–£33 LDO9.30pm

Lic ꟿ CTV Ᵽ

Credit cards ① ② ③ Ⓥ

London SW3 — London SW19

SW7

South Kensington
London plan **4** D3

Selected

Number Eight Hotel 8 Emperors Gate, South Kensington ☎01-370 7516 Plan 2: **5** *A2*

A small cheerful hotel where bedrooms are pleasantly decorated and provide many extra facilities. A buffet style breakfast is served by helpful staff.

14hc (10⇨ 4ﬁ) (6fb) CTV in all bedrooms Ⓡ B&b£41.50

Lic ꟿ Ᵽ

Credit cards ① ② ③ ⑤ Ⓥ

REMEMBER

Prices quoted in the gazetteer are minimum double room occupancy to maximum single room occupancy per person.

SW19

Wimbledon
London plan **4** C2

GH Trochee Hotel 21 Malcolm Rd, Wimbledon ☎01-946 1579 & 3924

17hc (2fb) CTV in all bedrooms Ⓡ B&bfr£22

ꟿ CTV 3P

Ⓥ

Wimbledon Hotel 78 Worple Rd, Wimbledon ☎01-946 9265

Hotel has modernised compact bedrooms, with limited comfortable lounge facilities and easy car parking.

12hc (3⇨ 3ﬁ) (4fb) CTV in all bedrooms ✗ Ⓡ B&b£26–£29

ꟿ CTV 10P

Credit cards ① ③

See advertisement on page 264

Worcester House 38 Alwyne Rd ☎01-946 1300

Hotel has compact, well-fitted bedrooms limited dining facilities and breakfast room service.

9ﬁ (1fb) CTV in all bedrooms ✗ Ⓡ LDO11am

ꟿ Ᵽ

Credit cards ① ② ③ ⑤

W1
West End; Piccadilly Circus, St Marylebone and Mayfair
London plan **4** D3/4

Hotel Concorde 50 Great Cumberland Pl ☎01-402 6169 Telex no 262070 Plan 1:**3** *D3*

Tastefully decorated and comfortable accommodation with good lounge. Well situated in the centre of London.

28hc (5⇌ 23ⓜ) (1fb) CTV in all bedrooms ✱ ✱B&bfr£42

Lic lift ⅏ CTV ₱

Credit cards 1 2 3 5

Georgian House Hotel 87 Gloucester Pl, Baker St ☎01-935 2211 Telex no 266079 Plan 1:**6** *D3*

A terraced house in busy road just off Marble Arch.

19hc (14⇌ 5ⓜ) (3fb) CTV in all bedrooms ✱ B&b£22–£25 (W only Nov–Mar)

Lic lift ⅏ CTV ₱ nc5yrs

Credit card 3

Hart House Hotel 51 Gloucester Pl, Portman Sq ☎01-935 2288 Plan 1:**7** *D3*

Imposing, five-storey terrace house with well-appointed bedrooms.

15hc (6⇌ 1ⓜ) (4fb) CTV in all bedrooms ✱ B&b£15–£25

⅏ ₱

Credit cards 1 2 3 Ⓥ

London W1 — London W2

Montagu House 3 Montagu Pl ☎01-935 4632

18hc (1ⓜ) (4fb) CTV in all bedrooms ✱ Ⓡ B&b£10–£25

⅏ CTV ₱

Credit cards 1 3 Ⓥ

W2
Bayswater, Paddington
London plan **4** C/D3/4

Ashley Hotel 15 Norfolk Sq, Hyde Park ☎01-723 3375 Plan 1:**1** *B3*
Closed 24–31 Dec

Situated in a quiet square close to Paddington Station.

16hc (6ⓜ) (1fb) CTV in all bedrooms ✱ B&b£13–£14.50

⅏ CTV ₱

Camelot Hotel 45 Norfolk Sq ☎01-723 9118 Telex no 268312 Plan 1:**2** *C3*

Friendly hotel providing modern facilities in a range of accommodation.

35hc (13⇌) (4fb) CTV in all bedrooms ✱ Ⓡ B&b£26.95–£43.45

⅏ CTV ₱

Credit card 3 Ⓥ

Dylan Hotel 14 Devonshire Ter Lancaster Gate ☎01-723 3280 Plan 1:**4** *B3*
Closed Xmas

Traditional style guesthouse, homely and comfortable.

18hc (2⇌ 5ⓜ) (3fb) ✱ Ⓡ B&b£15–£20 (W only Nov–Feb)

⅏ CTV ₱

Ⓥ

Garden Court Hotel 30–31 Kensington Gardens Sq ☎01-727 8304 Plan 1:**5** *A3*

Friendly, family-run, quietly situated hotel.

37hc (8⇌ 4ⓜ) (3fb) B&b£18–£25

Lic ⅏ CTV ₱

REMEMBER
Prices quoted in the gazetteer are minimum double room occupancy to maximum single room occupancy **per person.**

Pembridge Court Hotel 34 Pembridge Gdns ☎01-229 9977 Telex no 298363 rs Xmas

Very comfortable bedrooms with modern facilities. Separate restaurant 'Caps'

18hc (16⇌ 2fl) (4fb) CTV in all bedrooms B&b£35–£51.75 LDO11.30pm

Lic lift ♟ 2⌂

Credit cards [1] [2] [3] [5]

Slavia Hotel 2 Pembridge Sq ☎01-727 1316

Hotel offering reasonably priced simple accommodation.

31fl (8fb) B&b£17–£32 WB&b£107.10–£201.60 (W only Nov–Mar)

Lic lift ♟ CTV 2P (charge)

Credit cards [1] [2] [3] [5] (V)

GH Tria Hotel 35/37 St Stephens Gdns ☎01-221 0450 Telex no 266059

Imposing five storey terraced house.

42⇌ fl (5fb) ⍻ in 10 bedrooms CTV in all bedrooms ® B&b£20–£25

Lic lift ♟ CTV Ᵽ

Credit cards [1] [2] [3] [5]

W4
Chiswick
London plan **4** C3

Chiswick Hotel 73 Chiswick High Rd ☎01-994 1712

Attractive bedrooms and comfortable lounge. The basement houses a sauna and jacuzzi.

30hc (5⇌ 10fl) (7fb) CTV in all bedrooms LDO8.30pm

Lic ♟ CTV 15P sauna bath solarium

Credit cards [1] [2] [3] [5]

W8
Kensington
London plan **4** C3

Apollo Hotel 18–22 Lexham Gdns, Kensington ☎01-835 1133 Telex no 264189

Sister to Atlas Hotel, has many modern facilities and modest prices.

59hc (40⇌ 10fl) (4fb) CTV in all bedrooms ✗ B&b£24–£34

Lic lift ♟ CTV Ᵽ

Credit cards [1] [2] [3] [5] (V)

Atlas Hotel 24–30 Lexham Gdns, Kensington ☎01-373 7873 Telex no 264189 Plan 2: **1** *A2*

Modestly priced accommodation with many modern facilities.

70hc (13⇌ 37fl) (8fb) CTV in all bedrooms ✗ B&b£24–£34

Lic lift ♟ CTV Ᵽ

Credit cards [1] [2] [3] [5] (V)

W14
West Kensington
London plan **4** C3

Avonmore Hotel 66 Avonmore Rd ☎01-603 4296 Telex no 945922

Very comfortable accommodation offered by friendly proprietors.

9hc (3fb) CTV in all bedrooms ✗ ✻B&b£25–£30 WB&bfr£150 (W only Dec–Apr)

Lic ♟ CTV Ᵽ

Edward Lear Hotel 28–30 Seymour St ☎01-402 5401 London plan 1:**8** *D3*

30hc (5⇌ fl) (3fb) CTV in all bedrooms ✗ ® ✻B&bfr£27.60 CTV Ᵽ

Credit card [3]

WC1
Bloomsbury, Holborn
London plan **4** D4

Mentone Hotel 54–55 Cartwright Gdns, Bloomsbury ☎01-387 3927

Comfortable family accommodation, with public shower facilities and friendly service.

→

27hc (9⥰) (10fb) CTV in all bedrooms ✕ B&b£16–£21 WB&bfr£125 (W only Dec–Feb)

▥ ₱ 𝓡(hard)

LONGFRAMLINGTON
Northumberland
Map **12** NU10

Selected

INN Granby ☎(066570) 228
Closed Xmas Day

A charming stone-built village inn owned and managed by the friendly Hall family. The Granby has justifiably earned an excellent reputation for good food, hospitality and comfortable accommodation. Bedrooms, both in the inn and in the modern chalets adjacent are equally comfortable and well-appointed. There are two cosy bar lounges complete with oak beams.

3hc (1⇌) CTV in all bedrooms ✕ Ⓡ ✱B&b£16.50–£17.50 Bdi£26.25–£27.25 Bar lunch £2.85–£12.50 Dinner 8.30pm £10.75&alc

▥ 30P ⛟ nc8yrs

Credit cards 1 2 3

LONGLEAT
Wiltshire
Map **3** ST84

FH Mrs J Crossman **Stalls** *(ST806439)* ☎Maiden Bradley (09853) 323

Detached house built of Bath stone, originally the home farm for Longleat House. Sun terrace with trim lawns and garden to stream. Access off A362 at Corsley Lane End.

3hc (1fb) ✕ ✱B&b£10–£12 WB&bfr£70

▥ CTV 6P 281acres dairy

LONGRIDGE
Lancashire
Map **7** SD63

FH Mr F K Johnson **Falicon** *(SD629361)* Fleet Street Ln, Hothersall ☎Ribchester (025484) 583

Delightful sandstone farmhouse over 200 years old in pleasant rural surroundings. Bedrooms are very comfortable and well-equipped. Mrs Johnson enjoys cooking and offers freshly-prepared food for the discerning palate. Situated off the B6245 Longridge to Ribchester road.

3⇌ (1fb) ⁄in all bedrooms ✕ ✱B&b£16–£22 Bdi£27.50–£33.50 WBdifr£186.50 LDO5pm

▥ 6P nc10yrs 13 acres beef sheep

Ⓥ

LONGSDON
Staffordshire
Map **7** SJ95

FH Mr & Mrs M M Robinson **Bank End** *(SJ953541)* Old Leek Rd (½m SW off A53) ☎Leek (0538) 383638
Closed Xmas

Situated ½m S of village in a quiet lane overlooking the Endon Brook Valley and the Caldon Canal. The farmhouse is a fine sandstone building and more rooms are provided by modernised outbuildings on either side of the road.

5⇌⥰ (3fb) CTV in all bedrooms Ⓡ B&b£10–£14 Bdi£17–£21 LDO8.30pm

Lic ▥ CTV 10P ⊡heated ⌡ 62acres beef

See advertisement under Stoke-on-Trent

LOOE
Cornwall
Map **3** SX25
See plan on page 268

⊢⊣**GH 'Kantara'** 7 Trelawney Ter ☎(05036) 2093 Plan **1** *A4*
Feb–Nov

6hc (3fb) TV in 2 bedrooms B&b£8–£10 WB&b£56–£70

CTV 1⛍ ⌂

Credit cards 1 3 Ⓥ

Looe

GH Ogunquit Portuan Rd, Hannafore ☎(05036) 3105 Plan **2** *C1*

Feb–Nov

Personally-run guesthouse in an elevated position in Hannafore, West Looe. Affords superb views.

6hc (1fl) (2fb) ✱B&b£9–£12 Bdi£15–£18

🍽 CTV P

GH *Panorama Hotel* Hannafore Rd, Hannafore ☎(05036) 2123 Plan **3** *B2*

Apr–Oct

12hc (11⇌ 1fl) (4fb) CTV in 5 bedrooms TV in 1 bedroom LDO7pm

Lic 🍽 CTV 8P ⛵

Credit cards 1 3

GH St Aubyns Marine Dr, Hannafore, West Looe ☎(05036) 4351 Plan **4** *C1*

Etr–Oct

8hc (2⇌) (5fb) ✗ Ⓡ B&b£12–£17 WB&b£77–£112

CTV 4P

FH Mr & Mrs Hembrow **Tregoed** *(SX272560)* St Martins ☎(05036) 2718

Etr–Oct

Georgian-style manor house on high ground with sea view.

6hc (4fb) CTV in all bedrooms Ⓡ B&b£10–£12 Bdi£17–£19 WBdi£119–£133 LDO4pm

Lic CTV 15P ♨ ♪ 60acres dairy sheep

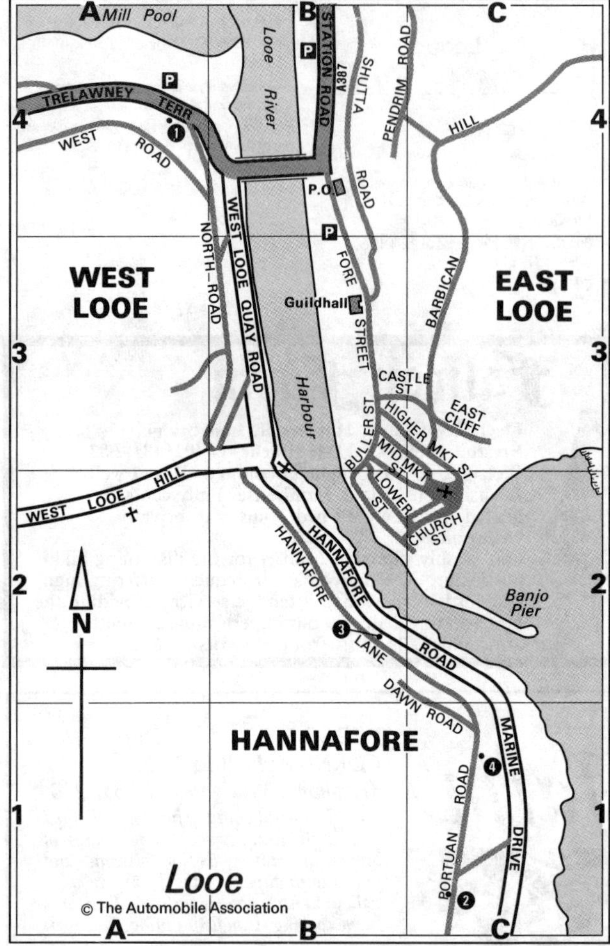

Looe

1 'Kantara' **2** Ogunquit **3** Panorama Hotel **4** St Aubyns

LOSTWITHIEL
Cornwall
Map **2** SX15

⊢⊣**FH** Mrs H Dunn **Pelyn Barn** *(SX091588)* Pelyn Cross ☎Bodmin (0208) 872451

Large farmhouse, formerly an old toll house, with large sun lounge affording scenic views. There is a well-kept lawn enclosure at rear.

3hc (1fb) B&b£9–£12

CTV 12P 1🚗 209acres mixed

Credit cards [2] [3]

LOUGHBOROUGH
Leicestershire
Map **8** SK51

GH De Montfort Hotel 88 Leicester Rd ☎(0509) 216061

9hc (1fb) CTV in all bedrooms Ⓡ B&b£12–£14.50 Bdi£17–£19.50 WBdifr£118 LDO4pm

Lic 🛋 CTV ₱̸

Credit cards [1] [3] Ⓥ

GH Sunnyside Hotel The Coneries ☎(0509) 216217

Conveniently situated for the town centre, this family run hotel offers compact, well-equipped bedrooms and is ideal for businessmen.

11hc CTV in 10 bedrooms ✗ Ⓡ in 10 bedrooms B&b£13–£14 Bdi£15.50–£19 LDO4pm

🛋 CTV 8P 3🚗 nc5yrs

Credit cards [1] [3] Ⓥ

LOWER BEEDING
West Sussex
Map **4** TQ22

FH Mr J Christian **Brookfield Farm Hotel** *(TQ212282)* Winterpit Ln, Plummers Plain ☎(040376) 568

An efficiently managed farmhouse with compact bedrooms, comfortable lounge and a popular lake and lawn to the rear.

12hc (1⇌ 8fl) (1fb) CTV in all bedrooms ✱B&b£20.12–£23 Bdi£31.05–£33.92 WBdifr£226.82 LDO9pm

Lic 🛋 CTV 100P (charge) ⛱ ⌐ 300acres mixed

Credit cards [1] [3]

LOWESTOFT
Suffolk
Map **5** TM59

GH Amity 396 London Road South ☎(0502) 2586

12hc (4fl) (3fb) CTV in all bedrooms Ⓡ ✱B&b£11–£12 Bdi£16–£17 WBdifr£90 LDO4pm

Lic 🛋 CTV 3P snooker solarium

Credit cards [1] [3]

GH Belmont 270 London Road South ☎(0502) 3867

Friendly family-run guesthouse within walking distance of sandy beach.

6hc (3fb) TV available in bedrooms Ⓡ ✱B&b£8–£8.50 Bdi£11–£11.50 WBdifr£69 LDO1pm

🛋 CTV ₱̸

Ⓥ

GH Clarendon Private Hotel 46 Kirkley Cliff ☎(0502) 87061

Private hotel facing seafront and close to Kensington Gardens.

10hc (2⇌ 3fl) (3fb) ⊁ in 2 bedrooms CTV in all bedrooms Ⓡ B&b£12–£18 Bdi£17–£23 WBdifr£105 LDO4pm

Lic 🛋 8P 1🚗 ⛱

Credit cards [1] [2] [3] Ⓥ

GH Hotel Katherine Kirkley Cliff Rd ☎(0502) 67858
Closed 25 Dec–4 Jan

Family-run hotel on south side of town overlooking Kensington Gardens.

10hc (5⇌ 2fl) (6fb) CTV in all bedrooms Ⓡ B&b£14–£21.50 Bdi£19.95–£27.45 WBdifr£122.50 LDO8pm

Lic 🛋 5P solarium

Credit cards [1] [2] [3] Ⓥ

GH Kingsleigh 44 Marine Pde ☎(0502) 2513
Closed Xmas

6hc (2fb) CTV in all bedrooms Ⓡ
*B&b£10–£14

6P nc3yrs

Ⓥ

GH *Lodge Private Hotel* London Rd South, Pakefield ☎(0502) 69805
Closed Xmas & New Year

This family managed hotel offers modern, comfortable accommodation in a friendly relaxed atmosphere.

7hc (2⇌ 3fl) (1fb) CTV in all bedrooms ✈ Ⓡ LDO6.30pm

Lic CTV 15P

Credit cards 1 2 3

Lowestoft — Low Row

GH Rockville House 6 Pakefield Rd ☎(0502) 81011 due to change to 581011
Etr–Oct & Xmas rs Nov–Etr

Small, family-managed establishment with good bedrooms and public lounge.

8hc (2⇌ 1fl) (1fb) CTV in all bedrooms ✈ (ex guide dogs) Ⓡ B&b£12.50–£20 Bdi£17.50–£25 WBdifr£92.50 LDO6pm

Lic P

Credit cards 1 3 Ⓥ

GH Seavilla Hotel 43 Kirkley Cliff Rd ☎(0502) 4657

Close to Kensington Gardens on A12. Good home cooking.

10hc (1⇌ 4fl) (1fb) CTV in all bedrooms Ⓡ B&b£15–£19 Bdi£20–£24 WBdifr£130 LDO7pm

Lic CTV 6P 2

Credit cards 1 2 3 Ⓥ

LOW ROW
North Yorkshire
Map **7** SD99

GH Peatgate Head ☎Richmond (0748) 86388 →

This charming 300-year-old house offers attractive accommodation. Excellent dinners are freshly-prepared by the proprietor.

6hc (2fl) ✖ Ⓡ ✱Bdi£22.50–£25

Lic ⅢCTV P

LUDDENDEN FOOT
West Yorkshire
Map **7** SE02

GH Collyers Hotel and Restaurant Burnley Rd ☎(0422) 882624

A mid-Victorian mill owner's house overlooking the Calder Valley affording spacious accommodation as well as a varied menu in the attractive restaurant.

6hc (2fb) CTV in all bedrooms Ⓡ ✱B&bfr£17.25 Bdifr£27.25 LDO9.30pm

Lic 14P

Credit cards 1 3

FH Mrs P Hitchin **Crib** *(SE026245)* ☎Halifax (0422) 883285
Mar–Oct

16th-century Pennine Farmhouse, with low beams and mullioned windows. In the hills overlooking the Calder Valley.

4hc (1⇌ 1fl) in 4 bedrooms CTV available in bedrooms ✖ B&b£8.50–£9.50 Bdi£14.50–£15.50 WBdifr£101.50

Ⅲ CTV 6P 2 nc5yrs 200acres dairy

Low Row — Lulworth

LUDFORD
Lincolnshire
Map **8** TF28

INN White Hart Magna Mile ☎Burgh-on-Bain (050781) 664

4fl Ⓡ B&b£13.50–£15 Bdi£15.50–£22 WB&bfr£94.50 Bar lunch £2.50–£6.50 Dinner 10.30pm £2.50–£6.50&alc

Ⅲ CTV 40P snooker

Credit card 1 Ⓥ

Credit Cards

1 Access/Euro/Mastercard

2 American Express

3 Barclaycard/Visa

5 Diners

LUDLOW
Shropshire
Map **7** SO57

GH Cecil Private Hotel Sheet Rd ☎(0584) 2442

Large modern house providing comfortable accommodation on edge of town.

11hc (1fb) Ⓡ; B&bfr£12 Bdifr£18.50 WBdi£129.50 LDO6.30pm

Lic Ⅲ CTV 10P 1

Ⓥ

INN Church Church St, Buttercross ☎(0584) 2174

Attractive 13th-century inn enjoying a town centre location just behind the Buttercross.

9⇌ fl (1fb) CTV in all bedrooms ✖ Ⓡ ✱B&b£15–£20 Bar lunch £1–£5.50 Dinner 9.30pm£6–£8.50&alc

Ⅲ

Credit card 3

LULWORTH
Dorset
Map **3** SY88

GH Gatton House Hotel ☎West Lulworth (092941) 252
Mar–Oct

Elevated position nestling into hillside with panoramic views.

8hc (4⇌ 4fl) (2fb) ⅔ in 1 bedroom CTV in all bedrooms Ⓡ B&b£15–£18.50 Bdi£22.70–£26.20 WBdi£149–£173

Lic ꟾꟾꟾ CTV 12P 2🚗 ⌂

Credit cards 1 3

GH Lulworth Hotel Main Rd ☎West Lulworth (092941) 230
Closed 24–26 Dec

Open rural setting leading to cove.

9hc (2⇌ 2fl) CTV in 8 bedrooms ✗ Ⓡ ✱B&b£11.25–£14 Bdi£19.75–£22 WBdifr£118.50 LDO7.30pm

Lic CTV 12P nc5yrs

Credit cards 1 3

LUSTLEIGH
Devon
Map **3** SX78

GH *Eastwrey Barton Hotel*
Moretonhampstead Rd ☎(06477) 338

Granite-built farmhouse standing in 3 acres of gardens; comfortable bedrooms and friendly service.

8hc (2⇌) LDO6pm

Lic CTV 10P nc8yrs

LUTON
Bedfordshire
Map **4** TL02

GH Ambassador Hotel 31 Lansdowne Rd ☎(0582) 31411
Closed Xmas & Boxing Day →

Friendly and comfortable house run by young proprietors.

14hc (10fl) (1fb) CTV in all bedrooms ® ✱B&b£20–£40 Bdi£24–£48 LDO8.45pm

Lic CTV 20P

GH Arlington Hotel 137 New Bedford Rd ☎(0582) 419614

Well-managed and comfortable commercial guesthouse.

19hc (1⇌ 5fl) (2fb) CTV in all bedrooms ® in 2 bedrooms B&b£17–£34 Bdi£24–£41 LDO8.30pm

Lic 25P

Credit cards 2 5

GH *Humberstone Hotel* 616–618 Dunstable Rd ☎(0582) 574399

Very comfortable and clean hotel where the welcome is warm and friendly.

10hc (2fl) (3fb) in 4 bedrooms CTV in all bedrooms ® LDO9pm

Lic 18P nc7yrs

Credit cards 1 3

GH Oakmore Hotel 29 Marsh Rd ☎Leagrave (0582) 576778

A comfortable and well-managed guesthouse, conveniently close to the town centre.

5hc (1⇌ 4fl) (2fb) CTV in all bedrooms ® B&b£31.05 Bdi£37.05–£41 WBdi£233.42–£258.30 LDO9.30pm

Lic CTV 12P

Credit card 1 3 Ⓥ

LUTTERWORTH
Leicestershire
See **Shearsby**

LYDFORD
Devon
Map **2** SX58

INN *Castle* ☏(082282) 242
Closed Xmas Day

7hc (2fb) CTV in all bedrooms Ⓡ LDO9.45pm

🏺 40P

INN Dartmoor ☏(082282) 221
Closed Xmas Day

Friendly inn with comfortable rooms and large menu. Situated on A386 between Tavistock and Okehampton.

6hc (4⇌) (1fb) CTV in 5 bedrooms TV in 1 bedroom Ⓡ B&bfr£11.50 WB&bfr£69 Lunch £2.20alc Dinner 9.55pm£11alc

Lic 🏺 50P

Credit cards 1 2 3 5 Ⓥ

LYME REGIS
Dorset
Map **3** SY39

GH Coverdale Woodmead Rd ☏(02974) 2882
Mar–Oct

Quiet location near to shops and sea.

9hc Ⓡ ✱B&b£8.50–£10 Bdi£13.25–£14.75 WBdi£81–£93 LDO5pm

🏺 CTV 12P

GH Kersbrook Hotel & Restaurant Pound Rd ☏(02974) 2596
rs Jan

Thatched 18th-century building in extensive picturesque gardens, overlooking Lyme Bay, at the top of the town, a few minutes walk from the centre.

11hc (5⇌ 6fl) (1fb) CTV in 6 bedrooms Ⓡ ✱B&b£17.50–£19.50 Bdi£27.50–£29.50 WBdifr£170 LDO8pm

Lic 🏺 CTV 14P nc15yrs in dining room

Credit cards 1 2 3 Ⓥ

GH Old Monmouth Hotel Church St ☏(02974) 2456
Closed Feb rs Dec & Jan

16th-century building opposite the parish church, a few minutes walk from the harbour.

6hc (1⇌ 2fl) (1fb) ✗ Ⓡ in 1 bedroom B&b£13–£18.50 WBdi£87–£120

Lic 🏺 CTV 6P nc8yrs

GH Rotherfield View Rd ☏(02974) 2811
Closed Xmas

Situated in quiet residential area with coastal and country views.

7hc (3fb) B&b£9–£10 Bdi£14–£15 WBdi£88.75–£97.75

Lic 🏺 CTV 7P

GH *White House* 47 Silver St ☏(02974) 3420
Apr–Oct

18th-century listed building close to beach, gardens and shops.

7hc (4fl) CTV in all bedrooms Ⓡ B&b£10.50–£13 WB&b£66–£82

Lic 🏺 7P nc10yrs

Ⓥ

LYNDHURST
Hampshire
Map **4** SU30

GH Bench View Southampton Rd ☏(042128) 2502
Closed Xmas

This friendly hotel is situated on the main Lyndhurst to Southampton road overlooking the attractive 'bench' area of the forest. Bedrooms are spacious and well-decorated and, as there is no lounge each room is equipped with a comfortable chair and colour television. There is a separate breakfast room.

8hc (5fb) CTV in all bedrooms Ⓡ B&b£10–£14 WBdi£66.50

9P

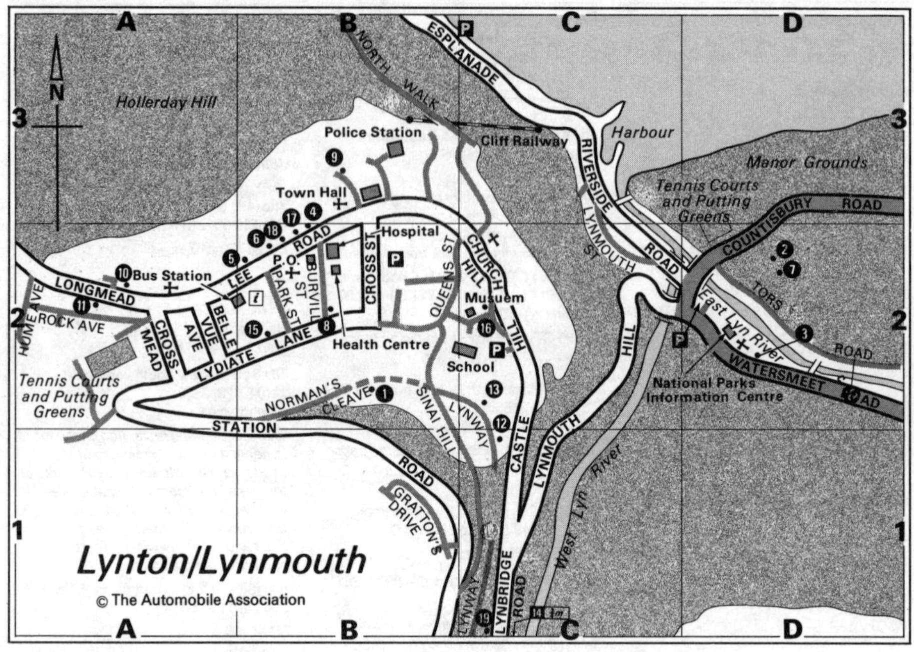

Lynmouth & Lynton

1 Alford House
2 Countisbury Lodge Hotel *(see under Lynmouth)*
3 East Lyn *(see under Lynmouth)*
4 Gable Lodge *(see under Lynton)*
5 Gordon House Hotel
6 Hazeldene *(see under Lynton)*
7 Heatherville *(see under Lynmouth)*
8 Horwood House *(see under Lynton)*
9 Ingleside Hotel *(see under Lynton)*
10 Kingford House Private Hotel *(see under Lynton)*
11 Longmead House *(see under Lynton)*
12 Lynhurst Hotel *(see under Lynton)*
13 Mayfair Hotel *(see under Lynton)*
14 Pine Lodge *(see under Lynton)*
15 Retreat *(see under Lynton)*
16 St Vincent *(see under Lynton)*
17 Southcliffe *(see under Lynton)*
18 Turret *(see under Lynton)*
19 Valley House Hotel *(see under Lynton)*

GH Whitemoor House Hotel
Southampton Rd ☎(042128) 2186
Closed 10 days Xmas

A very pleasant guesthouse, with good sized well-maintained rooms. Close to main road.

5hc (2fb) CTV in all bedrooms Ⓡ B&b£12–£15 WB&bfr£95

Lic ⋒ CTV 8P

LYNMOUTH
Devon
Map **3** SS74
See plan. See also **Lynton**

GH Countisbury Lodge Hotel
Countisbury Hill ☎Lynton (0598) 52388
Plan **2** *D2*

8hc (2⇌ 3⋒) (3fb) Ⓡ in 5 bedrooms B&b£13.50–£15 Bdi£19–£21 WBdi £125.25–£133.50 (W only Xmas wk) LDO7.30pm

Lic ⋒ CTV 8P

GH East Lyn 17 Watersmeet Rd
☎Lynton (0598) 52540 Plan **3** *D2*

8hc (2fb) ⊬ in 2 bedrooms CTV in all bedrooms B&b£10–£12.50 Bdi£15.50–£18 WBdifr£105 LDO4pm

Lic ⋒ CTV 5P 8🚗

Credit cards 1 3 ⓥ

GH Heatherville Tors Park (Guestaccom)
☎Lynton (0598) 52327 Plan **7** *D2*
Apr–Oct

Enthusiastically run Victorian guesthouse in elevated position, with nice warm atmosphere.

8hc (4⋒) (1fb) ✗ Ⓡ in 1 bedroom ✱B&b£12.50–£14 Bdi£19–£20.50 WBdifr£122 LDO5.30pm

Lic ⋒ CTV 8P nc7yrs

LYNTON
Devon
Map **3** SS74
See also **Lynmouth**

GH Alford House Alford Ter ☎(0598) 52359 Plan **1** *B2*

A Georgian residence in an elevated position overlooking the town, approached by a hilly path from the car park.

7hc (fb) ⊬ in all bedrooms CTV in 4 bedrooms ✱B&b£15.50–£17.20 Bdi£20.50–£22.50 LDO9pm

Lic CTV ⱣP nc7yrs

GH Gable Lodge Lee Rd ☎(0598) 52367
Plan **4** *B2*
Closed Dec & Jan

9hc (2⇌ 4⋒) (2fb) CTV in all bedrooms ✗ ⓇB&b£10–£11.75 Bdi£15.75–£17.50 WBdi£104.75–£116.35 LDO5pm

Lic ⋒ CTV 8P nc5yrs

GH Gordon House Hotel 31 Lee Rd
☎(0598) 53203 Plan **5** *B2*
Mar–Nov

A warm and friendly welcome awaits guests at this establishment. Originally built in the Victorian era the house has been tastefully restored yet still offers all modern facilities

7hc (1⇌ 6🚿) (1fb) CTV in all bedrooms ® B&b£12–£14 Bdi£20–£22 WBdifr£134 LDO7pm

Lic ⅏ CTV 7P

Ⓥ

GH Hazeldene 27–28 Lee Rd ☎(0598) 52364 Plan **6** *B2*
Closed 3–30 Nov

9hc (6⇌) (2fb) CTV in all bedrooms ® B&b£10.50–£14 Bdi£17.50–£21 WBdi£115–£135 LDO5pm

Lic ⅏ CTV 8P nc5yrs

Credit cards 1 2 3

Lynton

⟼**GH Horwood House** Lydiate Ln ☎(0598) 52334 Plan **8** *B2*
Apr–Oct

5hc (1fb) ® B&b£8.50–£9.50 Bdi£15–£16 WBdi£98–£105 LDO5pm

Lic CTV 6P ⌂ pool table

Ⓥ

GH Ingleside Hotel Lee Rd ☎(0598) 52223 Plan **9** *B3*
mid Mar–mid Oct

7hc (4⇌ 3🚿) (2fb) CTV in all bedrooms ✗ ® B&b£13–£17 Bdi£21–£25 WBdi£147–£175 LDO6pm

Lic ⅏ 10P nc5yrs

Ⓥ

See advertisement on page 276

GH Kingford House Private Hotel Longmead ☎(0598) 52361 Plan **10** *A2*
Apr–Oct →

8hc (4fl) (1fb) ✗ Ⓡ (charge) ✱B&b£9–£9.50 Bdi£14.25–£15 WBdifr£98.50 LDO4.30pm

Lic CTV 8P nc5yrs

Ⓥ

GH Longmead House 9 Longmead ☎(0598) 52523 Plan **11** *A2*
Feb–Nov

Attractively decorated and well-furnished accommodation in quiet residential area.

9hc (1fb) ✗ (ex guide dogs) Ⓡ B&b£9.50–£11 Bdi£16–£17.50 WBdifr£112 LDO5.30pm

Lic 🍴 CTV 8P nc5yrs

GH Lynhurst Hotel Lynway ☎(0598) 52241 Plan **12** *C1*
Mar–Oct

7hc (4⇌ 3fl) (1fb) TV in all bedrooms ⓇB&b£10–£11 Bdi£12–£14 WBdifr£78

Lic CTV P nc2yrs

GH Mayfair Hotel Lynway ☎(0598) 53227 Plan **13** *C2*

A family run establishment offering good home cooked meals and friendly service.
Closed Feb & Nov

10hc (5⇌ 3fl) (2fb) CTV in all bedrooms Ⓡ B&b£15–£18 Bdi£21–£24 WBdifr£135 LDO6.30pm

Lic 🍴 CTV 10P

Credit cards [1] [3] Ⓥ

Lynton — Lytham St Annes

GH Pine Lodge Lynway (access from Lynbridge Rd) ☎(0598) 53230 Plan **14** *C1*
Etr wk & mid May–Sep

8hc (1⇌ 2fl) Ⓡ B&b£12–£14 Bdi£17–£19 WBdifr£112

CTV 8P nc12yrs

Ⓥ

⊢**GH Retreat** 1 Park Gdns ☎(0598) 53526 Plan **15** *A2*
Mar–Oct

6hc (2fb) ✗ Ⓡ B&b£9 Bdi£14 WBdifr£90 LDOnoon

🍴 CTV 3P

Ⓥ

GH St Vincent Castle Hill ☎(0598) 52244 Plan **16** *C2*
Apr–Oct

Comfortable house offering good home-cooking.

6hc (1fl) (2fb) ✗ Ⓡ ✱B&b£8.50–£11 Bdi£14–£16.50 WBdi£100–£110 LDO4.30pm

Lic CTV 3P

Ⓥ

GH Southcliffe Lee Rd ☎(0598) 53328 Plan **17** *B2*
Mar–Dec

8hc (2⇌ 6fl) CTV in all bedrooms Ⓡ ✱B&b£11–£13 Bdi£18.50–£20.95 WBdi£125–£131 LDO6.30pm

Lic 🍴 7P nc5yrs

Credit cards [1] [3]

GH Turret Lee Rd ☎(0598) 53284 Plan **18** *B2*
Mar–Oct

6hc (2⇌) ✗ B&b£9–£10 WB&b£59.50–£66.50

CTV 5🚗 nc12yrs

GH Valley House Hotel Lynbridge Rd ☎(0598) 52285 Plan **19** *C1*

8hc (1fl) (2fb) CTV in 5 bedrooms Ⓡ ✱B&b£12.50–£14.50 Bdi£18.70–£29 WBdi£117.30–£186

Lic 🍴 CTV 8P

Credit cards [1] [2] [3] Ⓥ

LYTHAM ST ANNES

Lancashire
Map **7** SD32

⊢**GH Beaumont Private Hotel**
11 All Saints Road ☎(0253) 723958

Pleasant, well-furnished, family-run guesthouse in quiet side road.

9hc (4fb) Ⓡ B&b£8.50–£10 Bdi£11–£14 LDO4pm

Lic CTV ₱

Ⓥ

GH Cullerne's Hotel 55 Lightburne Av ☎(0253) 721753

Small, friendly house situated just off the promenade.

6hc (2fb) TV in all bedrooms Ⓡ B&b£12 Bdi£16.50 WBdi£115 LDOnoon

Lic 🍽 CTV 3P nc5yrs

GH Endsleigh Private Hotel 315 Clifton Drive South ☎(0253) 725622

Family run hotel close to sea front.

14hc (1⇌ 9♏) (3fb) CTV in 11 bedrooms ✗ Ⓡ B&b£12–£14 Bdi£16.50–£18 WBdi£92–£115 LDO4pm

Lic 🍽 CTV 8P

GH Harcourt Hotel 21 Richmond Rd ☎(0253) 722299

Closed Xmas & New Year

Small, personally-run, well-furnished guesthouse in quiet side road.

10hc (4fb) Ⓡ B&b£10.35–£10.92 Bdi£13.22–£13.80 WBdifr£92.57 (W Jul–mid Aug) LDO6pm

Lic 🍽 CTV 6P

Ⓥ

Lytham St Annes — Macclesfield

GH Lyndhurst Private Hotel 338 Clifton Drive North ☎(0253) 724343

A family-owned and run house close to town centre and sea.

12hc (1⇌) (4fb) CTV in 4 bedrooms Ⓡ B&b£12–£14 Bdi£17–£19 WBdifr£105

CTV 11P

Ⓥ

GH Strathmore 305 Clifton Drive South ☎(0253) 725478

10hc (2⇌ 3♏) (1fb) CTV in all bedrooms ✗ Ⓡ B&b £13.50–£15.25 Bdi£15.50–£18.25 WBdi£107.50–£120.75

Lic 🍽 10P nc12yrs

MABLETHORPE
Lincolnshire
Map **9** TF58

⊢⊣**GH Auralee** ☎(0521) 77660

Closed Xmas & Boxing Day

Friendly, comfortable, family-run seaside house for holiday and commercial trade.

8hc TV in all bedrooms ✗ Ⓡ B&b£8.50 Bdi£11.15 WBdifr£70 LDO9pm

Lic 🍽 CTV 9P nc2yrs

Ⓥ

MACCLESFIELD
Cheshire
Map **7** SJ97

GH Moorhayes Private Hotel 27 Manchester Rd ☎(0625) 33228

Closed 23 Dec–2 Jan

An attractive house set in its own grounds, in an elevated position close to the town centre with pleasantly furnished rooms and friendly proprietors.

7hc (2♏) (2fb) CTV in all bedrooms ✗ Ⓡ ✻B&b£8.30–£25

🍽 11P

Ⓥ

Credit Cards

1 Access/Euro/Mastercard

2 American Express

3 Barclaycard/Visa

5 Diners

MACHRIHANISH

Strathclyde *Argyllshire*
Map **10** NR62

Selected

GH Ardell House ☎(058681) 235
Closed Xmas & New Year rs Nov–Jan

David and Jill Baxter work hard to ensure that their guests have every comfort. Bedrooms are attractive with tea and coffee making facilities and colour televisions. Guests can relax in the first floor lounge. Dinners feature interesting 'Taste of Scotland' dishes. Magnificent views across the golf course to the islands of Jura and Islay. Winner of the 1986–7 AA Guesthouse of the Year Award.

7hc (1fl) Annexe: 3fl (1fb) CTV in 8 bedrooms TV in 1 bedroom Ⓡ B&b£14.50–£22 Bdi£23–£30 WBdi£168–£189

Lic CTV 12P

Ⓥ

MACHYNLLETH

Powys
Map **6** SH70

FH Mr & Mrs D Timms **Rhiwlwyfen** *(SH761983)* Forge ☎(0654) 2683
Apr–Oct

This remote 17th-century farmhouse is comfortably furnished. Guests can enjoy a peaceful stay amid beautiful surroundings.

2rm (2fb) Ⓡ ✱B&b£8.50–£10 Bdi£14.50–£16 WBdi£101.50–£112

CTV 6P 100acres beef sheep

Ⓥ

MAIDSTONE

Kent
Map **5** TQ75

GH Carval Hotel 56–58 London Rd ☎(0622) 62100

Attractive Victorian house located on a busy road into Maidstone. Well-maintained accommodation, comfortable and homely, with dining room overlooking the garden.

10hc (2fl) CTV in all bedrooms Ⓡ ✱B&b£12.50–£15

Lic CTV 8P

Credit cards 1 2 3 5

GH Kingsgate Hotel 85 London Rd ☎(0622) 53956

Comfortable, modern accommodation in appealing, late 19th-century house with modern extension.

17hc (3fb) CTV in 12 bedrooms ✱B&b£15–£19 Bdi£22.50–£23.50 WBdi£157.50–£164.50

Lic CTV 24P 6

GH Rock House Hotel 102 Tonbridge Rd ☎(0622) 51616
Closed 24 Dec–1 Jan

Small modern guesthouse with cheerful bedrooms and limited lounge facilities.

10hc (2fb) CTV in all bedrooms Ⓡ B&b£12.50–£21 WB&b£80–£140

CTV 7P nc1yr

Credit cards 1 3 Ⓥ

MALDON

Essex
Map **5** TL80

INN Swan Hotel Maldon High St ☎(0621) 53170

Small pub and restaurant with modestly furnished bedrooms.

6hc (2fb) in 1 bedroom TV in all bedrooms B&b£12–£16.50 Bdi£16–£24 WBdi£143.50 Lunch £4–£7.50&alc Dinner9pm £4.50–£10

CTV 30P 1

Credit cards 1 2 3 5

MALHAM

North Yorkshire
Map **7** SD96

GH Sparth House Hotel ☎Airton (07293) 315

Agreeable family run guesthouse in centre of this lovely Dales village.

10hc (1fl) (3fb) B&b£12.50–£16.50 Bdi£19.25–£23.25 WBdifr£120 LDO5pm

Lic CTV 7P

Ⓥ

See advertisement under Skipton

MALMESBURY

Wiltshire
Map **3** ST98
See Rodbourne

MALVERN

Hereford & Worcester
Map **3** SO74

GH *Bredon Hotel* 34 Worcester Rd ☎(06845) 66990
Closed 25 Dec–1 Jan

Georgian-style hotel near town centre. Relaxing lounge has good views of Severn Valley.

9hc (3 3fl) (2fb) CTV in all bedrooms Ⓡ LDO9.30pm

Lic CTV 10P

Credit cards 1 2 3

GH Sidney House Hotel 40 Worcester Rd ☎(06845) 4994

Listed Georgian building, fully restored to offer pleasant accommodation and attentive service.

7hc (3fl) (1fb) TV in all bedrooms Ⓡ B&b£12–£14 Bdi£19.50–£23.50 WBdifr£119 LDO2pm

Lic CTV 7P

Credit cards 1 2 3 5 Ⓥ

MAN, ISLE OF

Map **6**

BALLAUGH

Map **6** SC39

INN Ravensdale Castle Glen Rd ☎Sulby (0624 89) 7330
rs Nov–Mar

A Georgian/Victorian country inn, featuring a clock tower. Set in own grounds, it offers comfortable accommodation.

10hc (7⇌) (3fb) CTV in 3 bedrooms TV in 2 bedrooms Ⓡ B&b£13–£19.50 Lunch£2.75–£7&alc Dinner9pm£8–£9&alc

𝔐 CTV 70P ⌗

Credit cards ① ③ Ⓥ

DOUGLAS
Map **6** SC37

GH Ainsdale 2 Empire Ter, Central Prom ☎(0624) 76695

Pleasantly furnished and personally-run guesthouse.

21hc (7fb) Ⓡ ✱B&b£8–£8.50 Bdi£10–£10.50

CTV P̸ ⌂

GH Ascot Private Hotel 7 Empire Ter ☎(0624) 75081
Apr–Oct

Large, central private hotel providing good family entertainment.

32⇌ (6fb) CTV in all bedrooms ✖ Ⓡ ✱Bdi£16–£18 WBdifr£125

Lic lift 𝔐 P̸

Credit cards ① ③

GH Edelweiss Queens Prom ☎(0624) 75115

An attractive family run hotel situated facing the promenade and offering good all round value.

15hc (1⇌ 14fl) (2fb) CTV in all bedrooms ✖ Ⓡ ✱B&b£12.50–£13.80 Bdi£15.50–£16.80 LDO9pm

Lic lift CTV P̸ solarium

Credit cards ① ③

GH Gladwyn Private Hotel Queen's Prom ☎(0624) 75406
Etr–Sep

Modern well-furnished hotel overlooking Douglas Bay.

39hc (4fl) (15fb) B&b£10.50 Bdi£12.65–£13.65 WBdi£88.55–£95.55

Lic CTV P̸ snooker

Credit cards ① ③ Ⓥ

GH Holyrood Hotel 51 Loch Prom ☎(0624) 73790
Feb–Nov

Man, Isle of
—
Manchester

Personally supervised private hotel offering comfortable accommodation.

19hc (2fl) Lic CTV P̸ (10fb) ✖

GH *Hydro Hotel* Queen's Prom ☎(0624) 76870
May–Sep rs Etr

Large, well-furnished house on the sea front.

71hc (8⇌ 2fl) (27fb) ✖ Ⓡ LDO7pm

Lic lift 𝔐 CTV P̸

Credit cards ① ③ Ⓥ

GH Rosslyn 3 Empire Ter, Central Prom ☎(0624) 76056
3 Jan–28 Nov

Near promenade, this guesthouse is personally run by owners.

16hc (4⇌ 4fl) (3fb) CTV in 5 bedrooms ✖ Ⓡ B&b£10.50–£12.50 Bdi£12.50–£17 WBdifr£119

Lic 𝔐 CTV P̸ ⌂

Ⓥ

GH Rothesay Private Hotel 15–16 Loch Prom ☎(0624) 75274
Closed Dec & Jan

Well-furnished, family-run hotel with good bedrooms.

30hc (6fl) (2fb) CTV in all bedrooms ✱B&b£14–£17 Bdi£18–£21 LDO7.30pm

Lic lift CTV P̸

GH *Rutland Hotel* Queen's Prom ☎(0624) 21218
Etr–Oct

Large seafront hotel supervised by resident owners

107hc (12⇌ 13fl) (17fb) ✖ LDO7.30pm

Lic lift CTV P̸ ⌂

Credit cards ① ③

GH Welbeck Private Hotel Mona Dr ☎(0624) 75663

Well-furnished private hotel near promenade.

22⇌ fl (3fb) CTV in all bedrooms ✖ Ⓡ B&b£15–£18 Bdi£18.50–£22 WBdifr£130 LDO7pm

Lic lift 𝔐 CTV P̸

Ⓥ

PORT ERIN
Map **6** SC16

GH Regent House The Promenade ☎(0624) 833454

8hc (5⇌ 1fl) CTV in all bedrooms ✖ Ⓡ B&b£12–£13 Bdi£16.75–£18 LDO6.30pm

𝔐

Ⓥ

See advertisement on page 280

PORT ST MARY
Map **6** SC26

GH Mallmore Private Hotel The Promenade ☎(0624) 833179
May–6 Oct

Delightfully situated hotel overlooking the bay.

43hc (10fb) ✖ Ⓡ in 16 bedrooms ✱B&b£8–£8.30 Bdifr£11.50

CTV P ⌂ snooker

Credit cards ① ② ③ Ⓥ

MANCHESTER
Gt Manchester
Map **7** SJ89

GH Horizon Hotel 69 Palatine Rd, West Didsbury ☎061–445 4705

Modern hotel with well-equipped bedrooms in pleasant residential area.

15hc (8⇌ 7fl) (1fb) CTV in all bedrooms ✖ Ⓡ ✱B&bfr£18.50 Bdifr£24.50 WBdi£145 LDO5pm

Lic 𝔐 CTV 20P nc10yrs

Credit cards ① ③ Ⓥ

GH Kempton House Hotel 400 Wilbraham Rd, Chorlton-Cum-Hardy ☎061–881 8766
Closed Xmas & Boxing Day

Large semi-detached house with nice décor and furnishings. →

14hc (1fb) CTV in 5 bedrooms ✗ B&b£12–£15 Bdi£15–£18 LDO5pm

Lic ₩ CTV 9P

Ⓥ

GH New Central Hotel 144–146 Heywood St (Guestaccom) ☎061–205 2169

Closed Xmas–New Year

Double-fronted hotel in a residential area, yet convenient for city centre.

10hc ✗ Ⓡ B&b£15–£20 WB&b£100–£120 LDO7.30pm

Lic ₩ CTV 10P nc5yrs

Ⓥ

MAPPOWDER
Dorset
Map **3** ST70

FH Mrs A K Williamson-Jones ***Boywood*** *(ST733078)* ☎Hazelbury Bryan (02586) 416

1½m N unclass rd towards Hazelbury Bryan

3rm ✗

₩ CTV P ⌂ ⊡(heated) ℘(hard) 17acres beef poultry

MARGARET RODING (nr Gt. Dunmow)
Essex
Map **5** TL51

FH Mr & Mrs J Matthews **Greys** *(TQ604112)* Ongar Rd ☎ Good Easter (024531) 509

Apr–Oct

Small, comfortable farmhouse of some quality set away from main farm buildings.

3rm (2hc) ✗ Ⓡ available in bedrooms ✻B&bfr£10

₩ CTV 3P nc10yrs 340 acres arable sheep

MARGATE
Kent
Map **5** TR37

GH Beachcomber Hotel 2–3 Royal Esplanade, Westbrook ☎Thanet (0843) 221616

15hc (3fb) ✗ B&b£12–£13.50 Bdi£18–£19.50 WBdifr£107 LDO10pm

Lic CTV 1P ⌂

⊢**GH Charnwood Private Hotel** 20–22 Canterbury Rd ☎Thanet (0843) 224158

Old-fashioned, traditional accommodation under new and friendly management.

8hc (4fb) ✗ Ⓡ B&b£9–£11 Bdi£13–£15 WBdi£75–£90 LDO4pm

Lic ₩ CTV ₱

Credit cards ① ③ Ⓥ

GH *Galleon Lights Hotel* 12–14 Fort Cres, Cliftonville ☎Thanet (0843) 291703

Comfortable modernised accommodation, with a basement dining room and bar, facing the Winter Gardens.

20hc (5⇌ 3fl) (2fb) CTV in 11 bedrooms LDO5pm

Lic ₩ CTV ₱ nc10yrs

Credit cards ① ③

GH Greswolde 20 Surrey Rd, Cliftonville ☎ Thanet (0843) 223956

9hc (1⇌ 1fl) (2fb) CTV in all bedrooms Ⓡ ✻B&b£8.50–£11 Bdi£13.50–£16.25 LDO11am

Lic ₩ CTV ₱

Ⓥ

⊢**GH Tyrella Private Hotel** 19 Canterbury Rd ☎Thanet (0843) 292746

Closed Xmas & New Year

Small, family-run house, close to the sea with modern, well-decorated bedrooms.

7hc (4fb) CTV in 1 bedroom ✗ Ⓡ B&b£9–£10 Bdi£12.50–£13.50 WBdifr£70 LDO1pm

Lic ₩ CTV ₱ nc6yrs

Ⓥ

GH *Westbrook Bay House* 12 Royal Esp, Westbrook ☎Thanet (0843) 292700

Well-maintained bedrooms, some with excellent sea views, and tastefully furnished public rooms.

12hc (3fl) (4fb) ✗ LDO4.30pm

Lic ₩ CTV ₱

MARK CAUSEWAY
Somerset
Map **3** ST34

FH Mrs E Puddy **Croft** *(ST355475)* ☎Mark Moor (027864) 206

Etr–Xmas

Comfortable and well-decorated farmhouse with traditional furnishings throughout.

4hc ✗ B&bfr£9.75 Bdifr£12.50 WBdi£77 LDO4pm

CTV 3P 3🚗 nc14yrs 130acres dairy

MARLOW
Buckinghamshire
Map **4** SU88

GH Glade 75 Glade Rd ☎(06284) 4677

Small, modern house, family-run to a very high standard.

7hc (1fb) CTV in all bedrooms ✗ Ⓡ B&b£22–£26 Bdi£26–£30 WBdi£150–£175 LDO5pm

Lic ₩ 4P nc5yrs

Credit cards ① ③ Ⓥ

MARPLE
Cheshire
Map **7** SJ98

FH Mrs M G Sidebottom **Shire Cottage Ernocroft** *(SJ982910)* Marple Bridge ☎Glossop (04574) 66536 or 061-427 2377

Modern bungalow with good furnishings overlooking delightful farming country.

4hc (1fl) (1fb) ⚟ in 2 bedrooms CTV in all bedrooms ✗ Ⓡ ✻B&b£10–£13 Bdi£13.50–£17 WBdi£91–£110 LDO1pm

₩ CTV 6P ⌂ 180acres mixed

Ⓥ

MARSHGATE
Cornwall
Map **2** SX19

FH Mrs P Bolt ***Carleton*** *(SX153918)*
☎Otterham Station (08406) 252
Etr–Oct
Farmhouse is situated adjacent to the Boscastle road in Marshgate with views over the surrounding farmlands.

3rm (1fb) ✱

CTV 3P 120acres dairy

MARSTOW
Hereford & Worcester
Map **3** SO51

FH Mrs S C Watson **Trebandy** *(SO544203)* ☎Llangarron (098984) 230
Apr–Oct
Large, Georgian farmhouse situated in the remote Garron Valley, well off the A4137, 1m NW unclass rd. Ideal for peaceful stay.

2hc (2fb) ✱ Ⓡ ✱B&b£8.50–£9 WB&bfr£59.50

CTV 6P 286acres arable beef

Ⓥ

MARTON
Warwickshire
Map **4** SP46

FH Mrs P M Dronfield **Marton Fields** *(SP402680)* ☎(0926) 632410
Closed Xmas

Marshgate — Mathon

A large farmhouse on edge of quiet village. Proprietor Mrs Dronfield is an accomplished amateur artist and hopes to run specialised painting holidays.

4hc in all bedrooms ✱ Ⓡ B&b£10–£12 Bdi£17–£19 WBdifr£119 LDO6pm

CTV 10P 247acres arable beef

MARYBANK
Highland *Ross & Cromarty*
Map **14** NH45

FH Mrs R Macleod ***Easter Balloan*** *(NH484535)* ☎Urray (09973) 211
Etr–Oct
Roadside farmhouse standing in its own garden on edge of village.

5rm (4hc) (2fb) ✱ LDO8pm

CTV 10P 143acres mixed

Credit card 3

MARY TAVY
Devon
Map **2** SX57

FH Mrs B Anning **Wringworthy** *(SX500773)* ☎(082281) 434
Apr–Sep
2m S A386.

3rm (1fb) ✱ B&b£9.50–£10 Bdi£15–£16 LDO10am

CTV 3P 80acres beef dairy

MASHAM
North Yorkshire
Map **8** SE28

GH Bank Villa (Guestaccom) ☎Ripon (0765) 89605
Mar–Oct
Good home-cooking in comfortable, personally-run guesthouse.

7hc B&b£11.50–£14 Bdi£20.50–£23 WBdi£130 LDOnoon

Lic CTV 7P nc5yrs

Ⓥ

MATHON
Hereford & Worcester
Map **3** SO74

GH *Moorend Court* (Guestaccom) ☎Ridgway Cross (088684) 205
Large house set in 10 acres of grounds, offering comfortable accommodation in large rooms all with panoramic views.

7hc (1⇌) (3fb) TV in all bedrooms Ⓡ LDOnoon

40P (grass)

See advertisement on page 282

MATLOCK
Derbyshire
Map **8** SK36

FH Mrs M Brailsford **Farley** *(SK294622)* ☎(0629) 2533
Closed Xmas & New Year

Stone-built farmhouse, parts of which date back to 1610, set high in the Derbyshire hills. 1½m NNW unclass rd.

3hc (1fb) Ⓡ *B&b£10 Bdi£15 WBdifr£105

CTV 8P 225acres arable beef dairy

Ⓥ

Matlock

FH Mrs R A Groom **Manor** *(SK327580)*
Dethick ☎Dethick (062984) 246 due to change to (0629) 534246
Closed Dec

Large, beautifully preserved mid 16th-century Manor house, once home of Sir Anthony Babbington.

4hc (1fl) (1fb) CTV in 1 bedroom B&b£10–£12.50 Bdi£15.50–£19.50 WBdi£105.50–£129 LDO10am

CTV 4P nc8yrs 200acres beef sheep mixed

FH M Haynes **Packhorse** *(SK323617)*
Tansley ☎(0629) 2781 due to change to 582781

Former inn on much travelled Chesterfield to Manchester packhorse route. Tastefully furnished. Lawns and putting greens. 2m NE of Matlock off A632 at Tansley signpost.

5hc (3fb) B&b£9–£9.50 WB&bfr£63

CTV 20P nc3yrs 40acres mixed

FH Mrs J Hole **Wayside** *(SK324630)* Matlock Moor ☎(0629) 2967
Closed Xmas & New Year

Pleasant, modernised, stone-built farmhouse, adjacent to A632 Matlock–Chesterfield road.

6hc (2fb) ✖ ✱B&bfr£8.50

🍴 CTV 8P 60acres dairy

MATTISHALL
Norfolk
Map **9** TG01

FH Mrs M Faircloth **Moat Farm** *(TG049111)* ☎Dereham (0362) 850288
May–Oct

Simple but most comfortable accommodation in welcoming small, red-brick and pantiled farmhouse.

2hc (1fb) ✖ LDO6pm

CTV 2P nc4yrs 100acres arable beef sheep mixed

MAWGAN PORTH
Cornwall
Map **2** SW86

GH White Lodge Hotel ☎St Mawgan (0637) 860512
Mar–Nov

Large detached building situated in a prominent position and enjoying sea views. Good bedrooms and friendly services.

Matlock — Melksham

15hc (10🛁 🚿) (6fb) CTV in 12 bedrooms B&b£12.50–£16.25 Bdi£16.50–£20.50 WBdi£89–£135 LDO7.30pm

Lic 🍴 15P

Ⓥ

MAYFIELD
Staffordshire
Map **7** SK14

INN *Queen's Arms* ☎Ashbourne (0335) 42271

Situated on the A52 approximately 1 mile west of Ashbourne, this homely roadside inn offers clean, simple accommodation conveniently located for Alton Towers and the Peak National Park.

7hc (3fb) CTV in 6 bedrooms

CTV 20P

MELKSHAM
Wiltshire
Map **3** ST96

GH Longhope 9 Beanacre Rd ☎(0225) 706737

Comfortable, well-maintained stone-built house conveniently located on the edge of town.

7hc (3🛁 4🚿) (3fb) CTV in 6 bedrooms Ⓡ in 6 bedrooms B&b£12.50 Bdi£17.50 WBdi£125.50 LDO6pm

🍴 CTV 12P

GH Regency Hotel 10–12 Spa Rd ☎(0225) 702971

A terraced Regency house in town centre with attentive, friendly owners.

11hc (1🛁 4🚿) (1fb) CTV in all bedrooms Ⓡ B&b£15–£17 Bdi£20–£24 WBdifr£155 LDO8pm

Lic 🍴 CTV P̸

Credit cards ① ③ Ⓥ

Selected

GH Shaw Country Hotel Shaw ☎(0225) 702836
Closed 25–26 Dec

1½ NW off A365.

Delightful, 400-year-old farmhouse, covered in creepers, on outskirts of town. Its two lounges, breakfast room and bar are comfortably furnished.

11hc (1🛁 5🚿) (1fb) CTV in all bedrooms ✖ Ⓡ B&b£16–£24 Bdi£23.20–£31.20 LDO8pm

Lic 🍴 25P ⛳ ⛱(heated)

Credit cards ① ② ③ Ⓥ

GH York Church Walk ☎(0225) 702063
5hc (1fb) B&b£11 Bdi£18 WBdifr£120 LDO6pm
CTV P 2
Credit cards 1 3

MELMERBY
Cumbria
Map **12** NY63

FH Mrs M Morton **Meadow Bank** *(NY615375)* ☎Langwathby (076881) 652
Closed Dec & Jan
Comfortable bungalow adjacent to main farm building.
2rm (1fb) in 2 bedrooms B&b£8–£8.50 WB&bfr£55
CTV 3P 185acres arable beef dairy sheep
Ⓥ

MELTON MOWBRAY
Leicestershire
Map **8** SK71

GH Westbourne House Hotel 11A–15 Nottingham Rd ☎(0664) 63556
Closed Xmas
20hc (8) (2fb) CTV in all bedrooms B&b£15–£29 Bdi£20–£34 LDO7.15pm
Lic CTV 19P

MENDHAM
Suffolk
Map **5** TM28

FH Mrs J E Holden **Weston House** *(TM292828)* ☎St Cross (098682) 206
Apr–Oct
Fine old house approximately 300 years old, in 1 acre of garden with fishing nearby.
3hc (1fb) B&b£9 WB&b£56
CTV 6P 330acres arable beef dairy mixed

MENHENIOT
Cornwall
Map **2** SX26

FH Mrs S Rowe **Tregondale** *(SX294643)* ☎Liskeard (0579) 42407
Closed Xmas

Farm offering friendly atmosphere and attractive rooms. E of Liskeard, 1½m N of A38.
3rm (2hc) (1fb) Ⓡ B&b£9.50–£10 Bdi£13.50–£14.50 WBdifr£90 LDO6pm
CTV 3P shooting 180acres mixed
Ⓥ

MERE
Wiltshire
Map **3** ST83

INN Talbot Hotel The Square ☎(0747) 860427
Oak timbers abound both outside and inside this 16th-century village hostelry.
10rm (4 3) (2fb) CTV in all bedrooms Ⓡ in 1 bedroom B&b£18–£22 Bdi£26.50–£30.50 WBdifr£120 Lunch £5–£6.50&alc Dinner 9pm £8.50&alc
25P
Credit card 1 Ⓥ

MERIDEN
West Midlands
Map **4** SP28

GH Meriden Hotel Main Rd ☎(0676) 22005
Small friendly hotel offering good accommodation at competitive prices.
8hc (2fb) CTV available in bedrooms B&b£17.25–£25 Bdi£23.25–£28.25 LDOnoon
Lic CTV 15P
Ⓥ

MEVAGISSEY
Cornwall
Map **2** SX04

GH Headlands Hotel Polkirt Hill ☎(0726) 843453
Mar–Oct & Xmas
Large detached house, standing above road with magnificent sea views.
14hc (6) (3fb) B&b£11–£13 Bdi£17.50–£19.50 WBdi£113.75–£126.75 LDO7pm
Lic CTV 11P

GH Mevagissey House Vicarage Hill ☎(0726) 842427
Mar–Oct
Large, detached former rectory in elevated position with views to harbour.
6hc (1 3) (3fb) CTV in all bedrooms Ⓡ B&b£11–£18 Bdi£18.50–£25.50 WBdi£119.50–£168.50 LDOnoon
Lic 12P nc7yrs
Ⓥ

FH Mrs A Hannah **Treleaven** *(SW008454)* ☎(0726) 842413
Closed 15 Dec–7 Jan
Large detached farmhouse on a hill with lawned garden and swimming pool.
6 (1fb) CTV in all bedrooms Ⓡ B&b£12–£16 Bdi£18–£23 WBdifr£118 LDO8pm
Lic CTV 6P heated 200acres mixed
Credit cards 1 3 Ⓥ

INN *Ship* Fore St ☎(0726) 843324
5hc (1fb) LDO8.30pm
CTV

MIDDLESBROUGH
Cleveland
Map **8** NZ42

GH *Chadwick Private Hotel* 27 Clairville Rd ☎(0642) 245340
Spacious Edwardian style house with comfortable bedrooms.
6hc (1fb) LDO4pm
CTV

GH Grey House Hotel 79 Cambridge Rd ☎(0642) 817485
Closed 2 weeks Xmas & New Year
Sizeable rooms of charm and character, enhanced by proprietor's own paintings and drawings.
10hc (1 6) (1fb) CTV in 7 bedrooms Ⓡ B&b£14.25–£28 Bdi£19.75–£33.50 LDO7pm
CTV 10P

GH *Longlands Hotel* 295 Marton Rd ☎(0642) 244900

Converted end terrace house, well-suited to business people, with spacious and colourful rooms.

7hc (1fb) ✖ LDO5pm

Lic 𝍧 CTV 2P 6[garage]

MIDDLETON-ON-SEA
West Sussex
Map **4** SU90

GH Ancton House Hotel Ancton Ln ☎(024369) 2482

Cosy 16th-century guesthouse set in rural surroundings.

9hc (2[bath] 4[shower]) (2fb) Ⓡ B&b£13.50–£15.50 Bdi£17.50–£19.50 WBdi£116.38–£129.65

Lic 𝍧 CTV 5P 5[garage] ⌂

Credit card ③ Ⓥ

MIDDLETOWN
Powys
Map **7** SJ21

FH Mrs E J Bebb **Bank** *(SJ325137)* ☎Trewern (093874) 260
Etr–Oct

Situated on the A458 Shrewsbury–Welshpool road at the foot of the Breidden Hills with good views.

3rm (2hc) (1fb) ✖ B&bfr£9

𝍧 CTV P nc5yrs 30acres sheep

Middlesbrough — Milngavie

MIDHURST
West Sussex
Map **4** SU82
See **Bepton** and **Rogate**

MILBORNE PORT
Somerset
Map **3** ST61

FH Mrs M J Tizzard **Venn** *(ST684183)* ☎(0963) 250208

Attractive accommodation in a modern house, set back off main road on Shaftesbury side of village.

3rm (2hc) (2fb) TV available in bedrooms ✖ Ⓡ B&bfr£9.50 WB&bfr£56

𝍧 CTV P ⌂ 375acres dairy

MILFORD-ON-SEA
Hampshire
Map **4** SZ29

GH Seaspray 8 Hurst Rd ☎Lymington (0590) 42627

A small, delightful guesthouse facing the sea. Pretty, bright bedrooms, TV lounge and separate bar.

6hc (2[shower]) (1fb) CTV in all bedrooms ❋B&b£12–£20 Bdi£18.50–£26.50 WBdifr£130 LDO11am

Lic 𝍧 8P

MILLPOOL
Cornwall
Map **2** SW53

GH Chyraise Lodge Hotel ☎Penzance (0736) 763485

Tastefully furnished guesthouse in large, attractive gardens.

10hc (4[shower]) (2fb) ✖ Ⓡ B&b£10.50–£13.80 Bdi£16–£19.50 WBdifr£125 LDO9pm

Lic 𝍧 CTV 20P

Credit card ① Ⓥ

See advertisement under Praa Sands

MILNGAVIE
Strathclyde *Dunbartonshire*
Map **11** NS57

FH Mrs L Fisken **High Craigton** *(NS525766)* ☎041–956 1384

Off A809, two-storey painted stone-built farmhouse on hill-top with views over fields towards Glasgow.

2hc (1fb) ✖ B&b£9 WB&b£59.50

𝍧 CTV 10P 1100acres sheep

MILTON COMMON
Oxfordshire
Map **4** SP60

INN Three Pigeons ☎Great Milton (08446) 247
3⇌ ⋒ (1fb) CTV in all bedrooms ✗ Ⓡ B&bfr£25 WB&bfr£150 LDO10pm
⋒⋒ CTV 20P snooker
Credit cards 1 3 5 Ⓥ

MILTON KEYNES
Buckinghamshire
Map **4** SP83
See **Brickhill (Great), Gayhurst, Salford** and **Whaddon**

GH The Different Drummer 94 High St, Stony Stratford ☎(0908) 564733 Telex no 946240
Closed Xmas & New Year
A popular family-run residential hotel and restaurant with cosy bedrooms.
17hc (3⇌ 4⋒) (1fb) CTV in all bedrooms ✗ Ⓡ B&b£23.50–£35 LDO8.30pm
Lic ⊅
Credit cards 1 2 3 5 Ⓥ

MINEHEAD
Somerset
Map **3** SS94
See plan on page 287

Milton Common — Minster Lovell

GH Carbery Hotel Western Ln, The Parks ☎(0643) 2941 Plan **1** *A3*
Mar–Nov
7hc (2⇌ 3⋒) (2fb) CTV in all bedrooms ✗ Ⓡ ✱B&b£10–£12 Bdi£15–£17 WBdi£98.50 LDO7.15pm
Lic ⋒⋒ 7P 1⌂ nc10yrs

GH Dorchester Hotel 38 The Avenue ☎(0643) 2052 Plan **2** *C3*
13hc (3fb) ⚡ in all bedrooms CTV available in bedrooms ✗ Ⓡ available in bedrooms B&b£10.25–£11 Bdi£15–£16 WBdi£85.25–£90.75 LDO8.30pm
Lic ⋒⋒ 12P nc5yrs
Credit cards 1 3 Ⓥ

GH Gascony Hotel The Avenue ☎(0643) 5939 Plan **3** *C3*
Mar–Oct
Friendly and efficient guesthouse in a prime position.
14hc (2⇌ 7⋒) (3fb) CTV in 7 bedrooms Ⓡ ✱B&b£11–£12 WBdifr£87 LDO6.30pm
Lic CTV 10P
Credit cards 3 5 Ⓥ

GH Marshfield Tregonwell Rd ☎(0643) Plan **4** *C3*
Mar–Nov
A semi-detached 3-storey gabled residence offering well maintained accommodation within easy walking distance of the beach and town centre.
11hc (5⋒) (2fb) Ⓡ ✱B&b£9–£11.25 Bdi£13.50–£15.75 LDO7pm
Lic CTV 6P

GH Mayfair Hotel 25 The Avenue ☎(0643) 2719 Plan **5** *C3*
Etr–Oct
16hc (3⇌ 13⋒) (10fb) CTV in all bedrooms Ⓡ B&b£14.50–£15.50 Bdi£20–£21 WBdi£110–£120 LDO6pm
Lic ⋒⋒ 14P

MINSTER LOVELL
Oxfordshire
Map **4** SP31

FH Mrs K Brown **Hill Grove** *(SP334110)* ☎Witney (0993) 3120 due to change to 703120
Closed Xmas
A Cotswold stone-built farmhouse with extensive views over the Windrush Valley, with river running through. Off B4047 1½ m E of village towards Crawley village.
2rm ✗ Ⓡ ✱B&b£10.50–£12
⋒⋒ CTV 3P 200acres arable beef mixed

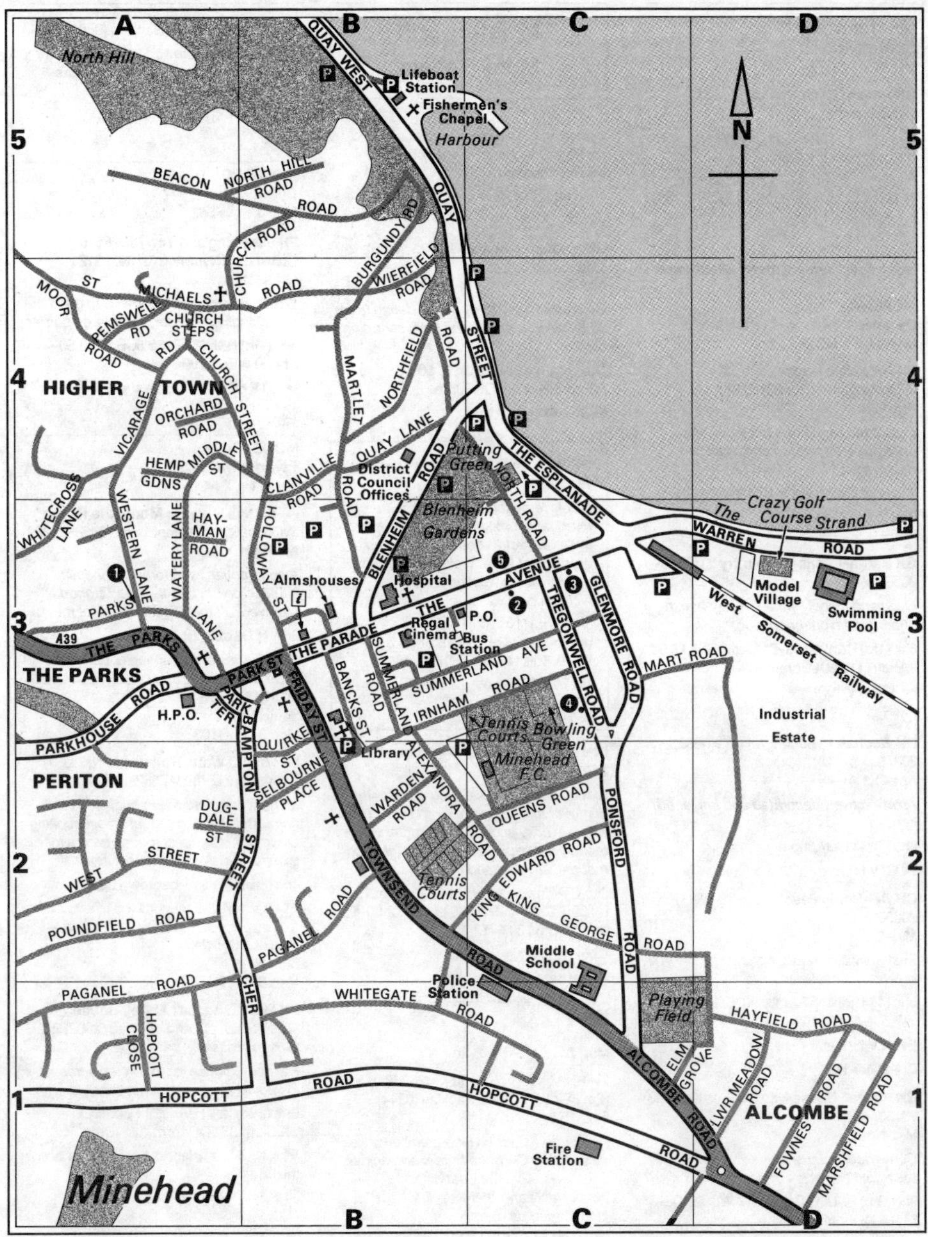

Minehead

1 Carbery Hotel
2 Dorchester Hotel
3 Gascony Hotel
4 Marshfield Hotel
5 Mayfair Hotel

Minsterworth — Monk Soham

MINSTERWORTH
Gloucestershire
Map **3** SO71

GH Severn Bank ☎(045275) 357
Closed Xmas
Pleasant and spacious guesthouse in six acres beside the river.
6hc (1⇌ 3fl) (4fb) CTV in all bedrooms ✗ Ⓡ B&b£14.50–£19 WB&b£101.50–£133
Lic 12P nc5yrs
Ⓥ
See advertisement under Gloucester

MOFFAT
Dumfries & Galloway *Dumfriesshire*
Map **11** NT00

GH Arden House High St (Guestaccom) ☎(0683) 20220
Apr–Oct
Converted sandstone bank building, attractively decorated and furnished, dating from 1738, in town centre.
7hc (4fl) (2fb) B&b£9–£12 Bdi£14–£17 LDO6pm
9P

GH Barnhill Springs Country ☎(0683) 20580
Quiet and friendly small country-house offering plain but good food.
6hc (1fb) B&b£10.50–£11 Bdi£17–£17.50 WBdifr£115 LDO6pm
Lic CTV 10P
Ⓥ

GH *Buchan* 13 Beechgrove ☎(0683) 20378
Apr–Oct
An attractively decorated and furnished house.
8hc (2fb) LDO7.30pm
CTV 6P

GH Del-Robin Beechgrove ☎(0683) 20050
Mar–Oct
Tastefully decorated Victorian house in a quiet residential road.
6hc (4fl) (2fb) Ⓡ B&b£9.50–£12 Bdi£15–£17.50 WBdifr£100
CTV 7P 1
Credit card 3

GH Hartfell House Hartfell Cres ☎(0683) 20153
Mar–Nov
Converted Victorian house to rear of the town with two acres of gardens.
9hc (3fb) B&bfr£10 Bdifr£17 WBdi£108–£110 LDO6pm
Lic CTV 10P
Ⓥ

GH *Rockhill* 14 Beechgrove ☎(0683) 20283
Mar–Oct
Charming house close to parkland and gardens. Neat, well-maintained accommodation.
10hc (4fb) LDO5pm
CTV 6P

GH St Olaf Eastgate, Off Dickson St ☎(0683) 20001
Apr–Oct
Converted two-storey house dating from 1880 situated just off the main shopping centre.
7hc (3fb) ✱B&b£9 Bdi£13.50 WBdifr£94.50 LDO6.30pm
4P 4

Selected

GH Well View Hotel Ballplay Rd ☎(0683) 20184
Nicely re-decorated interior, with good pine furnishings are to be found in this attractive house situated on outskirts of town. Well-kept gardens and adjoining woollen craft workshop.
8rm (6hc) (1⇌ 3fl) (2fb) Ⓡ in 4 bedrooms B&b£10–£18 Bdi£17.50–£26 WBdi£115.50 LDO7.45pm
Lic CTV 8P
Credit card 3

INN Black Bull Hotel Churchgate ☎(0683) 20206
A 16th-century inn situated close to the centre of this attractive small town. The bars are cosy and full of character with a friendly atmosphere. Bedrooms, though modest, are neat and modern.
3hc CTV in all bedrooms ✗ Ⓡ B&b£15 Bdi£20–£25 WBdifr£100 Lunch £2.50–£3 Dinner9pm £3.50–£7
5P
Credit card 3 Ⓥ

MOLD
Clwyd
Map **7** SJ26

FH Mrs A Brown **Hill** *(SJ263625)* Llong (2m SE of A5118) ☎Buckley (0244) 542415
This large detached Georgian house lies close to the Cheshire border and enjoys fine views. Accommodation is comfortable and there are attractive landscaped gardens.
3hc (1fb) ✗ Ⓡ B&b£9–£10
CTV 5P 300acres dairy mixed
Ⓥ

MOLESWORTH
Cambridgeshire
Map **4** TL07

INN *Cross Keys* ☎Bythorn (08014) 283
Village pub built in early 1900's, in quiet country location, offering fresh home-cooking.
3hc (1⇌ 1fl) Ⓡ LDO10.30pm
30P

MOLLAND
Devon
Map **3** SS82

FH Mrs P England **Yeo** *(SS785266)* ☎Bishop's Nympton (07697) 312
Apr–Oct
Well-maintained farmhouse with good furnishings and décor, set in large garden.
3hc (1fb) B&b£8.50–£9.50 Bdi£13.50–£14.50 WBdifr£90
CTV 6P 200acres sheep
Ⓥ

MONEYDIE
Tayside *Perthshire*
Map **11** NO02

FH Mrs S Walker **Moneydie Roger** *(NO054290)* ☎Almondbank (073883) 239
Apr–Sep
A substantial, two-storey farmhouse situated on unclassified road signed Methven, off the B8063, 2½m W of the A9.
2rm ✗ B&b£8–£8.50
2P 143acres arable sheep cattle mixed

MONKSILVER
Somerset
Map **3** ST03

FH Mrs S J Watts ***Rowdon*** *(ST082381)* ☎Stogumber (0984) 56280
Modern farmhouse with bright comfortable accommodation overlooking Quantock Hills. Ideal touring centre for Exmoor and West Somerset coast.
4hc (2fb) CTV in 1 bedroom LDO5pm
CTV 10P 300acres mixed

MONK SOHAM
Suffolk
Map **5** TM26

FH Mrs S E Bagnall **Abbey House** *(TM216656)* ☎Earl Soham (072882) 225
Closed Xmas
Former Victorian rectory in ten acres, including an open-air swimming pool.
3rm (2⇌) (2fb) B&bfr£14 Bdifr£21 WBdifr£133 LDO4pm
CTV 6P 10acres beef dairy sheep mixed

MONMOUTH
Gwent
Map **3** SO51

Selected

INN Queen's Head St James Street ☎(0600) 2767

Attractive small inn with bar of character and pretty bedrooms. Situated by Haberdashers school.

3hc (1⇌ 2fl) (3fb) CTV in all bedrooms Ⓡ B&b£17 WB&b£90 Lunch £1–£2.50&alc Dinner 10pm £1.50–£2.50&alc

ⅢCTV 6P

Credit cards 1 3 Ⓥ

MONTROSE
Tayside *Angus*
Map **15** NO75

GH *Linksgate* 11 Dorward Rd ☎(0674) 72273

Small, family run guesthouse in substantial stone villa close to the sea front.

9hc (2⇌) (3fb) CTV in 2 bedrooms LDO6pm

ⅢCTV 9P

FH Mrs A Ruxton **Muirshade of Gallery** *(NO671634)* ☎Northwaterbridge (067484) 209
Apr–Oct

Situated in beautiful countryside facing the Grampian mountain range, only 5m from the sea.

2hc (1fb) ✗ ✱B&b£7.50–£8.50 Bdi£12–£12.50 LDO4pm

CTV 3P 175acres arable

Ⓥ

MORCHARD BISHOP
Devon
Map **3** SS70

FH Mr & Mrs S Chilcott ***Wigham*** *(SS757087)* ☎(03637) 350

Very attractive thatched farmhouse of 16th century date. Carefully restored to provide stylish accommodation.

4hc (3⇌ 1fl) (3fb) CTV in all bedrooms ✗ Ⓡ

Lic ⅢCTV 9P ⛱heated U 11acres mixed

MORECAMBE
Lancashire
Map **7** SD46

GH Ashley Private Hotel 371 Marine Road East ☎(0524) 412034

Small family-run sea front guesthouse.

15hc (1⇌ 2fl) (4fb) CTV in all bedrooms ✗ Ⓡ B&b£12–£13 Bdi£14–£15 WBdifr£100 LDO4.30pm

Lic ⅢCTV 5P 1🚗

Credit cards 1 3 Ⓥ

GH Beach Mount 395 Marine Road East ☎(0524) 420753
Mar–Nov

Modern family-run hotel overlooking the bay.

26hc (22⇌) (3fb) CTV in 22 bedrooms Ⓡ B&b£11.75–£14.25 Bdi£17.50–£20 WBdi£105–£120 LDO7pm

Lic ⅢCTV 6P

Credit cards 1 2 3 5

⊢⊣**GH Ellesmere Private Hotel** 44 Westminster Rd ☎(0524) 411881
Apr–Nov

Small, friendly guesthouse with good home-made food.

5hc (2fb) CTV in all bedrooms ✗ B&b£7.50–£8 Bdi£9–£10 WBdifr£60 LDO5.15pm

ⅢCTV ⚡

Ⓥ

GH New Hazelmere Hotel 391 Marine Road East ☎(0524) 417876
May–Nov

Private hotel occupying a corner site on the promenade.

22hc (5⇌ 2ⓕ) (4fb) Ⓡ B&bfr£11.50 Bdifr£14.95 WBdifr£87.75

Lic CTV 1P

Ⓥ

GH Hotel Prospect 363 Marine Road East ☎(0524) 417819
Etr–Oct

Modern well-furnished hotel overlooking the bay.

14hc (12⇌) (5fb) CTV in all bedrooms Ⓡ B&bfr£10 Bdifr£14 WBdifr£98 LDO3pm

Lic 🍽 CTV 6P

Credit card ③ Ⓥ

GH Rydal Mount Private Hotel 361 Marine Road East ☎(0524) 411858
Etr–Oct

Nicely furnished sea front guesthouse.

14hc (3ⓕ) (4fb) Ⓡ ✱B&b£10.92–£11.50 Bdi£13.22–£13.80 WBdifr£90

Lic CTV 12P nc3yrs

Ⓥ

GH Stresa Private Hotel 96 Sandylands Prom ☎(0524) 412867
Etr–Oct

Morecambe — Moretonhampstead

9hc (2fb) ✗ Ⓡ ✱B&b£9.50–£10 Bdi£13–£13.50 WBdi£83–£87 LDO4.30pm

Lic 🍽 CTV P

Credit card ① Ⓥ

GH Hotel Warwick 394 Marine Road East ☎(0524) 418151

Pleasantly furnished modern sea front hotel.

23hc (2⇌ 9ⓕ) (4fb) CTV in 14 bedrooms TV in 2 bedrooms Ⓡ B&b£10–£12 Bdi£14–£18 WBdi£97 LDO6pm

Lic lift 🍽 CTV

Credit cards ① ② ③ ⑤ Ⓥ

GH Wimslow Private Hotel 374 Marine Rd East ☎(0524) 417804
Feb–Oct

A pleasant family-run hotel on the promenade overlooking the bay.

15hc (3ⓕ) (4fb) CTV in all bedrooms ✗ Ⓡ ✱B&b£11.50–£12.07 Bdi£16.10–£16.67 WBdifr£101.20 LDO4.30pm

Lic 🍽 CTV 3P 6🚗

Credit cards ① ③ Ⓥ

INN York Hotel Lancaster Rd ☎(0524) 418226

Main road pub near town centre offering spacious bedrooms.

12hc (8fb) CTV in all bedrooms Ⓡ B&b£10–£11.50

🍽 CTV 12P snooker

MORETONHAMPSTEAD
Devon
Map **3** SX78

GH Cookshayes 33 Court St ☎(0647) 40374
mid Mar–Oct

Large Victorian house set in well-kept gardens.

9hc (4ⓕ) (1fb) CTV in 8 bedrooms Ⓡ B&b£11–£12.50 Bdi£20–£24 WBdi£115–£122.50 LDO5.30pm

Lic 🍽 CTV 15P nc5yrs

Credit cards ① ③ Ⓥ

⊢⊣**GH Elmfield** Station Rd ☎(0647) 40327
Etr–Oct

Large detached house at the foot of Dartmoor, with some lovely views.

6hc (3ⓕ) (2fb) B&b£9–£10 Bdi£15–£16 WBdi£95–£98 LDO7pm

Lic 🍽 CTV 8P

GH Wray Barton Manor ☎(0647) 40246
8hc (2⇌ 1🚿) ⚡ in all bedrooms CTV in all bedrooms B&bfr£12 Bdifr£19.50 LDO2pm
Lic CTV 8P nc12yrs

MORETON-IN-MARSH
Gloucestershire
Map **4** SP13

GH Moreton House High St ☎(0608) 50747
Small personally-run house in the centre of town. Good home cooking.
12hc (1⇌ 3🚿) (1fb) CTV in 5 bedrooms TV in 7 bedrooms Ⓡ B&b£12.50–£16 Bdi£17.50–£30 LDO8pm
Lic 🕮 CTV 5P
Credit card 🄱 Ⓥ

⊢⊣**FH** Mr & Mrs Righton **Old Farm** *(SP205340)* Dorn (1m N off A429) ☎(0608) 50394
Apr–Sept
3hc (2fb) Ⓡ B&b£9–£10 WB&b£50–£60
CTV 10P 250acres mixed

MORFA NEFYN
Gwynedd
Map **6** SH23

GH Erw Goch Hotel ☎Nefyn (0758) 720539
Georgian house with good leisure facilities including snooker (¾ size table) and table tennis.
15hc (5fb) B&bfr£12
Lic 🕮 CTV 25P

MORTEHOE
Devon
Map **2** SS44
See also **Woolacombe**

Moretonhampstead — Moylegrove

Selected

GH Sunnycliffe Hotel (Guestaccom) ☎Woolacombe (0271) 870597
Closed Dec & Jan
All bedrooms in this attractive, well-furnished hotel have fine sea views. Public rooms and bar are comfortable, and the set menu offers good, well-cooked food.
8hc (4⇌ 4🚿) ⚡ in 4 bedrooms CTV in all bedrooms ✗ Ⓡ ✱B&b£17–£19 Bdi£22–£27 WBdi£143–£168 LDO6pm
Lic 🕮 10P nc12yrs

MORTIMER'S CROSS
Hereford & Worcester
Map **3** SO46

INN Mortimers Cross ☎Kingsland (056881) 238
An imposing roadside inn with an aviary and barbecue area in the rear gardens.
5hc (2fb) B&bfr£11.75 Lunchfr£1.95&alc Dinner 10.30pmfr£2.50&alc
🕮 20P 1🚗
Ⓥ

MOUNT
Cornwall
Map **2** SX16

⊢⊣**FH** Mr & Mrs J T Capper **Mount Pleasant** *(SX152680)* ☎Cardinham (020882) 342
Mar–Sep
Farmhouse situated 6m E of Bodmin in open country on the edge of Bodmin Moor. Own transport essential.
8hc (1⇌ 1🚿) (3fb) ✗ Ⓡ B&b£8–£9 Bdi£12–£14.50 WBdi£75–£85 LDO4pm
Lic 🕮 CTV 10P 6acres non-working
Ⓥ

MOUSEHOLE
Cornwall
Map **2** SW42

GH Tavis Vor ☎Penzance (0736) 731306
mid Mar–mid Oct
Delightful country house-style residence, in own grounds running to the edge of the sea.
7hc (3🚿) (1fb) Ⓡ ✱B&b£12.50–£15.50 Bdi£18–£21.50 WBdi£126–£147 LDO5pm
Lic 🕮 CTV 7P nc5yrs

MOY
Highland *Inverness-shire*
Map **14** NH73

GH Invermoy House ☎Tomatin (08082) 271
Formerly the local railway station, the main line still runs close by. 1½m off A9.
7hc (1🚿) Ⓡ B&b£10–£11.75 Bdi£18–£19.75 WBdifr£119 LDO7.30pm
Lic 🕮 CTV 10P
Credit cards 🄱 🄳

MOYLEGROVE
Dyfed
Map **2** SN14

FH Mrs J I Young **Cwm Connell** *(SN119461)* ☎(023986) 220
Closed Dec
Charming 200-year-old farmhouse in picturesque location with lovely views of sea and coastline. Comfortable bedrooms each with its own sitting/dining room and TV. There is a walled garden at the rear available to guests.
3rm (1hc) ⚡ in all bedrooms CTV in all bedrooms ✗ ✱B&b£8–£10 Bdi£11–£13 WBdi£77–£84 (W only Jul & Aug)
🕮 3P 1🚗 nc 5acres mixed

FH Mrs A D Fletcher **Penrallt Ceibwr** *(SN116454)* ☎(023986) 217
True Welsh hospitality, comfortable accommodation and delicious meals using home-grown produce at this farmhouse on the St Dogmaels/Newport coast road. Views of village and Cibwr Bay, where seals may sometimes be seen. →

6hc (3fb) B&b£10.50 Bdi£17 WBdifr£110 LDO7pm

Lic 𝍢 CTV 40P ⌂ 280acres arable dairy

MUIR OF ORD
Highland *Ross & Cromarty*
Map **14** NH55

⊢FH Mrs Fraser **Gilchrist** *(NH538493)* ☎(0463) 870243
Apr–Sep

Compact but comfortable house just outside the town.

2rm ⚡ in all bedrooms Ⓡ B&b£9–£10 Bdi£14–£16 WBdifr£98 LDO5pm

CTV 8P 160acres arable mixed

Ⓥ

MULL, ISLE OF
Strathclyde *Argyllshire*
Maps **10** & **13**

BUNESSAN
Map **10** NM32

GH Ardachy ☎(06817) 377
Mar–Nov

A comfortable and friendly family run guest house with compact bedrooms and good home cooking.

8hc (7🚿) (2fb) Ⓡ ✱B&b£16 Bdi£24

Lic CTV 8P

SALEN
Map **10** NM54

GH Craig Hotel ☎ Aros (06803) 347
Etr–15 Oct

Painted roadside hotel offering comfortable accommodation and friendly atmosphere.

7hc B&b£15–£18 Bdi£21–£25 WBdi£137–£175

Lic CTV 7P

Credit card 3 Ⓥ

TOBERMORY
Map **13** NM55

GH Harbour House 59 Main St ☎(0688) 2209
Apr–Oct rs Nov–Mar

A friendly family-run licensed guesthouse situated on the front overlooking Tobermory Bay.

9hc (1🛁) (2fb) CTV available in bedrooms Ⓡ ✱B&b£14–£16.50 Bdi£23–£25.50 LDO7.45pm

Lic CTV

MULLION
Cornwall
Map **2** SW61

GH Henscath House Mullion Cove ☎(0326) 240537
Closed Xmas–New Year

All main rooms have magnificient views, and there is a good atmosphere and good food.

6hc (3🛁 2🚿) (1fb) ✗ Ⓡ B&b£10.50–£12.50 Bdi£18.50–£20.50 WBdi£125–£138 LDO6.30pm

Lic 𝍢 CTV 8P

GH Trenowyth House Private Hotel Mullion Cove ☎(0326) 240486
Mar–Dec

Family hotel well-positioned offering good views.

6hc (1🛁 2🚿) (2fb) CTV in 4 bedrooms TV in 1 bedroom Ⓡ B&b£10–£13 Bdi£15–£18.50 WBdifr£123.02 LDO9.30pm

Lic 𝍢 CTV 20P ⌂ ⛵

Credit card 1

INN Old Inn Church Town ☎(0326) 240240
rs 24 Dec–1 Jan

Character inn with attractive bar, comfortable rooms and good food.

5hc (3⇌ 1ꟻ) TV in all bedrooms ✈ Ⓡ B&b£12–£16 Bar lunch £3alc Dinner 9.30pm £5alc

12P nc14yrs

Credit card 3

MUMBLES
West Glamorgan
Map **2** SS68
See also **Bishopston & Langland Bay**

GH Harbour Winds Private Hotel Overland Rd, Langland ☎Swansea (0792) 369298
Apr–Sep

Well-maintained comfortable detached house in own grounds.

8hc (1⇌ 1ꟻ) (3fb) Ⓡ B&b£13–£15 Bdi£19–£21 WBdi£120–£130 LDOnoon

ꟻ CTV 12P nc5yrs

Ⓥ

GH Shoreline 648 Mumbles Rd, Southend ☎Swansea (0792) 366322

Modestly appointed yet friendly guesthouse overlooking Swansea Bay.

14hc (5ꟻ) (3fb) CTV in all bedrooms ✈ Ⓡ ✱B&b£10–£16 Bdi£16.50–£22.50 Wbdifr£112 LDO6pm

Lic ꟻ CTV P

MUNGRISDALE
Cumbria
Map **11** NY33

FH Mr & Mrs G Wightman **Near Howe** *(NY286373)* ☎Threlkeld (059683) 678
Mar–Nov

Set in well-tended gardens at the end of a quiet lane 1½ miles from the A66. Very comfortable accommodation and good home cooking.

7hc (5ꟻ) (3fb) B&b£8–£10 Bdi£13–£15 WBdi£91–£105 LDO5pm

Lic ꟻ CTV 10P snooker 350acres beef sheep

FH Mrs J M Tiffin **Wham Head** *(NY373342)* Hutton Roof ☎Skelton (08534) 289
Mar–Oct

Traditional old farmhouse offering homely accommodation in quiet surroundings.

4rm (3hc) (2fb) ✱B&bfr£7.50 Bdifr£11.50 WBdifr£77 LDO4pm

CTV 8P 130acres dairy sheep mixed

INN Mill ☎Threlkeld (059683) 632
Closed Xmas day

Attractive 17th-century inn, recently refurbished, yet maintaining period details such as oak beams and open fireplaces. Cosy lounge and comfortable dining room. Good home-cooked snacks and meals.

8hc (1⇌ 1ꟻ) Ⓡ B&b£12.50–£13.50 Bdi£18.50–£20 WBdi£126–£136.50 Bar lunch fr75p Dinner 7pm £7.50–£8.50

ꟻ CTV 20P

Ⓥ

MUTFORD
Suffolk
Map **5** TM49

GH Beulah Hall Dairy Ln ☎Barnby (0502 76) 226

A personally run Georgian style house set in 6 acres of grounds incorporating a heated outdoor pool and small lake for private fishing. Comfortable bedrooms and elegant lounges create a relaxing atmosphere, and smoking is discouraged.

8hc (1⇌) ⚟ in 7 bedrooms CTV in all bedrooms ✈ Ⓡ B&b£13–£21 Bdi£22–£30 WBdifr£154 LDO1pm

Lic ꟻ CTV 20P 3 (heated) U

Ⓥ

NAILSWORTH
Gloucestershire
Map **3** ST89

GH Gables Private Hotel Tiltups End, Bath Rd (Guestaccom) ☎(045383) 2265
Closed Dec & Jan

A modestly appointed establishment.

6rm (5hc) (2fb) Ⓡ ✱B&b£10–£12.50 Bdi£16–£20 WBdi£112–£140 LDO8pm

Lic CTV 10P

Ⓥ

GH Orchard Close Springhill ☎(045383) 2503

In a quiet position yet near to town centre, with spacious, tasteful and comfortable rooms.

3hc (2⇌ 1ꟻ) (1fb) CTV in all bedrooms ✈ Ⓡ ✱B&b£fr£10 Bdifr£15 WBdifr£98 LDO10pm

ꟻ 3P

Ⓥ

NAIRN
Highland *Nairnshire*
Map **14** NH85

GH Bruach House 35 Seabank Rd ☎(0667) 54194
Closed Xmas & New Year rs Nov–Mar

A well-appointed house with attractive lounge and some nice family bedrooms.

8hc (3⇌) (3fb) Ⓡ B&b£12–£15 Bdi£19.50–£22.50 WBdifr£126 LDO5.30pm

ꟻ CTV 8P

Ⓥ

GH Greenlaws Private Hotel 13 Seafield St ☎(0667) 52738

Detached house with tasteful extension in residential area. Neat, well-equipped bedrooms in varying sizes and styles.

8hc (2⇌ 2ꟻ) (1fb) CTV in all bedrooms Ⓡ ✱B&b£13–£16 Bdi£21.50–£23.50 WBdifr£140 LDO7.30pm

Lic ꟻ CTV 8P

Selected

GH Sunny Brae Marine Rd ☎(0667) 52309
26 Mar–28 Oct

A modern purpose-built villa standing in its own gardens looking across Nairn Links and the Moray Firth. Mr Cruickshank is the perfect host while his wife Carole ensures that the simple menu offers the best of home cooking. The neat, bright bedrooms are compact, and guests can relax in the delightful, new sun lounge surrounded by a convivial friendly atmosphere.

10hc (1fb) CTV in all bedrooms Ⓡ B&b£14–£15.50 Bdi£20.50–£22 WBdi£136.50–£147 LDO5.30pm

Lic ꟻ CTV 14P

Ⓥ

See advertisement on page 294

NANTGAREDIG
Dyfed
Map **2** SN42

FH Mrs J Willmott **Cwmtwrch** *(SN497220)* ☎(026788) 238

Early 19th-century Welsh-stone farmhouse, carefully modernised and furnished.

6hc (1⇌ 3ꟻ) (2fb) CTV in 1 bedroom TV in 1 bedroom Ⓡ in 3 bedrooms B&b£12–£18 Bdi£20–£26 WBdi£120–£180 LDO9pm

Lic ꟻ CTV 20P 30acres mixed

Ⓥ

NANTWICH
Cheshire
Map **7** SJ65

FH Mrs S Allwood **Burland** *(SJ604534)* Wrexham Rd, Burland (3m W A534) ☎Faddiley (027074) 210

Spacious, comfortable accommodation on 200 acre dairy farm.

3hc (2ꟻ) TV in all bedrooms B&b£10–£17.50 Bdi£16–£27.50 WBdi£101–£157.50 LDO7pm

ꟻ 5P 205acres arable dairy

Ⓥ

NARBERTH
Dyfed
Map **2** SN11

GH *Blaenmarlais* ☎(0834) 860326
Closed Dec

Attractive country hotel in own grounds.

11hc (1⇌ 5ꟻ) (4fb) Ⓡ LDO6.30pm

Lic ꟻ CTV 20P 6 (hard)

FH Mrs I M Bevan **Jacob's Park** *(SN103158)* ☎(0834) 860525 →

A comfortable well-furnished farmhouse on A40.

3hc (1fb) ✱ B&bfr£9.50 Bdifr£13.50 WBdifr£80 LDO7.30pm

CTV 6P 28acres beef sheep

NARBOROUGH
Norfolk
Map **9** TF71

INN *Ship* Swaffham Rd ☎(0760) 337307

17th-century coaching inn, formerly a barge station, which aims to be a sporting hostelry. Shooting parties, coarse and trout fishing can be arranged.

6⇌fl CTV in all bedrooms
50P 3

NEAR SAWREY
Cumbria
Map **7** SD39

Selected

GH Garth ☎Hawkshead (09666) 373
Closed Dec

A charming Victorian Country house decorated and furnished to the highest standard while retaining all of its character. The individually styled bedrooms are spacious and comfortable. On cooler evenings the lounge boasts a roaring log fire and the elegant dining room is just the place in which to enjoy the excellent home cooking. Service is warm and friendly.

7hc (2fl) (1fb) CTV in 2 bedrooms Ⓡ B&b£12.75 Bdi£18.50–£19.50 WBdifr£129.50 LDO4pm

Lic CTV 10P

Ⓥ

See advertisement under Hawkshead

GH High Green Gate ☎Hawkshead (09666) 296
Mar–Oct rs Xmas–New Year

A small yet pleasant guesthouse with attractive gardens, in the heart of Beatrix Potter country.

Narberth — Nether Langwith

6hc (1⇌ 1fl) (3fb) B&b£11–£13.25 Bdi£17–£19 WBdi£109–£120 LDO6pm

CTV 7P

Ⓥ

GH Sawrey House Country Hotel ☎Hawkshead (09666) 387
Feb–Oct

Delightful house offering warm comfortable accommodation and good home-cooking.

10hc (4⇌ 3fl) (3fb) Ⓡ B&b£12–£15.50 Bdi£19.50–£23 WBdifr£135

Lic CTV 15P

NEATISHEAD
Norfolk
Map **9** TG32

GH Barton Angler Lodge Hotel Irstead Rd ☎Horning (0692) 630740

Secluded country house with relaxed atmosphere and quality restaurant offering 'country cuisine'.

6hc (1⇌ 3fl) CTV in 4 bedrooms Ⓡ B&b£14.50–£26 WB&b£101.50–£182 LDO9.30pm

Lic CTV 40P nc12yrs

Credit cards 1 2 3 5

Credit Cards

1 Access/Euro/Mastercard
2 American Express
3 Barclaycard/Visa
5 Diners

GH Regency Neatishead Post Office Stores ☎(0692) 630233

A 17th-century house situated in this quiet, unspoilt village in the heart of the Norfolk Broads offering friendly, comfortable accommodation.

5hc (2fb) CTV in 3 bedrooms Ⓡ ✱B&b£10–£15

CTV P

NEEDHAM MARKET
Suffolk
Map **5** TM05

GH Pipps Ford ☎Coddenham (044979) 208
Closed 2 wks Xmas

16th-century farmhouse close to the River Gipping, with delightful old-fashioned garden, surrounded by farmland and meadows. Entrance off roundabout junction A45/A140.

2⇌ in all bedrooms ✱ Ⓡ B&b£12–£20 Bdi£24.50–£32.50 LDO noon

Lic CTV 12P (hard) 8acres smallholding

NESSCLIFF
Shropshire
Map **7** SJ31

INN Nesscliff Hotel ☎(074381) 253

5hc (2fb) Ⓡ B&b£11.50 Bdi£14–£21.60 WBdi£98–£151.20 Lunchfr£4.45&alc Dinner 10pm£5–£8&alc

CTV 30P 2

NETHER LANGWITH
Nottinghamshire
Map **8** SK57

FH Mrs J M Ibbotson **Blue Barn** *(SK539713)* ☎Mansfield (0623) 742248
Closed 24–25 Dec

Roomy and relaxing Victorian farmhouse in the heart of Robin Hood country. 2½m NW of Cuckney, 2nd lane on the left off A616 to Creswell.

3rm (1hc) ✱ Ⓡ B&bfr£9

CTV 6P 2 250acres arable mixed

Ⓥ

NETLEY
Hampshire
Map **4** SU40

GH La Casa Blanca (formerly White House) 48 Victoria Rd ☎Southampton (0703) 453718
Closed 10 days Xmas & New Year

3 miles from Southampton this cosy, friendly guesthouse is well-situated for all the local attractions including Netley Abbey. Some pretty bedrooms, all with colour television.

7hc (1fb) CTV in all bedrooms ✗ Ⓡ ✱B&b£13–£15 Bdi£18.50–£20.50 WBdifr£122.50 LDO10am

ꟻ 2P Ⓥ

NETTLECOMBE
Dorset
Map **3** SY59

INN Marquis of Lorne ☎Powerstock (030885) 236
Closed Xmas Day

8hc (4ꟻ) (2fb) ✗ Ⓡ B&b£13.50–£16 Bdi£17.50–£23.50 WBdi£126–£147 Lunchfr£6.50&alc Dinner9.30pm£11alc

CTV 65P Ⓥ

See advertisement under Bridport

NEWARK
Nottinghamshire

See Laxton

NEWBOLD-ON-STOUR
Warwickshire
Map **4** SP24

⊢⊣**FH** Mrs J M Everett **Newbold Nurseries** *(SP253455)* ☎Alderminster (078987) 285
Mar–Oct

Modern farmhouse with large rooms and a quiet situation.

2rm (1hc) (1fb) B&bfr£9

ꟻ CTV 2P 25acres arable Ⓥ

NEWBOROUGH
Staffordshire
Map **7** SK12

FH Mrs B Skipper ***Chan Try View*** Moat Hill *(SK135247)* ☎Hoar Cross (028375) 200

This modern farmhouse, 1 mile S of the village on the slope of Moat Hill, offers friendly service and comfortable accommodation.

2rm (1fb) Ⓡ

ꟻ CTV 6P 55acres beef sheep

NEWBRIDGE
Lothian *Midlothian*
Map **11** NT17

FH Mr & Mrs W Pollock ***Easter Norton*** *(NT157721)* ☎031-333 1279
Apr–Sep

Small homely farmhouse in excellent position for motorway and Edinburgh Airport.

2rm (1fb) ✗

ꟻ CTV P 5acres poultry

NEWBURY
Berkshire
Map **4** SU46

INN Hare & Hounds Hotel Speen (1m W A4) ☎(0635) 47215 Telex no 847662

A well managed popular roadside inn with modern well appointed bedrooms and also offering a high standard of cooking.

7ꟻ Annexe: 15hc (7⇌ 8ꟻ) (1fb) CTV in all bedrooms Ⓡ B&b£15–£38 Lunch£5.50–£10&alc Dinner9.30pm£6.50–£11&alc

ꟻ 65P

Credit cards [1] [2] [3] [5]

NEWBY BRIDGE
Cumbria
Map **7** SD38

GH Furness Fells ☎ (05395) 31260
Mar–Oct

Attractive house with annexe overlooking large well-tended garden.

4hc Annexe: 2hc (2fb) ✗ Ⓡ B&b£10–£10.50 WB&bfr£66

Lic ꟻ CTV 10P nc3yrs

Ⓥ

NEWCASTLE ON CLUN
Shropshire
Map **7** SO28

⊢⊣**FH** Mr & Mrs Davies **Lower Duffryn** *(SO229822)* ☎ Clun (05884) 239
Mar–Nov

Pleasant, old farmhouse providing simple but well-maintained accommodation.

3hc (1fb) ✗ B&b£8–£9 Bdi£12.50–£13.50 WBdifr£85 LDO5pm

ꟻ CTV 3P 2🚗 130acres ✓ arable cattle sheep

Ⓥ

NEWCASTLE-UNDER-LYME
Staffordshire
Map **7** SJ84

GH Grove Court Hotel 100 Lancaster Rd ☎(0782) 614406

Comfortable well-equipped accommodation in a large Victorian house set within an acre of garden.

9⇌ ꟻ Annexe: 2⇌ ꟻ (2fb) CTV in all bedrooms Ⓡ B&b£15–£18.50 Bdi£20–£23.50

Lic ꟻ 12P

Credit cards [1] [3]

FH Mrs M J Heath ***Home*** *(SJ823454)* Keele ☎(0782) 627227
Apr–Oct

1¾m W along A5525.

2rm (1fb) TV in 1 bedroom ✗ Ⓡ LDO4.30pm

CTV 6P nc2yrs ✓ 250acres dairy sheep

NEWCASTLE UPON TYNE
Tyne & Wear
Map **12** NZ26

GH Avenue Hotel 2 Manor House Rd, Jesmond ☎091-281 1396
Closed Xmas Day & New Year's Day →

Small commercial hotel close to town centre, overlooking county cricket ground.

9hc (1fb) B&b£16.10–£28.75 Bdi£22.10–£30.75 WB&b£112.70–£201.25 LDO6.15pm

Lic CTV

Credit cards 1 2 5

GH Chirton House Hotel 46 Clifton Rd ☎091-273 0407

Comfortable and welcoming hotel offering good value home cooked dinners.

11hc (1 3) (3fb) CTV in 8 bedrooms B&b£17.25–£25.30 Bdi£24.15–£32.20 WBdifr£120 LDO5.30pm

Lic CTV 12P

Credit card 1

GH Clifton Cottage Dunholme Rd ☎091-273 7347

Simple but comfortable accommodation and helpful proprietors.

6hc (2fb) TV in all bedrooms Ⓡ B&b£11–£12

CTV 6P

Ⓥ

GH Western House Hotel 1 West Av, Gosforth ☎091-285 6812

Family run guesthouse offering modest accommodation in a convenient location.

14hc (3fb) TV in 2 bedrooms Ⓡ available in bedrooms LDO7.30pm

Lic CTV

Credit card 3 Ⓥ

NEW MILTON

Hampshire
Map **4** SZ29

GH Ashley Court Hotel 105 Ashley Rd ☎(0425) 619256

Family-run guesthouse with warm atmosphere and good home cooking. Comfortable, modern accommodation with bar and separate lounge. Conveniently situated for the New Forest and the South Coast.

8hc (5 3) (1fb) Ⓡ *B&b£16.50–£17.50 Bdi£22.50–£24.50 WBdifr£156 LDOnoon

Lic CTV 8P

Credit cards 1 3 Ⓥ

NEWNHAM BRIDGE

Hereford & Worcester
Map **7** SO66

Selected

FH Mrs E J Adams **Lower Doddenhill** *(SO661698)* ☎(058479) 223

Mar–Nov

In an elevated position with attractive views of the surrounding countryside is this 17th century farmhouse, home of the Adams family. It has three bedrooms, one with en-suite shower. Oak beams and attractive decor all add to its charm and appeal. The emphasis is on individual comfort and attention making every guest that stays here feel at home.

Winner for Midlands Region of the 1987/8 AA Farmhouse of the Year Award.

3hc (1) (1fb) in 3 bedrooms Ⓡ B&b£9.50–£12 Bdi£15.50–£18 LDOnoon

CTV 6P nc6yrs 230acres arable beef dairy sheep

Ⓥ

NEWPORT

Dyfed
Map **2** SN03

GH Cnapan Country House (Guestaccom) East St ☎(0239) 820575

Closed Feb rs Nov–Jan

A delightful village guesthouse with comfortable accommodation and good food, including specially wholefood lunches.

5 (1fb) CTV in 1 bedroom TV in 4 bedrooms Ⓡ B&b£14.50–£19.50 Bdi£22.50–£27.50 WBdifr£139.35 LDO9pm

Lic 6P

Credit cards 1 3

INN *Golden Lion* East St ☎(0239) 820321

Cosy inn of character with bright, well-equipped bedrooms.

10rm (9hc 5 4) (1fb) CTV in 9 bedrooms Ⓡ LDO9.30pm

CTV 10P sauna bath solarium

Credit cards 1 3

NEWPORT

Gwent
Map **3** ST38

GH Caerleon House Hotel Caerau Rd ☎(0633) 64869

Conveniently positioned for the town centre and M4 Link roads this comfortable guesthouse offers friendly, hospitable service.

8hc (1fb) CTV in all bedrooms Ⓡ B&b£13.50–£18 LDO9pm

Lic 8P

Ⓥ

NEWPORT

Isle of Wight
See **Wight, Isle of**

NEWQUAY

Cornwall
Map **2** SW86
See plan on pages 298–299

GH Arundell Hotel Mount Wise ☎(0637) 872481 Plan **1** *B1*

Large seasonal family hotel, comfortable and recently renovated.

37hc (10 11) (10fb) CTV in 31 bedrooms Ⓡ B&b£7–£15 Bdi£10.50–£18.50 WBdi£54–£96 LDO6pm

Lic CTV 32P 8 snooker sauna bath solarium

Credit cards 1 2 3 Ⓥ

⊢GH **Barrowcliff Hotel** Henver Rd ☎(0637) 873492 Plan **2** *E3*
May–Sep
23hc (1⇌ 6ⓜ) (6fb) CTV in all bedrooms ® B&b£7.50–£12 Bdi£9.50–£14.50 Wbdi£66.50–£101.50 LDO6.30pm
Lic CTV 20P nc3yrs
Credit cards 1 3

GH *Cherington Hotel* 7 Pentire Av ☎(0637) 873363 Plan **3** *A2*
Apr–Sep
Family hotel close to Pentire beach.
22hc (2⇌ 4ⓜ) (3fb)
Lic CTV 14P 2🚗

GH Copper Beech Hotel 70 Edgcumbe Av ☎(0637) 873376 Plan **4** *D2*
mid May–mid Oct
Well-appointed family hotel in peaceful area, adjoining Trenance Gardens.
14hc (2⇌ 6ⓜ) (3fb) ✖ B&b£11.50–£12.65 Bdi£14.95–£16.10 WBdifr£109.25 (W only Jun, Jul & Aug) LDO6pm
Lic ⅏ CTV 14P
Credit card 3

GH Fistral Beach Hotel Esplanade Rd, Pentire ☎(0637) 873993 Plan **5** *A2*
Mar–Nov & Xmas
Purpose built modern hotel with magnificent sea views and easy access to sandy beach.

Newquay

15hc (7ⓜ) (4fb) CTV in all bedrooms B&b£11.50–£18.50 Bdi£14–£20.80 WBdi£88.10–£134.70 LDO6.45pm
Lic ⅏ CTV 12P solarium
Credit cards 1 3 Ⓥ

GH *Gluvian Park Hotel* 12 Edgcumbe Gdns ☎(0637) 873133 Plan **6** *D2*
Apr–Oct
Comfortable modern family hotel close to sea front and Tolcarne beach.
23hc (2⇌ 16ⓜ) (7fb) CTV in all bedrooms ✖ ® LDO6.30pm
Lic ⅏ CTV 10P
Credit cards 1 3

GH Hepworth Hotel 27 Edgcumbe Av ☎(0637) 873686 Plan **7** *D2*
Apr–Sep
Modern comfortable family hotel, recently refurbished to high standards.
13hc (4ⓜ) (4fb) ✖ ® B&b£10–£15 Bdi£14.50–£19.50 WBdi£91–£120 (W only Jul–Aug) LDO6.30pm
Lic ⅏ CTV 12P

GH *Jonel* 88–90 Crantock St ☎(0637) 875084 Plan **8** *B2*
Small comfortable well-appointed terraced hotel, close to town.
12hc (2fb) ✖ ®
Lic CTV 7P
Ⓥ

GH Kellsboro Hotel 12 Henver Rd ☎(0637) 874620 Plan **9** *E3*
Etr–Oct
Well-appointed family hotel, close to beaches.
14hc (10⇌ 1ⓜ) (8fb) ⅟ in all bedrooms CTV in all bedrooms ® B&b£12.50–£15 Bdi£16–£20 WBdifr£120 LDO7pm
Lic ⅏ 20P ▭(heated)

GH *Links Hotel* Headland Rd ☎(0637) 873211 Plan **10** *B3*
Mar–Oct
Personally-run private hotel with well-equipped bedrooms.
15hc (9ⓜ) (3fb) CTV in all bedrooms LDO4.30pm
Lic ⅏ CTV P

GH Mount Wise Hotel Mount Wise ☎(0637) 873080 Plan **11** *C1*
Modern comfortable high rise property.
34hc (8⇌ 14ⓜ) Annexe: 2hc (17fb) CTV in all bedrooms ® ✱B&b£10–£16 Bdi£13–£19 W£83–£132 ⊭ LDO7pm →

Lic Lift 🍽 CTV 20P 6🚗 ⛳ ⛵(heated) sauna bath gymnasium

Credit card 1

GH Pendeen Hotel Alexandra Rd, Porth ☎(0637) 873521 Plan **12** *E3*
Etr–Nov

A modern private hotel only 200 yards from Porth Beach. Rooms are pleasant, and equipped with metred TV.

15hc (6🛁 6🚿) (5fb) CTV in 4 bedrooms ✗ B&b£10–£14.50 Bdi£16–£19.50 WBdi£74.50–£120.50 LDO6pm

Lic 🍽 CTV 15P

Ⓥ

GH Porth Enodoc 4 Esplanade Rd, Pentire ☎(0637) 872372 Plan **13** *A2*
Etr–Oct & Xmas

Large detached house standing in its own gardens overlooking the sea.

10🚿 (4fb) CTV available in bedrooms ✗ B&b£10–£13 Bdi£15–£18 WBdi£88–£112 (W only Jul–Aug) LDO5.30pm

Lic 🍽 CTV 12P

Selected

GH *Priory Lodge Hotel* Mount Wise ☎(0637) 874111 Plan **14** *C1*

Hotel of character set in its own grounds with attractive and comfortable rooms.

21hc (5🛁 11🚿)Annexe: 2🚿 (13fb) CTV in all bedrooms ✗ Ⓡ LDO7pm

Lic 🍽 CTV 25P ⛵ (heated)

Ⓥ

GH *Rolling Waves* Alexandra Rd, Porth ☎(0637) 873236 Plan **15** *E3*
Etr–Oct

Detached, modern guesthouse in elevated position with glorious views of Porth and Whipsiderry beaches.

9hc (3🚿) (3fb) ✗ LDO5pm

Lic CTV 10P

GH *Rumours Hotel* 89 Henver Rd ☎(0637) 872170 Plan **16** *E3*

Large modern guesthouse with pleasant public rooms and nicely appointed bedrooms.

Newquay

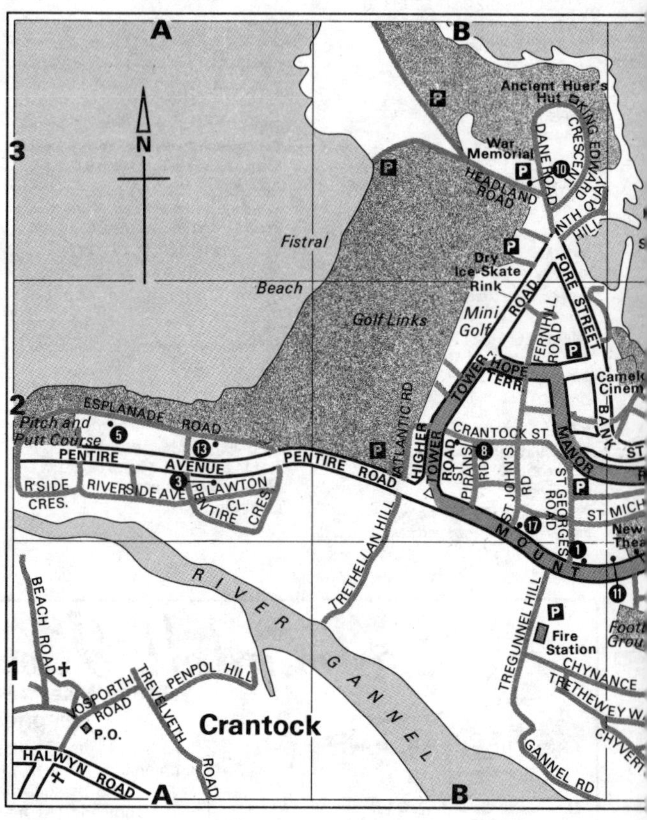

Newquay

1 Arundell Hotel
2 Barrowcliff Hotel
3 Cherington Hotel
4 Copper Beech Hotel
5 Fistral Beach Hotel
6 Gluvian Park Hotel
7 Hepworth Hotel

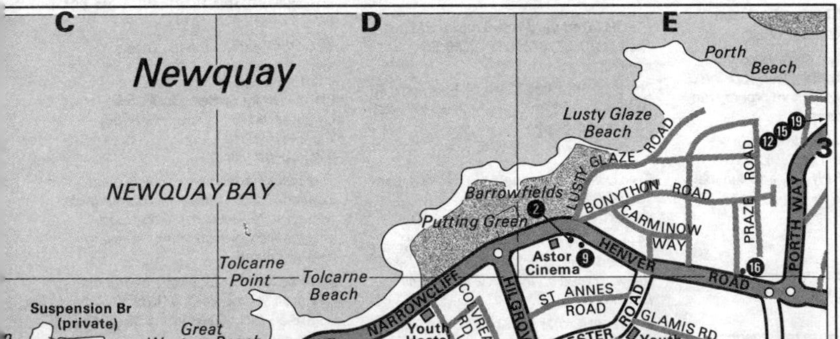

Newquay

8 Jonel
9 Kellsboro Hotel
10 Links Hotel
11 Mount Wise Hotel
12 Pendeen Hotel
13 Porth Endoc
14 Priory Lodge Hotel
15 Rolling Waves
16 Rumours Hotel
17 Tir Chonaill Lodge
18 Wheal Treasure
19 Windward Hotel

14rm (9hc 6⇨ 1⋒) (2fb) CTV in all bedrooms ✗ Ⓡ LDO10.30pm

Lic 🍽 18P 🏠 ⛱(heated)

Credit cards 1 2 3 5

⊢→**GH Tir Chonaill Lodge** 106 Mount Wise ☎(0637) 876492 Plan **17** *B2*

Centrally-situated friendly family guesthouse. Comfortable, well-appointed bedrooms. An establishment proudly-run by experienced owners.

8⇨ ⋒ (8fb) CTV in all bedrooms Ⓡ B&b£8.75–£12 Bdi£11.25–£14.25 WBdi£78.75–£99.75 (W only end Jun–beg Sep) LDO 5pm

Lic 🍽 CTV 8P

Ⓥ

⊢→**GH Wheal Treasure** 72 Edgcumbe Av ☎(0637) 874136 Plan **18** *D1/2*
May–Sep

Comfortable hotel, close to Trenance Gardens.

9hc (3⋒) (2fb) ✗ B&b£8–£11 Bdi£12–£15 WBdi£90–£100 (W only late Jul–Aug) LDO5.30pm

Lic 🍽 CTV 9P nc5yrs

Newquay — New Romney

⊢→**GH Windward Hotel** Alexandra Rd, Porth ☎(0637) 873185 Plan **19** *E3*
Etr–Oct

7hc (1⇨ 1⋒) (3fb) CTV in all bedrooms Ⓡ B&b£8–£10.50 Bdi£11–£14 WBdi £70–£95 (W only Jul–Sep)

Lic 🍽 CTV 10P

FH J C Wilson **Manuels** *(SW839601)* Lane ☎(0637) 873577
Closed Xmas–New Year

17th-century farmhouse in sheltered, wooded valley, 2m from Newquay. Take the west road off the A392 at Quintrill Downs.

5rm (2hc) (2fb) ✗ ✻B&bfr£7 Bdifr£11 WBdifr£77 (W only late May–Aug)

CTV 6P 🏠 44acres mixed

Ⓥ

NEW QUAY
Dyfed
Map **2** SN35

FH Mr & Mrs White **Nanternis** Nanternis *(SN374567)* (2m SW off A486) ☎(0545) 560181
Etr–Oct

Farmhouse of great character tucked away in a snug little village. Organic garden produce.

2hc (1fb) ⍁ in all bedrooms ✗ Ⓡ ✻B&b£8–£10 Bdi£12–£14 WBdi£84–£91 (W only mid Jul–Aug) LDOnoon

🍽 CTV 4P 8acres sheep goats

Ⓥ

FH Mr H Kelly **Ty Hen** *(SN365553)* Llwyndafydd (S of Cross Inn, A486) ☎(0545) 560346
mid Feb–mid Nov

This period farmhouse enjoys a quiet location. Accommodation is comfortable with en suite bedrooms. Good food, imaginatively prepared. Non-smoking establishment.

5⋒ Annexe: 2⋒ (4fb) ⍁ in 7 bedrooms CTV in all bedrooms Ⓡ ✻B&b£10–£15 Bdi£16.50–£21.50 WBdi£115.15–£143.50

Lic 🍽 CTV 20P 🏠 15acres sheep

Ⓥ

NEW ROMNEY
Kent
Map **5** TR02

GH Blue Dolphins Hotel & Restaurant Dymchurch Rd ☎(0679) 63224

9hc (1⇌ 1fl) (1fb) CTV in all bedrooms Ⓡ
✱B&b£13–£16 Bdi£26–£29 WBdifr£160
LDO9.30pm

Lic 🍽 CTV 15P

Credit cards 1 3 Ⓥ

NEWTON (nr Vowchurch)
Hereford & Worcester
Map **3** SO33

FH Mrs J C Powell **Little Green**
(SO335337) ☎Michaelchurch (098123) 205
Closed Xmas

Modernised farmhouse, once an inn, with friendly atmosphere.

3hc (2fb) B&b£7–£8.50 Bdi£12–£13
WBdifr£90

CTV 5P 50acres beef sheep

Ⓥ

NEWTON
Northumberland
Map **12** NZ06

FH Mrs C M Hargreaves **Cookhill**
(NY056654) ☎Stockfield (0661) 843117
Apr–Oct rs Nov–Mar

3rm (1fb) ✗ Ⓡ in 2 bedrooms B&b£10
WB&b£56

Lic 🍽 CTV 4P 23acres beef sheep mixed

Ⓥ

NEWTON ABBOT
Devon
Map **3** SX87

GH Lamorna Exeter Rd, Coombe Cross, Sandygate (3m N A380) ☎(0626) 65627

7hc (1fb) TV in all bedrooms ✗
✱B&b£11–£15 Bdi£17.50–£21.50
WBdifr£122.50 LDO6pm

Lic 🍽 CTV 15P 1🚗 (heated)

NEWTONMORE
Highland *Inverness-shire*
Map **14** NN79

GH *Alvey House Hotel* Golf Course Rd
☎(05403) 260
Jan–Oct

Detached house in 1½ acres of garden 50 yards from golf course.

7hc (4fl) (2fb) ✗LDO7.30pm

Lic 🍽 CTV 10P

GH Coig Na Shee Fort William Rd
☎(05403) 216
Feb–Nov

Spacious stone house in secluded garden setting with a very relaxing atmosphere and comfortable bedrooms. Gentle and friendly service from owners. The owner makes good use of local produce in many traditional Scottish dishes.

6hc (1⇌) (1fb) Ⓡ ✱B&b£11–£13 Bdi£18–£20 WBdifr£126 LDO5pm

🍽 CTV 8P

Ⓥ

GH Pines Hotel Station Rd ☎(05403) 271
Apr–17 Oct

6hc (1⇌ 5fl) (1fb) ✗ Ⓡ ✱B&b£14–£15
Bdi£21–£22 WBdifr£143 LDO6pm

Lic 🍽 CTV 6P nc6yrs

Ⓥ

NEWTON REGIS
Staffordshire
Map **4** SK20

FH Mrs M Lane **Newton House**
(SK278075) ☎Tamworth (0827) 830632

Extensive Georgian-style farmhouse in elevated village position.

5hc (1fb) ⊬ in 1 bedroom TV in 1 bedroom ✗ Ⓡ ✱B&b£9.50 Bdi£15
WBdifr£90 LDO2pm

🍽 CTV 6P 1🚗 (grass) 6acres mixed

NEWTON STEWART
Dumfries & Galloway *Wigtownshire*
Map **10** NX46

GH Corsbie Villa Corsbie Rd☎(0671) 2124

A well maintained hotel with neat compact bedrooms situated in a residential part of town.

9hc (1fb) ⊬ in all bedrooms ✱B&b£8
Bdi£11.50 LDO 6pm

Lic CTV 16P

Credit cards 1 3

GH Duncree House Hotel King St
☎(0671) 2001

Simple, inexpensive accommodation in a country lodge on outskirts of town.

6hc (5fb) B&b£9 Bdi£12 WBdifr£84
LDO5pm

Lic CTV 25P

Credit card 2 Ⓥ

FH Mrs Hewitson **Auchenleck**
(NX450709) Minnigaff ☎(0671) 2035
Etr–30 Oct

Large turreted farmhouse in an isolated position bordering Kiroughtree Forest and Glentrool National Park.

3hc ⊬ in all bedrooms ✗ Ⓡ B&b£9–£10
Bdi£14 WBdi£91

🍽 CTV 6P 103acres beef sheep

NEWTOWN
Powys
Map **6** SO19

FH L M & G T Whitticase **Highgate**
(SO111953) ☎(0686) 25981
Mar–Oct

15th-century black and white timbered farmhouse, in elevated position with commanding views over valley and hills. Rough shooting, fishing and ponies available.

3fl ✗ Ⓡ B&bfr£11.50 Bdifr£16.50
WBdifr£116LDO4.30pm

Lic 🍽 CTV P 250acres beef sheep mixed

Ⓥ

FH Mrs I Jarman **Lower Gwestydd**
(SO126934) Llanllwchaiarn ☎(0686) 26718
Mar–Dec

17th-century farmhouse with historical features both inside and out. 2m E off B4568.

3hc (2fb) ✗ Ⓡ ✱B&b£10–£10.50 Bdi£14–£14.50 WBdifr£95 LDO4pm

🍽 CTV 3P 200acres arable beef sheep

NITON
Isle of Wight
See **Wight, Isle of**

NORMANBY
North Yorkshire
Map **8** NZ90

FH D I Smith **Heather View** *(NZ928062)*
☎Whitby (0947) 880451
Mar–Oct

Attractive modern farmhouse, well-appointed and comfortable. Conveniently situated for coastal visits.

5hc (2fb) Ⓡ ✱B&b£8.50–£9 Bdi£11.50–£12.50 WBdifr£73 LDO2.30pm

🍽 CTV 5P nc5yrs 40acres mixed

Ⓥ

NORTHALLERTON
North Yorkshire
Map **8** SE39

GH Windsor 56 South Pde ☎(0609) 774100
Closed 24 Dec–2 Jan

Friendly proprietors offer hospitality and comfortable accommodation in this well managed guesthouse.

6hc (3fb) CTV in all bedrooms Ⓡ
B&b£11.50–£13.50 Bdi£17.25–£19.25
LDO3pm

🍽 CTV

NORTHAMPTON
Northamptonshire
Map **4** SP76

GH Poplars Hotel Cross St, Moulton
☎(0604) 43983
Closed Xmas wk

22hc (2⇌ 9fl) (4fb) TV in 5 bedrooms CTV in 17 bedrooms Ⓡ B&bfr£20 Bdifr£27
WBdifr£185 LDO6pm

Lic 🍽 CTV 22P

Credit card 1 Ⓥ

See advertisement on page 302

NORTH BERWICK
Lothian *East Lothian*
Map **12** NT58

GH Cragside 16 Marine Pde ☎(0620) 2879 →

Neatly appointed guesthouse on sea front in East Bay.

6hc (2fb) ✈ Ⓡ B&b£11 Bdifr£15.50 WBdifr£97.25 LDO6pm

CTV

Ⓥ

NORTH NIBLEY
Gloucestershire
Map **3** ST79

GH Burrows Court Nibley Gn, Dursley
☎Dursley (0453) 46230

Recently converted 18th-century weaving mill set in 1 acre of gardens with good views.

8hc (6⇌ 2fl) CTV in all bedrooms ✈ Ⓡ B&b£17.25–£24 Bdi£23–£33.50 WBdi£150–£192.50 LDO8pm

Lic 12P nc10yrs

Credit cards 1 3

NORTHOWRAM
West Yorkshire
Map **7** SE12

FH Mrs W Longbottom **Royd** *(SE107268)* Hall Ln ☎Halifax (0422) 206718
Apr–Sep (rs Oct–Mar prior bookings only)

Converted 19th-century farmhouse with spacious bedrooms. Farm has a stud of Arabian stallions, riding stables and guest stabling.

4rm (3fb) TV in 2 bedrooms Ⓡ *B&b£9 Bdi£14 WBdifr£98 LDOnoon

CTV 5P 22acres Arab horse stud beef poultry mixed

NORTH WALSHAM
Norfolk
Map **9** TG23

GH Beechwood Private Hotel
20 Cromer Rd ☎(0692) 403231
Closed 24 Dec–7 Jan

11hc (3⇌ 4fl) (5fb) B&b£14.50 Bdi£20–£25 WBdifr£130 LDO7pm

Lic CTV 12P nc5yrs

Ⓥ

NORTH WOOTTON
Somerset
Map **3** ST54

FH Mrs M White **Barrow** *(ST553416)*
☎Pilton (074989) 245
Feb–Nov

15th-century stone-built farmhouse on edge of village, situated between Wells, Glastonbury and Shepton Mallet.

3hc (1fb) ✈ Ⓡ B&b£9 Bdi£14 WBdi£90 LDO9am

CTV 4P 150acres dairy

Ⓥ

NORTON
Nottinghamshire
Map **8** SK57

FH Mrs J Palmer **Norton Grange** *(SK572733)* ☎Mansfield (0623) 842666
Etr–Oct

A 200-year-old stone-built farmhouse fronted by small gardens, at edge of village.

3rm (2hc) (1fb) in 2 bedrooms ✈ Ⓡ B&b£9.50–£10.50 WB&bfr£60

CTV 3P 172acres arable mixed

Ⓥ

NORWICH
Norfolk
Map **5** TG20

During the currency of this guide telephone numbers are due to change.

GH *Grange Hotel* 230 Thorpe Rd
☎(0603) 34734
Closed Xmas wk

39hc (4⇌ 35fl) (1fb) CTV in 38 bedrooms TV in 1 bedroom ✈ Ⓡ LDO8.30pm

Lic CTV 40P sauna bath solarium

Credit cards 1 2 3 5

GH Marlborough House Hotel
22 Stracey Rd, Thorpe Rd ☎(0603) 628005
12hc (2⇌ 3fl) (2fb) CTV in all bedrooms B&b£15–£20 Bdi£18–£23 WBdifr£115 LDO4.30pm
Lic 🍽 CTV 6P 2🚗

GH Wedgewood 42 St Stephens Rd ☎(0603) 625730
Closed 24–31 Dec
Situated on a busy main road close to the town centre and coach station.
11hc (3⇌ 4fl) (1fb) ⊁ in 2 bedrooms CTV in all bedrooms ✖ ® B&b£11–£20 WBdifr£70
🍽 7P
Credit cards 1 3 Ⓥ

NOTTINGHAM
Nottinghamshire
Map **8** SK53

GH Balmoral Hotel 55–57 Loughborough Rd, West Bridgford ☎(0602) 818588
Closed Xmas
Warm and welcoming hotel one mile south of city centre with modern well-equipped rooms.
34hc (26fl) CTV in all bedrooms ✖ ® B&b£17.25–£26 Bdi£25–£35 LDO7.45pm
Lic 🍽 CTV 35P
Credit cards 1 3

GH Bridgford Lodge 88/90 Radcliffe Rd, West Bridgford ☎(0602) 814042
Pair of semi-detached houses, converted to provide tasteful accommodation.
12hc (6fl) (3fb) CTV in all bedrooms ✖ ® LDO7pm
Lic 🍽 14P
Credit cards 1 3 Ⓥ

GH Crantock Hotel 480 Mansfield Rd ☎(0602) 623294
10hc (1⇌) (1fb) TV in 1 bedroom CTV in 1 bedroom ® ✱B&b£14.08–£16.96
Lic 🍽 CTV 30P

GH *Grantham Commercial Hotel* 24–26 Radcliffe Road, West Bridgford ☎(0602) 811373
Simple and businesslike accommodation close to Trent Bridge.
24hc (2fb) CTV in all bedrooms
🍽 CTV 8P 2🚗

GH Park Hotel 7 Waverley St ☎(0602) 786299
Conveniently situated for the theatres and shops, slightly north west of the town centre, this large house provides well appointed bedrooms.
15hc (11fb) CTV in all bedrooms ✖ ® ✱B&b£7.50–£12 Bdi£15.50–£20 LDO9.30pm
Lic
Credit cards 1 3

GH Waverley 107 Portland Rd, Waverley St ☎(0602) 786707
Closed 2 wks Xmas
15hc (2fb) ✱B&bfr£8 WB&bfr£56
🍽 CTV Ᵽ

GH Hotel Windsor 116 Radcliffe Rd, West Bridgford ☎(0602) 813773
Closed 25 & 26 Dec
Popular and impeccably maintained hotel one mile south of city centre on A6011.
43hc (6⇌ 37fl) (6fb) CTV in all bedrooms ✖ ® B&b£20.70–£27.60 Bdi£28.17–£35.07 LDO7.45pm
Lic 🍽 CTV 50P snooker solarium
Credit cards 1 2 3 Ⓥ

NUNEATON
Warwickshire
Map **4** SP39

GH Abbey Grange Hotel 100 Manor Court Rd ☎(0203) 385535 →

12hc (1⇌ 3fl) (1fb) CTV in all bedrooms ✗ Ⓡ B&b£14.50–£26.50 Bdi£21.45–£36.50 LDO9pm

Lic 🍽 25P

Credit cards 1 2 3 5 Ⓥ

GH Drachenfels Hotel 25 Attleborough Rd ☎(0203) 383030

8hc (1fl) (2fb) CTV in all bedrooms Ⓡ ✻B&b£11.25–£15.50 LDO8pm

Lic 🍽 8P

Credit card 1

NUNNEY
Somerset
Map **3** ST74

INN George Church St ☎(037384) 458

Attractive inn near Nunney Castle, with good restaurant and separate residents' lounge.

14rm (13hc) (8⇌ 5fl) (3fb) CTV in 9 bedrooms Ⓡ B&b£20–£30 Lunch fr£6.50&alc Dinner 9pm fr£7&alc

🍽 CTV 30P

Credit cards 1 2 3 5

NUTHURST
West Sussex
Map **5** TQ12

FH Mrs S E Martin **Saxtons** *(TQ199275)* ☎ Lower Beeding (040376) 231
Closed Xmas Day

There is a warm and friendly atmosphere and comfortable, homely accommodation at this Georgian farmhouse.

3hc (1fb) ✗ Ⓡ B&b£12–£15 Bdi£20–£23 WBdi£140–£161 LDO5pm

🍽 CTV 6P 2🚗 100acres sheep goats

Ⓥ

OAKAMOOR
Staffordshire
Map **7** SK04

INN Admiral Jervis Inn & Restaurant Mill Rd ☎(0538) 702187

18th-century inn with lots of character, providing comfortable accommodation. Conveniently situated for Alton Towers.

5hc (1⇌ 4fl) (4fb) TV in all bedrooms ✗ Ⓡ B&b£15–£18.50 Dinner 9.30pm £6.50&alc

🍽 20P

Credit cards 1 2 3 5

OAKFORD
Devon
Map **3** SS92

FH A Boldry **Newhouse** *(SS892228)* ☎(03985) 347
Closed Xmas

Comfortable 17th-century farmhouse with oak beams and inglenook fireplace.

3hc (1fb) ✗ Ⓡ B&b£9.50 Bdi£15 WBdi£94.50

🍽 CTV 3P ♪ 42acres beef

Ⓥ

See advertisement under Dulverton

OAKHAM
Leicestershire

See Empingham

OBAN
Strathclyde *Argyllshire*
Map **10** NM83
See plan

⊢⊣**GH Ardblair** Dalriach Rd ☎(0631) 62668 Plan **1** *C4*
Apr–Oct

Behind town centre overlooking the bay, convenient to swimming pool, bowling green and tennis courts.

16hc (4fb) ✗ B&b£8–£10 Bdi £13.75–£15.75 WBdifr£100 LDO5.30pm

CTV 10P

Credit card 2

GH *Crathie* Duncraggen Rd ☎(0631) 62619 Plan **2** *C3*
Etr–Oct

Modern house on a hill behind town centre, adjacent to McCaig's tower.

9hc (2fb) ✗ Ⓡ LDO5pm

Lic CTV 12P nc 2yrs

GH Foxholes Hotel Cologin (along unclass rd from junc with A816) ☎(0631) 64982
Plan **3** *B1*
Apr–Oct

Oban

Peacefully situated in a quiet glen 3 miles south of Oban. Bedrooms are tastefully furnished and well-equipped, the lounge opens onto a patio and gardens, with a small dining room adjacent, where appetising 'Taste of Scotland' dishes are served.

5hc (2⇌ 3⫪) CTV in all bedrooms Ⓡ Bdi£27–£29.50 WBdifr£189

Lic ⫶⫶ 5P nc12yrs

GH Glenburnie Private Hotel The Esplanade ☎(0631) 62089 Plan **4** *A5*
Apr–Oct

Grey stone-built hotel on sea front overlooking the island of Mull.

15hc (9⫪) (3fb) CTV in all bedrooms B&b£11.50–£20

⫶⫶ CTV 12P 1🚗 nc4yrs

⊢⊣**GH Heatherfield Private Hotel** Albert Rd ☎(0631) 62681 Plan **5** *C3*
Closed Feb

Pleasant house situated on hill behind town with ¾ acre of garden.

9hc (3fb) CTV in all bedrooms Ⓡ B&b£8.50–£11.50 Bdi£14–£17 WBdifr£110

Lic ⫶⫶ 10P

Ⓥ

⊢⊣**GH Kenmore** Soroba Rd ☎(0631) 63592 Plan **6** *C1*

White-painted stone house situated on A816 with small modern extension.

6hc (2fb) B&b£8.50–£9.50

CTV 12P

Ⓥ

GH Roseneath Dalriach Rd ☎(0631) 62929 Plan **7** *C4*
Closed Xmas

Attractive sandstone house in terrace on hillside offering views across bay to Kerrera.

10hc (1⫪) (1fb) CTV in 2 bedrooms ✗ Ⓡ in 1 bedroom ✱B&b£9–£12.50 Bdi£13–£16.50 WBdi£85–£125 LDO5pm

⫶⫶ CTV 8P

GH *Sgeir Mhaol* Soroba Rd ☎(0631) 62650 Plan **8** *C1*

Small friendly guesthouse on the A816 just outside town centre.

7hc (3fb) ✗ LDO6pm

⫶⫶ CTV 10P

GH Thornloe Albert Rd ☎(0631) 62879 Plan **9** *C4*

Large semi-detached house, convenient to many leisure facilities.

9hc (2fb) CTV in 2 bedrooms ✗ Ⓡ ✱B&b£10–£12.50 Bdi£15.50–£17.50 LDO4pm

⫶⫶ CTV 7P nc5yrs

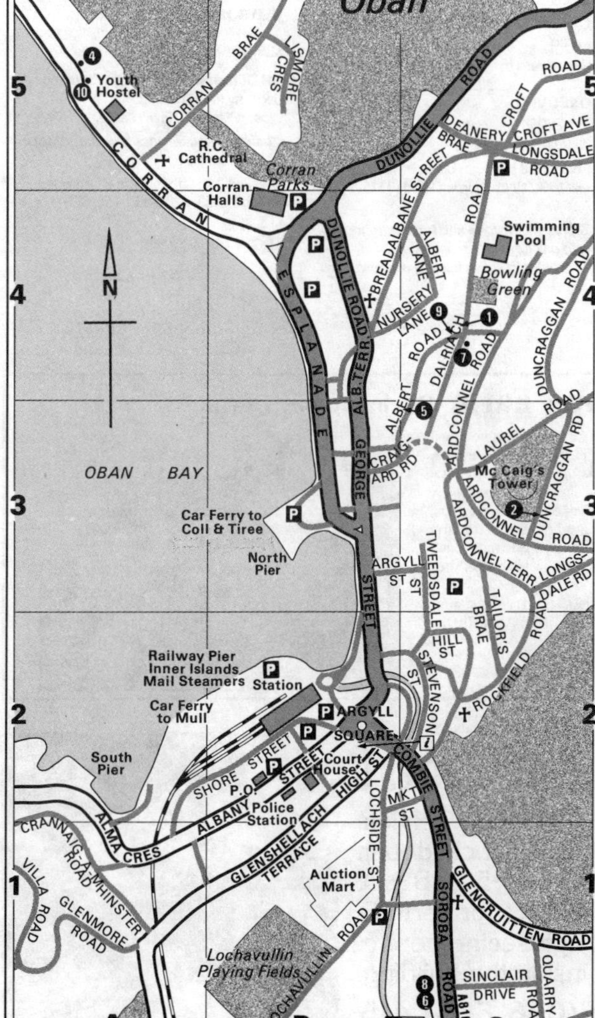

1 Ardblair
2 Crathie
3 Foxholes Hotel
4 Glenburnie Private Hotel
5 Heatherfield Private Hotel
6 Kenmore
7 Roseneath
8 Sgeir Mhaol
9 Thornloe
10 Wellpark Hotel

GH Wellpark Hotel Esplanade ☎(0631) 62948 Plan **10** *A5*
May–Sep
Semi-detached hotel built in granite and sandstone, offering good standard of accommodation in a seafront location.
17fl CTV in all bedrooms Ⓡ ✱B&b£14–£16 Bdi£20–£22 WBdi£129.27–£141.75 LDO7.30pm
▥ 12P nc3yrs

ODDINGTON
Gloucestershire
Map **4** SP22

INN Horse & Groom ☎Cotswold (0451) 30584
Closed Xmas evening rs 24–26 Dec
5rm (1⇌ 4fl) (1fb) CTV in 2 bedrooms ✖(ex guide dogs) Ⓡ B&b£16–£19.50 Bdi£21–£23 Bar lunch £1.50–£3.50alc Dinner 9.30pm £9 alc
▥ 40P

OKEHAMPTON
Devon
Map **2** SX59

GH Fowley House Tavistock Rd ☎(0837) 2294
Detached family run Edwardian residence situated beside the A30.
4hc (4fb) ✖ Ⓡ ✱B&b£9.50–£10.50 Bdi£14.50–£16 LDO6.30pm
Lic CTV 5P nc3yrs

FH Mrs K C Heard **Hughslade** *(SX561932)* ☎(0837) 2883
Closed Xmas
Devonshire farmhouse offering friendly service. Spectacular views of Dartmoor. Full-sized snooker table.
5hc (3fb) B&b£12–£14 Bdi£18–£18.50 WBdifr£95 LDO6pm
CTV 10P U snooker 600acres beef sheep mixed
Credit card ② Ⓥ

OKEOVER
Staffordshire
Map **7** SK14

FH Mrs E J Harrison **Little Park** *(SK160490)* ☎Thorpe Cloud (033529) 341
Apr–Oct
200-year-old stone and brick farmhouse with oak beams in most rooms. Outstanding views from all windows.
3hc (1fb) ✖ ✱B&b£8.50–£9 Bdi£13–£13.50 LDO10am
▥ CTV P nc3yrs 123acres dairy
Ⓥ

OLD DALBY
Leicestershire
Map **8** SK62

FH Mrs V Anderson ***Home Farm*** *(SK673236)* Church Ln ☎Melton Mowbray (0664) 822622
19th-century farmhouse, on edge of peaceful village in lovely Vale of Belvoir.
3hc (1fb) ✖
▥ CTV 5P ¾acre non-working

OLD SODBURY
Avon
Map **3** ST78

GH Dornden Church Ln ☎Chipping Sodbury (0454) 313325
Closed Xmas & New Year
Charming house, once a vicarage, set in lovely grounds.
9hc (2⇌ 1fl) (4fb) CTV in 5 bedrooms ✱B&b£12.50–£20 Bdi£18.50–£26 LDO3pm
▥ CTV 15P ℛ(grass)

ONICH
Highland *Inverness-shire*
Map **14** NN06

GH Glenmorven House ☎ (08553) 247
May–Oct

Nicely appointed guesthouse situated on the shores of Loch Linnhe with superb outlook.

7hc (1fl) (2fb) Ⓡ Bdi£20–£21.42 WBdi£140–£150 LDO7pm

Lic 🛏 20P

Ⓥ

GH *Tigh-A-Righ* ☎(08553) 255
Closed 22 Dec–7 Jan

A simple but friendly little roadside house lying to the north of the village.

5hc (3fb) LDO9pm

Lic 🛏 CTV 15P ♿

FH Mr & Mrs A Dewar **Cuilcheanna House** *(NN019617)* (Guestaccom)
☎(08553) 226
Etr–6 Oct

Large Victorian house with gardens set in sloping fields leading to Loch Linnhe. Excellent views over lochs and mountains.

8⇌ (2fb) Ⓡ ✱B&b£13–£15 Bdi£20–£22 WBdi£130–£140 LDO7.30pm

🛏 10P 🐄 120acres beef

Ⓥ

ORFORD
Suffolk
Map **5** TM44

INN King's Head Front St
☎(0394) 450271
Closed Jan

5hc (1fb) Ⓡ B&b£14–£17.50 Lunch £7alc Dinner 9pm £12alc

100P 1🚗

Credit card 5

OSWESTRY
Shropshire
Map **7** SJ22

GH Ashfield Country House Llwyn-y-Maen, Trefonen Rd ☎(0691) 655200
Closed Jan–Feb

Modern, purpose-built establishment 1½ miles south-west of town.

13⇌ (2fb) CTV in all bedrooms Ⓡ B&b£20–£30 Bdi£25–£40 WBdi£150–£250LDO9pm

Lic 🛏 50P

Ⓥ

OTTERY ST MARY
Devon
Map **3** SY19

GH Fluxton Farm Hotel Fluxton
☎(040481) 2818

Sixteenth-century Devon longhouse enjoying a peaceful setting to the South of the town. Accommodation is neat and the proprietors give a pleasant welcome.

10hc (3⇌ 2fl) (2fb) Ⓡ B&b£13.50–£16.50 Bdi£18.50–£22.50 WBdifr£135 LDO5.30pm

Lic 🛏 CTV 15P 🎾(grass) 🏌 snooker

Ⓥ

FH Mrs S Hansford **Pitt Farm** *(SY089966)*
☎(040481) 2439
Closed Xmas

6rm (1hc) (2fb) ✗ Ⓡ ✱B&b£9.50–£11 Bdi£13.50–£15 WBdi£94.50–£105 LDO5pm

CTV 8P 190acres mixed

Ⓥ

OXENHOPE
West Yorkshire
Map **7** SE03

FH Mrs A Scholes ***Lily Hall*** *(SE023362)*
Uppermarsh Ln ☎Haworth (0535) 43999
Closed Xmas

Stone built smallholding rearing cattle and geese, overlooking the moors near Haworth.

4hc ✗

🛏 CTV 12P nc5yrs 9acres mixed smallholding

Credit card 2

OXFORD
Oxfordshire
Map **4** SP50

GH Bravalla 242 Iffley Rd ☎(0865) 241326

Small and homely guesthouse.

6hc (2fl) (2fb) CTV in all bedrooms Ⓡ B&b£10–£16

🛏 CTV 6P

Ⓥ

See advertisement on page 308

GH Brown's 281 Iffley Rd ☎(0865) 246822

Homely family guesthouse, well-decorated and clean accommodation. 1m from city.

6hc (1fb) CTV in 3 bedrooms TV in 3 bedrooms Ⓡ B&b£10–£15

🛏 CTV 3P

See advertisement on page 308

GH Burren 374 Banbury Rd ☎(0865) 513513

Clean, well-decorated family house with spacious accommodation. →

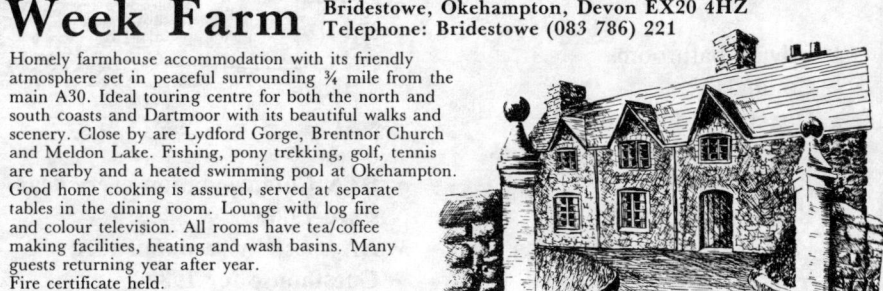

Credit Cards

1 Access/Euro/Mastercard
2 American Express
3 Barclaycard/Visa
5 Diners

7⇌ fl (3fb) CTV in 5 bedrooms TV in 2 bedrooms ✱ Ⓡ ✱B&b£13–£15

Ⓜ CTV 6P nc5yrs

Ⓥ

GH Combermere 11 Polstead Rd ☎(0865) 56971

Small, friendly place, close to city centre, in residential area.

8hc (4fl) (2fb) CTV in 5 bedrooms TV in 3 bedrooms ✱ Ⓡ B&b£12–£15

Ⓜ 3P

GH Conifer 116 The Slade, Headington ☎(0865) 63055

Oxford

Small, family-run establishment providing clean, comfortable bedrooms.

8hc (1⇌ 2fl) (1fb) CTV in all bedrooms ✱ Ⓡ B&b£14–£22

Ⓜ 8P ⇝(heated)

GH Courtfield Private Hotel 367 Iffley Rd ☎(0865) 242991

Small, family-run house with modern, well-decorated bedrooms.

6hc (1⇌ 3fl) (1fb) TV in all bedrooms ✱ B&b£14–£17

Ⓜ CTV 6P 2🚗 nc3yrs

Ⓥ

GH Dial House 25 London Rd, Headington (2m E) ☎(0865) 69944 Closed Xmas & New Year

8hc (2⇌ 2fl) (3fb) ⁄ in all bedrooms CTV in all bedrooms Ⓡ B&b£14–£16

Ⓜ 8P nc6yrs

GH Earlmont 322–324 Cowley Rd ☎(0865) 240236 Closed Xmas

Friendly guesthouse with modern standards.

5hc Annexe: 7hc (5fb) ⊁ in 2 bedrooms CTV in 8 bedrooms TV in 4 bedrooms ✗ Ⓡ B&b£12–£13

Ⅲ CTV 10P 1🚗 nc5yrs

Ⓥ

GH *Falcon* 88–90 Abingdon Rd ☎(0865) 722995

Closed 15 Dec–15 Jan

Accommodation here is above average and the lounge is comfortable.

Oxford

10hc (2fb) ✗

Ⅲ CTV 10P

GH *Galaxie Private Hotel* 180 Banbury Rd ☎(0865) 515688

Situated just one mile from the city centre, this small hotel is run by resident proprietors. Bedrooms are compact and homely.

33hc (6⇌ 9⩡) (3fb) CTV in all bedrooms lift Ⅲ CTV 26P

GH Green Gables 326 Abingdon Rd ☎(0865) 725870

Closed 20 Dec–7 Jan

Detached family house about a mile south of the city centre.

8hc (3⩡) (2fb) CTV in all bedrooms ✗ Ⓡ B&b£13–£17

Ⅲ CTV 8P

Credit card ③ Ⓥ

GH Highfield West 188 Cumnor Hill ☎(0865) 863007

Situated two miles from the town centre this small modern hotel has tastefully decorated bedroom accommodation and an outdoor swimming pool.

5hc (1⇌ 2ffl) (1fb) CTV in all bedrooms Ⓡ B&bfr£13.50 6P ⛱(heated)

GH Micklewood 331 Cowley Rd ☎(0865) 247328

Clean and homely accommodation.

6hc (2fb) CTV in 3 bedrooms TV in 3 bedrooms ✱ B&b£11.50–£12

🍴 CTV 6P

GH Pickwicks 17 London Rd, Headington ☎(0865) 750487

Comfortable, detached corner house with good bedrooms.

8hc (3⇌ 3ffl) (2fb) CTV in all bedrooms ✱ Ⓡ B&b£15–£22 Bdi£20–£27

🍴 CTV 12P 1🚗

GH Pine Castle 290 Iffley Rd ☎(0865) 241497

Homely guesthouse with comfortable, well-furnished rooms.

6hc (2fb) CTV in 4 bedrooms TV in 2 bedrooms Ⓡ ✱B&b£11–£15

🍴 CTV 3P

Ⓥ

GH Red Mullions 23 London Rd, Headington ☎(0865) 64727
Closed 23 Dec–2 Jan

Spacious detached house with own garden offering comfortable, modern bedrooms.

9hc (2⇌ 4ffl) (4fb) CTV in 6 bedrooms ✱ Ⓡ B&b£15–£18

🍴 CTV 10P nc5yrs

GH Tilbury Lodge 5 Tilbury Ln, Botley ☎(0865) 862138

Spotlessly kept modern accommodation in quiet almost rural area away from city centre.

8hc (5⇌ ⋒) (3fb) ✕ ✻B&b£13–£16.50 CTV 7P 2garages

Ⓥ

GH Westwood Country Hotel Hinksey Hill Top ☎(0865) 735408 Telex no 295141

Closed 17 June–1 Jul & 22 Dec–2 Jan

Small hotel in lovely woodland setting on outskirts of the city.

26hc (14⇌ 12⋒) (5fb) CTV in all bedrooms ✕(ex guide dogs) Ⓡ ✻B&b£22.50–£24.50 LDO8pm

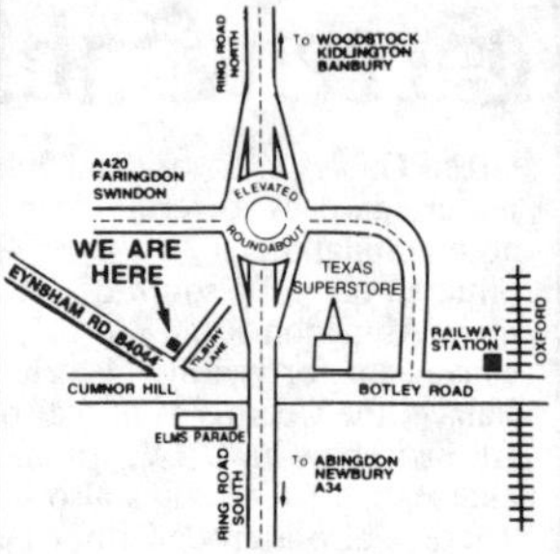

Lic CTV 25P ♿ gymnasium

Credit cards 1 2 3 5 Ⓥ

GH Willow Reaches Private Hotel 1 Wytham St ☎(0865) 721545

rs 15 Dec–Jan

Small, homely guesthouse in a quiet residential area.

9hc (2⇌ 2⋒) (2fb) CTV in all bedrooms ✕ Ⓡ B&b£15–£30 Bdi£20–£38 WB&bfr£96.50 LDO6.30pm

Lic CTV 3P 3garages

Credit cards 2 3 5 Ⓥ

OXHILL

Warwickshire

Map **4** SP34

FH Mrs S Hutsby **Nolands** *(SP312470)* ☎Kineton(0926) 640309

Closed Xmas

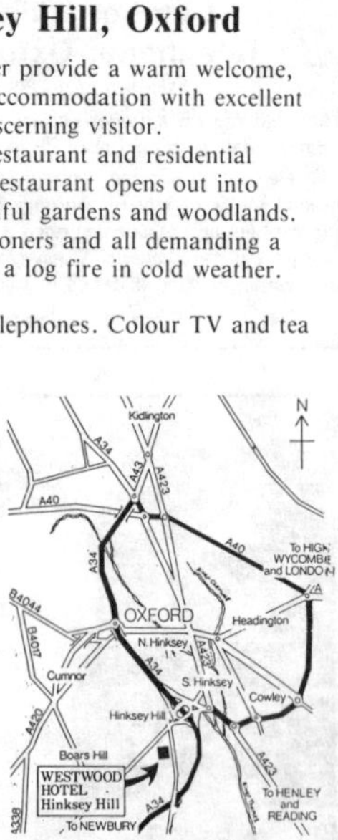

Attractive modern farm set in a peaceful valley 1m E of Pillarton Priors on A422. Comfortable, well-equipped bedrooms are in annexe adjoining farmhouse. Nearby lake offers fine woodland walks and fishing.

Annexe: 6hc (1⇌ 3⫚) (3fb) CTV in 4 bedrooms ✖ Ⓡ B&b£7–£12 Bdifr£15 LDOam

⫶ CTV 6P 4⌂ nc5yrs ⟋ 300acres arable

OXWICH
West Glamorgan
Map **2** SS58

GH Oxwich Bay Hotel Gower
☎Swansea (0792) 390329
Closed 24 & 25 Dec

Family holiday hotel, close to the beach.

14hc (2fb) ✖ Ⓡ B&b£13.25–£18 Bdi£20.75–£25.50 WBdi£119–£133LDO11pm

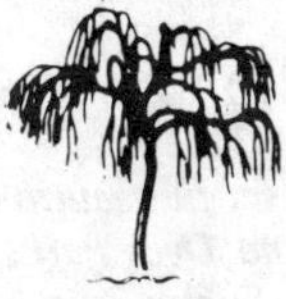

Lic ⫶ CTV 40P

Credit cards 1 2 3 5 Ⓥ

PADOG
Gwynedd
Map **6** SH85

FH Mrs E A Jones **Pant Glas** *(SH846513)* Pentrefoelas Rd ☎Pentrefoelas (06905) 248
Etr–Oct

3m W of Betws-y-Coed, S of A5

3hc (1fb) ✖ ✱B&b£8–£9 Bdi£12.50–£14 LDO3pm

CTV P 181acres beef sheep

Ⓥ

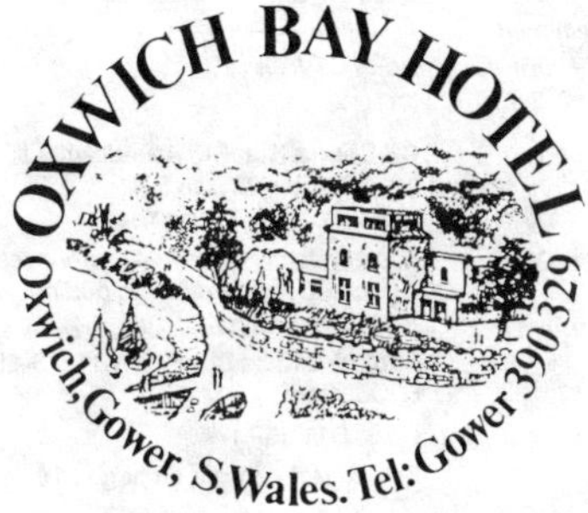

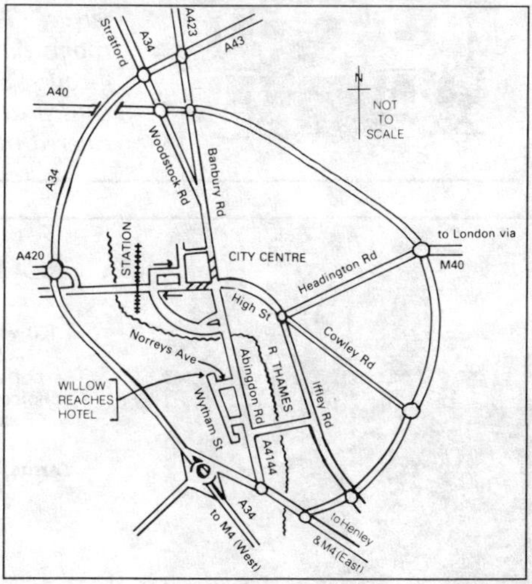

PADSTOW
Cornwall
Map **2** SW97

GH Alexandra 30 Dennis Rd ☎(0841) 532503
Mar–Oct

6hc (2fb) CTV in all bedrooms ✗ Ⓡ B&b£9.75–£10.75 Bdi£15–£15.75 WBdifr£100 LDOnoon

5P nc5yrs

Credit card ③

GH Dower House Private Hotel Fentonluna Ln ☎(0841) 532317

A house of character with comfortable bedrooms and friendly service.

9hc (1⇌ 3fl) (4fb) CTV available in bedrooms Ⓡ ✱B&b£13–£18 Bdi£24–£26.50 WBdi£104–£138.50 LDO7pm

Lic ™ CTV 9P

Credit card ①

GH Tregea Hotel High St ☎(0841) 532455

8hc (2fb) Ⓡ B&b£12.45–£16.75 Bdi£17.65–£23.30 WBdifr£114 LDO1pm

Lic ™ CTV 8P

GH Woodlands Hotel Treator ☎(0841) 532426

At Treator 1m W B3276.

9⇌ fl (3fb) CTV in 8 bedrooms Ⓡ available in bedroms B&b£11.50–£13.50 Bdi£18.50–£20.50 WBdifr£126.50 LDO5pm

Lic ™ CTV 15P

PAIGNTON
Devon
Map **3** SX86
See plan

GH Bayview Hotel 6 Cleveland Rd ☎(0803) 557400 Plan **1** *C1*

A bright, friendly, modern establishment within walking distance of the sea front.

10hc (3fb) ✗ Ⓡ ✱B&b£9–£11 Bdi£12–£15 WBdi£75–£98

Lic ™ CTV 10P

Ⓥ

GH *Beresford* 1 Adelphi Rd ☎(0803) 551560 Plan **2** *C2*
Closed Oct, Xmas & New Year

8hc (4fl) (1fb) ✗ Ⓡ LDO10am

Lic ™ CTV 3P

See advertisement on page 316

GH *Brackencroft* 3 St Andrews Rd ☎(0803) 556773 Plan **3** *B2*

Pleasantly-furnished villa within walking distance of sea-front lawns.

10hc (5fb) LDO6pm

™ CTV 5P

GH Cambria Hotel Esplanade Rd, Sea Front ☎(0803) 559256 Plan **4** *C3*

25hc (1fl) (4fb) Ⓡ B&b£14–£18 Bdi£16–£20 WBdifr£120 LDO6pm

Lic ™ CTV 2P

GH Channel View Hotel 8 Marine Pde ☎(0803) 522432 Plan **5** *C4*
Closed Xmas & New Year rs Nov–Jan

12hc (9fl) (3fb) CTV in all bedrooms Ⓡ B&bfr£10 Bdifr£13 WBdifr£67.50 (W only Whit–Sept) LDOnoon

Lic ™ CTV 10P

Ⓥ

GH Cherra Hotel 15 Roundham Rd ☎(0803) 550723 Plan **6** *B1*
Mar–Oct, Xmas & New Year

Friendly, family-run private hotel close to harbour. Good garden with putting green.

14hc (3fl) (7fb) CTV in all bedrooms Ⓡ B&b£10–£13 Bdi£13–£16 WBdi£75–£90 LDO5.30pm

Lic ™ CTV 15P 1🚗

See advertisement on page 316

GH Clennon Valley Hotel 1 Clennon Rise ☎(0803) 550304 Plan **7** *B1*
Closed Xmas

This small but charming hotel is personally run by the owners who offer friendly, hospitable service. Bedrooms are comfortable and well-equipped and the public rooms cosy

.12hc (1⇌ 9⋔) (3fb) CTV in 10 bedrooms ✱B&b£10–£13.50 Bdi£15–£17 W£85–£115 ⱡ LDO5pm

Lic 🍴 CTV 12P

GH Danethorpe Hotel 23 St Andrews Rd ☎(0803) 551251 Plan **8** *B1*
Closed Xmas & New Year

Bright, spotlessly clean private hotel with spacious public rooms.

8hc (3⋔) (1fb) CTV in all bedrooms Ⓡ ✱B&b£9–£11 Bdi£13–£15 WBdi£85–£100 LDO5.30pm

Lic 🍴 10P

Credit cards ① ③ Ⓥ

See advertisement on page 316

Paignton

GH Preston Sands Hotel 12 Marine Pde, Preston ☎(0803) 558718 Plan **9** *C4*

16hc (13⋔) (4fb) CTV in 7 bedrooms TV in 1 bedroom Ⓡ in 2 bedrooms B&b£9.50–£15 Bdi£15–£20 WBdi£92–£130 LDO4pm

Lic 🍴 CTV 12P nc6yrs

⊢⊣**GH Radford Hotel** 28–30 Youngs Park Rd ☎(0803) 559671 Plan **10** *B1*

14hc (5fb) B&b£6.60–£10 Bdi£8.50–£12.50 WBdi£56–£87 LDO4pm

Lic 🍴 CTV 4P pool table

GH Redcliffe Lodge Hotel 1 Marine Dr ☎(0803) 551394 Plan **11** *C4*
Mar–mid Nov

17hc (10⇌ 7⋔) (2fb) CTV in all bedrooms ✗ Ⓡ B&b£16–£20 Bdi£23–£27 WBdifr£129

Lic 🍴 CTV 20P ⌂

Credit cards ① ② ③ Ⓥ

See advertisement on page 317

GH Hotel Retreat 43 Marine Dr ☎(0803) 550596 Plan **12** *C4*
Etr–Sep

Comfortable, family-owned private hotel in spacious gardens on the sea front.

15hc (3⇌) (2fb) CTV in 14 bedrooms Ⓡ in 3 bedroomsB&b£10–£15 Bdi£15.50–£20 WBdi£95–£130 ⱡ LDO6pm

Lic CTV 14P

Credit cards ① ③

GH St Weonard's Private Hotel 12 Kernou Rd ☎(0803) 558842 Plan **13** *B2*
Mar–Oct

8hc (2 ⋔) (4 fb) ✗ Ⓡ ✱B&b£8–£12 Bdi£11–£15 WBdi£77–£90 LDO5pm

Lic CTV 2P

Ⓥ

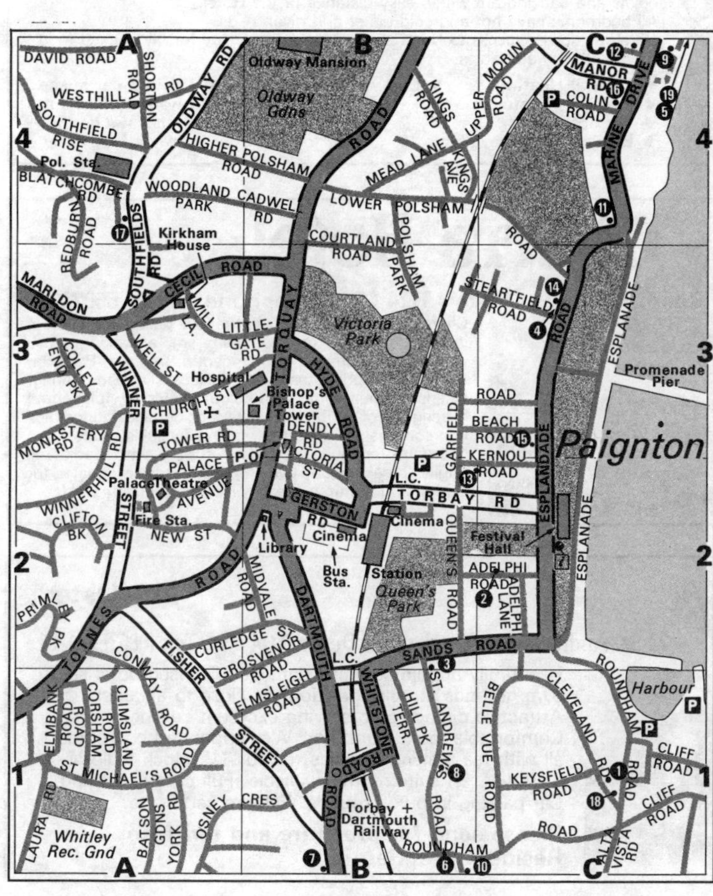

Paignton

1 Bayview Hotel
2 Beresford
3 Brackencroft
4 Cambria Hotel
5 Channel View Hotel
6 Cherra Hotel
7 Clennon Valley Hotel
8 Danethorpe Hotel
9 Preston Sands Hotel
10 Radford Hotel
11 Redcliffe Lodge Hotel
12 Hotel Retreat
13 St Weonard's Private Hotel
14 Sattva Hotel
15 Sealawn Hotel
16 Sea Verge Hotel
17 South Mount Hotel
18 Sunnybank Private Hotel
19 Torbay Sands Hotel

GH Sattva Hotel 29 Esplanade Rd ☎(0803) 557820 Plan **14** *C3*

Friendly, private hotel with comfortable, modern bedrooms. Adjacent to seafront.

20hc (3⇨ 7ⓕ) (6fb) CTV in all bedrooms ✕ ® B&b£11.50–£19.50Bdi£15–£22.50 WBdi£92.50–£138.50 LDO5pm

Lic 🍽 CTV 11P

Credit cards 1 3 ⓥ

GH Sealawn Hotel Sea Front ☎(0803) 559031 Plan **15** *C2*

Paignton

Friendly Victorian holiday hotel opposite sea front. Cosy atmosphere and modern well-equipped bedrooms.

14hc (6⇨ 5ⓕ) (3fb) CTV in all bedrooms ✕ ® B&b£11–£16 Bdi£14–£19 WBdi£77–£119 LDO6pm

Lic 🍽 CTV 14P 🏠

ⓥ

GH Sea Verge Hotel Marine Dr, Preston ☎(0803) 557795 Plan **16** *C4*
Closed Xmas

As its name suggests, this family-run hotel lies close to the sea front. Excellent bedroom accommodation.

12hc (5ⓕ) (1fb) CTV in all bedrooms ✕ ✱B&b£12–£15 Bdi£18–£20 WBdifr£140 LDO5pm

Lic 🍽 CTV 14P nc12yrs

Credit cards 1 3

Sattva Hotel

ESPLANADE, PAIGNTON, SOUTH DEVON
Telephone: 0803/557820

A modern Hotel situated on the level in the centre of the sea front. Residential licence, excellent cuisine, choice of menu. Radio intercom, tea & coffee making facilities and colour TV in all rooms. Entertainment. Most rooms en suite including the ground floor. Central heating. Car Park. An ideal centre for touring Devon and nearby beauty spots.

Write or telephone for further details to the proprietors: Mr & Mrs T W Nadin

SEALAWN HOTEL

Sea Front, Paignton, South Devon
Telephone: 0803 559031
Arrive as visitors, leave as friends

Situated right on the sea front and overlooking spacious greens but just a few minutes walk from the town centre and the many attractions and nightspots that Paignton offers. Renowned for excellent food, good service and creating a happy relaxed atmosphere for all our guests. All rooms are comfortably furnished and have the modern facilities required to make your holiday an enjoyable one. Ample parking. Open all year. Proprietors Tony & Sheena Codd.

Redcliffe Lodge

1 Marine Drive, Paignton TQ3 2NJ
Reception (0803) 551394
Visitors (0803) 525643

RIGHT ON THE BEACH . . . The Hotel is situated in one of Paignton's finest sea front positions in its own grounds with an easy level walk to most facilities including two safe sandy beaches, harbour, theatre, shops and town centre.

DINE IN STYLE . . . Sea air sharpens appetites remarkably. Meals in our sunny dining-room overlooking the sea front are to be lingered over and savoured. We are proud of our cuisine, the result of careful thought to give pleasure, variety and interest.

All principle rooms and most of the bedrooms have extensive seaviews. All bedrooms en-suite with colour TV, radio and intercom to reception; tea making facilities on request. Ground floor bedrooms available. Hotel is heated throughout making it ideal for early or late holidays, mid-week bookings accepted. Large car park –perfect touring centre. Colour brochure on request from resident proprietors Iris & Kevin Roughley.

The Sea Front Hotel that is all things to all people.

GH South Mount Hotel 7 Southfield Rd ☎(0803) 557643 Plan **17** *A4*
Apr–Oct rs Nov–Mar
A friendly welcome and personal service is asssured by the owners of this charming character guesthouse. It is set amid attractive mature gardens in a quiet yet convenient location.
9hc (2fl) (1fb) B&b£9.50–£10.50 Bdi£12.50–£14.50 WBdifr£95
Lic CTV 5P

GH Sunnybank Private Hotel 2 Cleveland Rd ☎(0803) 525540 Plan **18** *C1*
Friendly, personal service at comfortable private hotel.
12hc (2fl) (4fb) B&b£9–£12.50 Bdi£13–£15.50 WBdifr£75
Lic CTV 7P nc2yrs
Credit card 1 V

GH *Torbay Sands Hotel* Sea Front, 16 Marine Pde, Preston ☎(0803) 525568 Plan **19** *C4*
12hc (3fb) LDO1pm
Lic CTV 7P

PAISLEY
Strathclyde *Renfrewshire*
For accommodation details see **Glasgow Airport**

PANTYGELLI (nr Abergavenny)
Gwent
Map **3** SO31

FH Mrs M E Smith **Lower House** *(SO314159)* Old Hereford Rd ☎Abergavenny (0873) 3432
Etr–Oct
Isolated stone-built farmhouse with mountain views, 3m from Abergavenny.
3hc B&b£8–£8.50 WB&bfr£56
CTV 6P 200acres arable beef sheep

PARBOLD
Lancashire
Map **7** SD41

INN Wayfarer Alder Ln ☎(02576) 2542

Attractive cottage-style building (C1668) with well furnished bedrooms and extensive a la carte menu.
3hc (2⇌ 1fl) CTV in all bedrooms ® B&b£7.50–£15 Bdi£11.50–£30 WBdi fr£120 Lunch fr£5.95&alc Dinner10pm £5.95–£8.95&alc
CTV 30P
Credit cards 1 3 V

PARKMILL (nr Swansea)
West Glamorgan
Map **2** SS58

FH Mrs D Edwards **Parc-le-Breos House** *(SS529896)* ☎Swansea (0792) 371636
1½m NW off A4118.
8rm (5hc 2fl) B&b£10.50–£11.50 Bdi£14–£15 WBdi £98–£105 LDO6pm
CTV P U snooker 55acres mixed
V

PARRACOMBE
Devon
Map **3** SS64

FH Mr H Bearryman **Lower Dean** Trentishoe ☎(05983) 215
Feb–mid Dec
Set amidst 13 acres of farmland with pigs, ducks and chickens, this friendly farmhouse offers good home cooking in an informal atmosphere. Horse-riding available.
7hc (1⇌) (4fb) CTV available in bedrooms B&b£10.50–£11.50 Bdi £15.50–£16.50 WBdifr£93
Lic CTV 7P U snooker gymnasium 13acres mixed

PATELEY BRIDGE
North Yorkshire
Map **7** SE16

Selected

GH Grassfields Country House Hotel ☎Harrogate (0423) 711412
Mar–Oct
In the valley of the River Nidd and surrounded by four acres of mature grounds and neat gardens this charming Georgian residence provides peaceful country accommodation. The spacious bedrooms are well equipped and good home cooking is served in the attractive dining room not far from the comfortable lounge and lounge bar.
9hc (5⇌ 4fl) (3fb) ® B&b£16.50–£17.50 Bdi£24.50–£25.50 WBdi£161–£168 LDO7pm
Lic CTV 24P

GH Roslyn 9 King St ☎Harrogate (0423) 711374
Mar–Oct
Ideally placed in a delightful Dales town on the river Nidd, Roslyn House offers good food and hospitality in pleasant surroundings. The bedrooms are full of charm and character yet well-equipped with modern facilities. There is also a cosy lounge and a friendly bar.
6hc (1⇌ 5fl) CTV in all bedrooms ® B&b£11–£19 Bdi£18.50–£26.50 WBdifr£120 LDO4pm
Lic 3P nc

PATRICK BROMPTON
North Yorkshire
Map **8** SE29

GH Elmfield House Arrathorne, Bedale (2m N unclass towards Catterick Camp) ☎Bedale (0677) 50558
Guests can enjoy a peaceful stay at this exceptionally well appointed pebble-dashed house set on the edge of the Yorkshire Dales and approached by a long farm track.

3hc (2fl) (1fb) B&bfr£9 Bdifr£15 WBdifr£105

Lic ₩ CTV 6P

Ⓥ

See advertisement under Bedale

PEEBLES
Borders *Peeblesshire*
Map **11** NT24

GH Lindores Old Town ☎(0721) 20441

Neat house with combined lounge and dining room.

5hc (3fb) ✗ B&b£9–£10 WB&b£63–£70

₩ CTV 3P

GH Whitestone House Innerleithen Rd ☎(0721) 20337

Neat, well-maintained guesthouse to E of town. Combined lounge and dining room.

5hc (2fb) ✗ B&b£9–£10

₩ CTV 5P

Ⓥ

FH Mrs J M Haydock **Winkston** *(NT244433)* Edinburgh Rd ☎(0721) 21264 Etr–Oct

Nicely decorated farmhouse 1½ miles north of town off Edinburgh road. Shower room only, no bath.

3hc ✗ Ⓡ B&b£8.50–£9.25

₩ CTV 4P 15acres sheep

Ⓥ

PELYNT
Cornwall
Map **2** SX25

FH Mrs L Tuckett **Trenderway** *(SX214533)* ☎Polperro (0503) 72214 Etr–Oct

Friendly accommodation and stylish bedrooms at this 16th-century farmhouse situated off the beaten track yet just 2 miles from Polperro and Looe.

3hc ✗ B&b£12–£14

₩ CTV 2P 1🚗 nc10yrs 600acres arable

PEMBROKE
Dyfed
Map **2** SM90

GH High Noon Lower Lamphey Rd ☎(0646) 683736

Modern family-run guesthouse offering relaxed accommodation and attentive service.

8hc (1fb) B&b£8.95–£9.50 Bdi£13.20–£13.75 WBdifr£88 LDO5pm

Lic ₩ CTV 7P

PENARTH
South Glamorgan
Map **3** ST17

GH Albany Hotel 14 Victoria Rd ☎Cardiff (0222) 701598

Stone-built house in quiet road with residents' bar.

14hc (1⇌ 4fl) (4fb) CTV in all bedrooms ✱B&b£13–£15.50 LDO7.30pm

₩ CTV P

Credit cards 1 3

PENCARREG
Dyfed
Map **2** SN54

INN Red Lion ☎Llanybyther (0570) 480018

Good, homely food and comfortable bedrooms at cosy inn.

3hc (2fl) Ⓡ ✱B&b£10–£12 Bdi£14.50–£16.50 WBdi£85–£98 Lunch fr£4.50&alc High Tea £2.50–£4.50 Dinner9.30pm fr£5&alc

₩ CTV 26P

Credit cards 1 3 Ⓥ

PENMACHNO
Gwynedd
Map **6** SH75

FH M Jones **Tyddyn Gethin** *(SH799514)* ☎(06903) 392 Feb–Nov

Farm situated high on mountainside with panoramic views of the surrounding country.

3hc ✗ Ⓡ B&b£8.50–£9.50 Bdi£12.50–£14.50 LDO5pm

CTV P 80acres arable beef mixed sheep

Ⓥ

PENNANT
Dyfed
Map **2** SN56

GH Bikerehyd Farm (Guestaccom) ☎Nebo (09746) 365 Feb–Nov

Accommodation is in three carefully restored 14th-century cottages adjacent to main building. Full of character.

3hc Annexe: 3fl CTV in 3 bedrooms Ⓡ B&b£14–£17 Bdifr£24–£27 WBdifr£130 LDO6pm

Lic ₩ CTV P nc8yrs

PENRHYNDEUDRAETH
Gwynedd
Map **6** SH63

FH Mrs P Bayley **Y Wern** *(SH620421)* Llanfrothen (2m N off B4410) ☎(0766) 770556

Large 17th-century house with good family bedrooms. Ideal location for touring Southern Snowdonia.

5hc (4fb) ✗ B&b£10–£12 Bdi£15.50–£17.50 WBdi£100–£115

₩ CTV 6P

110acres beef sheep

Ⓥ

PENRITH
Cumbria
Map **12** NY53

GH Brandelhow 1 Portland Pl ☎(0768) 64470

Town centre house offering neat, comfortable accommodation.

6rm (5hc) (3fb) CTV in all bedrooms Ⓡ B&b£8.50–£10 Bdi£12.50–£15 WBdifr£98 LDO5pm

₩ CTV 1P

Ⓥ

GH Limes Country Hotel Redhills Stainton (2m W A66) ☎(0768) 63343

A spacious yet unpretentious house situated 1m W of junction 40 on the M6. The friendly family service extends to providing hot water bottles on cool nights. Breakfast is a treat with home-made jam and marmalade and free-range eggs.

6hc (5fb) ✗ Ⓡ B&b£10–£12.50 Bdi£16–£18.50 WBdi£100–£120 LDO5pm

Lic ₩ CTV 8P

Credit card 3 Ⓥ

GH Pategill Villas Carleton Rd ☎(0768) 63153

Spacious guesthouse in its own attractive gardens.

10hc (6fb) B&b£10.50–£11

Lic ₩ CTV 10P

Ⓥ

GH Woodland House Hotel Wordsworth St ☎(0768) 64177

Elegant red-sandstone house with attractive public rooms.

8hc (3⇌ 1fl) (2fb) ⊁ in all bedrooms CTV in all bedrooms ✗ Ⓡ B&b£12–£14.50 Bdi£18–£20.50 WBdifr£113.50 LDO4.30pm

Lic ₩ CTV 10P 1🚗

PENRUDDOCK
Cumbria
Map **12** NY42

Selected

FH Mrs S M Smith **Highgate** *(NY444275)* ☎Greystoke (08533) 339 Feb–Nov

A high level of thoughtfulness and attention to detail is apparent throughout this charming 18th-century farmhouse. All bedrooms are individually decorated and two have brass beds. A comfortable lounge and dining room. Home-cooked dinners are of a good standard. A good base for touring and recreational facilities. Situated on the A66 Penrith to Keswick road 1m E of village and 4m W of M6 junc 40.

3hc (1fb) CTV in all bedrooms ✗ Ⓡ B&b£10–£12 WB&bfr£70 LDO5pm

₩ CTV 3P nc5yrs 400acres mixed

Ⓥ

PENYBONT
Powys
Map **3** SO16

GH Ffaldau Country House Llandegley (2m E A44) ☎(059787) 421
Good home-cooking is a speciality at this authentic 16th-century crook-frames farmhouse.
3hc (1🛁) Ⓡ B&b£10.50–£12.50 Bdi£19–£21 WBdi£126–£142 LDO9pm
Lic 🍽 CTV 25P
Ⓥ

PENZANCE
Cornwall
Map **2** SW43
See plan

GH *Beachfield Hotel* The Promenade ☎(0736) 62067 Plan **1** *B1*
Mar–Nov
32hc (12🛁) (2fb) Ⓡ
Lic 🍽 CTV 🅿

GH Bella-Vista Private Hotel
7 Alexandra Ter, Seafront ☎(0736) 62409 Plan **2** *A1*
Simple, homely guesthouse with views over Mounts Bay.
10hc (5fb) CTV available in bedrooms Ⓡ ✱B&b£10–£12 Bdi£15–£17 WBdi£98–£112 LDO5pm

Lic 🍽 CTV 8P nc3yrs
Credit cards 1 3 Ⓥ

⊢⊣**GH Blue Seas Hotel** 13 Regent Ter ☎(0736) 64744 Plan **3** *D2*
Regency terraced house, comfortably appointed offering friendly service.
10hc (1⇌ 6🛁) (3fb) CTV in all bedrooms ✗ B&b£9–£12.50 Bdi£14–£17.50 WBdi£98–£112 LDO6.30pm
Lic 🍽 12P nc5yrs
Ⓥ

⊢⊣**GH Camilla Hotel** Regent Ter ☎(0736) 63771 Plan **4** *C2*
Character Regency residence overlooking seafront promenade with comfortable friendly family atmosphere, positioned close to parks and town centre amenities.
10hc (1⇌ 2🛁) (2fb) CTV in 5 bedrooms B&b£9–£12.50 Bdi£14–£17.50 WBdi£95–£120 LDO6pm
Lic 🍽 CTV 6P
Ⓥ
See advertisement on page 322

GH Carlton Private Hotel ☎(0736) 62081 Plan **5** *B1*
Apr–19 Oct
Small modest family hotel, personally-run, and positioned on sea front offering commanding views.
12hc (5🛁) CTV in all bedrooms ✗ Ⓡ B&b£10–£15 Bdi£16–£21 WBdifr£90 LDO4pm
Lic CTV 🅿 nc12yrs
Ⓥ

⊢⊣**GH Dunedin** Alexandra Rd ☎(0736) 62652 Plan **6** *A2*
Closed Jan & Feb
Very comfortable, small, personally-run guesthouse positioned close to sea front.
9hc (4fb) CTV in all bedrooms Ⓡ B&b£9–£10.50 Bdi£14–£15.50 WBdi£85–£99 LDO5pm
Lic 🍽 CTV 1🚗(charge) nc3yrs

GH Georgian House 20 Chapel St ☎(0736) 65664 Plan **7** *C3*
Situated opposite the Admiral Benbow Inn this centrally postioned hotel offers tastefully furnished bedrooms.
12hc (4⇌ 2🛁) (4fb) CTV in all bedrooms Ⓡ B&b£11.50–£16.10 Bdi£18–£22.60 WBdifr£126 LDO7.30pm
Lic 🍽 CTV 11P
Credit cards 1 3 Ⓥ

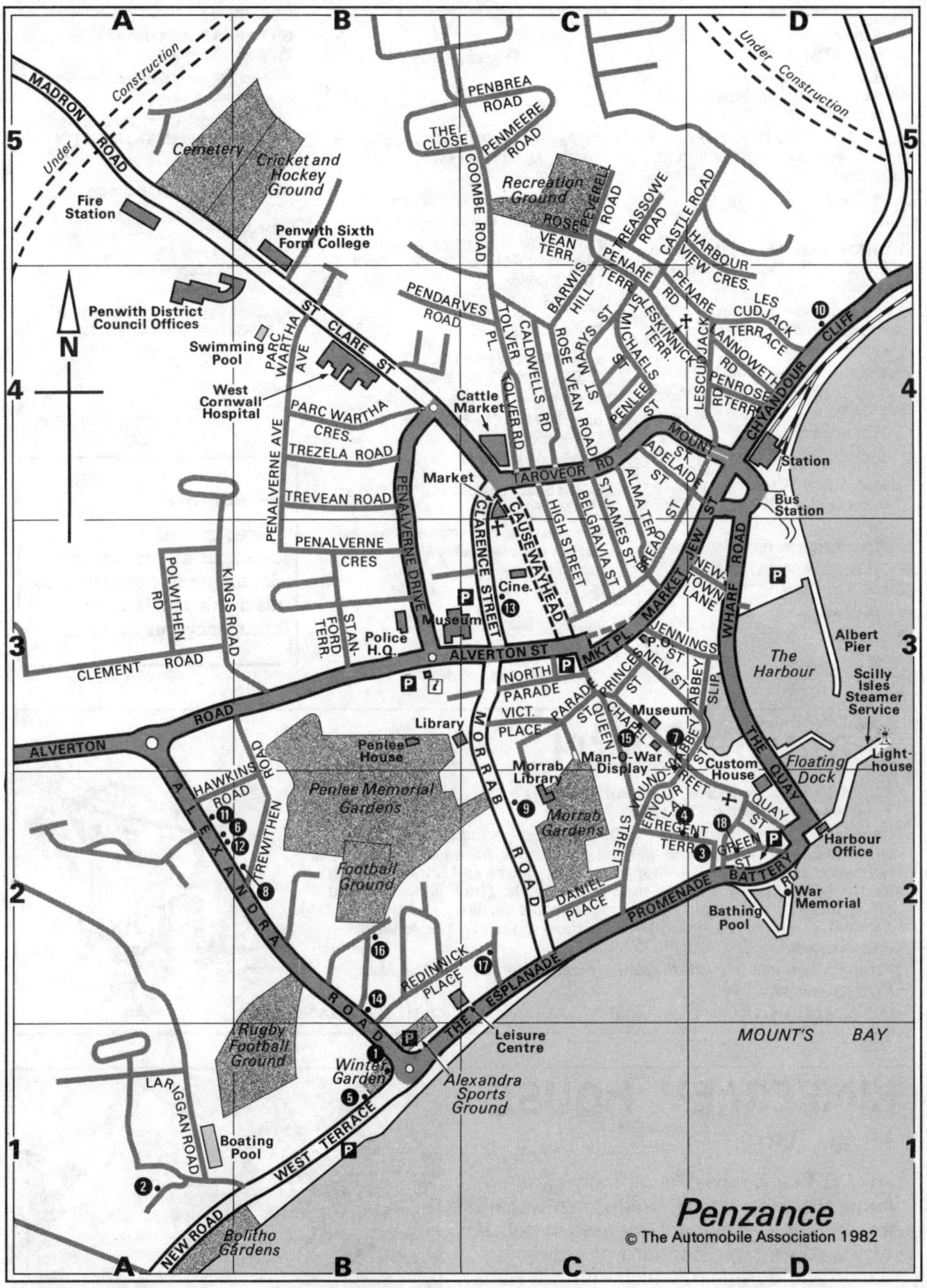

Penzance

1 Beachfield Hotel
2 Bella-Vista Private Hotel
3 Blue Seas Hotel
4 Camilla Hotel
5 Carlton Private Hotel
6 Dunedin
7 Georgian House
8 Holbein House Hotel
9 Kimberley House
10 Mount Royal Hotel
11 Penmorvah Hotel
12 Pentrea Hotel
13 Shobnall House
14 Trenant Private Hotel
15 Trevelyan Hotel
16 Trewella
17 Willows

GH Holbein House Hotel Alexandra Rd ☎(0736) 65008 Plan **8** *B2*

Small comfortable family hotel, personally-run and positioned in quiet area leading to sea front.

10hc (3⇌ 7fl) (7fb) CTV in all bedrooms Ⓡ B&b£12–£17 Bdi£18–£23 WBdifr£120 LDO8.30pm

Lic ⊞ CTV P̸

Credit cards ① ③

⊢GH **Kimberley House** 10 Morrab Rd (Guestaccom) ☎(0736) 62727 Plan **9** *C2* Jan–Oct

Small tastefully furnished residence offering warm and friendly welcome from resident proprietors.

9hc (2fb) CTV in 6 bedrooms ✗ Ⓡ B&b£9–£10 Bdi£14.50–£15.50 WBdi£92–£98 LDO5pm

Lic ⊞ CTV 4P nc5yrs

Credit cards ① ③

GH Mount Royal Hotel Chyandour Cliff ☎(0736) 62233 Plan **10** *D4* Mar–Oct

Small family hotel facing sea and harbour.

9hc (4⇌) (3fb) ✱B&b£12–£14 WB&b£80.50–£94.50

⊞ CTV 6P 4🚗

Ⓥ

Penzance

GH Penmorvah Hotel Alexandra Rd ☎(0736) 63711 Plan **11** *A2* Closed Xmas

Personally-run private hotel with comfortable accommodation.

10hc (5⇌ 5fl) (4fb) CTV in all bedrooms Ⓡ ✱B&b£13–£14 Bdi£20–£22 WBdi£115–£130 LDO6pm

Lic ⊞ P

Credit cards ① ② ③

⊢**GH Pentrea Hotel** Alexandra Rd ☎(0736) 69576 Plan **12** *A2*

9hc (2fl) (2fb) CTV in all bedrooms Ⓡ B&b£9–£11 Bdi£14–£16 WBdifr£87 LDO6pm

Lic ⊞ CTV P̸

⊢**GH Shobnall House** 10 Clarence St ☎(0736) 63374 Plan **13** *C3*

A personally run guesthouse in a central position affording homely accommodation.

9hc (2fb) CTV in all bedrooms Ⓡ B&b£8.50–£10 Bdi£13–£14.50 WBdi£80–£90 LDO6.30pm

Lic CTV 2P

Credit cards ① ③ Ⓥ

GH Trenant Private Hotel Alexandra Rd ☎(0736) 62005 Plan **14** *A2*

A personally-run guesthouse, close to local amenities.

10hc (4fl) (5fb) CTV in all bedrooms Ⓡ B&bfr£9.50 Bdifr£15 WBdifr£100 LDO4pm

Lic CTV P nc5yrs

GH Trevelyan Hotel 16 Chapel St ☎(0736) 62494 Plan **15** *C3* Closed Xmas

17th-century property offering comfortable accommodation within town centre.

8hc (1⇌ 1fl) (4fb) ✗ Ⓡ ✱B&b£8.50–£9.50 Bdi£14–£15 WBdifr£95 LDOam

Lic ⊞ CTV 8P

REMEMBER

Prices quoted in the gazetteer are minimum double room occupancy to maximum single room occupancy per person.

⊢GH **Trewella** 18 Mennaye Rd ☎(0736) 63818 Plan **16** *B2*
Apr–Oct

Cosy little guesthouse with good home-cooking about two minutes from sea front.

8hc (1⥂) (3fb) Ⓡ B&b£7.75–£8.75 Bdi£11.25–£12.25 WBdi£76.50–£83.50 LDO4.30pm

Lic 𝍖 CTV ⁄P nc3yrs

Ⓥ

GH Willows Cornwall Ter ☎(0736) 63744 Plan **17** *C2*

Victorian corner house with attractive gardens.

7hc (1fb) Ⓡ in 6 bedrooms B&b£10.50–£11.50 Bdi£18.50–£19.50 WBdifr£136 LDO4.30pm

𝍖 CTV 6P nc5yrs

Ⓥ

INN Yacht The Promenade ☎(0736) 62787 Plan **18** *D2*
Mar–Oct

This pleasant inn has uninterrupted views across Maints Bay, an Art Deco style bar and recently refurbished bedrooms.

6hc (1fb) ✗ Ⓡ ✱B&bfr£10 Bdifr£14 Bar lunch £4–£6&alc Dinner £4–£6&alc

CTV 8P

PERRANPORTH
Cornwall
Map **2** SW75

GH Cellar Cove Hotel Droskyn Way ☎Truro (0872) 572110

14hc (4fb) CTV in all bedrooms Ⓡ B&b£11–£13 Bdi£16.50–£18.50 WBdi£100–£125

Lic CTV 20P ⌂ pool table table tennis games room

Credit cards 1 3 Ⓥ

GH Fairview Hotel Tywarnhayle Rd ☎Truro (0872) 572278
Apr–Oct

Good views from this comfortable family hotel.

15hc (6⥂) (6fb) ⁄ in 2 bedrooms Ⓡ B&b£10–£11.50 Bdi£14.50–£16 WBdi£85–£110 LDO10pm

Lic 𝍖 CTV 8P 3⌂ pool table

Credit cards 1 3

GH Lamorna Private Hotel Tywarnhayle Rd ☎Truro(0872) 573398

Comfortable personally-run small family hotel.

9hc (4fb) Ⓡ B&b£9–£10.50 Bdi£15.50–£17.50 WBdi£103.50–£114 LDO7pm

Lic CTV ⁄P

Ⓥ

GH Villa Margarita Country Hotel Bolingey ☎Truro (0872) 572063

Exceptionally well-appointed colonial-style villa in an acre of well-tended gardens. Imaginative table d'hote menus served by caring owners.

5hc (3⥂) Annexe: 2⥂ (1fb) TV available in bedrooms ✗ Ⓡ B&b£13–£14.50 Bdi£22.50–£24 WBdi£135–£144 LDO6pm

Lic CTV 8P nc8yrs ⌂ solarium

Ⓥ

PERTH
Tayside *Perthshire*
Map **11** NO12

GH Clark Kimberley 57–59 Dunkeld Rd ☎(0738) 37406

A small, well-maintained guesthouse on the main road. Cheerful owners ensure a friendly welcome and good service. Bedrooms are modern and comfortable.

8hc (5fb) CTV in all bedrooms Ⓡ ✱B&b£9–£10

𝍖 CTV 12P

Ⓥ

GH *Clunie* 12 Pitcullen Cres ☎(0738) 23625
Closed Xmas & New Year
A plesant stone built house situated on the outskirts of the city providing well maintained, compact bedrooms with private facilities and comfortable public rooms.
7hc (1⇌ 4fl) (3fb) CTV in all bedrooms ✈ Ⓡ
Ⓜ 7P

GH Darroch 9 Pitcullen Cres ☎(0738) 36893
A very pleasant guesthouse set on the northern outskirts of the city.
6hc (3fl) (2fb) CTV in all bedrooms Ⓡ ✱B&b£10–£15 Bdi£16–£21 WBdifr£112 LDO4pm
Ⓜ CTV 10P
Ⓥ

⊢⊣**GH Gables** 24–26 Dunkeld Rd ☎(0738) 24717
Two adjoining houses on a busy junction N of the town.
8hc (3fb) CTV in 5 bedrooms Ⓡ B&b£9–£10 Bdi£14–£15 WBdi£95–£105 LDO4pm
Lic Ⓜ CTV 8P
Credit cards 1 3 Ⓥ

GH Iona 2 Pitcullen Cres ☎(0738) 27261
Small well-appointed house with modern bedrooms and pleasant public rooms. Close to town centre.
6hc (2fb) Ⓡ B&b£10–£12 Bdi£15–£17 WBdi£100–£114
Ⓜ CTV 5P
Credit card 2 Ⓥ

GH Pitcullen 17 Pitcullen Cres ☎(0738) 26506
A stone-built guesthouse providing comfortable bedrooms on a bed-and-breakfast basis.
6hc (1fl) (2fb) CTV in all bedrooms ✈ Ⓡ B&bfr£10 Bdifr£15 LDO6
Ⓜ CTV 6P

PETERSFIELD
Hampshire
See also **Rogate**

PETWORTH
West Sussex
Map **4** SU92

GH Almshouses (Guestaccom) Tillington ☎(0798) 43432
2hc (1fl) Annexe: 2hc (1⇌ 1fl) (1fb) CTV in all bedrooms Ⓡ ✱B&b£15–£18 WB&b£98–£119
Ⓜ CTV 6P nc10yrs
Credit cards 1 3 Ⓥ

PEVENSEY BAY
East Sussex
Map **5** TQ60

GH Napier The Promenade ☎Eastbourne (0323) 768875
10hc (5fl) (3fb) TV in 1 bedroom CTV in 4 bedrooms ✈ Ⓡ B&b£10–£12 Bdi£15–£17 WBdifr£75 LDO4.10pm
Lic Ⓜ CTV 7P

PICKERING
North Yorkshire
Map **8** SE88

GH Bramwood 19 Hallgarth ☎(0751) 74066
In a quiet position close to the town centre, this town house offers neat and pleasant accommodation. The home cooked dinners are especially recommended and smoking is not allowed.
6hc (2fb) ⊬in al bedrooms ✈ Ⓡ B&b£10–£14 Bdifr£15 LDO6.30pm
Lic CTV 6P
Credit cards 1 2 3

GH Cottage Leas Country Middleton ☎(0751) 72129
Converted 18th-century farmhouse with antique bric-a-brac.
12hc (6⇌ 6fl) (3fb) CTV in 10 bedrooms TV in 2 bedrooms Ⓡ B&bfr£8 Bdifr£25.50 LDO9pm
Lic Ⓜ 50P 4🚗 ⚲(hard) solarium
Credit cards 1 3 5 Ⓥ

PIDDLETRENTHIDE
Dorset
Map **3** SY79

INN The Poachers ☎(03004) 358
This attractive small inn can be found on the edge of the village. An annexe provides comfortable bedroom accommodation. Pretty garden by a stream.
2⇌ fl CTV in all bedrooms Ⓡ B&b£12–£15 WB&b£80–£95 Lunch £4.50alc Dinner 9pm£4.50alc
Ⓜ 30P
Ⓥ

PILSDON
Dorset
Map **3** SY49

FH K B Brooks **Monkwood** *(SY429986)* ☎Broadwindsor (0308) 68723
(5m NW of Bridport off the Broadoak-Marshwood Rd)
Closed Xmas
Thatched farmhouse with pleasant views. Charmouth 6m.
2rm (1fb) ✈ ✱B&bfr£8
CTV P 230acres beef dairy sheep mixed

PILTON
Somerset
Map **3** ST54

GH Long House (Minotels) ☎(074989) 701
mid Feb–mid Nov
Delightful little hotel in 17th-century building set in charming historic village.
7hc (3⇌ 3fl) (1fb) B&b£17 Bdi£25.50 WBdi£140 LDO6.30pm
Lic Ⓜ 10P nc5yrs
Credit cards 1 2 3 5 Ⓥ

The Almshouses

TILLINGTON,
NR. PETWORTH
WEST SUSSEX
GU28 0RA
Telephone: Petworth
(0798) 43432
(From overseas dial
44 798 43432)

Pretty and comfortable conversion of two Almshouses and Piggery Grade II listed. Built in local stone, the House, together with the hidden rooms behind the wall, overlook lovely views to the South Downs.
Bedrooms are well furnished, TV, radio, tea/coffee making facilities. Electric blankets/ bottles on request. Full central heating. Garden. Ample parking. Telephone.
Separate Ground Floor SUITE. 1/2 bedrooms both en-suite with own sitting room & kitchenette. Sleeps 2-5 people. Also self catering. Superb views to South Downs.
Wide selection pubs/excellent restaurants nearby. Ideal base for touring, antiques, National Trust Gardens, or just to relax.
Break rates Oct — Mar.
Heathrow or Gatwick 1 hour.
From £14-£20 per person per night.
Directions: From Petworth A272 (Midhurst). After reaching sign TILLINGTON 3rd drive on left.
Member of GUESTACCOM/ COUNTRY HOMES.
Access or Visa accepted.

COTTAGE LEAS COUNTRY HOTEL

AND LICENSED RESTAURANT
Middleton, Nova Lane, Pickering, North Yorkshire YO18 8PN
Telephone: STD 0751 72129

Recommended: Ashley Courtenay
Les Routiers.
Member English Tourist Board
All cards taken.

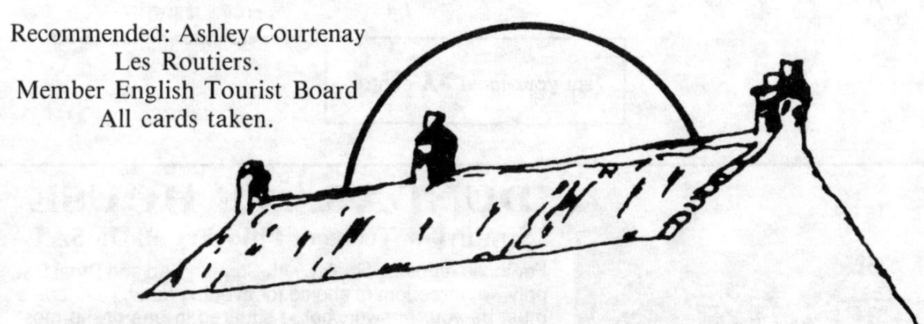

★ Secluded country setting.
★ 12 bedrooms, all en-suite.
★ 2 Four-poster rooms.
★ Tea making in all rooms.
★ Snug bar.
★ Colour TV all rooms.
★ Tennis court and solarium.
★ Cycle hire.
★ Fire certificate.
★ Bar meals, evening dinners.
★ Send for brochure to resident proprietors: Jean and Stephen Whitaker.

PITLOCHRY
Tayside *Perthshire*
Map **14** NN95
See plan

GH Adderley Private Hotel
23, Toberargan Rd ☎(0796) 2433
Plan **1** *C3*
Etr–mid Oct
Small family-run hotel, close to town centre.
8hc (3⇌) (1fb) Ⓡ B&b£10.80–£11.90 Bdi£16.80–£17.90 LDO5pm
CTV 9P nc6yrs
Ⓥ

Selected

GH Balrobin Hotel Higher Oakfield☎(0796) 2901 Plan **2** *D3*
Apr–13 Nov
A traditional Scottish stone house set in own grounds on elevated site with panoramic views. One can relax in well-appointed bedrooms, pleasant public rooms and enjoy the friendly atmosphere and personal attention provided by the owners.
12hc (1⇌ 9fl) (1fb) CTV in all bedrooms Ⓡ B&b£12–£15 Bdi£17.50–£23 WBdi£120–£155 LDO7.30pm
Lic 12P nc10rs
Ⓥ

GH Craigmore 27 West Moulin Rd ☎(0796) 2123 Plan **3** *C3*
Mar–Oct
A secluded location for this stone built house with cottage annexe. Comfortable, well-maintained accommodation.
7hc (2⇌ 5fl) Annexe: 7hc (3fl) (4fb) (ex in Annexe) B&b£10–£12.50 Bdi£17–£19.50 WBdifr£130 LDO6.30pm
Lic CTV 14P
Ⓥ

Selected

GH Dundarave House Strathview Ter ☎(0796) 3109 Plan **4** *B3*
Apr–Oct
A charming Victorian house, specialising in bed and breakfast only, set in formal terraced gardens in a secluded location. Quality accommodation with well appointed bedrooms and a comfortable period lounge. A hearty Scottish breakfast is served in the tastefully decorated dining room. The owners aim to provide personal and friendly attention in relaxing surroundings.
7hc (5⇌) (1fb) CTV in all bedrooms Ⓡ B&b£16.50–£17.50 WB&b£112–£119
7P
Ⓥ

GH Duntrune 22 East Moulin Rd ☎(0796) 2172 Plan **5** *D3*
Mar–Oct
Pleasantly furnished house.
7hc (5fl) (1fb) CTV in all bedrooms Ⓡ B&b£11.50–£12.50
8P nc5yrs
Ⓥ

GH Fasganeoin Hotel Perth Rd ☎(0796) 2387 Plan **6** *D2*
May–Oct rs Apr
Attractive large house standing in its own grounds at southern entrance to the town.
9hc (4fb) B&b£12–£14.50 Bdi£20.50–£23.50 WBdi£131.50–£152 LDO7.30pm
Lic 20P
Ⓥ

Visit your local AA centre

GH Faskally Home Farm ☎(0796) 2007
Plan **7** *A4*
Apr–Oct
Pleasant 'U-shaped' building on west side of B8019 north of Pitlochry. Sheltered from Loch Faskally by trees.
8rm (6hc) (2fb) P ✱B&b£8.50
P

GH Torrdarach Hotel Golf Course Rd ☎(0796) 2136 Plan **8** *B4*
Etr–mid Oct
7hc (1⇌ 2fl) CTV in all bedrooms Ⓡ B&b£13–£15.50 Bdi£19.50–£22 WBdifr£129.50 LDO5.45pm
Lic 8P
Ⓥ
See advertisement on page 328

GH Well House Private Hotel 11 Toberargan Rd ☎(0796) 2239 Plan **9** *C3*
Mar–Oct
Pleasant, small, family-run, private hotel offering wholesome dinners and personal attention.
6hc (3fl) (1fb) CTV in all bedrooms Ⓡ ✱B&b£11–£13 B&b£70–£80 LDO7.30pm
Lic CTV 8P
Credit cards 1 3

PLUCKLEY
Kent
Map **5** TQ94

FH Mrs F Harris **Elvey** *(TQ916457)* ☎(023384) 442
Detached converted oasthouse and stableblock with extensive views over the Weald. Comfortable bedrooms. Traditional meals served in Kentish Barn restaurant.
10hc (7⇌ 3fl) (6fb) CTV in all bedrooms Ⓡ ✱B&b£15.50–£25.50 Bdi£25.50–£35.50 WBdi£168.50–£248.50 LDO6pm
Lic 40P 75acres mixed
Credit cards 3 5 Ⓥ
See advertisement on page 328

Pitlochry

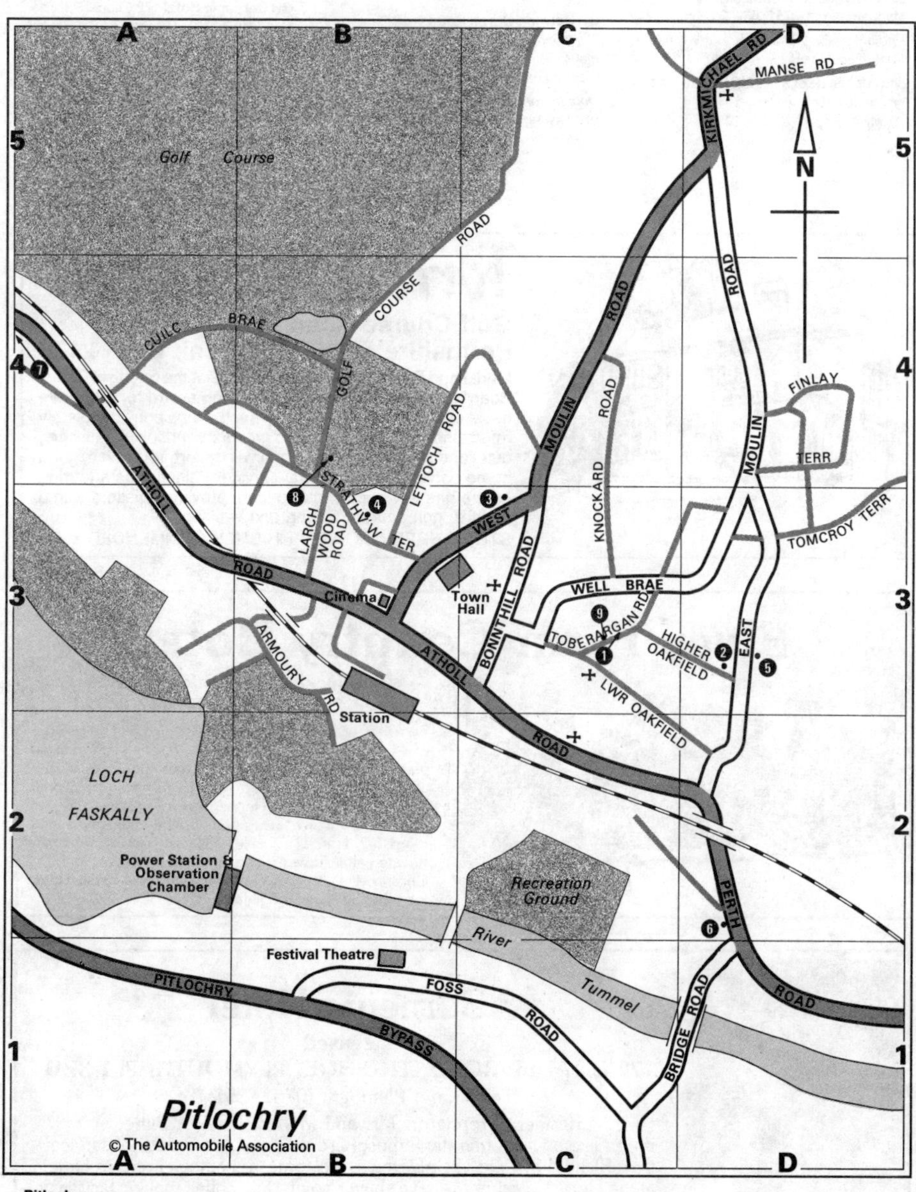

Pitlochry

1 Adderley Private Hotel
2 Balrobin Hotel
3 Craigmore
4 Dundarave
5 Duntrune
6 Fasganeoin Hotel
7 Faskally Home Farm
8 Torrdarach Hotel
9 Well House Private Hotel

PLYMOUTH
Devon
Map **2** SX45
See plan on pages 330–331

GH Benvenuto 69 Hermitage Rd, Mannamead ☎(0752) 667030 Plan **1** *E8*
End of terrace Victorian property 1 mile from the city centre.
8hc (1fb) Ⓡ B&b£9.50–£10 Bdi£13.50–£14 WBdifr£87.50
Lic 𝌆 CTV 2🚗
Ⓥ

Plymouth

GH Bowling Green Hotel 9–10 Osborne Pl, Lochyer St, The Hoe ☎(0752) 667485 Plan **2** *C2*
Closed Xmas
Double-fronted Georgian hotel overlooking Drake's famous bowling green.

12hc (3⇨ 1⋒) (3fb) CTV in all bedrooms Ⓡ ✱B&b£12–£17 WB&bfr£144
𝌆 CTV no P
Credit cards 1 3 Ⓥ

GH Carnegie Hotel 172 Citadel Rd, The Hoe ☎(0752) 225158 Plan **3** *B3*
Closed Xmas wk
9hc (2fb) ✖ Ⓡ LDO7.30pm
Lic 𝌆 CTV no P
Credit cards 1 2 3 5

GH Chester 54 Stuart Rd, Pennycomequick ☎ (0752) 663706 Plan **4** *A7*

Georgian House Hotel

and Fourposter Restaurant

51 Citadel Road, The Hoe, Plymouth
Telephone: (0752) 663237

All rooms are en suite with colour TV, tea and coffee making facilities, hair dryer, trouser press and direct dial telephone. Cocktail bar and candle-lit restaurant. Situated on The Hoe, 5 minutes from ferry. English and Continental cuisine cooked by proprietor's wife. All major credit cards taken.

Resident proprietors: Noel and Virginia Bhadha

Harrabeer Country House Hotel

Harrowbeer Lane, Yelverton, Devon PL20 6EA

Peacefully located on edge of Dartmoor yet only 9 miles from Plymouth this small friendly licensed hotel caters all year for those on business or on holiday. Comfortable bedrooms with en-suite facilities, colour television and tea/coffee makers. Superb freshly prepared food. Secluded gardens, moorland views, outdoor swimming pool. Golf, walking, fishing, riding, all nearby. Bargain breaks. Visa — Access — Amex — Diners.

Telephone: Yelverton (0822) 853302

See gazetteer entry under Yelverton

Drake's View Hotel

33, Grand Parade, West Hoe, Plymouth, Devon.
Telephone: (0752) 221500 Proprietress: Mrs. Jill Russell

Sample the delights of this popular hotel, favoured by world-wide yachtsmen, business people, actors from nearby Theatre Royal, honeymooners, families who just want to relax.

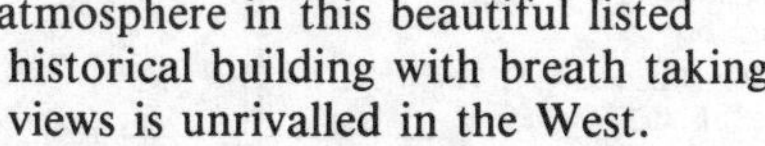

The welcoming, caring atmosphere in this beautiful listed historical building with breath taking views is unrivalled in the West.

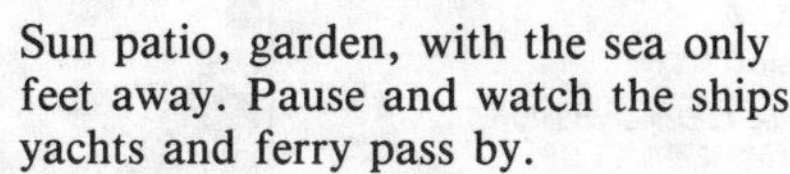

Sun patio, garden, with the sea only feet away. Pause and watch the ships, yachts and ferry pass by.

Tea and coffee making facilities, colour TV in all rooms, licensed bar, sun loungers provided, drinks served by your friendly proprietress. Central heating, pets welcome.
Highest Standards maintained.
Two minutes drive Brittany Ferry and Theatre Royal.

Plymouth

1 Benvenuto
2 Bowling Green Hotel
3 Carnegie Hotel
4 Chester
5 Cranbourne Hotel
6 Drakes View Hotel
7 Dudley
8 Gables End Hotel
9 Georgian House Hotel
10 Headland Hotel
11 Kildare
12 Lockyer House Hotel
13 Merville Hotel
14 Olivers Hotel
15 Riviera Hotel
16 Russell Lodge Hotel
17 St James Hotel
18 Smeaton's Tower
19 Trillium

Detached house in large, walled garden, 1m from city centre; walking distance to shops and Hoe.

11hc (2🚿) (2fb) CTV in all bedrooms ✱B&b£9.50–£12.50 Bdi£14.50–£17.50 LDO10am

Lic 卌 CTV 7P

GH Cranbourne Hotel 282 Citadel Rd, The Hoe ☎(0752) 263858 Plan **6** *C3*

Modern comforts are provided in this end of terrace Georgian hotel.

10hc (3fb) CTV in all bedrooms Ⓡ B&b£10–£14 WB&b£70–£98

Lic 卌 CTV 3🚗

Credit cards ① ③

GH Drakes View Hotel 33 Grande Pde, West Hoe ☎(0752) 221500 Plan **6** *B1*
Closed Xmas

Listed building facing Drake's Island with glorious views over the Sound. Comfortable bedrooms.

7hc (3fb) 🚭in all bedrooms CTV in all bedrooms Ⓡ B&b£12.50–£25

Lic 卌 CTV ⌂

Credit cards ① ③ Ⓥ

GH Dudley 42 Sutherland Rd, Mutley ☎(0752) 668322 Plan **7** *D8*
rs Xmas

Double-fronted house in quiet residential street.

6hc (3fb) CTV in all bedrooms Ⓡ B&b£10–£13 Bdifr£16 WBdifr£95 LDO9am

卌 CTV P

Credit cards ① ③

GH Gables End Hotel 29 Sutherland Rd, Mutley ☎(0752) 220803 Plan **8** *D7*

7hc (3fb) ✗ Ⓡ ✱B&b£10–£11 Bdi£15–£16 WBdifr£100 LDO4pm

卌 CTV 3🚗(charged)

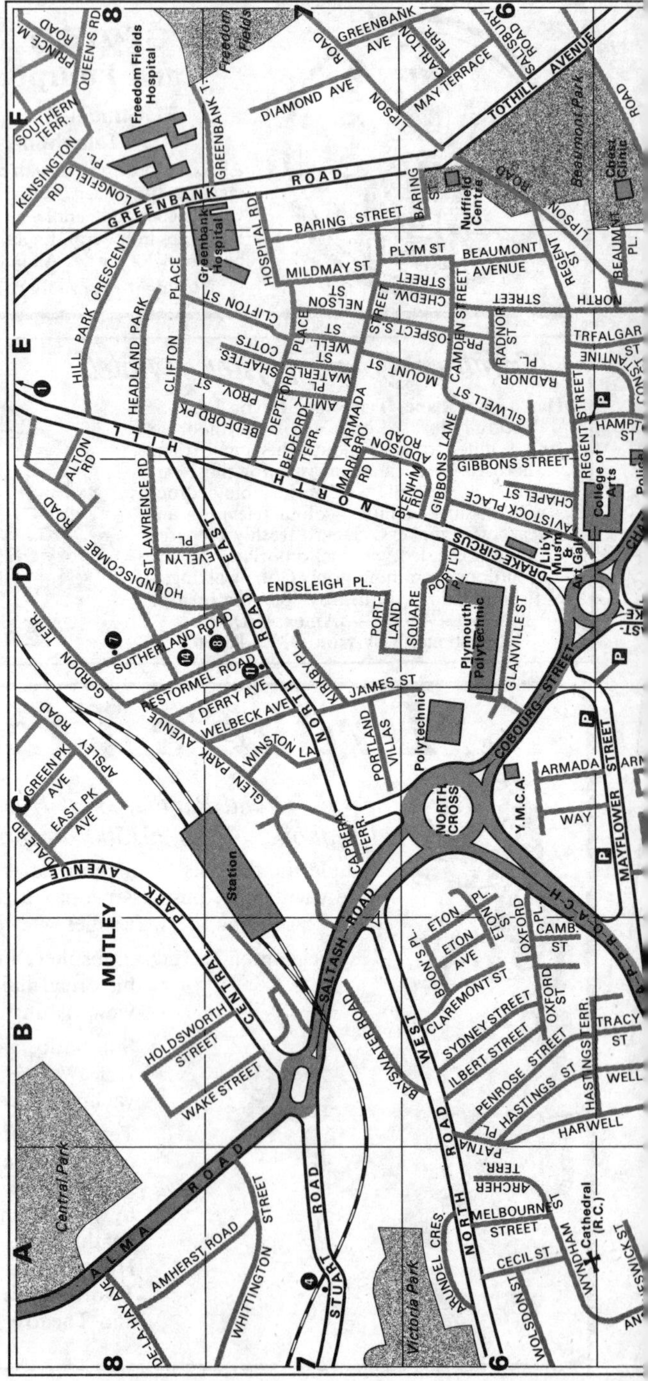

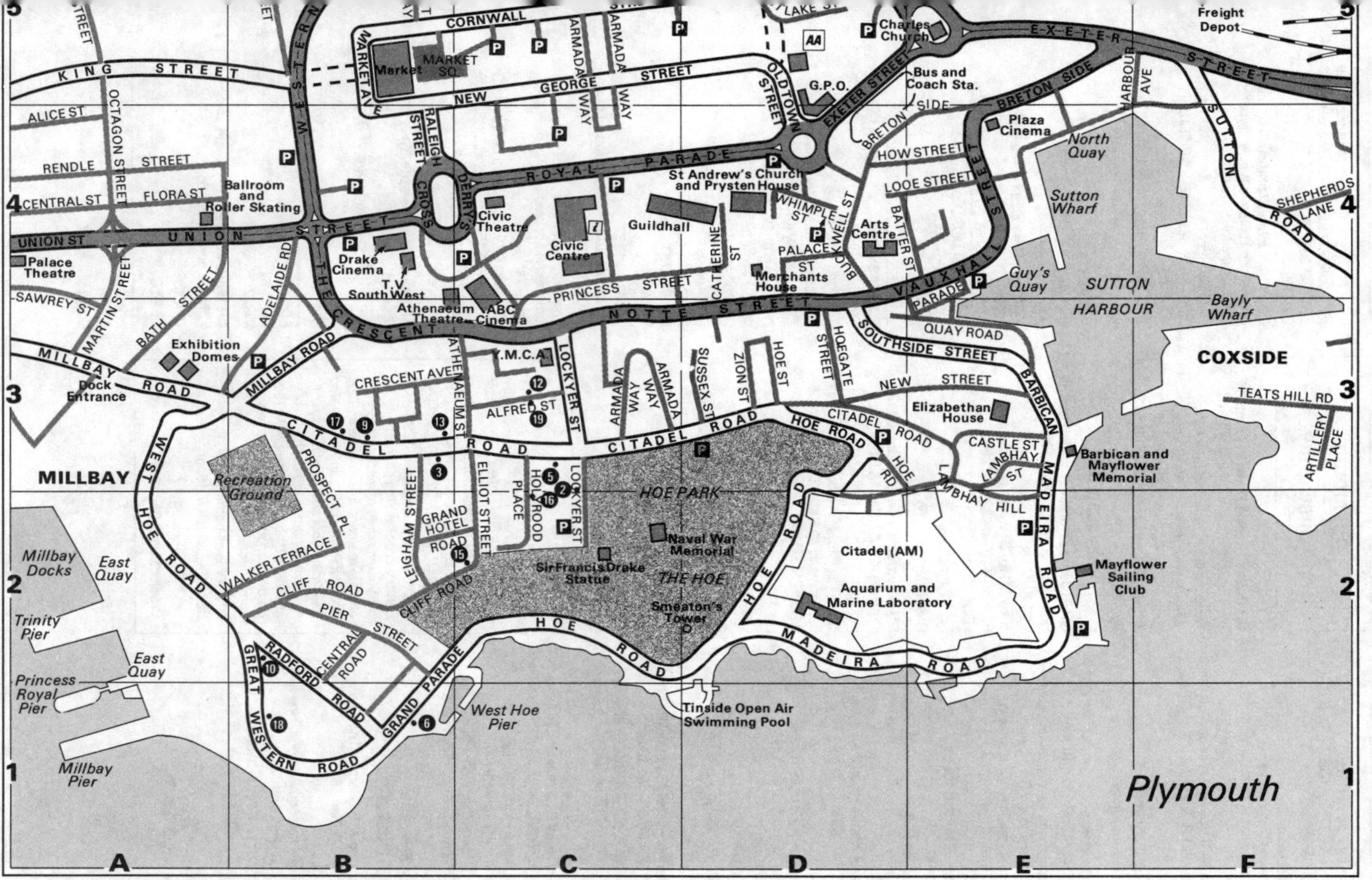

Plymouth
Freight Depot
CORNWALL
Market
MARKET SQ.
MARKET AVE
KING STREET
NEW GEORGE STREET
ARMADA WAY
OLDTOWN STREET
EXETER STREET
Charles Church
AA
G.P.O.
Bus and Coach Sta.
BRETON SIDE
HARBOUR AVE
SUTTON ROAD
SHEPHERDS LANE
ALICE ST
OCTAGON STREET
RENDLE STREET
CENTRAL ST
FLORA ST
Ballroom and Roller Skating
UNION ST
UNION STREET
Palace Theatre
SAWREY ST
MARTIN STREET
BATH STREET
ADELAIDE RD
WESTERN
RALEIGH STREET
DERRY'S CROSS
ROYAL PARADE
Civic Theatre
Drake Cinema
T.V. South West
Athenaeum Theatre
ABC Cinema
Civic Centre
Guildhall
St Andrew's Church and Prysten House
WHIMPLE ST
BUCKWELL ST
PALACE ST
Merchants House
CATHERINE ST
PRINCESS STREET
NOTTE STREET
THE CRESCENT
HOW STREET
LOOE STREET
BATTER ST
Arts Centre
Plaza Cinema
VAUXHALL STREET
PARADE
North Quay
Sutton Wharf
Guy's Quay
SUTTON HARBOUR
Bayly Wharf
COXSIDE
TEATS HILL RD
ARTILLERY PLACE
QUAY ROAD
SOUTHSIDE STREET
BARBICAN
NEW STREET
Elizabethan House
HOEGATE STREET
HOE ST
ZION ST
SUSSEX ST
ARMADA WAY
LOCKYER ST
Y.M.C.A.
ALFRED ST
ATHENAEUM ST
CRESCENT AVE
MILLBAY ROAD
Exhibition Domes
Dock Entrance
MILLBAY
CITADEL ROAD
HOE ROAD
CASTLE ST
LAMBHAY ST
LAMBHAY HILL
HOE RD
Barbican and Mayflower Memorial
HOE PARK
Naval War Memorial
Sir Francis Drake Statue
THE HOE
Smeaton's Tower
Citadel (AM)
Aquarium and Marine Laboratory
MADEIRA ROAD
Mayflower Sailing Club
Recreation Ground
PROSPECT PL.
LEIGHAM STREET
GRAND HOTEL ROAD
ELLIOT STREET
HOLYROOD PLACE
WEST HOE ROAD
WALKER TERRACE
CLIFF ROAD
PIER STREET
CENTRAL ROAD
RADFORD ROAD
GREAT WESTERN ROAD
GRAND PARADE
West Hoe Pier
Tinside Open Air Swimming Pool
Millbay Docks
East Quay
Trinity Pier
Princess Royal Pier
Millbay Pier
A
B
C
D
E
F
1
2
3
4
5

GH Georgian House Hotel 51 Citadel Rd, The Hoe ☎(0752) 663237 Plan **9** *B3*
Closed 23 Dec–5 Jan

Terraced hotel offering well-equipped bedrooms and imaginative menu. Situated close to the famous Hoe and the Barbican.

10hc (4⇌ 6⋒) (1fb) CTV in all bedrooms Ⓡ B&b£20–£21 Bdi£30–£32 LDO9.30pm

Lic ⅏ CTV 3P

Credit cards 1 2 3 5

See advertisement on page 329

GH *Headland Hotel* Radford Rd, West Hoe ☎(0752) 660866 Plan **10** *B2*

Lounge corner hotel with easy access to Plymouth Hoe and the Barbican.

Annexe: 28rm 15hc (7⇌ 6⋒) (5fb) Ⓡ

⅏ CTV

GH *Kildare* 82 North Road East ☎(0752) 29375 Plan **11** *D7*

8hc (1⇌) (3fb) ✗ Ⓡ

⅏ CTV ℗

GH Lockyer House Hotel 2 Alfred St, The Hoe ☎ (0752) 665755 Plan **12** *C3*
Closed Xmas

An end of terrace Georgian house situated in quiet side street, although close to city centre.

6hc (1fb) B&b£9.90 Bdi£17

Lic ⅏ CTV ℗

Ⓥ

⊢⊣**GH Merville Hotel** 73 Citadel Rd, The Hoe ☎(0752) 667595 Plan **13** *B3*

10hc (3fb) Ⓡ B&b£9–£10 Bdi£14.95–£15.95 WBdifr£104.65 LDO3pm

Lic ⅏ CTV 2P

GH Olivers Hotel 33 Sutherland Rd, The Hoe ☎(0752) 663923 Plan **14** *D8*

Victorian building with friendly atmosphere and excellent food.

6hc (1fb) CTV in all bedrooms ✗ Ⓡ B&b£13.50–£18 Bdi£21.50–£26 W£130–£161– LDOnoon

Lic ⅏ CTV 3P nc11yrs

Credit cards 1 2 3 5 Ⓥ

GH Riviera Hotel 8 Elliott St, The Hoe ☎(0752) 667379 Plan **15** *C2*
Closed Xmas

Personally run hotel on Plymouth Hoe with very well equipped bedrooms.

11hc (6⇌) (2fb) CTV in all bedrooms Ⓡ ✱B&b£13–£20 Bdi£19–£26 WBdi£128–£175 LDO9.30pm

Lic ⅏ ℗

Credit cards 1 2 3 5 Ⓥ

GH Russell Lodge Hotel 9 Holyrood Pl, The Hoe ☎(0752) 667774 Plan **16** *C2*

Terraced Georgian residence just 5 minutes walk from city centre.

10hc (2fb) CTV in all bedrooms ✗ Ⓡ ✱B&b£10.50–£11.50 WB&b£50–£72

⅏ CTV 3P

Credit cards 1 2 3 5 Ⓥ

GH St James Hotel 49 Citadel Rd, The Hoe ☎(0752) 661950 Plan **17** *B3*
Closed Xmas

10⇌⋒ (2fb) CTV in all bedrooms Ⓡ B&b£16–£20 Bdi£22.95–£26.95 LDO6.30pm

Lic ⅏ ℗ nc6yrs

Credit cards 1 3 Ⓥ

GH Smeaton's Tower 44 Grand Pde ☎(0752) 221007 Plan **18** *B1*
rs Xmas

18hc (1⋒) (5fb) ⅟in 4 bedrooms CTV in all bedrooms ✗ Ⓡ B&b£10–£15 Bdifr£15 WBdifr£105 LDO8.30pm

Lic ℗

Credit card 3

GH *Trillium* 4 Alfred St, The Hoe (Guestaccom) ☎ (0752) 670452 Plan **19** *C3*
Closed 2 wks Xmas

5hc (1fb) ✗ Ⓡ LDO4pm

Lic ⅏ CTV 3P nc5yrs

Credit cards 1 2 3

POCKLINGTON
Humberside
Map **8** SE74

Selected

GH Barnby Moor Country Hotel
Hull Rd Barnby Moor (Guestaccom) (2m W off A1079) ☎(0759) 302700

A converted and restored 17th-century coaching inn offering a pleasant mixture of modern and antique features. The original stables and stableyard now contain a heated swimming pool and there is also a half sized snooker table. The attractive dining room overlooks the garden and all bedrooms are very comfortable.

4⋒ CTV in all bedrooms ✗ Ⓡ B&b£19–£30 LDO7.15pm

Lic 30P ⩯(heated) U

Credit cards 1 3

⊢⊣**FH** Mr & Mrs Pearson **Meltonby Hall** *(SE 800524)* Meltonby (2m N unclass) ☎(0759) 303214
Etr–Oct

Large 18th-century farmhouse on the edge of the Yorkshire Wolds. Situated 2½m N of the town in attractive countryside.

2rm (1fb) ✗ B&b£7.50–£8 Bdi£12.50 WBdi£84

⅏ CTV P 118acres mixed

Ⓥ

POLBATHIC
Cornwall
Map **2** SX35

⊢⊣**GH Old Mill** ☎St Germans (0503) 30596

8hc (2fb) B&b£9–£9.50 Bdi£14–£16 WBdifr£95 LDO7.30pm

Lic CTV 12P 1🚗

Ⓥ

POLMASSICK
Cornwall
Map **2** SW94

GH Kilbol Country House Hotel ☎Mevagissey (0726) 842481

7hc (3⇌) (1fb) B&b£13.80–£17.25 Bdi£19.55–£21.85 WBdifr£133.40

Lic ⅏ CTV 12P ⩯

Credit cards 1 2 3 5 Ⓥ

POLPERRO
Cornwall
Map **2** SX25

GH Landaviddy Manor Landaviddy Ln ☎(0503) 72210

Charming country house of Cornish stone, furnished in keeping with its style and character.

10hc (4⋒) CTV available in bedrooms Ⓡ ✱B&b£11–£15 Bdi£18–£24 LDO8.30am

Lic ⅏ CTV 12P 1🚗 nc5yrs

Credit cards 1 2 3 Ⓥ

GH Lanhael House ☎(0503) 72428
Mar–Oct

6hc (1⋒) ⅟ in all bedrooms ✗ B&b£12–£18

⅏ CTV 7P nc14yrs ⩯

POLZEATH
Cornwall
Map **2** SW97

GH *White Lodge* Old Polzeath ☎Trebetherick (020886) 2370

10hc (2fb)

Lic ⅏ CTV 10P

PONSWORTHY
Devon
Map **3** SX77

FH Mr & Mrs Fursdon **Old Walls** *(SX697745)* ☎Poundsgate (03643) 222
Mar–Oct

Farmhouse standing in its own small estate in isolated position, on Dartmoor. Pleasant atmosphere.

3rm B&b£11.77–£14.77

▥ 4P 36acres calf rearing

PONTARDULAIS
West Glamorgan
Map **2** SN50

FH Mr & Mrs G Davies ***Croft*** *(SN612015)* Heol-y-Barna ☎(0792) 883654
Closed Xmas & New Year

Situated in elevated position with open aspect to the Gower Peninsula and the Loughor Estuary. Approx ½m from A48.

3hc (1fb) LDOnoon

▥ CTV 3P nc5yrs 5 acres beef small holding

PONTFAEN
Dyfed
Map **2** SN03

FH Mrs S Heard **Tregynon** *(SN054345)* ☎Newport(0239) 820531

A comfortable, beamed 16th-century farmhouse in the foothills of the Preseli mountains. Vegetarian and wholefood meals are a speciality. 3m E of village, off unclass road joining B4313 and Newport. 5m from Newport sands.

6hc (2⊓) (3fb) ✈ Ⓡ B&b£11.50–£14.50 Bdi£18–£21 WBdi£119–£140 LDO8.45pm

Lic ▥ CTV P ⌂ 10acres sheep

Ⓥ

PONTLLYFNI
Gwynedd
Map **6** SH45

GH Bron Dirion Hotel ☎Clynnogfawr (028686) 346
Mar–Oct

Detached country house in quiet rural situation.

9hc (4fb) ✱B&bfr£10 Bdifr£14.50 WBdifr£92 LDO6.30pm

Lic ▥ CTV 10P

Ponsworthy — Porlock

PONTYPRIDD
Mid Glamorgan
Map **3** ST09

INN White Hart Hotel 1 High St ☎(0443) 405922

Central location amidst shops. Traditional, popular hostelry with disco bar and pool. Well-fitted bedrooms.

4hc (1fb) CTV in all bedrooms ✈ Ⓡ B&bfr£18

Lic ▥ CTV 15P snooker

POOLE
Dorset
Map **4** SZ09
For locations and additional guesthouses see **Bournemouth**

GH Avoncourt Private Hotel 245 Bournemouth Rd, Parkstone ☎(0202) 732025 Branksome & Westbourne plan **61** *A3*

Simple guesthouse with comfortable bedrooms and lounge.

6hc (3fb) ✈ B&b£8.50–£15 Bdi£13–£19 WBdifr£85

Lic ▥ CTV 5P 1🚗

Credit Cards

1 Access/Euro/Mastercard
2 American Express
3 Barclaycard/Visa
5 Diners

GH Grovefield Hotel 18 Pinewood Rd, Branksome Park ☎(0202) 766798 Branksome & Westbourne plan **67** *A1*
Mar–Sep

An attractive, quietly situated small hotel.

11hc (7⇌) (2fb) CTV in 7 bedrooms Ⓡ B&b£17.30–£21.80 Bdi£23.70–£29 WBdi£115–£157 LDO5pm

Lic ▥ CTV 12P nc5yrs

GH *Redcroft Hotel*
20 Pinewood Rd, Branksome Park ☎(0202) 763959 Branksome & Westbourne plan **73** *B1*

Situated in a quiet residential area opposite entrance to Branksome Dene Chine. Comfortable, well-furnished rooms.

10hc (4⇌ 1⊓) (3fb) CTV in all bedrooms ✈ Ⓡ LDO4.30pm

Lic ▥ CTV 12P nc5yrs

GH Sheldon Lodge 22 Forest Rd, Branksome Park ☎(0202) 761186 Branksome & Westbourne plan **75** *A2*
Closed Xmas & New Year

Detached guesthouse in quiet area with attractive public rooms and good bedrooms.

14hc (8⇌ 6⊓) (4fb) Ⓡ B&b£15.50–£20 Bdi£21.50–£26 WBdi£126–£150 LDO7pm

Lic ▥ CTV 13P solarium

Ⓥ

PORLOCK
Somerset
Map **3** SS84

GH Gables Hotel ☎(0643) 862552
Mar–Oct

7hc (1⇌) Ⓡ B&b£11–£12.50 Bdi£18–£19.50 WBdi£120–£128 LDO10.30am

Lic ▥ CTV ▶ nc12yrs

Ⓥ

GH Lorna Doone Hotel High St ☎(0643) 862404

A comfortable guesthouse offering good home-cooking. →

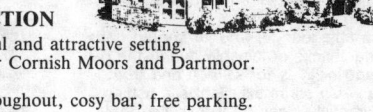

11hc (1⇌ 1⋔) (2fb) ✖ ✻B&b£11.50–£13.50 Bdi£17.50 WBdi£113.50 LDO8.30pm

Lic 卌 CTV 9P

Credit cards 1 3 Ⓥ

GH Overstream Parson St ☎ (0643) 862421
Etr–Oct

8hc (4⋔) (3fb) CTV in all bedrooms ✖ ✻B&b£10.50–£13 Bdi£15.50–£18 WBdifr£108.50 LDO7pm

Lic lift 15P

PORTESHAM
Dorset
Map **3** SY68

GH Millmead Country Goose Hill ☎Abbotsbury (0305) 871432
Feb–Nov

The friendly proprietors offer good facilities, comfortable bedrooms and wholesome food. A non-smoking establishment.

8hc (2⇌ 2⋔) (1fb) ✗ in all bedrooms CTV in all bedrooms B&bfr£15 Bdifr£24.25 WBdifr£154 LDO6pm

Lic 卌 12P nc10yrs

Credit cards 1 3 Ⓥ

PORTHALLOW
Cornwall
Map **2** SW72

GH Gallen Treath ☎St Keverne (0326) 280400
Closed Dec

Offering comfort and good food in attractive surroundings.

6hc (2⋔) (2fb) CTV in all bedrooms Ⓡ B&bfr£10.50 Bdifr£14.50 WBdifr£94

Lic 卌 CTV 5P

Credit cards 1 2 3 5

See advertisement under Lizard

PORTHCAWL
Mid Glamorgan
Map **3** SS87

⊢⊣**GH Collingwood Hotel** 40 Mary St ☎(065671) 2899

Modestly appointed establishment.

8hc (4fb) B&b£9 Bdi£13.50 WBdi£87 LDO5pm

Lic 卌 CTV P̸

Credit card 3 Ⓥ

⊢⊣**GH Minerva Private Hotel** 52 Esplanade Av (Guestaccom) ☎(065671) 2428

8hc (2⇌) (3fb) CTV in all bedrooms Ⓡ B&b£9 Bdi£14 WBdi£95 LDO6pm

Lic 卌 CTV P̸

Ⓥ

PORTHCOTHAN BAY
Cornwall
Map **2** SW87

GH *Bay House* ☎Padstow (0841) 520472
28 Mar–3 Oct

17hc (1fb)

Lic CTV 17P

PORTHCURNO
Cornwall
Map **2** SW32

⊢⊣**FH** Mr M B Silcox **Corniché Trebehor** *(SW376244)* ☎Penzance (0736) 871685
Feb–Oct rs Xmas

Well appointed, modern farmhouse. Situated 2m from village, 2m from Lands End and 8m from Penzance. Ideal for touring.

6hc (1fb) B&b£8.50–£10 Bdi£12.50–£14 WBdi£82–£94 (W only Jul & Aug) LDO4.30pm

Lic 卌 CTV 8P nc6yrs 200acres dairy

Ⓥ

PORTHMADOG
Gwynedd
Map **6** SH53

⊢⊣**GH Oakleys** The Harbour ☎(0766) 512482
Apr–Nov

Detached Victorian house in quiet town position.

8hc (1⇌ 2⋔) (3fb) ✖ B&b£8.50–£9.50 Bdi£13.50–£15 WBdi£90–£100 LDO5pm

Lic CTV 18P nc5yrs

Ⓥ

GH Owen's Hotel High St ☎(0766) 512098
Mar–Oct

A small family hotel in the town centre.

11hc (3⇌ 3⋔) (3fb) CTV in 7 bedrooms Ⓡ B&b£12–£16 Bdi£17–£21 WBdifr£110 LDO6pm

Lic 卌 CTV 3P 5🚗

Credit card 1 Ⓥ

PORTHTOWAN
Cornwall
Map **2** SW64

GH Porthtowan Beach Hotel ☎(0209) 890228

This family holiday hotel enjoys spectacular views from its elevated position.

17hc (1⇌ 10⋔) (5fb) B&b£12–£13 Bdi£17.50 WBdifr£115 LDO5pm

Lic 卌 CTV 16P pool table

Ⓥ

PORT ISAAC
Cornwall
Map **2** SW98

GH Bay Hotel 1 The Terrace ☎Bodmin (0208) 880380
Etr–Oct

Double-fronted building in elevated position overlooking sea.

11hc (5fb) B&b£11–£13.50 Bdi£16–£19 WBdi£94–£114.50 LDO7pm

Lic CTV 10P

GH *Fairholme* 30 Trewetha Ln ☎Bodmin (0208) 880397
rs Xmas

Detached double-fronted building on main road leading to Port Isaac.

7hc (3fb) ✖ LDO10am

卌 CTV 8P

GH St Andrews Hotel The Terrace
☎Bodmin (0208) 880240
Mar–Nov

Personally-run hotel with lovely views of sea and countryside.

13hc (3⇌ 4fl) (5fb) ® B&b£12.50–£16.50 Bdi£21–£25 WBdi£134.50–£155.50 LDO8.30pm

Lic ₩ CTV 14P

PORTNANCON
Highland *Sutherland*
Map **14** NC46

GH Port-na-Con House Loch Eriboll
☎Durness (097181) 367
Mar–Oct rs Feb & Nov

Beautifully located on W shore of Loch Eriboll by the old pier. A former harbour store converted to provide compact, comfortable accommodation.

4hc (2fb) ® B&b£9.50–£13.50 Bdi£16.75–£20.75

Lic ₩ 6P

Credit card 3

PORTON
Wiltshire
Map **4** SU13

INN Porton Hotel ☎Idmiston (0980) 610203

8hc CTV in all bedrooms B&b£12.50–£15 WB&bfr£105 Lunch £5alc Dinner10pm £6alc

₩ 30P 2

Credit cards 1 3 Ⓥ

See advertisement under Salisbury

PORTPATRICK
Dumfries & Galloway *Wigtownshire*
Map **10** NX05

GH Blinkbonnie School Brae ☎(077681) 282

Jan–Oct

Extremely well-maintained, extended bungalow with outstanding views of village and harbour. Accommodation is bright and compact and the friendly proprietors provide good meals.

6hc (1fb) ® *B&b£8.50–£11.50 Bdi£14–£17 LDO5pm

₩ CTV 10P

PORTREATH
Cornwall
Map **2** SW64

INN *Portreath Arms* The Square
☎(0209) 842534

7hc (5fl) CTV in all bedrooms ® LDO9pm

50P nc14yrs

Credit card 3

PORTREE
Isle of Skye, Highland *Inverness-shire*
See **Skye, Isle of**

PORT ST MARY
Isle of Man
See **Man, Isle of**

PORTSMOUTH & SOUTHSEA
Hants
Map **4** SZ69
See plan on pages 336–337

GH *Abbeville Hotel* 26 Nettlecomb Av, Southsea ☎(0705) 826209 Plan **1** *F2*

Delightful family hotel with a warm, friendly atmosphere, furnished to include homely bric-a-brac and antiques. Bedrooms are comfortable and there is good home cooking.

11hc (2fb)

₩ CTV P

See advertisement on page 338

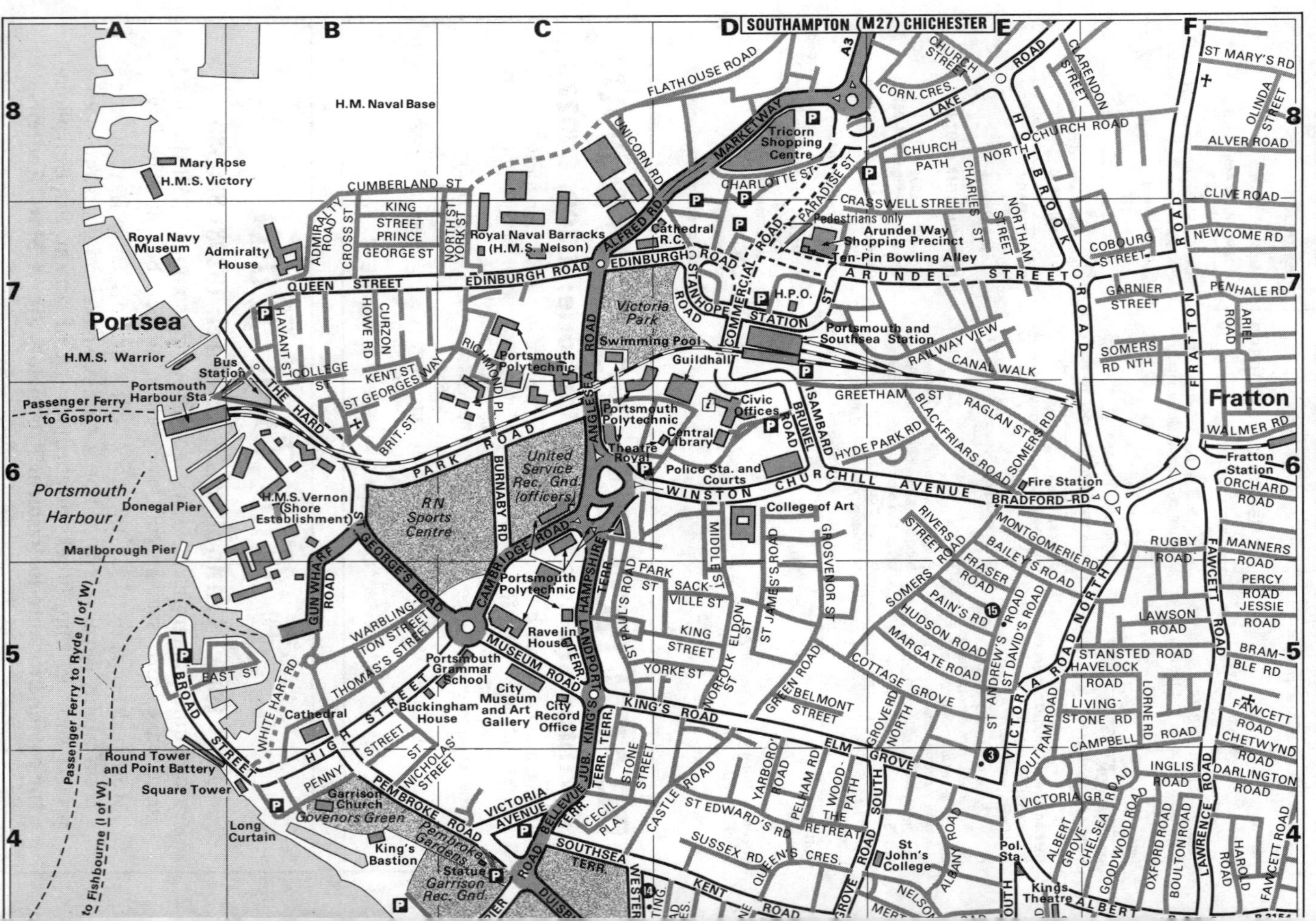
SOUTHAMPTON (M27) CHICHESTER
Fratton
Fratton Station
FRATTON ROAD
FAWCETT ROAD
HOLBROOK ROAD
ARUNDEL STREET
Tricorn Shopping Centre
MARKETWAY
Arundel Way Shopping Precinct
Ten-Pin Bowling Alley
Pedestrians only
COMMERCIAL ROAD
Portsmouth and Southsea Station
H.P.O.
Civic Offices
Guildhall
Central Library
Police Sta. and Courts
College of Art
Victoria Park
Swimming Pool
Portsmouth Polytechnic
Theatre Royal
Cathedral R.C.
ANGLESEA ROAD
HAMPSHIRE TERR
LANDPORT TERR.
KING'S TERR.
WINSTON CHURCHILL AVENUE
VICTORIA ROAD NORTH
ELM GROVE
KING'S ROAD
Kings Theatre
Pol. Sta.
St John's College
United Service Rec. Gnd. (officers)
BURNABY RD
RN Sports Centre
PARK ROAD
CAMBRIDGE ROAD
MUSEUM ROAD
Ravelin House
City Museum and Art Gallery
City Record Office
Portsmouth Grammar School
Buckingham House
Royal Naval Barracks (H.M.S. Nelson)
EDINBURGH ROAD
QUEEN STREET
THE HARD
H.M. Naval Base
Mary Rose
H.M.S. Victory
Royal Navy Museum
Admiralty House
Bus Station
Portsmouth Harbour Sta
H.M.S. Warrior
Portsea
Passenger Ferry to Gosport
Portsmouth Harbour
Donegal Pier
Marlborough Pier
H.M.S. Vernon (Shore Establishment)
GUN WHARF ROAD
ST GEORGE'S ROAD
HIGH STREET
Cathedral
WHITE HART RD
BROAD STREET
EAST ST
Round Tower and Point Battery
Square Tower
Long Curtain
King's Bastion
Garrison Church
Govenors Green
Pembroke Gardens
Statue
Garrison Rec. Gnd.
PEMBROKE ROAD
Passenger Ferry to Ryde (I of W)
to Fishbourne (I of W)
A3
A
B
C
D
E
F
4
5
6
7
8

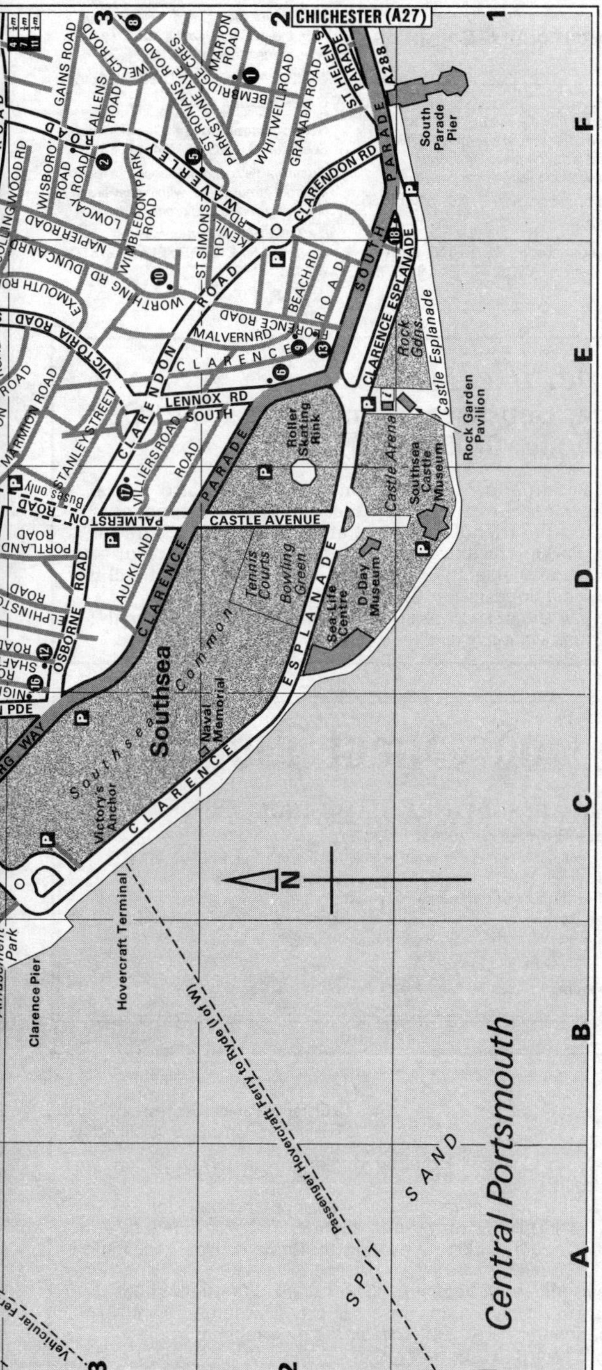

Portsmouth

1 Abbeville Hotel
2 Amberley Court
3 Astor House
4 Beaufort Hotel
5 Birchwood
6 Bristol Hotel
7 Chequers Hotel
8 Collingham
9 Gainsborough House
10 Goodwood House
11 Lyndhurst
12 Orleans
13 Rock Gardens Hotel
14 Ryde View
15 St Andrews Lodge
16 Somerset Private Hotel
17 Upper Mount House Hotel
18 White House Hotel

GH Amberley Court 97 Waverley Rd, Southsea ☎(0705) 735419 Plan **2** *F3*

Pleasant family-run guesthouse of some quality.

9hc (1fl) (3fb) ✗ Ⓡ B&b£10 Bdi£14.50 WBdifr£75 LDO5.30pm

CTV ✗

GH Astor House 4 St Andrew's Rd, Southsea ☎(0705) 755171 Plan **3** *E4*

Very comfortable and homely establishment with antique furniture.

7hc (4fb) CTV in all bedrooms Ⓡ B&b£9.50–£10 WB&bfr£65

CTV ✗

Ⓥ

GH *Beaufort Hotel* 71 Festing Rd, Southsea ☎(0705) 823707 Plan **4** *F3*
Closed Xmas

Smart, homely, comfortable hotel close to gardens and seafront. Modern, well-equipped bedrooms, separate lounge and basement dining room.

16hc (2⇨) (5fb) ✗ in 2 bedrooms ✗

CTV 8P nc3yrs

Credit Cards 1 3

GH Birchwood 44 Waverley Rd, Southsea ☎(0705) 811337 Plan **5** *F3*

Small terraced guesthouse situated some distance from the sea front. Comfortable, if old-fashioned, bedrooms.

6hc (2fl) (2fb) ✗ in 2 bedrooms CTV in all bedrooms ✗ Ⓡ B&b£9.50–£12 Bdi£13.50–£16 WBdi£75–£90 LDO6pm

CTV ✗

See advertisement on page 338

GH Bristol Hotel 55 Clarence Pde, Southsea ☎(0705) 821815 Plan **6** *E2*
Closed Xmas

Four-storey Victorian house overlooking seafront gardens and Southsea Common.

13hc (9fl) (7fb) CTV in 9 bedrooms TV in 4 bedrooms ✗ (ex guide dogs) Ⓡ B&b£13.50–£15.50 Bdi£18.50–£20.50 WBdifr£120 →

Lic CTV 7P

Credit cards 1 3 Ⓥ

GH Chequers Hotel Salisbury Rd, Southsea ☏(0705) 735277 Plan **7** *F3*

Comfortable hotel in quiet residential area with simple accommodation and good public areas.

13hc (3fb) TV in 2 bedrooms B&b£15–£16 Bdi£21–£22 WBdi£85–£110 LDO6.30pm

Lic CTV 12P

Credit cards 1 3 Ⓥ

GH Collingham 89 St Ronans Rd, Southsea ☏(0705) 821549 Plan **8** *F3*
Closed 24–26 Dec

Portsmouth & Southsea

Compact, friendly establishment with comfortable modern bedrooms. Well-maintained accommodatioan with combined lounge and dining room.

6hc (3fb) Ⓡ B&b£9.50–£10.50 WB&bfr£63

CTV

GH Gainsborough House 9 Malvern Rd, Southsea ☏(0705) 822604 Plan **9** *E2*

Well-established guesthouse, 2 minutes from the sea front, with a warm, welcoming atmosphere.

7hc (2fb) Ⓡ B&b£9.50–£10 WB&bfr£63

CTV nc3yrs

GH Goodwood House 1 Taswell Rd, Southsea ☏(0705) 824734 Plan **10** *E3*

Comfortable accommodation in a friendly informal atmosphere, within easy reach of shopping centre and promenade.

8hc (1fb) TV in all bedrooms Ⓡ ✱B&b£12.50–£13.50 Bdi£17.50–£18.50 WBdifr£111

Lic

GH Lyndhurst 8 Festing Gv, Southsea ☎(0705) 735239 Plan **11** *F3*

Cosy guesthouse with a homely atmosphere and a good level of comfort. Compact dining room and separate TV lounge.

7hc Ⓡ B&bfr£10 Bdifr£13.50–£14 WBdifr£78.75 LDOnoon

ᛗ CTV ₱

GH Orleans 37 Shaftesbury Rd, Southsea ☎(0705) 812424 Plan **12** *D3*

A personally run small house with comfortable and clean accommodation.

Portsmouth & Southsea

6hc (2fb) ✈ Ⓡ B&b£9

CTV 3P

GH Rock Gardens Hotel Clarence Rd Southsea ☎(0705) 833018 Plan **13** *E2*
Closed Xmas

Quietly-situated house with modern bedrooms and a large dining room. Bar and separate lounge. Friendly, personal service is offered at this family-run establishment.

14hc (6⇌ 6fl) (1fb) CTV in all bedrooms ✈ Ⓡ ✱B&b£13–£17 Bdi£19.50–£23.50 WBdi£95–£130 LDO7pm

Lic ᛗ CTV 8P

Credit cards 1 3

GH Ryde View 9 Western Pde, Southsea ☎(0705) 820865 Plan **14** *C4*
Closed Xmas

Family hotel overlooking common with sea views from front-facing bedrooms. Close to all amenities. Accommodation is modern and well-equipped with bedrooms on four floors, a basement dining room and comfortable lounge bar.

→

14hc (6fl) (6fb) CTV in all bedrooms ® B&b£12–£18.50

Lic ¶¶ CTV ₱

Credit cards 1 5 ⓥ

GH St Andrews Lodge
65 St Andrews Rd, Southsea ☎(0705) 827079 Plan **15** *E5*
Closed 20 Dec–2 Jan

Bright, modern bedrooms and friendly service at this comfortable guesthouse.

9hc (5fb) TV in 1 bedroom ✗ ® ✻B&b£10.50–£11 WB&bfr£66.50

¶¶ CTV ₱

ⓥ

Credit Cards

1 Access/Euro/Mastercard

2 American Express

3 Barclaycard/Visa

5 Diners

GH Somerset Private Hotel 16 Western Pde, Southsea ☎(0705) 822495
Plan **16** *C3*

Well-maintained and efficiently managed with a friendly atmosphere. Some bedrooms on the top floors have extensive views of the harbour.

19hc (5fl) (8fb) CTV in all bedrooms ® B&b£15 Bdi£19–£21 WBdifr£126–£135 LDO7.15pm

Lic ¶¶ CTV ₱

Credit cards 1 3 ⓥ

GH Upper Mount House Hotel The Vale, Clarendon Rd, Southsea ☎(0705) 820456
Plan **17** *D3*

Listed three-storey building set to the rear of a main road in a quiet lane.

11hc (2⇌ 7fl) (3fb) CTV in all bedrooms ® B&b£13–£18.50 Bdi£18–£24 WBdi£90–£128 LDO6pm

Lic ¶¶ CTV 7P

Credit cards 1 3 ⓥ

GH White House Hotel 26 South Parade, Southsea ☎(0705) 823709 Plan **18** *F2*
Closed Xmas

A small, exclusive hotel facing the sea. Some of the modern bedrooms have sea views.

14hc (5fl) (1fb) CTV in all bedrooms ® ✻B&b£11.50–£19 Bdi£18.50–£26 WBdifr£117 LDO7pm

Lic ¶¶ CTV ₱

Credit cards 1 2 3 5

POUNDSGATE
Devon
Map **3** SX77

GH Leusdon Lodge (Guestaccom)
☎(03643) 304

150-year-old granite-built house on edge of Dartmoor, offering traditional English fare.

9hc (2⇌ 1fl) (2fb) CTV available in bedrooms ® ✻B&b£10.50–£22 Bdi£22–£30 WBdi£163–£200 LDO8pm

Lic ¶¶ CTV 12P

Credit cards 1 2 3 5

PRAA SANDS
Cornwall
Map **2** SW52

GH La Connings ☎Penzance (0736) 762380
May–Sep

Chalet-style guesthouse surrounded by farmland and adjacent coast.

6hc (1⇨ 2🚿) (2fb) ✱B&b£8–£13 Bdi£13–£18 WBdi£91–£126 LDO6pm

Lic 🍽 CTV 8P ⛺ ⛱(heated)

GH White House Hotel Castle Dr ☎Penzance (0736) 762100
Apr–Oct

Friendly, relaxed hotel, with an easy, level walk to the beach.

10hc (3fb) TV available in bedrooms ✗ Ⓡ ✱B&b£10–£12 Bdi£17–£19 WBdi£110–£124 LDOnoon

Lic 🍽 CTV 12P

Credit cards 1 3 Ⓥ

See advertisement under Penzance

PRESTATYN
Clwyd
Map **6** SJ08

GH Bryn Gwalia Inn 17 Gronant Rd ☎(07456) 2442
rs 23 Dec–2 Jan

Edwardian house in residential area, short walk to shops.

8hc (1⇨ 4🚿) (1fb) CTV in all bedrooms ✗ Ⓡ B&b£18–£22 Bdi£22–£32 WBdi£135–£190 LDO9pm

Lic 🍽 24P

Credit card 1

GH Hawarden House 13 Victoria Rd ☎(07456) 4226

6hc (5fb) CTV in 5 bedrooms ✱B&b£7.50–£9.50 Bdi£11–£13 WBdifr£63 LDO11am

Lic 🍽 CTV 5P

Ⓥ

PRESTEIGNE
Powys
Map **3** SO36

FH Mrs K Owens **Broadheath** *(SO339633)* ☎(0544) 267416
Apr–Oct

Charming character farmhouse in secluded position.

3rm (2hc) (1fb) ✗ Ⓡ ✱B&b£9–£10 WB&b£60–£67

CTV 3P 300acres mixed

Ⓥ

PRESTON
Lancashire
Map **7** SD52

GH Fulwood Park Hotel 49 Watling Street Rd ☎(0772) 718067
Closed Xmas Day & Boxing Day

Extensively modernised family-run hotel.

20hc (7⇨ 7🚿) (2fb) CTV in 6 bedrooms TV in 4 bedrooms ✗ (ex guide dogs) Ⓡ B&b£17.87–£22 Bdi£24–£29 LDO7.15pm

Lic CTV 24P 1🚘 ♿

Credit cards 1 2 3 5 Ⓥ

GH Tulketh Private Hotel 209 Tulketh Rd, Ashton ☎(0772) 728096

Comfortable modern accommodation is provided in this Victorian-style hotel.

7hc (1🚿) (1fb) CTV in 3 bedrooms TV in 4 bedrooms Ⓡ B&b£22.40–£27.60 Bdi£31–£36.22 WBdifr£227.70 LDO7.30pm

Lic 🍽 CTV 20P

Credit card 1 Ⓥ

GH Withy Trees 175 Garstang Rd, Fullwood ☎(0772) 717693
Closed Xmas

Mainly commercial, simple-style guesthouse offering bed-and-breakfast only. 2m N on A6.

10hc (2fb) ✗ B&b£11–£12 WB&b£77–£84

20P

Ⓥ

PRESTWICK
Strathclyde *Ayrshire*
Map **10** NS32

GH Fairways 19 Links Rd ☎(0292) 70396

Nicely appointed with bright cheerful bedrooms. Overlooking the golf course.

→

6hc (1fb) B&b£11.50–£12.50 Bdi£15.50–£19 WBdifr£103

Lic 🍽 CTV 8P ⌂

Ⓥ

Selected

GH Fernbank 213 Main St ☎(0292) 75027

Mr and Mrs Wright offer first-class hospitality in a relaxed and friendly atmosphere at their comfortable, tastefully-appointed guesthouse. Bedrooms are bright and attractive – four have en-suite facilities. Two small but cosy lounges and good home cooking add to the appeal of Fernbank.

7hc (4ﬁ) ✗ B&b£11–£14 Bdi£17–£20 WBdi£116–£137 LDO5.30pm

🍽 CTV 7P nc5yrs

Ⓥ

GH Kincraig Private Hotel 39 Ayr Rd ☎(0292) 79480

Attractive red-sandstone villa on main road with neatly appointed good-sized rooms.

6hc (1fb) Ⓡ B&b£10 Bdi£15 WBdifr£100 LDO5pm

Lic 🍽 CTV 8P nc3yrs

PWLLHELI
Gwynedd
Map **6** SH33

GH *Sea Haven Hotel* West End Pde ☎(0758) 612572
Apr–Nov

Friendly holiday hotel facing a lovely sandy beach.

10hc (4ﬁ) (8fb) CTV in 8 bedrooms Ⓡ LDO10pm

Lic CTV P

Credit cards 1 2 3

⊢⊣**FH** Mrs M Hughes **Bryn Crin** *(SH379358)* ☎(0758) 612494
Apr–Oct

Large spacious farmhouse situated on hillside with panoramic views of Cardigan Bay and Snowdonia. Situated off unclass road.

3rm (2hc) (2fb) ✗ B&b£8.50–£9 WB&bfr£56

CTV 3P 80acres sheep

Ⓥ

FH Mrs J E Ellis **Gwynfryn** *(SH364357)* ☎(0758) 612536
Closed Xmas

Large granite-built farmhouse, surrounded by 2 acres of gardens and woodland, bordered to the south by a stream. 1m NW.

3hc ✗ ✱B&b£7.50–£10 Bdi£12.50–£15 Wfr£49.50 M

🍽 CTV 3P nc7yrs 90acres dairy

QUEEN CAMEL
Somerset
Map **3** ST52

INN Mildmay Arms ☎Yeovil (0935) 850456

7hc (2ﬁ) (2fb) CTV in all bedrooms Ⓡ ✱B&b£12.50–£17.50 Bdi£25 LDO10pm

35P snooker

Credit card 1 2

See advertisement under Yeovil

RAGLAN
Gwent
Map **3** SO40

INN *Cripple Creek* Bryngwyn (2m W off A40) ☎(0291) 690256

Off old Abergavenny rd, ¾ mile from Raglan. Modern Accommodation combined with old-world charm.

3hc LDO10.30pm

🍽 CTV 40P

RAMSGATE
Kent
Map **5** TR36

⊢⊣**GH Jalna Hotel** 49 Vale Sq ☎Thanet (0843) 593848
Closed Xmas

Located in a quiet residential part of the town, with well-maintained bedrooms and a basement dining room.

9hc (5ﬁ) (5fb) ✗ B&b£9–£12 Bdi£13.50–£16 WBdi£70–£91 LDOnoon

Lic 🍽 CTV 3P nc2yrs

Ⓥ

GH St Hilary Private Hotel 21 Crescent Rd ☎Thanet (0843) 591427

Cheerful compact bedrooms, basement dining room, situated in residential area.

7hc (4fb) ✗ B&b£10–£17 Bdi£13–£23 WBdi£65–£72 (W only Jul & Aug) LDO3.30pm

Lic CTV P nc4yrs

Credit card 1 Ⓥ

REMEMBER

Prices quoted in the gazetteer are minimum double room occupancy to maximum single room occupancy per person.

RASKELF
North Yorkshire
Map **8** SE47

Selected

GH Old Farmhouse (Guestaccom) ☎Easingwold (0347) 21971
18 Jan–20 Dec

Standing close to the village centre and 2 miles from Easingwold, this charming converted farmhouse is the perfect location from which to tour the North York moors and the city of York. The friendly proprietors are justifiably proud of their excellent home cooking. Bedrooms are comfortable and the public rooms are warm and welcoming.

10hc (5⇌ 5ﬁ) (2fb) B&b£13.50–£18.50 Bdi£21–£26.50 LDOnoon

Lic 🍽 CTV 15P

Ⓥ

RAVENGLASS
Cumbria
Map **6** SD09

GH St Michael's Country Muncaster ☎(06577) 362

Old village school of sandstone and granite, converted to provide comfortable accommodation.

9hc (1⇌) (1fb) ✗ Ⓡ B&b£11 Bdi£17 LDO5pm

Lic CTV 20P

RAVENSCAR
North Yorkshire
Map **8** NZ90

GH Smugglers Rock Country ☎Scarborough (0723) 870044
Apr–Oct

Converted and restored farmhouse, close to moors and sea.

9hc (3⇌ 4ﬁ) (2fb) B&b£11–£13 Bdi£16–£18 WBdifr£99 LDO4.30pm

Lic 🍽 CTV 10P snooker

Ⓥ

RAVENSTONEDALE
Cumbria
Map **12** NY70

⊢⊣**FH** Mrs M Wildman **Ellergill** *(NY737015)* ☎Newbiggin-on-Lune (05873) 240
Mar–Nov

Friendly guesthouse enjoying a peaceful location. Traditional home-cooking served amid a relaxed atmosphere.

4rm (1hc) (1fb) ⚟ in all bedrooms ✗ Ⓡ B&bfr£8.50 Bdifr£13.50 WBdifr£90

CTV 6P 300acres dairy sheep

Ⓥ

INN Fat Lamb Country Cross Bank (Guestaccom) ☎Newbiggin-on-Lune (05873) 242

17th-century farmhouse, now an inn, has comfortable accommodation and well appointed restaurant.

9hc (5⇔) (3fb) CTV in 2 bedrooms Ⓡ B&b£15–£18 Bdi£26–£29 WBdi£159.25–£177.59 Lunch£10.50&alc Dinner9.30pm £10&alc

CTV 50P ♿

READING
Berkshire
Map **4** SU77

GH Aeron 191 Kentwood Hill, Tilehurst ☎(0734) 424119

Professionally-run clean and friendly establishment. 3m W off A329.

9hc Annexe: 10hc (1fb) CTV in all bedrooms Ⓡ B&b£18–£19 Bdi£24–£25 LDO8.15pm

Lic 20P

Credit cards 1 3

GH Private House Hotel 98 Kendrick Rd ☎(0734) 874142
Closed Xmas

Comfortable and cheerful establishment offering good accommodation, run by friendly proprietors.

7hc B&b£17–£18

Lic CTV 6P nc12yrs

GH Thames House Hotel 18/19 Thameside ☎(0734) 507951

10hc (4⇔) (1fb) CTV in all bedrooms Ⓡ B&b£15–£17.50 LDO8pm

Lic CTV 14P

Credit cards 1 3

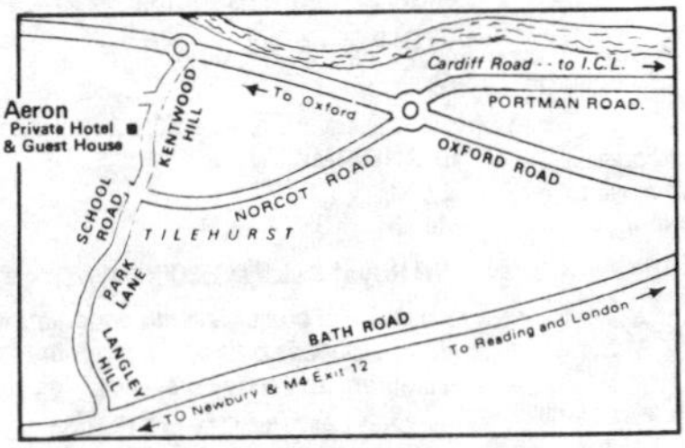

REDCAR
Cleveland
Map **8** NZ62

GH Claxton House Private Hotel
196 High St ☎(0642) 486745
Closed 24 Dec–2 Jan

Accommodation here is clean and comfortable and there is an interesting lounge dining room.

15rm (6fl) (2fb) ✱B&b£10.35–£13.23 Bdi£14.38

Lic ᗰ CTV 10P snooker

REDDITCH
Hereford & Worcester
Map **7** SP06

GH Old Rectory Ipsley Ln ☎(0527) 23000

A very hospitable hotel set in a new town, within peaceful surroundings.

10hc (6⇌ 4fl) ✖ B&b£20–£28 Bdi£29–£37 WBdi£203–£259 LDOnoon

Lic ᗰ CTV 16P 2🚗 ⌂

Credit card ① Ⓥ

REDHILL (nr Bristol)
Avon
Map **3** ST46

FH Mrs M J Hawkings **Hailstones** *(SS502638)* ☎Wrington (0934) 862209
Etr–Dec

Farmhouse in quiet, yet convenient position with pleasant dining room and croquet lawn.

4rm (3hc) (1fl) (2fb) ✖ ⊁ in 3 bedrooms Ⓡ in 1 bedroom ✱B&b£10–£15

ᗰ CTV 4P 150acres dairy sheep mixed

Ⓥ

REDHILL
Surrey
Map **4** TQ25

Redcar — Rhes-y-Cae

Selected

GH Ashleigh House Hotel 39 Redstone Hill ☎(0737) 764763
Closed Xmas

Very comfortable homely accommodation with outstanding hospitality.

9hc (1fl) (1fb) ✖ B&b£15–£18

ᗰ CTV 9P ≏(heated)

REDMILE
Leicestershire
Map **8** SK73

FH Mr & Mrs P Need **Peacock** *(SK791359)* (Guestaccom) ☎Bottesford (0949) 42475

Modernised 280-year-old farmhouse situated in the Vale of Belvoir, close to Castle. Small licensed restaurant.

4hc Annexe: 2hc (1⇌ 1fl) (3fb) TV in 2 bedrooms ✖ Ⓡ in 2 bedrooms ✱B&b£11.50–£17 Bdi£19.50–£22 WBdifr£120 LDO8.30pm

Lic ᗰ CTV 30P ⌂ ⊟ snooker solarium 5acres non-working

Credit card ① Ⓥ

REETH
North Yorkshire
Map **7** SE09

GH Arkleside Hotel ☎Richmond (0748) 84200
Mar–Oct

A quaint village house in a most attractive setting. Resident proprietors offer friendly service and good value dinners.

7hc (4fl) CTV in all bedrooms Ⓡ B&b£14–£17 Bdi£24–27 WBdifr£150 LDO7pm

Lic ᗰ 7P 3🚗

REIGATE
Surrey
Map **4** TQ25

GH Cranleigh Hotel 41 West St (Minotel) ☎(0737) 223417

An efficient, well-managed hotel, with well-equipped modern bedrooms, an outdoor heated swimming pool and rear garden.

10hc (6⇌) (2fb) CTV in all bedrooms ✖ Ⓡ B&b£26–£38 Bdi£35–£47 LDO9pm

Lic ᗰ CTV 6P ⊟(heated)

Credit cards ① ② ③ ⑤ Ⓥ

GH Priors Mead Blanford Rd ☎(0737) 248776

Comfortable family-run hotel with good size bedrooms. Quietly located.

9hc (1⇌) (3fb) Ⓡ B&b£13.50–£16

ᗰ CTV 6P nc5yrs

Ⓥ

RHANDIRMWYN
Dyfed
Map **3** SN74

INN Royal Oak ☎(05506) 201

Small, inn of character with panoramic views. Spotless bedrooms, modern restaurant and cosy bars.

5hc (2⇌ 1fl) (1fb) CTV in 3 bedrooms B&b£11.75–£14.75 WB&bfr£88.50 Bar lunch99p–£4.50 Dinner10.30pm£8.95alc 20P

Credit cards ① ③ Ⓥ

RHES-Y-CAE
Clwyd
Map **7** SJ17

INN *Miners Arms* ☎Halkyn (0352) 780567

Part 16th-century village inn in quiet rural situation.

8hc (1fb) CTV in 3 bedrooms TV in 5 bedrooms ✖ LDO10pm

ᗰ CTV 150P

RHOS-ON-SEA
Clwyd
Map **6** SH88
See **Colwyn Bay**

RHYD
Gwynedd
Map **6** SH64

FH Mrs N Griffiths **Bodlondeb** *(SH637420)* ☎Penrhyndeudraeth (0766) 770640
Etr–Oct

Bright, modern accommodation in farmhouse on the B4410. Ideal base for touring Southern Snowdonia.

3hc (1fb) B&bfr£7.50 Bdifr£11.50 WBdifr£80 LDO5pm

CTV P 420acres beef sheep

Ⓥ

RHYL
Clwyd
Map **6** SJ08

GH *Pier Hotel* 23 East Pde ☎(0745) 50280
Closed Xmas

Mid-terrace, on seafront, short walk to shops.

11hc (1 1) (3fb) LDO3pm

Lic CTV 2P solarium

GH Toomargoed Private Hotel 31–33 John St ☎(0745) 4103
Etr–Oct

Double-fronted mid-terrace in residential area off Marine Parade.

15hc (8fb) B&b£8–£10 Bdi£10.50–£12.50 WBdi£65

Lic CTV

Ⓥ

RICHMOND
North Yorkshire
Map **7** NZ10

GH *Pottergate* 4 Pottergate ☎(0748) 3826

Small, cosy house on fringe of town centre.

6hc (2fb) TV in all bedrooms Ⓡ

Lic CTV 2P 2

Selected

FH Mrs M F Turnbull **Whashton Springs** *(NZ149046)* (3m W on unclass rd) (Guestaccom) ☎(0748) 2884
Closed Xmas & New Year

A delightful 650-acre mixed farm, high in the hills of 'Herriot' country, only 3m from town. Guests are welcome to wander around the farm and explore the countryside. While Mrs Turnbull is busy preparing the wholesome farmhouse-style meal, Mr Turnbull chats to guests. The old stone farmhouse offers three very spacious bedrooms, furnished in keeping with the age of the house. While the rooms in the converted outbuildings are smaller they are equally comfortable and furnished in stripped pine. The charming lounge has a log fire and the quaint dining room offers superb views.

Winner for North Region of the 1987/8 AA Farmhouse of the Year Award.

3hc (1) CTV in all bedrooms Ⓡ B&b£11–£18 Bdi£18.50–£25.50 WBdi£119–£132 LDOam

Lic 10P (nc5yrs dinner) 600acres arable beef sheep mixed

Ⓥ

RIEVAULX
North Yorkshire
Map **8** SE58

FH Mrs M E Skilbeck **Middle Heads** *(SE584869)* ☎Bilsdale (04396) 251
Mar–Nov

Old stone-farmhouse of character, comfortably furnished and with a homely atmosphere, 1m E of B1257 and 3m NW of Helmsley.

3rm (1fb) in all bedrooms
*B&b£8.50–£9 WB&bfr£59.50

CTV 6P 170acres arable beef sheep mixed

RINGWOOD
Hampshire
Map **4** SU10

GH Little Forest Lodge Poulner Hill ☎(0425) 478848

An elegant country-style house in attractive gardens, well-secluded from the busy A31. Each bedroom is individually and tastefully decorated. The comfortable lounge features a Jacobean fireplace originally from Poole town hall. Mrs Martin, the friendly and charming proprietress will ensure all guests a pleasant stay. .

5hc (2 2) (2fb) CTV in all bedrooms Ⓡ B&b£17–£23 Bdi£25–£31 WBdi£165–£199 LDO4pm

Lic CTV 10P 2

Ⓥ

See advertisement on page 346

GH Little Moortown House Hotel 244 Christchurch Rd ☎(0425) 471404

Georgian building close to the centre of this pleasant market town. Bedrooms are well-equipped and offer good facilities. Comfortable, well-furnished lounge and dining room.

6hc (4) (1fb) CTV in all bedrooms Ⓡ B&b£20–£25 Bdi£25–£34.50 WBdi£150–£186 LDO9.30pm

Lic 8P

Credit cards 1 2 3

RIPLEY
Derbyshire
Map **8** SK45

GH Britannia 243 Church St, Waingroves ☎(0773) 43708

Modern detached house, 1½ miles south of Ripley.

6hc (1) (1fb) Ⓡ B&b£14.50 Bdi£20 LDOnoon

CTV 10P

RIPON
North Yorkshire
Map **8** SE37

GH Crescent Lodge 42 North St
☎(0765) 2331
Closed Xmas

Early 18th-century town house retaining lovely period rooms and fine Georgian staircase.

12hc (4fb) CTV in all bedrooms ✗ Ⓡ
B&b£10–£11 WB&bfr£70

Lic 🍽 CTV ✗P

GH *Nordale* 1 & 2 North Pde ☎(0765) 3557

Accommodation here is simple, but clean and the lounge is comfortable.

12hc (4fb) Ⓡ LDO5pm

Lic CTV 14P

⊢⊣Old Country 1 The Crescent ☎(0765) 2162

A graceful old Victorian house of character with spacious bedrooms and interesting public rooms.

7hc (6fb) ⚡ in 4 bedrooms TV in 2 bedrooms ✗ Ⓡ in 3 bedrooms
B&bfr£8.50 WBfr£56

🍽 CTV 10P

Ⓥ

ROBIN HOOD'S BAY
North Yorkshire
Map **8** NZ90

⊢⊣FH Mrs P Featherstone **Croft Farm** *(NZ941051)* Fylingthorpe ☎Whitby (0947) 880231
Apr–Oct

Comfortable accommodation on edge of village with good views of moors and sea.

2rm (1hc) (1fb) ⚡ in 2 bedrooms ✗
B&b£9–£9.50WB&bfr£63M

CTV 45acres dairy

ROCHE
Cornwall
Map **2** SW96

Selected

GH *Greystones* Mount Pleasant
☎(0726) 890863

Although a new building, tasteful furnishing, including many antiques, has created an olde-worlde atmosphere.

7hc (2⇌ 5fl) (2fb) LDO7.30pm

🍽 CTV 10P 1🚗 U

See advertisement under Bodmin

ROCHESTER
Northumberland
Map **12** NY89

⊢⊣FH Mrs J M Chapman **Woolaw** *(NY821984)* ☎Otterburn (0830) 20686

Comfortable farmhouse in a tranquil setting with lovely views over surrounding countryside.

2rm (1fb) ✗ B&b£9 Bdi£12 WBdi£80 LDO7.30pm

🍽 CTV P ✓ 740acres beef sheep

INN Redesdale Arms ☎Otterburn (0830) 20668

This cosy stone-built inn offers neat bedrooms and a good range of bar meals. On A68.

12hc (2⇌) (1fb) CTV in all bedrooms Ⓡ
✱B&b£12.50–£15.50 Lunch£3.50alc High Tea£1.50alc Dinner9pm£5alc

🍽 30P 2🚗

Credit cards 1 3 5 Ⓥ

ROCK
Cornwall
Map **2** SW97

GH Roskarnon House Hotel
☎Trebetherick (020886) 2329
Mar–Nov

15hc (4⇌ 2fl) (5fb) CTV in 4 bedrooms TV in 1 bedroom ✗ B&b£12.50–£17.50 Bdi£17.50–£25 WBdifr£110 LDO8pm

Lic CTV 14P 2🚗

Ⓥ

RODBOURNE (nr Malmesbury)
Wiltshire
Map **3** ST98

FH Mrs C M Parfitt **Angrove** *(ST949842)*
☎Malmesbury (0666) 822982
May–Sep

A typical Cotswold-style farmhouse backed by woodland and bordered by the River Avon where trout and coarse fishing is available. 1m NW unclass.

3hc ✗ Ⓡ ✱B&b£8–£10 WB&b£57

🍽 CTV 10P nc ✓ 204acres beef

See advertisement under Malmesbury

ROGART
Highland *Sutherland*
Map **14** NC70

Selected

⊢⊣FH Mrs J S R Moodie **Rovie** *(NC716023)* ☎(04084) 209
Apr–Oct

A charming stone farmhouse in lovely surroundings set in its own grounds bordered by a river. Bedrooms are spacious, well-decorated and comfortable. Public rooms are comfortable and there is a separate lounge with colour television. Morning tea is served in rooms and the food reflects good use of local produce. Warm hospitality and personal service by proprietors is the main aim here.

6hc (1fb) B&b£9–£10 Bdi£16–£17 WBdifr£112 LDO6.30pm

CTV 8P putting 120acres beef sheep

ROGATE
West Sussex
Map **4** SU82

— Selected —

FH Mrs J C Francis **Mizzards** (Guestaccom) *(SU803227)*
☎(073080) 656
Closed Xmas

A beautiful old farmhouse, skilfully modernised in a peaceful setting by a small river. Off A272 between Petersfield and Midhurst.

3⇌fl CTV in all bedrooms ✗ B&b£13–£18

🅿 10P 2🚗 nc6yrs ⛱(heated) 13½acres sheep

Ⓥ

See advertisement on page 348

ROMFORD
Gt London
Map **5** TQ58

GH Repton Private Hotel 18 Repton Dr, Gidea Park ☎(0708) 45253
23 Dec–1 Jan

8hc CTV in all bedrooms B&b£13.80–£18.40

🅿 CTV

ROMSEY
Hampshire
Map **4** SU32

GH *Adelaide House* 45 Winchester Rd
☎(0794) 512322

Small homely house on the edge of the town.

5hc ✗

🅿 CTV 5P

GH Chalet Botley Rd, Whitenap ☎(0794) 514909

Comfortable house set in quiet residential area.

3hc Annexe: 2⇌ (2fb) CTV in 4 bedrooms ✗ B&b£10–£12 WB&b£70–£84

🅿 CTV 6P

Ⓥ

ROSLIN
Lothian *Mid Lothian*
Map **11** NT26

INN Olde Original Rosslyn 4 Main St
☎031-440 2384

Early 18th-century inn, full of character, providing a good standard of modern accommodation. Pleasant, popular bars.

6hc (5⇌ 1fl) CTV in all bedrooms Ⓡ ✱B&b£18.75 Bdi£23.75–£30 Lunch90p–£6 High Tea£5–£6&alc Dinner10pm£5–£14&alc

🅿 14P

Credit cards 1 2 3 Ⓥ

ROSS-ON-WYE
Hereford & Worcester
Map **3** SO52

For details of farmhouse accommodation in the vicinity, see **Marstow** and **St Owen's Cross**

GH Arches Country House Walford Rd
☎(0989) 63348
Closed Xmas & New Year

6hc (1⇌) (2fb) ⚟ in 1 bedroom CTV in 2 bedrooms Ⓡ B&b£10–£12.75 Bdi£17.50–£20 WBdifr£99 LDO5pm

Lic 🅿 CTV 9P 🏠

Ⓥ

GH Bridge House Hotel Wilton ☎(0989) 62655
Closed Xmas

Cosy little hotel on edge of town with garden sloping to banks of the River Wye.

8hc (1⇌ 2fl) (1fb) CTV in 5 bedrooms ✗ B&b£12.50–£17.50 Bdi£19.50–£24.50 LDO9pm

Lic 🅿 CTV 16P

GH Brookfield House Ledbury Rd
☎(0989) 62188
rs Nov, Dec & Jan

Comfortable rooms and pleasant welcoming proprietors at the guesthouse which is close to the town centre.

8hc (1⇌ 2fl) TV in 3 bedrooms CTV in 5 bedrooms Ⓡ B&b£11–£12.50 WB&b£69–£78

Lic 🅿 CTV 10P

Credit cards 1 3 Ⓥ

GH *Ryefield House* Gloucester Rd
☎(0989) 63030
Jan–Oct

7hc (1⇌ 1fl) (3fb) Ⓡ LDO4.30pm

Lic 🅿 CTV 10P

GH Sunnymount Hotel Ryefield Rd (Guestaccom) ☎(0989) 63880
Closed Xmas

Personally-run house in quiet area of town offering friendly attentive service.

6hc (1⇌ 1fl) ✗ B&b£12–£14 Bdi£19.50–£21.50 WBdi£124–£138 LDO6.30pm

Lic 🅿 CTV 7P

Credit card 3 Ⓥ

ROSTON
Derbyshire
Map **7** SK14

⟼**FH** Mrs E K Prince **Roston Hall** *(SK133409)* ☎Ellastone (033524) 287
May–Sep

Former manor house, part Elizabethan and part Georgian, in centre of quiet village. Ideal for touring the Peak District.

2rm (1hc) (1fb) ✗ Ⓡ B&b£9–£10 WB&b£60–£68

TV 4P nc13yrs 90acres arable beef

Ⓥ

ROTHBURY
Northumberland
Map **12** NU00

GH Orchard High St ☎(0669) 20684
Closed Xmas

Delightful house in town centre, tastefully fitted throughout. →

6hc (3⫟) (1fb) CTV in all bedrooms ✗ Ⓡ B&b£12–£13 Bdi£19.50–£21 WBdi£131–£142 LDO7pm

Lic 🍴 ⌿P

Ⓥ

ROTHLEY
Leicestershire
Map **9** SK51

GH *Limes Hotel* 35 Mountsorrel Ln
☎Leicester (0533) 302531
Closed Xmas

Friendly, efficiently run hotel with comfortable bedrooms and pleasant bar.

11hc (3⫟) CTV in all bedrooms Ⓡ LDO9pm

Lic P ⌂

ROTTINGDEAN
East Sussex
Map **5** TQ30

⊢⊣**GH Braemar House** Steyning Rd
☎Brighton (0273) 34263

Family-run comfortable and homely accommodation, near the Downs.

16hc (2fb) B&b£9–£10 WB&bfr£63

🍴 CTV ⌿P

Ⓥ

GH Corner House Steyning Rd
☎Brighton (0273) 34533

In a beautiful village, this small guesthouse offers comfortable accommodation.

6hc (1fb) CTV in 5 bedrooms TV in 1 bedroom Ⓡ B&b£10–£10.50 WB&b£63–£66.15

🍴 ⌿P nc

ROWLEY REGIS
West Midlands
Map **7** SO98

GH Highfield House Hotel Holly Rd
☎021-559 1066
Closed Xmas

Busy hotel in heart of the Black Country having predominance of single rooms.

14hc (1⇌ 1⫟) ✗ Ⓡ in 2 bedrooms B&b£14–£17.50 Bdi£20–£23.50 LDOnoon

Lic 🍴 CTV 12P nc10yrs

ROWTON
Shropshire
Map **7** SJ61

⊢⊣**FH** Mrs V I Evans **Church** *(SJ614198)*
☎High Ercall (0952) 770381

300-year-old farmhouse providing simple but comfortable accommodation.

4hc (1⫟) (1fb) Ⓡ B&b£9–£15 Bdi£15–£21 WBdifr£100 LDO5pm

🍴 CTV 7P ⌂ 40acres dairy pig sheep

Ⓥ

ROXTON
Bedfordshire
Map **4** TL15

FH Mrs J Must **Church** 41 High St *(TL153545)* ☎(0234) 870234

Fully modernised farmhouse in a quiet village. Close to river.

2rm (1hc) (1fb) Ⓡ B&b£11–£12.50 WB&b£70

🍴 CTV 6P 66acres arable

Ⓥ

RUCKHALL
Hereford & Worcester
Map **3** SO44

Selected

Inn The Ancient Camp ☎Golden Valley (0981) 250449

Situated on an Iron Age Camp on high ground with spectacular views of the River Wye, this modernised inn offers extremely well equipped accommodation. Mr and Mrs Hague are convivial hosts, and Nova Hague makes full use of local produce in the preparation of interesting and varied meals.

3hc (1⇌ 2fl) CTV in all bedrooms ✗ Ⓡ B&b£17.50–£20 WB&b£122.50–£140 Bar lunch£6alc Dinner9.30pm£10alc

CTV 30P nc6yrs

RUDYARD
Staffordshire
Map **7** SJ95

FH Mrs E J Lowe **Fairboroughs** *(SJ957609)* ☎Rushton Spencer (02606) 341
Closed Xmas

4½m NW of Leek off A523 then off unclass rd.

3hc (1fb) Ⓡ available in bedrooms B&b£8–£9.50 LDOprevious day

CTV 4P 150acres beef sheep

Large stone-built farmhouse with grounds stretching to the edge of Rudyard Lake, with splendid views to distant hills.

3rm (2hc) (1fb) ✗ B&bfr£8.50 WB&bfr£59.50

CTV 4P 100acres dairy

RUFFORTH
North Yorkshire
Map **8** SE55

GH Wellgarth House Wetherby Rd ☎(090483) 592
Closed 25 & 26 Dec

A large well appointed modern house on the edge of the village.

8hc (3fl) (1fb) CTV in all bedrooms ✗ Ⓡ B&b£9.50–£14 Bdifr£14 LDO5pm

CTV 8P

RUGBY
Warwickshire
Map **4** SP57

GH Avondale 16 Elsee Rd (Guestaccom) ☎(0788) 78639

Traditional Victorian house in residential area close to town centre. Comfortable accommodation in a relaxed and friendly atmosphere. Ideally situated for the surrounding tourist areas.

7hc (1fl) (1fb) CTV in 3 bedrooms ✗ Ⓡ in 3 bedrooms B&b£11–£15 Bdi£16.50–£20.50 WBdifr£105 LDO3pm

CTV 8P 1🚗

Ⓥ

GH Mound Hotel 17–19 Lawford Rd ☎(0788) 3486
Closed 5 days Xmas

18hc (4fl) (4fb) TV in 17 bedrooms CTV in 1 bedroom ✗ B&b£15.50–£16.50 Bdi£23–£24 LDO3pm

Lic CTV 14P

Credit card 1

RUISLIP
Gt London
London plan **4** A5
(pages 258–259)

GH *Barn Hotel* West End Rd ☎(08956) 36057
Closed 24 Dec–1 Jan

17th-century house with relaxed friendly atmosphere offering comfortable period or modern bedrooms.

58⇌fl (6fb) CTV in all bedrooms Ⓡ LDO9.30pm

Lic CTV 60P (heated) sauna bath gymnasium

Credit cards 1 2 3

RUSHTON SPENCER
Staffordshire
Map **7** SJ96

FH Mrs J Brown **Barnswood** *(SJ945606)* ☎(02606) 261
Closed 23 Dec–6 Jan

RUSKIE
Central *Perthshire*
Map **11** NN60

FH Mrs S F Bain **Lower Tarr** *(NN624008)* ☎Thornhill (078685) 202
May–Oct

Large, well-maintained 200-year-old farmhouse, fully modernised and with good views over rolling hill land.

2rm (1hc) (1fb) ✗ Ⓡ B&b£8 Bdi£12.50–£13 WBdifr£85 LDO4pm

CTV P 210acres arable beef sheep mixed

Ⓥ

RUSTINGTON
West Sussex
Map **4** TQ00

GH Kenmore Claigmar Rd ☎(0903) 784634
rs Xmas

Close to shops and sea front with modern well-appointed rooms.

5hc (1⇌ 2fl) (2fb) CTV in all bedrooms Ⓡ B&b£11.25–£14.75 WB&b£70.25–£91.25

CTV 5P

GH Mayday Hotel 12 Broadmark Ln ☎(0903) 771198
Closed Oct

A delightful large detached building close to sea front offering good, honest English cooking.

10hc (6fl) (1fb) CTV in all bedrooms ✗ Ⓡ *B&b£20–£25 Bdi£25.50–£31 WBdi£158.50–£176 LDO7pm

Lic CTV 12P nc6yrs

Credit card 1

RUTHIN
Clwyd
Map **6** SJ15

⊢⊣**FH** Margaret E Jones **Pencoed** *(SJ107538)* Pwllglas ☎Clawdd Newydd (08245) 251
Closed Xmas

Stone-built farmhouse with timbered ceilings overlooking the Vale of Clwyd.

3hc (2fb) B&b£8–£9 Bdi£11–£12 WBdifr£80

ṁ CTV P 160acres mixed

Credit card [3]

RYDAL
Cumbria
See **Ambleside**

RYDE
Isle of Wight
See **Wight, Isle of**

RYE
East Sussex
Map **5** TQ92

GH Jeakes House Mermaid St ☎(0797) 222828

An interesting historic house set in a picturesque cobbled street, affording pretty bedrooms mostly with private facilities.

7rm (6hc 2🛁 1🚿) (1fb) CTV in all bedrooms Ⓡ ✱B&bfr£14

ṁ Ᵽ

GH *Little Saltcote* 22 Military Rd ☎(0797) 223210
Closed Xmas wk

Attractive, Victorian family house providing comfortable accommodation.

5hc (1🛁) (2fb) TV in all bedrooms ✗ Ⓡ

ṁ 4P

GH Mariner's Hotel 15 High St ☎(0797) 223480

17th-century house retaining some of its old-world charm including original beams. Comfortable rooms.

12hc (10🛁1🚿) (2fb) CTV in all bedrooms Ⓡ B&bfr£28

Lic ṁ Ᵽ ⛺

Credit cards [1] [2] [3] [5]

GH Old Borough Arms The Strand ☎(0797) 222128

Skilfully modernised house built in 1720 into the original medieval town walls.

9🚿 (3fb) CTV in all bedrooms Ⓡ B&b£15–£16 Bdi£21–£22 WBdifr£135 LDO8pm

Lic ṁ CTV 2P

Credit cards [1] [3] Ⓥ

GH *Playden Oasts Hotel* Playden ☎(0797) 223502
Mar–Oct

A pair of converted oast houses with some round rooms. Bedrooms are furnished in pine with modern facilities and friendly staff serve good quality food.

5🛁 (2fb) CTV in all bedrooms Ⓡ LDO9.30pm

Lic ṁ CTV 20P

Credit cards [1] [2] [3]

⊢⊣**FH** Mrs P Sullivin **Cliff Farm** *(TQ933237)* Iden Lock ☎Iden (07978) 331
Mar–Oct

Elevated farmhouse run by charming young couple. Extensive views of Romney Marsh; also free coarse fishing on River Rother. Comfortable bedrooms served by a shower room. 2m NE on Military road.

3hc (1fb) Ⓡ ✱B&b£9–£10.50

ṁ CTV 6P 6acres small holding

Ⓥ

ST AGNES
Cornwall
Map **2** SW75

⊢⊣**GH Penkerris** Penwinnick Rd ☎(087255) 2262

Attractive, detached house in lovely garden on the edge of the village.

5hc (3fb) TV in all bedrooms Ⓡ B&b£8–£10 Bdi£13–£15 WBdi£75–£90 (W only 15 Jul–20 Aug) LDO10am

CTV 8P

Ⓥ

GH Porthvean Hotel Churchtown ☎(087255) 2581
Closed Xmas & Jan

Comfortable village-centre guesthouse with friendly owners, also Frin's Restaurant with some vegetarian dishes.

7hc (5🚿) (3fb) Ⓡ B&bfr£13.80–£21.85 WB&b£82.80–£116.80 LDO9pm

Lic CTV 8P

Credit cards [1] [3] Ⓥ

ST ALBANS
Hertfordshire
Map **4** TL10

GH Ardmore House 54 Lemsford Rd ☎(0727) 59313

A detached family house with pleasant garden. Very neat, modern accommodation.

14hc (5🚿) (3fb) CTV in all bedrooms ✗ Ⓡ B&b£14.95–£32.20

ṁ 20P

GH Melford 24 Woodstock Road North ☎(0727) 53642

Converted family house with well-kept accommodation. Some bedrooms are rather small but guests can relax in the lounge.

12hc (4🚿) (3fb) Ⓡ B&b£20.70–£34.50

Lic ṁ CTV 12P

Ⓥ

ST ANDREWS
Fife
Map **12** NO51

⊢⊣**GH Albany** 56 North St ☎(0334) 77737
Closed Jan

Neat and compact terraced house.

10hc (3fl) (2fb) ⊬ in 2 bedrooms TV in 5 bedrooms CTV in 5 bedrooms Ⓡ B&b£8–£12.50 Bdi£13.50–£18 WBdi£90–£120 LDO5pm

Lic ⚹ 𝙋

GH Argyle 127 North St ☏(0334) 73387
Apr–Oct

Large private hotel on prominent corner site, with spacious bedrooms and good lounge accommodation.

21hc (1⇌ 12fl) (5fb) CTV in all bedrooms Ⓡ B&b£12–£18 Bdi£18–£24 WBdi£115–£150 LDO6pm

Lic ⚹ CTV 𝙋 nc2yrs

Credit cards 1 3 Ⓥ

GH *Arran House* 5 Murray Park ☏(0334) 74724

Family-run guesthouse offering good standard of accommodation near sea front and golf course.

6hc (3fl) (4fb) Ⓡ

⚹ CTV 𝙋

⊢GH **The Auld** Murray Park ☏(0334) 74314

Situated on one of the town's main streets, this smart house has been carefully maintained so that none of its original character is lost.

4hc (1fb) ✗ Ⓡ B&b£9–£13

⚹ CTV 𝙋

St Andrews

GH Beachway House 4–6 Murray Pk ☏(0334) 73319
Jan–mid Nov

Conversion of two adjoining houses in between town centre and sea.

13hc (7fl) (3fb) CTV in all bedrooms Ⓡ B&b£10–£16 Bdi£22 WBdi£145 LDO5pm

⚹ 𝙋

Ⓥ

⊢**GH Bell Craig** 8 Murray Pk ☏(0334) 72962

A neat house with combined lounge/dining room.

6hc (1⇌ 5fl) (3fb) CTV in all bedrooms Ⓡ B&b£9–£16 WB&bfr£80

⚹ CTV 𝙋 solarium

Ⓥ

GH Cleveden House 3 Murray Pl ☏(0334) 74212

Nicely decorated house in side street between town centre and sea.

6hc (2fb) ✱B&b£10–£13

⚹ CTV

Ⓥ

⊢**GH Craigmore** 3 Murray Pk ☏(0334) 72142

Smartly decorated, comfortable guesthouse conveniently situated for town centre and the Old Course.

6hc (1⇌ 1fl) (4fb) CTV in 2 bedrooms Ⓡ B&b£9–£15 WB&b£59.50–£95

⚹ CTV 𝙋

Ⓥ

GH Number Ten 10 Hope St ☏(0334) 74601
Jan–Oct

Attractively decorated hotel in terraced row off town centre.

10hc (2⇌ 4fl) (4fb) CTV in 4 bedrooms Ⓡ B&b£11–£16 Bdi£17.50–£22.50 WBdi£112–£150

⚹ CTV 𝙋

GH West Park House 5 St Mary's Pl ☏(0334) 75933
Closed Dec

Small but stylish detached Georgian house close to town centre. Attractive dining room also open to non-residents, including à la carte dinners.

5hc (3fl) (1fb) CTV in all bedrooms ✗ Ⓡ B&b£10.50–£17.50 Bdi£19–£26 LDO5pm

Lic ⚹ 𝙋

GH Yorkston Hotel 68 & 70 Argyle St ☏(0334) 72019
rs Xmas Day, Boxing Day & 1–2 Jan

Neatly appointed house on roadside leading into town from west.

11hc (1⇌ 1ffl) (3fb) ✗ Ⓡ ✱B&b£12–£14 Bdi£19.30–£21.80 WBdifr£125 LDO6.30pm

Lic 𝍖 CTV ✗P

Ⓥ

⊢⊣**FH** Mrs A Duncan **East Balrymouth** *(NO537142)* ☏(0334) 73475
Apr–Oct

Spacious and well-furnished Victorian farmhouse overlooking St Andrews Bay. Situated 1½m S of St Andrews on A917.

3rm (2hc) ⅄ in all bedrooms ✗ B&b£9–£10 Bdi£15–£16

CTV 3P 400acres arable beef sheep

ST AUBIN
Jersey
See **Channel Islands**

ST AUSTELL
Cornwall
Map **2** SX05

GH Alexandra Hotel 52–54 Alexandra Rd ☏(0726) 74242
Closed Xmas

14hc (4ffl) (6fb) CTV in all bedrooms Ⓡ B&b£10.50–£14.50 Bdi£14.50–£18.50 WBdi£96–£108 LDO5pm

Lic 𝍖 CTV 16P

Credit cards 1 2 3 Ⓥ

GH *Cornerways* Penwinnick Rd ☏(0726) 61579

6hc (2fb) CTV in 1 bedroom LDO4pm

Lic 𝍖 CTV 15P

GH Selwood House Hotel 60 Alexandra Rd ☏(0726) 65707
Closed 24–31 Dec

This comfortable family-run guesthouse is situated close to the town centre. Good food and friendly services.

12hc (3ffl) (4fb) CTV in 3 bedrooms ✗ Ⓡ B&b£10.50–£16.50 Bdi£15.50–£21.50 WBdifr£98 LDO9pm

St Andrews — St Buryan

Lic 𝍖 CTV 10P

Credit cards 1 2 3 Ⓥ

ST BLAZEY
Cornwall
Map **2** SX05

⊢⊣**GH Moorshill House Hotel** Rosehill ☏Par (072681) 2368
Closed Xmas

17th-century house situated along private drive.

5hc (2ffl) (2fb) ✗ B&b£9 Bdi£13 WBdi£80 LDO9pm

Lic 𝍖 CTV 8P nc3yrs

Ⓥ

ST BRIAVELS
Gloucestershire
Map **3** SO50

GH Stowe Court ☏Dean (0594) 530214
Closed 24 Dec–3 Jan

17th-century country house in rural location, furnished with antiques and offering friendly atmosphere and good food.

3hc (1ffl) (1fb) TV in 1 bedroom CTV in 2 bedrooms Ⓡ B&b£10–£20 Bdi£18.50–£28.50 WBdi£119.50–£140.50 LDOnoon

𝍖 6P ⌂

Ⓥ

INN Travellers Rest Stowe Green ☏Dean (0594) 530424

Enjoying an isolated location on an unclassified road between St Briavels and Coleford. A welcoming atmosphere and friendly service is provided by Edna Bennett and her staff. Comfortable accommodation and good food.

4rm (1fb) ✗ ✱B&bfr£11 Bdifr£14 Lunch fr£1 Dinner10.15pm fr£3

CTV 36P pool table

ST BRIDES-SUPER-ELY
South Glamorgan
Map **3** SO17

GH Sant-y-Nyll ☏Peterston-super-Ely (0446) 760209

A beautifully proportioned country house set in the Vale of Glamorgan, under the personal supervision of the resident proprietors Mr and Mrs Renwick.

6hc (1⇌) CTV in all bedrooms Ⓡ B&bfr£15 Bdifr£22 WBdifr£132

Lic 𝍖 20P

See advertisement under Cardiff

ST BURYAN
Cornwall
Map **2** SW42

GH Higher Trevorian Hotel and Restaurant ☏(0736) 810348

Friendly family hotel offering relaxed happy atmosphere and home-cooking.

9hc (2ffl) (2fb) Ⓡ B&b£9.50–£12.80 Bdi£16.50 LDO8.30pm

Lic 𝍖 CTV 10P ⌂

Credit cards 1 3

⊢⊣**FH** Mr & Mrs W Hosking **Boskenna Home** *(SW423237)* ☏(0736) 810250
Etr–Sep

Farmhouse with pleasant spacious rooms and traditional furniture. In a convenient position with beaches a few miles away.

3rm (1hc) (1fb) ✗ B&b£8 Bdi£13 WBdi£91

CTV 6P ⌂ 73acres arable dairy

⊢⊣**FH** Mrs M R Pengelly **Burnewhall** *(SW407236)* ☏(0736) 810200
mid May–mid Oct rs Wed

Spacious former 'gentleman's residence' with all bedrooms having sea views. A footpath from the farmhouse leads to a secluded bay affording safe bathing.

3hc (2fb) B&b£7.50–£8.50 Bdi£12.50–£13.50 WBdifr£80 LDO4pm

CTV 3P 150acres dairy

Credit card 3

ST CATHERINE'S
Strathclyde *Argyllshire*
Map **10** NN10

GH Thistle House ☎Inveraray (0499) 2209
May–mid Oct
Spacious detached Victorian house on Loch Fyne with attractive rooms and loch views.
6hc (3🛁) (1fb) ✗ Ⓡ B&bfr£12.50 WB&bfr£87.50
🏛 10P nc
Ⓥ

ST CLEARS
Dyfed
Map **2** SN21

INN Black Lion Hotel ☎(0994) 230700
Modestly appointed village inn.
11hc (2🛁) (1fb) CTV in 7 bedrooms TV in 1 bedroom Ⓡ in 6 bedrooms B&b£11–£20 Bdi£20–£29 WBdi£115–£125 Lunch £3–£8&alc Dinner9.30pm £5.50–£9&alc
🏛 CTV 25P snooker
Ⓥ

ST CLEMENT
Jersey
See **Channel Islands**

ST DAVIDS
Dyfed
Map **2** SM72

GH Alandale 43 Nun St ☎(0437) 720333
Closed Dec
6hc (1fb) Ⓡ B&b£10–£10.50 Bdi£16.50 WBdifr£100 LDO6.30pm
🏛 CTV ⱣP nc10yrs

GH *Pen-y-Daith* 12 Millard Pk ☎(0437) 720720
Apr–Dec
Comfortable modern house, neat and well-maintained.
8hc (2fb)
Lic 🏛 CTV P

GH The Ramsey Lower Moor ☎(0437) 720321
7hc (1fb) Ⓡ ✱B&b£12–£18 Bdi£18.50–£24.50 WBdifr£120
Lic CTV 10P
Ⓥ

GH Redcliffe House 17 New St (Guestaccom) ☎(0437) 720389
Apr–Oct
A small family-run guesthouse near the town centre.
6hc (2fb) CTV in 4 bedrooms ✗ Ⓡ B&bfr£10 Bdifr££15.50 WBdifr£100
🏛 CTV 2P nc6yrs
Ⓥ

GH Y Glennydd 51 Nun St ☎(0437) 720576
Apr–Oct
Traditional proprietor run guesthouse.
10hc (4fb) ✗ Ⓡ B&bfr£10 Bdifr£16.75 WBdifr£100 LDO4pm
Lic 🏛 CTV
Ⓥ

ST ERME
Cornwall
Map **2** SW85

FH Mrs F Hicks ***Pengelly*** *(SW856513)* Trispen ☎Mitchell (0872) 510245
rs Etr–Sep
Attractive, well-built farmhouse. Good central base for touring Cornwall.
3hc (1fb) ✗
CTV 4P nc10yrs 230acres mixed

⊢⊣**FH** Mrs B Dymond **Trevispian Vean** *(SW850502)* Trispen ☎Truro (0872) 79514
Mar–Sep
Extensively modernised farmhouse, clean and well-maintained. Large sun lounge at the front.
12hc (6🛁) (7fb) ✗ B&b£8–£9 Bdi£11–£13 WBdifr£80 LDO4.30pm
CTV 20P 300acres arable beef pig sheep

ST HELIER
Jersey
See **Channel Islands**

ST IVES
Cambridgeshire
Map **4** TL37

GH Olivers Lodge Hotel 50 Needingworth Rd ☎(0480) 63252
7hc (2fb) CTV in 6 bedrooms TV in 1 bedroom ✗ Ⓡ B&b£18.50 Bdi£25
Lic 🏛 14P
Credit cards 1 3
See advertisement on page 354

ST IVES
Cornwall
Map **2** SW54
See plan on page 355

⊢⊣**GH Bay View** Headland Rd, Carbis Bay ☎Penzance (0736) 796469
Plan **1** *B1*
Extended chalet bundalow in quiet residential area. Friendly owners provide good home cooking.
9hc (2🛁) (3fb) ⚡ in 9 bedrooms ✗ B&b£9–£12 Bdi£12–£15 WBdi£84–£105 LDO6pm
Lic CTV 9P 2🚗
Ⓥ

GH Blue Mist The Warren ☎Penzance (0736) 795209 Plan **2** *B4*
Etr–Oct
A comfortable and relaxed guesthouse, with well-appointed bedrooms, in centre of town. Seaviews from most bedrooms.
9hc (2fb) CTV in all bedrooms Ⓡ ✱B&b£9.20–£10.35 Bdi£13.80–£16.67 WBdifr£77.70 LDO5.30pm
nc3yrs
Ⓥ

GH Channings Hotel Talland Rd ☎(0736) 795681 Plan **3** *B4*
Etr–Sep
A lively family hotel in a good position enjoying views of the bay.
12hc (6fl) (3fb) ® ✱B&b£9–£17 LDO7.15pm
Lic CTV 12P

⊢⊣**GH Chy-an-Creet Private Hotel** Higher Stennack ☎Penzance (0736) 796559 Plan **4** *A5*
Soundly appointed, personally-run residence with grounds and gardens. Close to town centre.
10hc (1⇌ 6fl) (4fb) CTV in 4 bedrooms ® B&b£8.50–£11.50 Bdi£12.50–£21.50 WBdifr£87 (W only Jul & Aug) LDO4pm
Lic 🍽 CTV 16P ⌂
Credit cards 1 3 Ⓥ

GH *Cottage Hotel* Carbis Bay ☎Penzance (0736) 796351 Plan **5** *B2*
May–Oct
Modern hotel in four acres of wooded grounds, overlooking St Ives Bay.
59⇌ (51fb) CTV in all bedrooms ✖ ® LDO7.30pm
Lic lift 🍽 CTV 100P ⌂ ⌒(heated) squash snooker sauna bath
Credit cards 1 3

St Ives

— Selected —

GH Dean Court Hotel Trelyon Av ☎Penzance (0736) 796023 Plan **6** *B4*
Apr–Oct
Charming small hotel overlooking bay with particularly well-equipped bedrooms.
12hc (6⇌ 6fl) CTV in all bedrooms ✖ ® B&b£19–£26 Bdi£23–£31 WBdi£135–£155 (W only Jun–Aug) LDO4pm
Lic 🍽 12P nc
Ⓥ

GH Hollies Hotel Talland Rd ☎Penzance (0736) 796605 Plan **7** *B4*
A very friendly family guesthouse offering good home cooking, well furnished bedrooms, bar and lounge.
10hc (2⇌ 8fl) (4fb) CTV in all bedrooms ✖ ® B&b£12–£17.50 Bdi£18–£23.50 WBdi£106–£148 LDO5pm
Lic 🍽 CTV 12P
Ⓥ

GH *Island View* 2 Park Ave ☎Penzance (0736) 795111 Plan **8** *B4*
Mar–Oct
Bright and homely guesthouse enjoying fine views across town and harbour. Tasty traditional fare is served.
10hc (4fb) CTV in all bedrooms ® LDO6.30pm
P

GH Kandahar & Cortina The Warren ☎Penzance (0736) 796183 Plan **9** *B4*
Closed Xmas & New Year
Two delightful character cottages in the heart of old St Ives at the waters edge.
11hc (2fl) (1fb) CTV in all bedrooms ® B&b£9.50–£15 WB&b£66.50–£84
🍽 CTV
Ⓥ
See advertisement on page 356

⊢⊣**GH Kynance** The Warren ☎Penzance (0736) 796636 Plan **10** *B4*
Closed Xmas wk
8hc (1fl) (1fb) TV in all bedrooms ✖ ® B&b£9–£12 WB&b£63–£84
🍽 CTV
Ⓥ

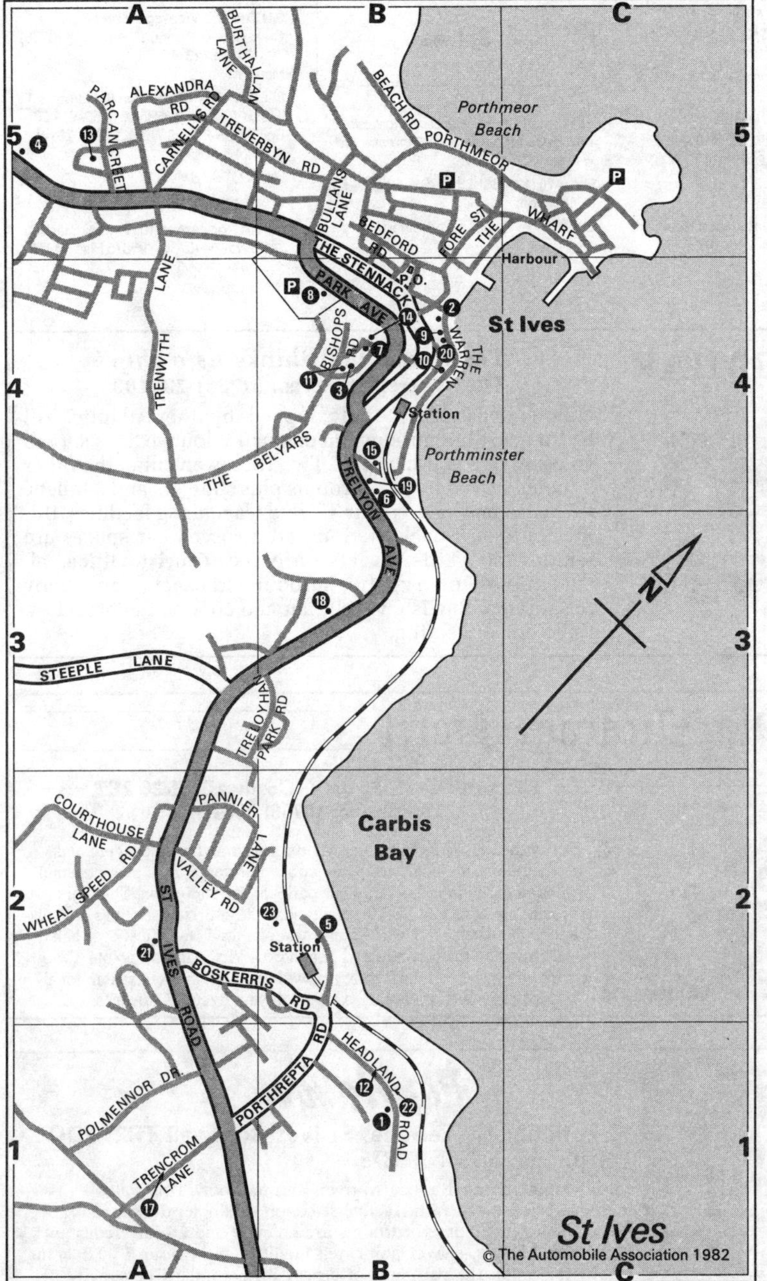

St Ives

1 Bay View
2 Blue Mist
3 Channings Hotel
4 Chy-an-Creet Private Hotel
5 Cottage Hotel
6 Dean Court Hotel
7 Hollies Hotel
8 Island View
9 Kandahar & Cortina
10 Kynance
11 Lyonesse Hotel
12 Monowai Private Hotel
13 The Old Vicarage Hotel
14 Pondarosa
15 Primrose Valley Hotel
16 Rosemorran Private Hotel
17 Hotel Rotorua
18 St Merryn Hotel
19 Shun Lee Private Hotel
20 Sunrise
21 Thurleston
22 Tregorran Hotel
23 White House Hotel

GH Lyonesse Hotel 5 Talland Rd ☎Penzance (0736) 796315 Plan **11** *B4*
Mar–Sep

Comfortable family hotel in good position with views of bay.

15hc (7fl) (6fb) CTV available in bedrooms ✈ Ⓡ available in bedrooms B&b£10–£14 Bdi£15–£19 WBdifr£90 LDO6.30pm

Lic CTV 10P ⌂ pool table

⊢⊣**GH Monowal Private Hotel** Headland Rd, Carbis Bay ☎Penzance (0736) 795733 Plan **12** *B1*
May–Sep

Family hotel, friendly and comfortable, with pleasant gardens and unrestricted views of St Ives Bay.

9hc (4fl) (1fb) B&b£8.50–£10 Bdi£11–£15 LDO6.30pm

Lic ꟾꟾꟾ CTV 7P nc5yrs ⌂(heated)

Ⓥ

St Ives

GH The Old Vicarage Hotel Parc-An-Creet (Guestaccom) ☎Penzance (0736) 796124 Plan **13** *A5*
Mar–Oct

8hc (2⇌ 2fl) (3fb) CTV in 6 bedrooms TV in 2 bedrooms Ⓡ *B&b£13.50–£14.50 Bdi£21.25–£22.25 WBdi£112–£120 (W only Jul & Aug)

Lic ꟾꟾꟾ CTV 12P

Credit cards 1 3 Ⓥ

⊢⊣**GH Pondarosa** 10 Porthminster Ter ☎Penzance (0736) 795875 Plan **14** *B4*

Guests can enjoy a warm welcome and good home cooking at this conveniently positioned hotel close to the town and beach.

9hc (1⇌) (4fb) CTV in all bedrooms ® in 8 bedrooms B&b£7.50–£9.50 Bdi£13.50–£15 WBdi£94.50–£112.50

卌 CTV 9P nc4yrs

Ⓥ

GH Primrose Valley Hotel Primrose Valley ☎Penzance (0736) 794939 Plan **15** *B4*
Mar–Oct rs Nov–Feb

Pleasant, small family hotel ideally positioned about 100yds from Porthminster beach.

11hc (5⇌ 1fl) (6fb) ✗ B&b£10.56–£19.21 Bdi£15.56–£24.21 WBdi£99.70–£152.70𝓁 (W only Jul–Aug) LDO6pm

Lic CTV 18P

GH *Hotel Rotorua* Trencrom Ln, Carbis Bay ☎Penzance (0736) 795419 Plan **17** *A1*
Etr–Oct rs Nov–Etr

Purpose-built in quiet lane just off St Ives rd, close to Carbis Bay.

13⇌fl (10fb) ⚟ in 2 bedrooms CTV in 1 bedroom TV in 1 bedroom ® LDO5pm

Lic 卌 CTV 10P ⌂ ≏

St Ives

GH *St Merryn Hotel* Trelyon ☎Penzance (0736) 795767 Plan **18** *B3*
Mar–Nov

16hc (11⇌) (8fb) ✗ LDO6pm

Lic 卌 CTV 20P

GH *Shun Lee Private Hotel* Trelyon Av ☎Penzance (0736) 796284 Plan **19** *B4*
15 Mar–Oct

Family-owned hotel in superb location overlooking bay and harbour.

11hc (3⇌ 8fl) (1fb) ✗ B&b£17–£22 LDO6pm

Lic 卌 CTV 10P nc5yrs

⊢GH **Sunrise** 22 The Warren ☎Penzance (0736) 795407 Plan **20** *B4*
Closed Dec

Picturesque and welcoming cottage guesthouse close to the sea in old part of town.

8hc (3⇌ 1fl) (2fb) CTV in 2 bedrooms TV in 6 bedrooms ® B&b£9–£12.50 WB&b£63–£87.50

CTV

Ⓥ

⊢GH **Thurleston** St Ives Rd, Carbis Bay ☎Penzance (0736) 796369 Plan **21** *A2*
Mar–Oct

Attractive detached granite house with friendly service and public rooms of character.

8hc (1⇌ 2fl) (3fb) ✗ ® available in bedrooms B&b£7.50–£10 Bdi£11–£15 WBdifr£77 (W only Jul–Aug)

Lic 卌 CTV 6P

See advertisement on page 358

GH Tregorran Hotel Headland Rd, Carbis Bay ☎Penzance (0736) 795889 Plan **22** *B1*
Apr–Oct & Xmas

Small, well-appointed family-run hotel with good sports facilities.

15hc (8fl) (3fb) ✗ ® B&b£11.50–£14.50 Bdi£15–£18.50 LDO6.30pm

Lic 卌 CTV 18P ≏(heated) gymnasium

Ⓥ

GH *White House Hotel* The Valley, Carbis Bay ☎Penzance (0736) 797405 Plan **23** *B2*
May–Oct

Situated at the foot of a wooded valley a few yards from Carbis Bay beach.

10hc (4⇌ 1fl) (3fb) ✗ ® LDO4.30pm

Lic 卌 CTV 10P

ST JOHN'S IN THE VALE
Cumbria
Map **11** NY32

FH Mrs M E Harrison **Shundraw** *(NY308236)* ☎Threlkeld (059683) 227
Etr–Oct

Large, well-maintained, stone-built farmhouse, parts of which date from 1712. In elevated position with views across valley.

4rm (1fb) B&b£7.50 WB&b£49

TV 4P 50acres sheep

ST JUST
Cornwall
Map **2** SW33

GH Boscean Country Hotel (Guestaccom) ☎Penzance (0736) 788748

Well-appointed charming country house. Peaceful location, just a short walk from sea.

9hc (7 2) (3fb) Ⓡ B&b£12.50–£15 Bdi£19–£21.50 WBdi£118–£126 LDO7pm

Lic CTV 12P

GH Boswedden House Cape Cornwall ☎Penzance (0736) 788733
Feb–Nov rs Xmas

Comfortable Georgian family house in peaceful surrounding.

7hc (5) (1fb) *B&b£10.50–£11.50 Bdi£14.50–£16.50 WBdifr£97 LDOnoon

Lic CTV 6P (heated)

Ⓥ

GH Kenython ☎Penzance (0736) 788607

Friendly welcome and good honest food. Situated at end of a ½m farm track.

4hc (2) (2fb) TV available in 1 bedroom B&b£9–£12 Bdi£15–£18 WBdi£102–£123

CTV 4P (grass)

ST JUST-IN-ROSELAND
Cornwall
Map **2** SW83

St John's in the Vale — St Marys

Selected

GH Rose-Da-Mar Hotel ☎St Mawes (0326) 270450
Apr–Oct

An attractive detached building, offering good food and friendly service, with views over River Fal.

8hc (4 1) (1fb) B&b£14.23–£18.64 Bdi£23.73–£28.14 WBdifr£192.06 LDO7pm

Lic CTV 9P nc11yrs

FH Mrs W Symons **Commerrans** *(SW842375)* ☎Portscatho (087258) 270
Etr–Oct

Pleasant modernised farmhouse, attractively decorated throughout, and situated in a large garden.

4rm (3hc) (1fb) Ⓡ in 3 bedrooms B&b£8–£9 Bdi£12.50–£13.50 WBdi£87.50–£90 LDO9am

CTV 6P nc1yr 61acres arable sheep

Credit Cards

1 Access/Euro/Mastercard
2 American Express
3 Barclaycard/Visa
5 Diners

ST KEYNE
Cornwall
Map **2** SX26

GH Old Rectory Country House Hotel (Guestaccom) ☎Liskeard (0579) 42617

Secluded former Rectory dating from the 16th century. Some four-poster beds.

8hc (4 3) CTV in all bedrooms Ⓡ B&b£17–£20 Bdi£26.50–£29.50 WBdi£185.50–£207.50 LDO7.30pm

Lic CTV 14P

Credit cards 1 3

FH Mr & Mrs P Cummins **Badham** *(SX249590)* ☎Liskeard (0579) 43572
Mar–Dec

Traditional Cornish farmhouse, carefully modernised to retain some original features. Set in lovely wooded valley.

5hc (2fb) in 5 bedrooms Ⓡ B&b£11.50–£12.50 Bdi£18.50–£19.50 WBdi£118–£124 LDO6pm

Lic CTV 20P (hard) 4acres small holding

Ⓥ

FH Mr V R Arthur **Killigorrick** *(SX228614)* ☎Liskeard (0579) 20559

Pleasant farmhouse in peaceful surroundings. 3½m from Liskeard, 500yds W off Duloe–Dobwalls Rd.

4hc (2fb) CTV in 1 bedroom *B&bfr£8.50

CTV 6P nc5yrs 21acres mixed

ST LAWRENCE
Isle of Wight
See **Wight, Isle of**

ST MARTIN
Jersey
See **Channel Islands**

ST MARYS
Isles of Scilly
No Map
See **Scilly, Isles of**

ST MARY'S LOCH
Borders *Selkirkshire*
Map **11** NT22

INN Tibbie Shiels ☎Cappercleuch (0750) 42231
Closed Xmas Day rs Nov–Jan
Historic little inn standing in a picturesque loch-side position.
6hc (1fb) Ⓡ available in bedrooms B&b£12–£12.50 Bdi£17–£18 WBdifr£126 Bar lunch £3.50–£4 High Tea £3.80–£6 Dinner9pm (8pm summer) £3.50–£4&alc
CTV 35P
Credit cards 1 3

ST OWEN'S CROSS
Hereford & Worcester
Map **3** SO52

FH Mrs F Davies **Aberhall** *(SO529242)* ☎Harewood End (098987) 256
Mar–Oct rs Nov–Feb
Cosy little farmhouse with basement games room and hard tennis court in grounds.
3hc in all bedrooms Ⓡ ✱B&b£9–£10 Bdi£13.50–£15 WBdifr£91 LDO5pm
CTV 3P nc12yrs (hard) snooker 132acres arable beef
Ⓥ

ST PETER PORT
Guernsey
See **Channel Islands**

ST PETER'S VALLEY
Jersey
See **Channel Islands**

ST SAMPSON'S
Guernsey
See **Channel Islands**

ST SAVIOUR
Guernsey
See **Channel Islands**

ST TEATH
Cornwall
Map **2** SX08

FH Mrs S M Mewton **Hillcrest** *(SX056809)* ☎Bodmin (0208) 850258
Closed 20 Dec–1 Jan
A detached farmhouse situated on the edge of the village.
2hc (1fb) B&b£8–£8.50 Bdifr£13.50 WBdifr£94.50
CTV 3P 19acres mixed
See advertisement under Camelford

SALCOMBE
Devon
Map **3** SX73

GH Bay View Hotel Bennett Rd ☎(054884) 2238
Mar–Sep
Small private hotel in a commanding position with unrestricted views of estuary and coastline.
10hc (1⇌) (2fb) Ⓡ in 3 bedrooms ✱B&b£15–£22 WB&bfr£100
Lic CTV 8P
Credit cards 1 3 Ⓥ

GH Charborough House Hotel Devon Rd ☎(054884) 2260
Jan–Sep
9hc (1⇌ 6fl) (2fb) CTV in all bedrooms Ⓡ B&b£16–£25 Bdi£25–£32 WBdi£150–£180 LDO8pm
Lic 10P
Credit cards 1 3 Ⓥ

GH *Lodge* Higher Town, Malborough ☎Kingsbridge (0548) 561405
6hc (1⇌ 3fl) Ⓡ LDO9pm
Lic CTV 8P nc9yrs

GH Lyndhurst Hotel Bonaventure Rd ☎(054884) 2481
Closed Xmas & New Year rs Nov–Feb
6hc (5fl) (1fb) in all bedrooms CTV in all bedrooms Ⓡ B&b£11.50–£13.50 Bdi£17–£18.50 WBdifr£119 LDO7pm
Lic CTV 4P nc7yrs
Credit cards 1 3 Ⓥ

GH Torre View Hotel Devon Rd ☎(054884) 2633
Etr–Oct
A cosy guesthouse run by friendly proprietors with commanding views of the estuary.
6hc (2⇌ 2fl) Ⓡ ✱B&bfr£13.50 LDO6pm
Lic CTV 4P

GH Trennels Private Hotel Herbert Rd ☎(054884) 2500
Good views of Salcombe, the estuary and the countryside from this friendly, personally-run hotel.
10hc (1⇌ 3fl) (1fb) in all bedrooms B&b£12–£14 Bdi£17.50–£19.50 WBdi£110–£120 LDO10am
Lic CTV 8P nc14yrs

GH Woodgrange Private Hotel Devon Rd (Minotel) ☎(054884) 2439
Mar–Oct
10hc (6⇌ 2fl) (2fb) CTV in all bedrooms Ⓡ B&b£14–£16 Bdi£23–£25 WBdi£129.50–£154 LDOnoon
Lic 12P
Credit cards 1 2 3 5
See advertisement on page 360

SALEN
Isle of Mull, Strathclyde *Argyllshire*
See **Mull, Isle of**

SALFORD
Bedfordshire
Map **4** SP93

INN Red Lion Country Hotel ☎Milton Keynes (0908) 583117
10hc (6⇌) CTV in all bedrooms Ⓡ ✱B&b£20–£34 Bar lunch £1–£2.20 Dinner 9.30pm £6.50alc
40P nc3yrs
Credit cards 1 2 3 5

SALFORD
Gt Manchester
Map **7** SJ89

GH Hazeldean Hotel 467 Bury New Rd
☎061-792 6667
rs Xmas wk
Large and well-equipped family-run house with good restaurant.
21hc (11⇌ 6fl) (2fb) CTV in all bedrooms Ⓡ B&b£23.40–£41.74 Bdifr£28 WBdi£195.60–£335 LDO8.30pm
Lic 🍽 CTV 21P
Credit cards 1 2 3 5

SALISBURY
Wiltshire
Map **4** SU12

GH Byways House 31 Fowlers Rd
☎(0722) 28364
17hc (10fl) (3fb) CTV in all bedrooms ✈ Ⓡ available in bedrooms B&b£12–£15
🍽 12P 1🚗

GH Glen Lyn 6 Bellamy Ln, Milford Hill
☎(0722) 27880
Large, comfortably furnished Victorian home situated in quiet cul-de-sac close to city centre.
6hc (2⇌ 1fl) (1fb) ⚔ in 1 bedroom CTV in all bedrooms ✈ Ⓡ B&b£12–£15 WB&b£72–£90
🍽 6P nc12yrs
Ⓥ

Salford — Sandown

GH Hayburn Wyke 72 Castle Rd
☎(0722) 24141
Handsome gabled corner house beside public park.
6hc (1fl) (2fb) CTV in all bedrooms ✈ B&bfr£11.50
🍽 CTV 5P 1🚗 nc8yrs

GH Holmhurst Downton Rd ☎(0722) 23164
Detached brick-built villa situated on main A338 adjacent to Cathedral.
8hc (5fl) (2fb) ⚔ in 1 bedroom ✈ B&b£10–£11
🍽 CTV 8P nc5yrs

INN Old Bell 2 St Ann Street ☎(0722) 27958
Small, personally-run inn dating from the 14th century, with comfortable bedrooms. Parking arranged on request.
7hc (1⇌ 6fl) ✈ Ⓡ ✱B&b£40–£48 (1 or 2 persons)
🍽 CTV P 🚌 nc14yrs solarium
Credit cards 1 2 3 5

INN White Horse Hotel Castle St
☎(0722) 27844
Closed Xmas Day & Boxing Day rs Sun
Red brick, corner-sited property in town centre with good bedrooms and neat restaurant.
12hc (5⇌) (2fb) CTV in all bedrooms B&b£16–£19 Bdi£23–£26 WBdifr£175 Lunch £4.50–£6.80&alc Dinner 9pm £6.95&alc
🍽 CTV 8P 6🚗 🚌
Credit cards 1 3 5

SALTDEAN
East Sussex
Map **5** TQ30
See also **Brighton & Hove**

GH *Linbrook Lodge* 74 Lenham Av (Guestaccom) ☎Brighton (0273) 33775
Closed Nov
House built on a slope in quiet residential area, all rooms have bright and colourful décor.
8hc (4fl) (3fb) CTV in 5 bedrooms TV in 1 bedroom Ⓡ LDO4pm
Lic 🍽 CTV 8P

SANDOWN
Isle of Wight
See **Wight, Isle of**

SANDPLACE
Cornwall
Map **2** SX25

GH Polraen Country House Hotel
☎Looe (05036) 3956
An attractive and comfortable country house built of Cornish stone in the early 1700s. Reputed to have once been a coaching inn.
5hc (1⇌ 4fl) (2fb) CTV in all bedrooms Ⓡ
✱B&b£16–£18 Bdi£24–£26 WBdifr£161.50 LDO6pm
Lic 21P
Credit cards 1 3 Ⓥ

SANDWICH
Kent
Map **5** TR35

INN *Fleur De Lis* Delf St ☎(0304) 611131
4hc (1fb) TV in all bedrooms Ⓡ LDO9.30pm
CTV
Credit cards 1 2 3 5

SANNOX
Isle of Arran, Strathclyde *Buteshire*
See **Arran, Isle of**

SANQUHAR
Dumfries & Galloway *Dumfriesshire*
Map **11** NS71

GH Drumbringan 53 Castle St (Guestaccom) ☎(06592) 409 due to change to (0659) 50409
Tidy, comfortable house with open-plan lounge/dining room standing on the town's main street.
5hc (2fb) B&b£9–£10 Bdi£13–£14 WBdi£88–£95
Lic CTV 6P

INN Blackaddie House Hotel
Blackaddie Rd ☎(06592) 270 due to change to (0659) 50270
Detached country house, near River Nith, popular with businessmen.
7hc (1⇌ 4fl) (2fb) CTV in all bedrooms Ⓡ
✱B&b£10–£15 Bdi£18–£23 WBdifr£125 Lunch£8&alc Dinner8.15pm£8&alc
25P
Credit card 1 Ⓥ

SANTON BRIDGE
Cumbria
Map **6** NY10

INN *Bridge* ☎Wasdale (09406) 221
19hc (14⇌ 5fl) (3fb) Ⓡ LDO9pm
CTV

SARISBURY GREEN
Hampshire
Map **4** SU50

GH Dormy ☎Locks Heath (04895) 2626
Small, homely guesthouse with friendly, family service.
7hc (1⇌ 2fl) (1fb) CTV in 5 bedrooms TV in 2 bedrooms Ⓡ B&b£12–£20
CTV 18P
Ⓥ

SAUNDERSFOOT
Dyfed
Map **2** SN10

GH *Claremont Hotel* St Brides Hill
☎(0834) 813231
Apr–Oct
Modest family residence in an elevated position close to beaches and town.
20hc (6fl) (5fb) CTV in all bedrooms Ⓡ LDO7.30pm
Lic CTV 30P (heated) pool table
Credit cards 1 3
See advertisement on page 362

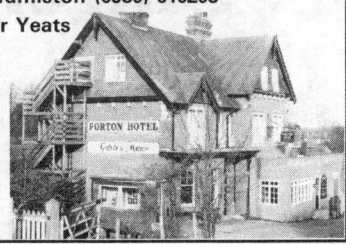

GH Harbour Light Private Hotel 2 High St ☎(0834) 813496
Closed Dec

Cheerful, small hotel with residents bar. A few minutes from harbour and beach.

12hc (6fb) TV available in bedrooms ✈ Ⓡ ✱B&b£9.50–£12.50 Bdi£14–£15.50 WBdifr£89 LDO3pm

Lic 🍽 CTV 9P

Credit cards 1 3 Ⓥ

GH Jalna Hotel Stammers Rd ☎(0834) 812282
Mar–Oct

Purpose-built, well-maintained hotel. Few minutes walk to beach and harbour.

14hc (8⇌ 6fl) (8fb) CTV in all bedrooms Ⓡ B&b£13–£15 Bdi£18–£20 WBdi£117–£138 LDO6.30pm

Lic 🍽 CTV 14P solarium

Credit cards 1 3

GH Merlewood Hotel St Brides Hill ☎(0834) 812421
Etr–Nov

Modern family-run hotel standing in elevated position overlooking the bay.

30⇌ (15fb) CTV in all bedrooms ✈ B&b£19–£21 Bdi£22–£24 WBdi£120–£145 (W only Jul & Aug) LDO7pm

Lic 🍽 CTV 30P ⌂ ≈ pool table

Credit card 3

Saundersfoot — Saxelby

GH Rhodewood House Hotel St Brides Hill ☎(0834) 812200

Comfortable, friendly hotel in quiet road overlooking Carmarthen Bay.

33hc (18⇌ 9fl) (6fb) CTV in all bedrooms Ⓡ B&b£16–£26 Bdi£23–£31 WBdi£145–£195 LDO10pm

Lic 🍽 CTV 70P ⌂ snooker solarium

Credit cards 1 2 3 5 Ⓥ

GH Sandy Hill Sandy Hill Rd ☎(0834) 813165
Mar–Oct

Well-converted farmhouse in a rural setting offering good home-cooking.

5hc (3fb) CTV in all bedrooms Ⓡ ✱B&b£9.50–£10 Bdi£13–£14 WBdi£91–£98 (W only Jul & Aug)

Lic 🍽 7P nc3yrs ≈

Ⓥ

GH Vine Farm The Ridgeway ☎(0834) 813543

Guests can enjoy a comfortable stay in a friendly atmosphere in this character building where imaginative food is served.

6hc (1⇌ 3fl) (2fb) CTV in 1 bedroom ✱B&bfr£11 Bdi£14.85–£19.50 WBdi£108–£130 LDO6pm

Lic CTV 10P nc2yrs

SAWLEY
Lancashire
Map **7** SD74

GH Spread Eagle Hotel ☎Clitheroe (0200) 41202

Superbly furnished bedrooms, with lots of extra facilities, are in converted store barn.

10hc (7⇌ 3fl) (2fb) CTV in all bedrooms ✈ Ⓡ ✱B&b£37–£39 Bdi£48.50 LDO9pm (9.30pm Sat)

Lic 🍽 80P

Credit cards 1 2 3 5 Ⓥ

SAXELBY
Leicestershire
Map **8** SK62

FH Mrs M A Morris **Manor House** *(SK701208)* ☎Melton Mowbray (0664) 812269
Etr–Oct

The manor house, parts of which date back to the 12th- and 15th-centuries, is situated on the edge of the village. 5m from Melton Mowbray.

3hc (2fb) Ⓡ B&bfr£9.50 Bdifr£15.50 WBdifr£103 LDOnoon

CTV 6P 125acres dairy sheep

SAXMUNDHAM
Suffolk
Map **5** TM36

GH Torrington Chantry Rd ☎(0728) 3106

A neat comfortable hotel quietly situated near the town centre, convenient for the station.

4hc in all bedrooms Ⓡ *B&bfr£9.50 Bdifr£17 LDOnoon

CTV 6P nc7yrs

See advertisement on page 364

SCARBOROUGH
North Yorkshire
Map **8** TA08
See plan

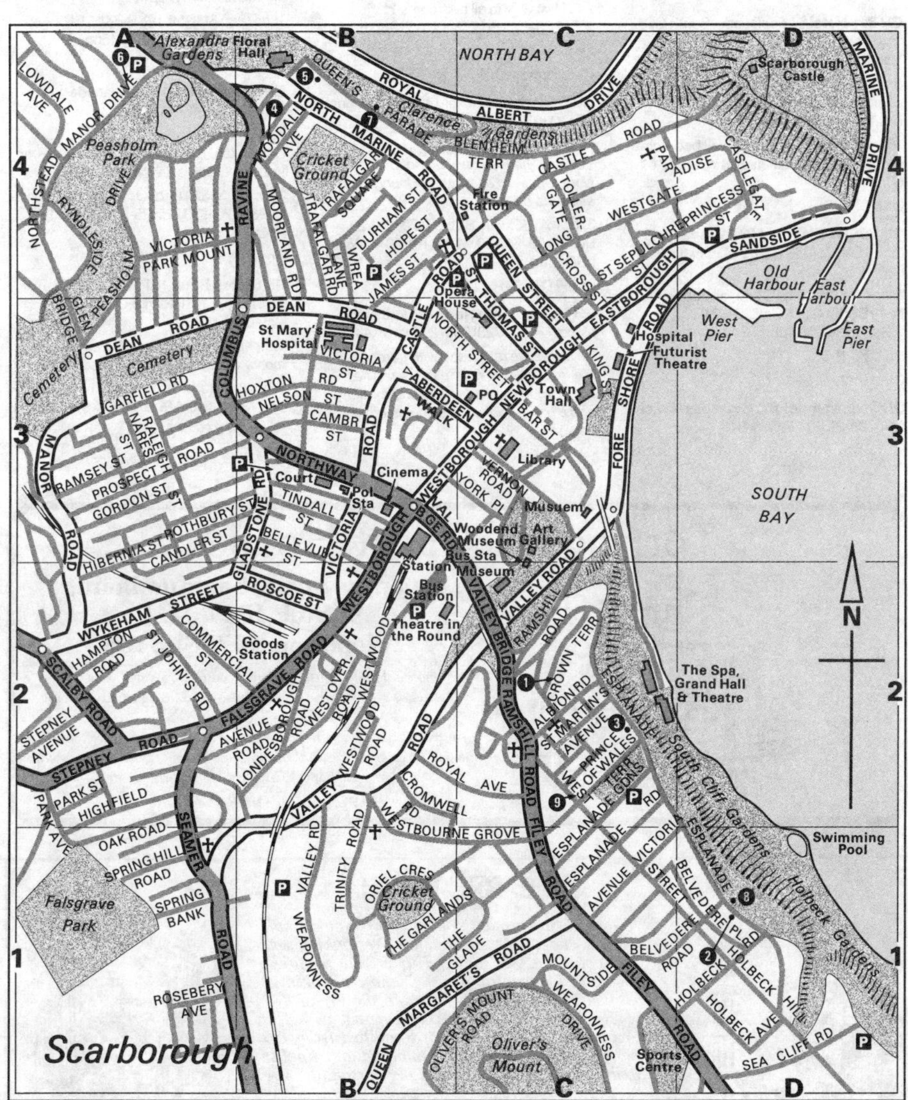

Scarborough

1 Avoncroft Hotel
2 Bay Hotel
3 Burghcliffe Hotel
4 Dolphin Hotel
5 Geldenhuis Hotel
6 Manor Heath Hotel
7 Paragon Hotel
8 Premier Hotel
9 Sefton Hotel

Scarborough

GH Avoncroft Hotel 5–7 Crown Ter ☎(0723) 372737 Plan **1** *C2*

Modest, tidy accommodation in a terrace of listed Georgian buildings.

34hc (1⇌ 10fl) (12fb) ⅟in 4 bedrooms CTV in all bedrooms Ⓡ ✱B&b£11.50–£13.50 Bdi£14–£16 WBdi£93–£105

Lic ᗰ CTV 10P ⌂

Ⓥ

GH Bay Hotel 67 Esplanade, South Cliff ☎(0723) 373926 Plan **2** *D1*
Mar–Nov

Stone-built house overlooking sea, with comfortable public rooms and smart basement dining area.

18hc (2⇌ 16fl) (2fb) CTV in all bedrooms Ⓡ B&b£20–£23 Bdi£25–£28 WBdifr£161 LDO6pm

Lic lift ᗰ 8P

GH Burghcliffe Hotel 28 Esplanade, South Cliff ☎(0723) 361524 Plan **3** *C2*
Feb–Nov

14hc (2⇌ 4fl) (6fb) CTV in all bedrooms ⋈ Ⓡ B&b£14–£18 Bdi£20–£24 WBdifr£136 LDO4pm

Lic CTV P̸

Credit card ③ Ⓥ

GH Dolphin Hotel 151 Columbus Ravine ☎(0723) 374217 Plan **4** *B4*

A mid-terrace house close to North Bay offering good accommodation and home cooked dinners served by the friendly resident owners.

7hc (4fl) CTV in all bedrooms ⋈ Ⓡ ✱B&b£9–£15 Bdi£13–£20 LDO6pm

Lic CTV P̸

Credit cards ① ③

GH Geldenhuis Hotel 145–147 Queens Pde ☎(0723) 361677 Plan **5** *B4*
Etr–Oct

Terraced houses on sea front overlooking North Bay with comfortable lounge and separate bar lounge.

32hc (6fl) (5fb) Ⓡ B&b£12.20–£13.20 Bdi£14.50–£15.50 WBdi£101.50–£108.50 LDO6pm

Lic ᗰ CTV 24P

GH Manor Heath Hotel 67 Northstead Manor Dr ☎(0723) 365720 Plan **6** *A4*

An attractive residence with gardens to the front and parking to the rear. The accommodation is tasteful and modern and a home cooked five course dinner is served.

18hc (1⇌ 9fl) (6fb) CTV in 10 bedrooms ✱B&b£9.20–£12.75 Bdifr£12.70 LDO6.30pm

Lic CTV 16P

GH Paragon Hotel 123 Queens Prom ☎(0723) 372676 Plan **7** *B4*
Closed Xmas

A comfortable sea front hotel run by affable resident proprietors.

15hc (2⇌ 3fl) (5fb) Ⓡ ✱B&b£10.50–£14.50 Bdifr£13.50 LDO5.45pm

Lic CTV P̸ nc5yrs

GH Premier Hotel 66 Esplanade ☎(0723) 361484 Plan **8** *D1*
Mar–Oct

Comfortable, family-run hotel overlooking the bay. Dinners are good value.

20hc (17⇌ 3fl) (5fb) CTV in all bedrooms Ⓡ B&b£20–£23 Bdi£25–£28 WBdi£161 LDO6.30pm

Lic lift ᗰ 8P

GH Sefton Hotel 18 Prince of Wales Ter ☎(0723) 372310 Plan **9** *C2*
Mar–Oct

Victorian town house with spacious public rooms and some charming bedrooms.

16hc (2⇌) (2fb) ⋈ Ⓡ B&b£11.50–£12 Bdi£13–£13.50 WBdi£91–£94.50

Lic lift ᗰ CTV P̸ nc4yrs

Ⓥ

SCILLY, ISLES OF
No map

ST MARY'S

Selected

GH Brantwood Hotel Rocky Hill ;☎Scillonia (0720) 22531
Apr–10 Oct

Just 20 minutes walk from the town and harbour this single-storey guesthouse offers well-equipped bedrooms of individual style. Cosy lounge and attractive dining room. Run by resident proprietors, David and Dorothy Oxford, who are responsible for the excellent cuisine and fine hospitality.

4⊞ CTV in all bedrooms ✗ Ⓡ B&b£30 Bdi£38–£45 WBdi£266–£315 LDO6.30pm

Lic 卌 nc10yrs

Credit cards 1 2 3

Selected

GH Carnwethers Country House Carnwethers, Pelistry Bay ☎Scillonia (0720) 22415
23 Mar–Oct

Perched above the secluded bay of Pelistry, in a beautiful part of St Mary's, stands this very friendly country-house retreat. Tastefully furnished bedrooms, a cosy lounge and fresh home-cooking are among the attractions along with a swimming pool discreetly tucked away in the gardens.

7hc (4⇌ 1⊞) (1fb) CTV available in bedrooms Ⓡ Bdi£20–£25 WBdi£140–£175 LDO6.30pm

Lic 卌 CTV 4P nc5yrs ⩯(heated) sauna bath

GH Four Seasons Little Porth, Hugh Town ☎Scillonia (0720) 22793
26 Mar–2 Dec

5hc (2⇌ ⊞) (1fb) ⚟ in 1 bedroom CTV in 3 bedrooms TV in 2 bedrooms ✗ Ⓡ Bdi£19.55–£24.15 WBdi£136.85–£169.05 LDOnoon

Lic 卌 ℗ nc7yrs

Ⓥ

SCOTCH CORNER
North Yorkshire
Map **8** NZ20

Selected

INN Vintage Hotel ☎Richmond (0748) 4424
Closed Xmas Day & New Year rs Sun

A popular hotel situated on the A66 just minutes from the A1. A warm welcome is assured by the charming proprietors and their friendly staff. Bedrooms are small but cosy. The rustic-style lounge and bar features a wealth of chunky stone and wood. The extensive menus in both bar and restaurant are good value with generous portions and well-presented.

8hc (4⇌ 1⊞) CTV in all bedrooms ✗(ex guide dogs) Ⓡ B&b£17.25–£29 Bdi£26.25–£41.50 WBdifr£175 Lunch £6.95–£7.95&alc Dinner9.15pm £9.75–£10.75&alc

卌 50P

Credit cards 1 3 Ⓥ

SEAFORD
East Sussex
Map **5** TV49

GH Avondale Hotel 5 Avondale Rd ☎(0323) 890008

Small, family-run house with friendly atmosphere.

11hc (1⇌) (4fb) 🚭in 6 bedrooms CTV in all bedrooms ✈ B&b£10.50–£12.50 Bdi£16.50–£18 WBdifr£123 LDO7pm

🪑 CTV P

SEASCALE
Cumbria
Map **6** NY00

GH Cottage Black How ☎(09467) 28416

Delightful guesthouse at edge of Seascale with high standard of accommodation and lovely fells views.

8hc (7⇌ 1fl) (1fb) CTV in all bedrooms ✈ Ⓡ B&bfr£16 Bdifr£22 WBdifr£129.50 LDO9am

🪑 CTV 10P

SEATON (nr Looe; 7m)
Cornwall
Map **2** SX35

GH Blue Haven Hotel Looe Hill ☎Downderry (05035) 310
Apr–Oct

6hc (3fl) (2fb) CTV in 1 bedroom B&b£9.50–£14.50 Bdi£15–£20 WBdi£95–£120 LDO8pm

Lic CTV 6P

Ⓥ

SEATON
Devon
Map **3** SY29

GH Eyre House Queen St ☎(0297) 21455

9hc (4fb) CTV in 4 bedrooms Ⓡ ✱B&b£9–£10 WB&b£63

Lic 🪑 CTV 10P 🏊

GH *Harbourside* 2 Trevelyan Rd ☎(0297) 20085

Personally-run guesthouse with pleasant atmosphere, adjacent to seafront.

7hc (3fb) TV/CTV available in bedrooms Ⓡ LDO5pm

🪑 CTV 10P

GH Mariners Hotel Esplanade ☎(0297) 20560
Mar–Dec

Neat, clean accommodation on seafront offering good, well-prepared English and Continental dishes.

10hc (3⇌ 7fl) (1fb) CTV in all bedrooms Ⓡ B&b£17.50–£21 Bdi£25–£28 WB&bfr£110 LDO5pm

Lic 🪑 CTV 10P

Credit card [1]

⊢**GH St Margarets** 5 Seafield Rd ☎(0297) 20462
Mar–Nov

Large double-fronted house overlooking playing fields. Close to town centre.

9hc (7fl) (5fb) CTV in all bedrooms Ⓡ B&b£8–£9.50 Bdi£13.50–£15 WBdifr£87.50 LDO8.30pm

Lic 🪑 6P ⌂

Ⓥ

SEAVIEW
Isle of Wight
See **Wight, Isle of**

SEBERGHAM
Cumbria
Map **11** NY34

⊢**FH** Mrs E M Johnston **Bustabeck** *(NY373419)* ☎Raughton Head (06996) 339
May–Sep

Stone-built farmhouse dating from 1684. Cosy lounge and dining room feature some magnificent oak beams.

3rm (1fb) 🚭 in all bedrooms ✈ B&bfr£9 Bdifr£12 LDOnoon

CTV 5P 72acres dairy mixed

Ⓥ

SEDGEFIELD
Co Durham
Map **8** NZ32

Selected

INN Dun Cow High St ☎(0740) 20894

A quaint village inn restored to offer comfortable accommodation while retaining its original old world charm. An interesting range of bar meals is available in the cosy lounge bars. The dining room complete with beams and natural stone walls, serves traditional country fare and specialities from the charcoal grill. The bedrooms are cosy with warm red carpets, white rough-cast beamed walls and ceilings. Staff are cheerful, helpful and friendly.

6hc CTV in all bedrooms Ⓡ ✱B&b£15–£25 Bdi£20–£40 WBdifr£205.50 Lunch£6.50–£8.50&alc Dinner10pm £7.70–£12.70&alc

🪑 25P

Credit cards [1] [2] [3] [5] Ⓥ

SEDLESCOMBE
East Sussex
Map **5** TQ71

FH Mr & Mrs Keenor **Whydown** *(TQ782168)* Crazy Ln ☎(042487) 258
Closed 17–31 Dec

2hc ✈ ✱B&b£12 WB&b£72

🪑 CTV 2P 7.5acres poultry

Ⓥ

SELBY
North Yorkshire
Map **8** SE63

GH Hazeldene 32–34 Brook St (A19) ☎(0757) 704809
Closed Xmas wk

Friendly guesthouse near the town centre with homely accommodation. Comfortable TV lounge and separate breakfast room.

7hc (2fb) ✈ Ⓡ B&b£10–£12

CTV 5P

SELKIRK
Borders *Selkirkshire*
Map **12** NT42

GH Hillholm 36 Hillside Ter ☎(0750) 21293
Mar–Sep
A spotlessly maintained, well-decorated and furnished house on the south side of town.
3hc ✗ B&bfr£10.50
CTV nc10yrs

SEMLEY
Wiltshire
Map **3** ST82

INN Benett Arms ☎East Knoyle (074783) 221 Telex no 41671
Closed Xmas Day
Delightful setting on village green opposite church.
2hc (1 1) Annexe: 3 CTV in all bedrooms Ⓡ B&b£16–£20 Bdi£21–£34 WBdifr£200 Lunch £6.50&alc Dinner9.45pm £6.50&alc
30P
Credit cards 1 2 3 5 Ⓥ

SENNEN
Cornwall
Map **2** SW32

GH Old Manor ☎(073687) 280
Closed 23–28 Dec
8hc (3fb) ✗ Ⓡ B&b£8–£12 Bdi£13–£17 WBdi£91–£119 LDO8.30pm
Lic CTV 50P
Credit cards 1 3 Ⓥ

GH Sunny Bank Hotel Sea View Hill ☎(073687) 278
Closed Xmas
11hc (2fb) ✻B&b£8.50–£10 Bdi£13.45–£14.95 WBdi£94–£104 LDO8.30pm
Lic CTV 12P

SETTLE
North Yorkshire
Map **7** SD86

GH Liverpool House Chapel Sq ☎(07292) 2247
Closed Xmas Day & Boxing Day
Charming 200-year-old house of great character, in quiet part of town.
8hc ✗ Ⓡ B&b£12–£14 Bdi£19–£21 WBdi£126–£133 LDO10am
Lic CTV 8P
Ⓥ

SEVENOAKS
Kent
Map **5** TQ55

GH Moorings Hotel 97 Hitchin Hatch Ln ☎(0732) 452589
Cosy homely hotel run by friendly proprietor.
9rm (4hc 1) Annexe: 2 (1fb) CTV in all bedrooms ✗ Ⓡ B&b£13.50–£21
Lic 15P
Credit cards 1 3

SHALDON
Devon
See **Teignmouth**

REMEMBER
Prices quoted in the gazetteer are minimum double room occupancy to maximum single room occupancy **per person.**

SHANKLIN
Isle of Wight
See **Wight, Isle of**

SHAP
Cumbria
Map **12** NY51

GH *Brookfield* ☎(09316) 397
Closed Jan
A friendly, welcoming house with a comfortable lounge and good meals served in the attractive restaurant.
6hc (3fb) ✗ LDO7.30pm
Lic CTV 25P 6

FH E & S Hodgson **Green Farm** *(NY551121)* ☎(09316) 619
Etr–Sep
Large farmhouse dating from 1705, on A6 1½m M6.
3rm (2hc) (2fb) ✗ Ⓡ B&b£8.50
CTV 4P 167acres mixed

SHAWBURY
Shropshire
Map **7** SJ52

FH Mrs S J Clarkson **Longley** *(SJ602228)* Stanton Heath ☎(0939) 250289
Closed Xmas wk
250 year old attractive brick and tile farmhouse is located within easy distance of Ironbridge and Shrewsbury.
2rm Annexe: 1 (2fb) B&b£8–£10 WB&bfr£56
CTV 4P 15acres arable sheep

FH G C Evans **New** *(SJ586215)* Muckleton ☎(0939) 250358
Modern farmhouse with large, newly furnished and extremely comfortable rooms. 2m NE of Shawbury off A53 on unclass rd.
4hc (1) CTV in all bedrooms ✗ Ⓡ B&b£9–£11 Bdi£15–£17 WBdi£100–£110
CTV 10P nc3yrs 70acres arable sheep
Ⓥ

SHEARSBY
Leicestershire
Map **4** SP69

FH Mrs A M Knight **Knaptoft House** *(SP619894)* Brungtingthorpe Rd ☎Peatling Magna (053758) 388 (due to change to Leicester (0533) 478388)

3hc (4fb) Ⓡ B&b£9.50–£11 Bdi£15–£17 WBdifr£104.50

🕮 CTV 10P ✔ 145acres mixed sheep

Credit card 1 Ⓥ

FH Mrs S E Timms **Wheathill** *(SP622911)* Church Ln ☎Peatling Magna (053758) 663
Closed Xmas

Old brick-built farmhouse retaining original beams and inglenook fireplaces.

3rm (1hc) ⊁ in 1 bedroom ✖ Ⓡ B&b£9.50–£10 Bdi£15–£15.50 WBdi£95–£100

🕮 CTV 3P 133acres dairy

SHEFFIELD
South Yorkshire
Map **8** SK38

GH Lindum Hotel 91 Montgomery Rd ☎(0742) 552356
Closed Xmas

Victorian town house with well-equipped bedrooms and cosy public areas.

10hc (1fb) CTV in all bedrooms Ⓡ ✱B&bfr£15.50 Bdifr£21 LDO6pm

Lic 🕮 CTV 5P

Ⓥ

GH Millingtons 70 Broomgrove Rd (off A625 Ecclesall Rd) ☎(0742) 669549

A smartly fitted and furnished terraced guesthouse.

6hc (2⋒) CTV in all bedrooms ✖ Ⓡ B&b£14–£17 WB&bfr£71

🕮 CTV 4P nc12yrs

Ⓥ

SHELFANGER
Norfolk
Map **5** TM18

FH Mrs D A Butler ***Shelfanger Hall*** *(TM109832)* (S of village off B1077) ☎Diss (0379) 2094
Apr–Oct

A pink-washed, brick-built 16th-century farmhouse encircled by a moat.

3hc (1fb) ✖

🕮 CTV 10P nc8yrs 400acres dairy

SHELSLEY BEAUCHAMP
Hereford & Worcester
Map **3** SO76

FH Mr & Mrs Moore **Church House** *(SO729627)* ☎(08865) 393
Apr–Sep

Imposing 18th-century farmhouse on the banks of the River Teme, offering good English cooking.

2hc (1⇌) Ⓡ B&b£10–£10.50 Bdi£15.50–£16 WB&bfr£70 LDO10am

🕮 CTV 10P

200acres arable poultry sheep mixed

Ⓥ

SHEPTON MALLET
Somerset
Map **3** ST64

INN Kings Arms Leg Sq ☎(0749) 3781
Closed 24–25 Dec rs Sun

17th-century inn of charm and character with pretty bedrooms and good fresh food.

3hc TV available in bedrooms Ⓡ ✱B&b£13.25–£15.50 Bar lunch fr£2.50

🕮 CTV 30P 🚗 nc10yrs

Ⓥ

SHERBOURNE
Warwickshire
Map **4** SP26
See **Warwick**

SHERFIELD ON LODDON
Hampshire
Map **4** SU65

GH Wessex House Hotel ☎Basingstoke (0256) 882243
Closed 10 days Xmas

Attractive, smart well-equipped hotel in neat grounds.

8⇌ CTV in all bedrooms ✖ Ⓡ B&b£31–£39 LDO9.30pm

Lic 🕮 12P nc5yrs

Credit cards 1 3

See advertisement under Basingstoke

SHERIFF HUTTON
North Yorkshire
Map **8** SE66

GH Rangers House Sheriff Hutton Park (Guestaccom) ☎(03477) 397

Interesting and unusual building with minstrel's gallery and ornate marble fireplace, as well as attractive garden.

6hc (2⇌ 2⋒) (1fb) ✖ B&b£19–£25 Bdi£26–£35 WBdifr£207 LDO9.30pm

Lic 🕮 CTV 30P 🏠

SHERINGHAM
Norfolk
Map **9** TG14

GH Beacon Hotel Nelson Rd ☎(0263) 822019
May–Sep

7hc (3⋒) ✖ Ⓡ B&b£13.50–£15.50 Bdi£17.50–£19.50 WBdi£106–£120 LDO7pm

Lic 🕮 CTV 7P nc12yrs

Credit cards 1 3

GH Camberley House Hotel 62 Cliff Rd ☎(0263) 823101
May–Sep

7hc (6⋒) (3fb) Ⓡ B&b£10–£13 Bdi£15–£18 WBdi£99–£119 LDOnoon

Lic 🕮 CTV 10P 🏠

Ⓥ

GH *Melrose Hotel* 9 Holway Rd ☎(0263) 823299
Mar–Dec
Family-owned and run hotel near town centre.
10hc (2fb) Ⓡ LDO2pm
Lic 𝍩 CTV 10P
Credit card ① ③

SHETLAND
Map **16**

LERWICK
Map **16** HU44

GH Glen Orchy 20 Knab Rd ☎(0595) 2031
Large house on top of hill overlooking Lerwick Harbour.
7hc (1⇨) (1fb) CTV in 2 bedrooms ✗ Ⓡ B&b£11–£15 Bdi£16–£25 WBdifr£175 LDO5pm
𝍩 CTV ⍉ ⌂
Ⓥ

SHIPDHAM
Norfolk
Map **8** TF90

GH Pound Green Hotel & Restaurant Pound Green Ln ☎Dereham (0362) 820165
Private family run hotel set in one acre of secluded lawned gardens with heated outdoor swimming pool.
14hc (7⇨) (3fb) CTV in 7 bedrooms Ⓡ B&b£16.50–£24 Bdi£25.25–£32.75 WBdi£176.75–£229.25
Lic 𝍩 CTV 55P 2🚗 ⩯(heated) snooker
Credit cards ① ③ Ⓥ

SHIPSTON-ON-STOUR
Warwickshire
Map **4** SP24

INN *Bell* Sheep St ☎(0608) 61443
7hc (2⇨) (1fb) Ⓡ CTV in all bedrooms LDO9.30pm
Lic 𝍩 CTV 24P
Credit cards ① ② ③ ⑤

INN *White Bear* High St (Guestaccom) ☎(0608) 61558
Friendly town centre inn with comfortable attractive bedrooms.
9hc (3⇨ 6⇨) (2fb) Ⓡ CTV in all bedrooms LDO9.30pm
𝍩 20P
Credit cards ① ② ③ ⑤

SHIRWELL
Devon
Map **2** SS53

⊢⊣**FH** Mrs J. Lyford **Woolcott** *(SS600388)* ☎(027182) 216
Situated in a quiet picturesque area on the foothills of Exmoor. The bedrooms overlook the unspoilt Devon countryside 1½ NE off A39.
3rm (2fb) ✗ B&b£7.50 Bdi£10 WBdifr£70 LDO4pm
𝍩 CTV 6P 25acres beef sheep
Ⓥ

SHOREHAM-BY-SEA
West Sussex
Map **4** TQ20

GH *Pende-Shore Hotel* 416 Upper Shoreham Rd ☎(07917) 2905
Closed 24 Dec–1 Jan
Very smart private hotel with added personal touches. There is a bistro-style restaurant and a bar.
14hc (1⇨) (2fb) TV in 6 bedrooms ✗ Ⓡ LDO7pm
Lic 𝍩 CTV 8P

SHOTTLE
Derbyshire
Map **8** SK34

GH Shottle Hall Farm ☎Cowers Lane (077389) 276
Closed Xmas
9hc (3fb) ⊬ in all bedrooms Ⓡ B&b£15.50–£17.50 Bdi£23.50–£25.50 WBdifr£161 LDO6pm
Lic 𝍩 CTV 30P
Ⓥ
See advertisement under Derby

SHREWSBURY
Shropshire
Map **7** SJ41
See also **Bomere Heath**

GH Cannock House Private Hotel 182 Abbey Foregate ☎(0743) 56043
Closed 23 Dec–2 Jan
7hc (1fb) B&b£10–£10.50
𝍩 CTV 5P

GH Fieldside Hotel 38 London Rd ☎(0743) 53143
Situated on A5112, 1½m SE of town centre. Comfortable accommodation for both tourists and commercial guests.
7hc (1⇨5⇨) CTV in all bedrooms ✗ Ⓡ B&b£20–£25 Bdi£26–£31 LDO8pm
Lic 𝍩 10P 2🚗 nc11yrs
See advertisement on page 370

GH *Sandford House Hotel* St Julians Friars ☎(0743) 3829
Closed 2 wks Dec–Jan
Listed building close to town centre and river walks.
7hc (1⇨ 1⇨) (1fb) CTV in all bedrooms Ⓡ
Lic 𝍩 CTV ⍉ ⌂
Credit cards ① ③

GH Sydney House Hotel Coton Cres, Coton Hill ☎(0743) 54681
Edwardian house, north of town centre, offering modern, well-maintained accommodation.
7hc (1⇨ 1⇨) (2fb) CTV in all bedrooms ✗ ✱B&b£11–£18 Bdi£17.50–£24.50 WBdifr£114.75 LDO7.30pm
Lic 𝍩 8P 1🚗
Ⓥ

FH Mrs P A Roberts **The Day House** *(SJ465104)* Nobold (2½m SW between A488 & A49) ☎(0743) 860212
Closed Xmas & New Year →

Mostly built in the 1840s, this rambling farmhouse is surrounded by attractive gardens in a peaceful area 2½ miles SSW of the town centre and provides spacious accommodation.

3rm (1hc) (3fb) CTV in all bedrooms ✖ Ⓡ ✱B&b£12–£14

CTV 10P 1🏠 400acres arable dairy

SIDMOUTH
Devon
Map **3** SY18

GH Canterbury Salcombe Rd ☎(03955) 3373
Mar–Oct

7hc (1⇌ 4⋒) (3fb) Ⓡ B&b£11–£13 Bdi£15.50–£17.50 WBdifr£102 LDO5pm

Lic CTV 6P

Ⓥ

GH Roehurst Private Hotel Bickwell Valley ☎(03955) 2147

An attractive mock Tudor house located in a wooded valley about ten minutes walk from the town centre.

5hc (1fb) ⊬ in all bedrooms ✖ Ⓡ B&b£12–£15 Bdi£15.50–£19.50 WBdi£90–£117

₩ CTV 6P nc8yrs

Ⓥ

GH Ryton House 52–54 Winslade Rd ☎(03955) 3981
Feb–Nov

Victorian converted semis in residential road. Well-situated for town centre and seafront.

9hc (3fb) Ⓡ ✱B&b£8–£9.50 Bdi£12.50–£14 WBdifr£84 (W only 1–19 Aug) LDO4.30pm

₩ CTV 9P ⌂

Ⓥ

Credit Cards

1 Access/Euro/Mastercard

2 American Express

3 Barclaycard/Visa

5 Diners

GH Sid Valley Farm Hotel Synderborough Ln, Sidbury (2m N A375) ☎Sidbury (03957) 274

This detached 17th-century extended farmhouse has fine countryside views and attentive service.

12hc ✖ ✱B&b£14–£17 Bdi£21–£24 LDO7pm

Lic CTV 18P ⛵(heated) ♩

SILLOTH
Cumbria
Map **11** NY15

GH Nith View 1 Pine Ter ☎(0965) 31542

A lovely guesthouse overlooking the Solway Firth with attractive and comfortable bedrooms.

8hc (4⋒) (4fb) CTV in 1 bedroom TV in 3 bedrooms Ⓡ B&b£11 Bdi£15 WBdi£100 LDO4pm

Lic ₩ CTV 8P 1🚗

Ⓥ

SKEGNESS
Lincolnshire
Map **9** TF56

GH Chatsworth Hotel North Pde ☎(0754) 4177
May–Oct & Xmas rs Mar, Apr & Nov

22hc (8⇌ 5fl) (5fb) CTV available ® *B&b£13.75–£16 Bdi£18.50–£20.75 WBdi£115–£130 LDO7.30pm

Lic 🍽 CTV 8P 4🚗

Credit cards 1 3 Ⓥ

Selected

GH Crawford Hotel South Pde
☎(0754) 4215
Etr–Oct & Xmas

A family run hotel in the true sense of the word, the Crawford is a delightful small hotel in a prime position overlooking the beach. The South family are excellent hosts and the hospitable relaxed atmosphere and personal attention ensure an enjoyable stay. Good home-cooked food. A heated indoor pool, hydro massage spa, games room and TV lounge are among the facilities here.

20hc (10⇌ 7fl) (8fb) CTV available in 8 bedrooms ® B&b£15.50–£20.50 Bdi£20.50–£24.50 WBdifr£120.75 LDO5pm

Lic lift 🍽 CTV 8P (heated) jacuzzi

Credit card 1 Ⓥ

SKIPTON
North Yorkshire
Map **7** SD95

Skegness — Skye, Isle of

GH Craven House 56 Keighley Rd
☎(0756) 4657

Family-run guesthouse with good all round facilities.

7hc (2⇌) CTV in 2 bedrooms ® B&b£11–£12 Bdi£18–£20 LDO4pm

🍽 CTV 🅿

GH Fairleigh 24 Bell Vue Ter, Broughton Rd ☎(0756) 4153

A small, family-run house with a homely atmosphere, close to town centre.

5hc (2fb) ✗ *B&bfr£10 Bdifr£15

CTV 10P

GH Highfield Hotel 58 Keighley Rd
☎(0756) 3182
Closed Xmas–16 Jan

Pleasant stone-house in Victorian-style, close to town centre.

10hc (3⇌ 2fl) (1fb) CTV in all bedrooms ® B&b£12–£14 Bdi£17–£19 LDO6.30pm

Lic CTV 🅿

Credit card 3

INN Red Lion Hotel High St ☎(0756) 60718

Cosy well-furnished inn (the oldest building in Skipton).

4hc (2⇌) (1fb) CTV in all bedrooms ✗ ® *B&b£10.50–£12.50

Lic 🍽 CTV 4P

SKIPTON-ON-SWALE
North Yorkshire
Map **8** SE37

GH *Skipton Hall* ☎Thirsk (0845) 567457

Stone-built Georgian farmhouse with comfortable spacious rooms of character; standing in own grounds by the village centre.

7hc (2⇌ 2fl) LDO7pm

Lic 🍽 CTV 12P ⛳(grass)

Credit cards 1 2 3

SKYE, ISLE OF
Highland *Inverness-shire*

DUNVEGAN
Map **13** NG24

GH *Roskhill* Roskhill (3m S A863)
☎(047022) 317
Mar–Nov

A friendly comfortable guesthouse with an attractive stone walled dining room.

5hc (2fb) ® LDO6pm

Lic 🍽 CTV 6P

See advertisement on page 372

ISLE ORNSAY
Map **13** NG71

GH Old Post Office House ☎(04713) 201
Apr–Sep

Tidy garden with pleasant hill and sea views.

4rm (3hc) Annexe: 2hc (4fb) Ⓡ B&b£9–£10

CTV 10P

PORTREE
Map **13** NG44

GH Bosville Bosville Ter ☎(0478) 2846
May–Sep

Well-maintained rough-cast building overlooking harbour and Raasay.

13hc (5⥂) (2fb) CTV in 1 bedroom TV in 1 bedroom Ⓡ *B&b£13.50–£16.50 Bdi£19.50–£22.50 WBdifr£132 LDO8pm

Lic CTV 10P

Ⓥ

GH Craiglockhart Beaumont Cres ☎(0478) 2233
Closed Dec

Comfortable house in pleasant seafront location overlooking the harbour and Raasay.

4hc (2⥂) Annexe: 6hc (1fb) Ⓡ B&b£11.50–£14

CTV 4P

GH Quiraing Viewfield Rd ☎(0478) 2870

6hc (2⥂) (2fb) Ⓡ B&b£9–£12

CTV 8P

FH Mrs M Bruce **Cruachanlea** *(NG513373)* Braes ☎Sligachan (047852) 233
Closed 20 Dec–10 Jan

A modernised farmhouse, now with accommodation all on ground floor. Outstanding views to Isle of Raasay. Situated on B883, 5 miles SE of Portree.

4hc (2fb) Ⓡ B&b£8.50–£9 Bdi£13–£13.50

CTV 6P 15acres sheep

FH Sylvia P MacDonald **Upper Ollach** *(NG518362)* Braes ☎Sligachan (047852) 225
May–Sep

Grey, stone crofting farm in hilly farmland with gardens and trees screening the house. Close to coastline, 6½m SE of Portree on B883.

2rm (1fb) ✗ B&bfr£8.50 Bdifr£12

CTV 3P 8acres arable poultry sheep

Ⓥ

WATERLOO
Map **13** NG62

GH Ceol-na-Mara ☎Broadford (04712) 323
Etr–Sep

6hc (1fb) ✗ Ⓡ *B&b£8.50 Bdi£14.50–£15.50 WBdifr£98 LDO9pm

CTV 6P

SLAIDBURN
Lancashire
Map **7** SD75

Selected

GH Parrock Head Country House Hotel Woodhouse Ln ☎(02006) 614
Feb–Nov

A tastefully modernised 17th-century farmhouse set in picturesque countryside surrounded by fells. Guests are guaranteed a memorable stay in such appealing accommodation comprising of excellent bedrooms and delightful public rooms. The food offered here is expertly prepared and cooked and service is friendly and attentive.

3⇌ Annexe: 6⇌ (1fb) CTV in all bedrooms Ⓡ B&b£19.50–£21 LDO8pm

Lic 20P

Credit card 2 Ⓥ

SLEAFORD
Lincolnshire
Map **8** TF04

GH *The Mallards* 6–8 Eastgate ☎(0529) 303062

12rm (11hc 2⇌ 4⫪) (2fb) CTV in all bedrooms Ⓡ LDO8.30pm

Lic 🍽 CTV 4P

Credit cards 1 2 3 5

SLEDMERE
Humberside
Map **8** SE96

INN Triton ☎Driffield (0377) 86644

Good value accommodation in a period inn in this attractive estate village.

6hc (2⇌ 2⫪) (1fb) CTV in all bedrooms Ⓡ B&b£10.50–£18 Bdi£15–£24 WBdifr£105 Lunch£4–£6 High tea fr£3 Dinner10pm £4.50–£6.50

🍽 CTV 30P

Credit cards 1 3 5 Ⓥ

SLINFOLD
West Sussex
Map **4** TQ13

GH Park Stane St (Guestaccom) ☎(0403) 790723

7hc (4⫪) (1fb) CTV in all bedrooms ✗ Ⓡ B&b£18 WB&b£126

🍽 CTV 12P

Credit cards 1 3 Ⓥ

SLOUGH
Berkshire
Map **4** SU97

GH Colnbrook Lodge Bath Rd, Colnbrook(3m E A4) (Guestaccom) ☎(0753) 685958
Closed 24 &25 Dec

A cosy house with a friendly, informal atmosphere within easy reach of Heathrow Airport.

8hc (1⇌ 1⫪) (2fb) ✗ Ⓡ B&b£16–£22 WB&bfr£110

Lic 🍽 CTV 12P ⌂

Ⓥ

SMEATON, GREAT
North Yorkshire
Map **8** NZ30

FH Mrs N Hall **Smeaton East** *(NZ349044)* ☎(060981) 336
May–Sep rs Oct–Apr Closed Xmas & New Year

A 17th-century working farm situated on the edge of the village affording spacious well maintained rooms of period character, and serving traditional English cooking of some note.

3hc ✗ B&b£9–£10 Bdi£14–£16.50 WB&bfr£63 LDO10am

🍽 CTV 4P nc7yrs 120acres dairy mixed

Ⓥ

SOLVA
Dyfed
See **Llandeloy**

SOMERTON
Somerset
Map **3** ST42

GH Church Farm School Ln, Compton Dundon ☎(0458) 72927
Closed Xmas–New Year

Picturesque, thatched cottage located in fine surroundings, close to main routes.

2hc (1⇌ 1⫪) Annexe: 3hc (2⇌ 1⫪) (1fb) CTV in all bedrooms Ⓡ B&b£13.50 Bdi£22 WBdifr£140.50 LDO5.30pm

Lic 🍽 6P

SOPWORTH
Wiltshire
Map **3** ST88

FH Mrs D M Barker **Manor** *(ST826865)* ☎Didmarton (045423) 676
Etr–Oct

3rm (1fb) B&b£9–£10 WB&bfr£50

TV 5P 300acres mixed

SOURTON
Devon
Map **2** SX51

Selected

GH Collaven Manor Country House Hotel ☎Bridestowe (083786) 522

15th century manor house set in 5 acres of grounds, tastefully decorated and furnished. Offering comfortable accommodation and excellent bedrooms.

8hc (6⇌ 2fl) CTV in all bedrooms Ⓡ ✱B&b£18–£36 LDO9.30pm

Lic 30P nc12yrs clay pigeon shooting croquet

Credit cards 1 3

SOUTHAMPTON
Hampshire
Map **4** SU41
See plan

GH Banister House Hotel 11 Brighton Rd, off Banister Rd ☎(0703) 221279 Plan **1** *B4*
Closed 25 & 26 Dec

Private hotel with warm and friendly atmosphere. Popular bar meals and dining room.

23hc (1⇌ 2fl) (3fb) CTV in 22 bedrooms Ⓡ available in bedrooms B&b£16.50–£22 Bdi£21.50–£27 WBdi£150.50 LDO7.45pm

Lic 14P

Credit card 1 3 Ⓥ

GH Brookvale 4 Brookvale Rd Portswood ☎(0703) 55617 Plan **2** *C5*
Closed 1 wk Xmas

9hc (2fb) TV in all bedrooms Ⓡ ✱B&b£11 Bdi£15.60 WB&b£68 LDOam

CTV 13P

GH Elizabeth House Hotel 43/44 The Avenue ☎(0703) 224327 Plan **3** *B5*

Modern accommodation is available at this well appointed hotel comprising of neat bedrooms, generous lounge and dining room; cellar bar and full range of services.

23hc (7⇌ 10fl) (2fb) CTV in all bedrooms Ⓡ B&b£17.50–£28 LDO9.15pm

Lic 20P

Credit cards 1 2 3 5 Ⓥ

GH Hunters Lodge Hotel 25 Landguard Rd, Shirley ☎(0703) 227919 Plan **4** *A3*
Closed 17 Dec–7 Jan

Professionally-managed with friendly service, this hotel has modern, well-equipped bedrooms. There are also generous bar and lounge amenities.

18hc (4⇌ 2fl) (2fb) in 1 bedroom CTV in all bedrooms Ⓡ B&b£16.10–£18.40Bdi£23–£32.20 WBdifr£161 LDO6pm

Lic CTV 16P 4

Credit cards 1 3 Ⓥ

GH Linden 51 The Polygon ☎(0703) 225653 Plan **5** *A3*
Closed Xmas wk

Two terraced houses set in the heart of the city centre. Well-decorated and comfortably furnished.

12hc (4fb) Ⓡ B&b£10–£11 WB&b£70–£80

CTV 7P

Ⓥ

GH Lodge 1 Winn Rd, The Avenue ☎(0703) 557537 Plan **6** *B5*
Closed Xmas wk

Quietly-situated Tudor-style hotel close to the city centre. Well-equipped bedrooms are complemented by good lounge and bar amenities. Extensive services are available.

14hc (2⇌) (2fb) CTV in 10 bedrooms Ⓡ ✱B&b£fr£15.50 Bdifr£22 WBdi£135–£182 LDO9pm

Lic CTV 10P

Credit cards 1 3 Ⓥ

GH Madison 137 Hill Ln ☎(0703) 333374 Plan **7** *A4*

Well-maintained, small but comfortable guesthouse with lounge. Friendly and efficient service.

10hc (1fl) (3fb) TV in 9 bedrooms Ⓡ in 9 bedrooms ✱B&b£10–£15 Bdi£15–£20 LDOnoon

CTV 7P

Ⓥ

GH *Rosida Garden Hotel* 25–27 Hill Ln ☎(0703) 228501 Plan **8** *A3*
rs 22 Dec–2 Jan

Friendly, family hotel with well-equipped modern bedrooms and public facilities.

29hc (27⇌ fl) (4fb) CTV in all bedrooms Ⓡ LDO9pm

Lic lift CTV 30P (heated)

Credit cards 1 3

GH St Regulus Hotel 5 Archers Rd ☎(0703) 224243 Plan **9** *B4*

Large Victorian hotel set in quiet residential area.

27⇌fl (3fb) CTV in all bedrooms B&bfr£13 LDO6.30pm

Lic CTV P

SOUTH BRENT
Devon
Map **3** SX66

FH M E Slade **Great Aish** *(SX689603)* ☎(03647) 2238
Closed Dec

Situated near Dartmoor National Park. Extensive views of countryside from farmhouse.

5hc (3fb) B&b£8.50–£9 WB&b£59.50–£60.50

CTV 6P 60acres beef dairy mixed

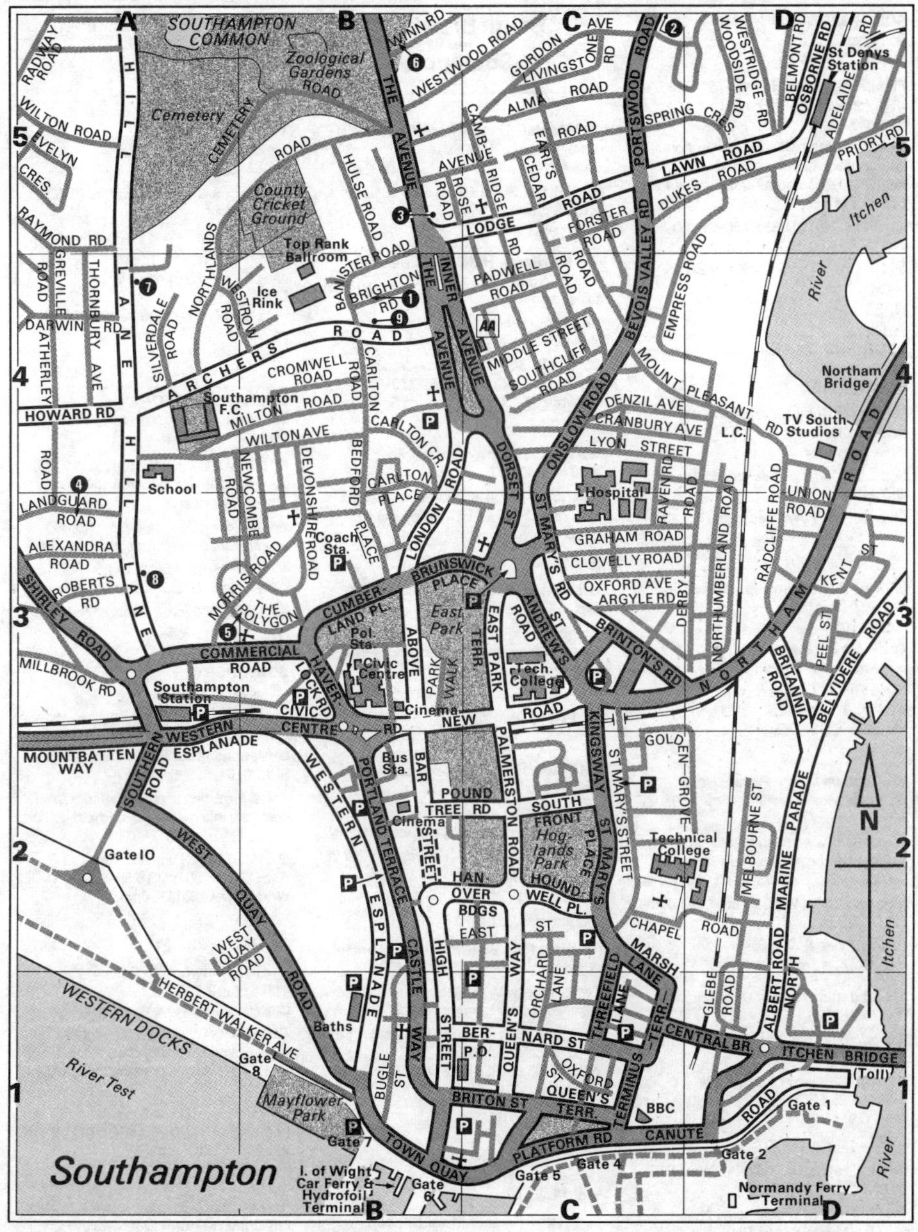

Southampton

1 Banister House Hotel
2 Brookvale
3 Elizabeth House Hotel
4 Hunters Lodge Hotel
5 Linden
6 Lodge
7 Madison
8 Rosida Garden Hotel
9 St Regulus Hotel

SOUTH BREWHAM
Somerset
Map **3** ST73

FH Mrs D Dabinett **Holland** *(ST732357)* ☎Upton Noble (074985) 263
Apr–mid Sep

Quietly situated with fine views of open countryside. A former dairyhouse with comfortable bedrooms and excellent bathrooms.

4rm (3hc) (1fb) Ⓡ B&b£9.50–£10.50 WB&b£63–£70

CTV 4P 1 nc5yrs 250acres dairy sheep

Ⓥ

SOUTHEND-ON-SEA
Essex
Map **5** TQ88

GH Argyle Hotel 12 Clifftown Pde ☎(0702) 339483
Closed 3 wks Xmas

Small, comfortable hotel overlooking sea and public gardens.

11hc (3fb) CTV in all bedrooms B&b£11–£13 WB&b£72.50–£80

Lic CTV nc5yrs

GH Bay 187 Eastern Esp, Thorpe Bay ☎(0702) 588415
Closed Xmas

Small, comfortable sea-front hotel with some modern bedroom facilities.

7hc (1fb) CTV in all bedrooms Ⓡ ✱B&b£10–£13 Bdi£14.50–£17.50 WBdi£95–£110 LDOnoon

CTV 3P

GH *Cobham Lodge Private Hotel* 2 Cobham Rd, Westcliff-on-Sea ☎(0702) 346438

Larger hotel with much to offer, attractive modern bedrooms, smart dining room, two lounges and a full size snooker table.

30hc (6 10) (4fb) CTV in all bedrooms LDO6.30pm

Lic CTV snooker

Credit cards 1 3 5

GH Gladstone Hotel 40 Hartington Rd ☎(0702) 62776

A comfortable hotel providing modern accommodation.

7hc (2fb) CTV in all bedrooms ✱B&b£8.25–£9.50 Bdi£13–£13.50 WBdifr£91 LDOam

Lic CTV nc3yrs

GH Marine View 4 Trinity Av, Westcliff-on-Sea ☎(0702) 344104

6hc (1fb) CTV in all bedrooms Ⓡ £10.50–£11.50WB&bfr£75

CTV

GH Mayfair 52 Crowstone Av, Westcliff-on-Sea ☎(0702) 340693
Closed Nov–Feb

6hc (1fb) ✱B&b£9–£9.50 Bdi£12.50–£13.50 WBdi£70–£74 LDO4pm

CTV 4P nc5yrs

GH Mayflower Hotel 5–6 Royal Ter ☎(0702) 340489
Closed Xmas

Grade II listed Regency building overlooking the sea.

23hc (4) (3fb) CTV in all bedrooms Ⓡ in 4 bedrooms B&b£13.50–£20.70 WB&bfr£94.50

CTV 2P

GH Regency Hotel 18 Royal Ter ☎(0702) 340747

12hc (5fb) CTV in all bedrooms Ⓡ B&b£16 Bdi£22–£25 WBdi£154–£175 LDO8pm

Lic CTV 1P

Ⓥ

GH Terrace Hotel 8 Royal Ter ☎(0702) 348143
Closed mid Dec–mid Jan

Small, homely, clifftop guesthouse with excellent sea views.

9hc (3fb) Ⓡ B&b£11–£12 WB&b£66–£72

Lic CTV nc10yrs

Ⓥ

GH Tower Hotel 146 Alexandra Rd ☎(0702) 348635

Large hotel situated in a quiet residential area offering well-equipped bedrooms.

13hc (2) (1fb) CTV in 12 bedrooms TV in 1 bedroom Ⓡ B&b£14–£22

Lic CTV

Credit cards 1 2 3 5

GH West Park Private Hotel 11 Park Rd, Westcliff-on-Sea ☎(0702) 330729

Larger hotel with many modern bedroom facilities and welcoming service.

21hc (13 3) CTV in all bedrooms Ⓡ in 14 bedrooms B&b£22–£32 WB&b£138.60–£201.60LDO6.30pm

Lic CTV 16P

Credit cards 1 3 Ⓥ

SOUTH LAGGAN
Highland *Inverness-shire*
Map **14** NN29

FH Mr P Fraser **Allt-na-Sithean** *(NN 293968)* Spean Bridge ☎Invergarry (08093) 311
May–Oct

A white-painted, semi-detached cottage set back from the main road 3m S of Invergarry. Compact, well-kept accommodation.

3rm (1hc) (1fb) B&b£8–£8.50 Bdi£13–£13.50 WBdifr£91 LDO6.30pm

CTV 3P 50acres mixed

Ⓥ

SOUTH LUFFENHAM
Leicestershire
Map **4** SK90

INN Boot & Shoe ☎Stamford (0780) 720177

Typical English stone-built inn, with lots of character, near Rutland Water.

4hc CTV in all bedrooms Ⓡ B&b£11–£12.50
Lunch£7.50alcDinner9.30pm£7.50alc

20P

Ⓥ

SOUTH PETHERTON
Somerset
Map **3** ST41

FH Mrs M E H Vaux **Rydon** *(ST427173)* Compton Durville ☎(0460) 40468
Etr–Oct rs winter

Attractive, mellow, stone farmhouse in a quiet location. Well-appointed throughout.

4hc (1fb) Ⓡ B&b£11–£11.50 Bdi£18–£20 WBdifr£120 LDO4pm

CTV 6P 150acres arable sheep mixed

Ⓥ

SOUTHPORT
Merseyside
Map **7** SD31
See plan on pages 378–379

GH Ambassador Private Hotel 13 Bath St ☎(0704) 43998 Plan **1** *A2*

A well-furnished and comfortable small hotel, set in a quiet side road just off Lord St.

8hc (6) (4fb) CTV in all bedrooms Ⓡ B&b£13–£18.50 Bdi£18.50–£23 WBdi£115–£120 LDO6pm

Lic 6P

Credit cards 1 3 Ⓥ

GH Brentwood 16 Duke St ☎(0704) 41185 Plan **2** *C3*
Closed Xmas & New Year

Pleasant well-furnished guesthouse, family owned and run, offering a warm welcome. Close to the famous Lord Street.

9hc (1) (3fb) CTV in 8 bedrooms TV in 1 bedroom Ⓡ B&b£8–£9.50 Bdi£11.50–£13 WBdifr£75 LDO3pm

CTV 5P

Ⓥ

GH Crimond Hotel 28 Knowsley Rd (Guestaccom) ☎(0704) 36456 Plan **3** *D3*

Comfortable and well-equipped hotel in quiet side road. Heated indoor swimming pool.

10hc (5 5) (2fb) CTV in all bedrooms Ⓡ B&b£23–£25 Bdi£31–£33 WBdi£194–£214 LDO7.30pm

Lic 𝍎 12P ⊡(heated) sauna bath

Credit cards 1 2 3 5 Ⓥ

GH Fairway Private Hotel 106 Leyland Rd ☎(0704) 42069 Plan **4** *D3*
Mar–Oct

Large, well-furnished house in quiet area.

9hc (4⋒) (4fb) CTV in 8 bedrooms ✗ Ⓡ B&b£11–£12 Bdi£14–£15 WBdifr£94 LDO5pm

Lic CTV 14P nc1yr

GH *Franklyn Hotel* 65 The Promenade ☎(0704) 40290 Plan **5** *D3*

Southport

Large, well-appointed hotel facing the sea and offering good value.

28hc (6fb) Ⓡ LDO7pm

Lic 𝍎 CTV 20P

Credit card 3

GH Fulwood Private Hotel 82 Leyland Rd ☎(0704) 30993 Plan **6** *E3*

Large detached family house situated in a quiet side road.

11hc (1fb) Ⓡ B&b£12 Bdi£16 WBdi£99 LDOnoon

Lic 𝍎 CTV 9P

GH The Gables Private Hotel 110 Leyland Rd ☎(0704) 35554 Plan **7** *D3*
Apr–Oct

A well-furnished hotel situated in a quieter part of the resort. Above average bedroom facilities.

9hc (2⇌ 6⋒) CTV in all bedrooms ✗ Ⓡ B&b£13.50–£14.50 Bdi£17.50–£19.50 WBdi£115–£125 LDO3pm

Lic 𝍎 CTV 9P nc12yrs

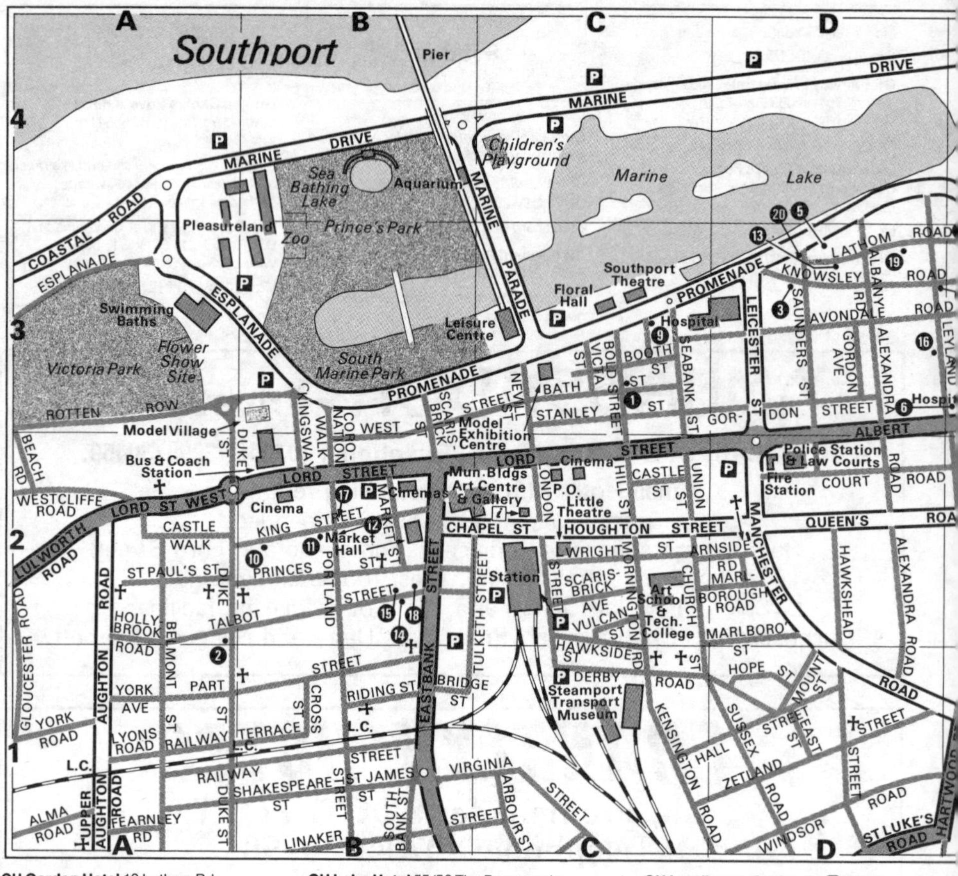

GH Garden Hotel 19 Latham Rd ☎(0704) 30244 Plan **8** *E3*

Friendly guesthouse in quiet side road.

9hc (3fb) CTV in all bedrooms Ⓡ ✱B&b£8–£10 Bdi£13.50–£15 WBdifr£100

Lic 🍴 CTV

Ⓥ

GH Lake Hotel 55/56 The Promenade ☎(0704) 30996 Plan **9** *C3*

This well furnished hotel is ideally located on the promenade.

20hc (10fl) (5fb) CTV in all bedrooms Ⓡ ✱B&b£12–£14.50 Bdi£15–£17.50

Lic CTV 14P

Credit card 3

⊢⊣**GH Lyndhurst** 101 King St ☎(0704) 37520 Plan **10** *B2*

7hc CTV in all bedrooms ✱ Ⓡ B&b£9 Bdi£13 WBdi£85 LDOnoon

Lic 🍴 CTV 2P nc5yrs

Ⓥ

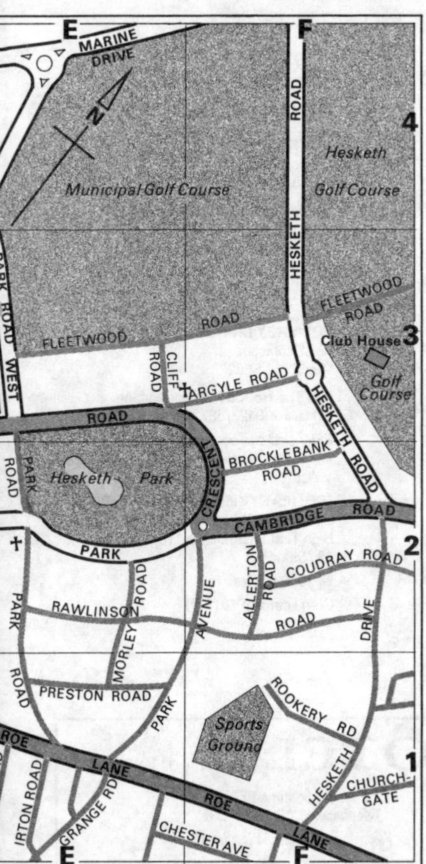

Southport

1 Ambassador Private Hotel
2 Brentwood
3 Crimond Hotel
4 Fairway Private Hotel
5 Franklyn Hotel
6 Fulwood Private Hotel
7 Gables Private Hotel
8 Garden Hotel
9 Lake Hotel
10 Lyndhurst
11 Newholme
12 Oakwood Private Hotel
13 Orleans Christian Hotel
14 Rosedale Hotel
15 Sidbrook Hotel
16 Sunningdale Hotel
17 Talbot Hotel
18 White Lodge Private Hotel
19 Whitworth Falls Hotel
20 Windsor Lodge Hotel

↦**GH Newholme** 51 King St ☎(0704) 30425 Plan **11** *B2*
Closed Xmas day & Boxing day

Small, well-furnished house personally-run by resident family.

6hc (3fb) ✗ Ⓡ B&b£8–£8.50 Bdi£10.50–£11.50 WBdi£75

M CTV 3P

Ⓥ

GH Oakwood Private Hotel 7 Portland St ☎(0704) 31858 Plan **12** *B2*
Etr–Nov

Family-run guesthouse, small but well-furnished and with good facilities.

6hc (2fl) (2fb) CTV in all bedrooms ✗ Ⓡ B&b£13–£15 Bdi£18–£20

Lic M CTV 8P nc5yrs

GH *Orleans Christian Hotel* 6–8 Lathom Rd ☎(0704) 38430 Plan **13** *D3*

Family-run hotel which 'encourages Christian fellowship, friendliness and happiness'. No smoking in house.

35hc (8fb) ⊬ in all bedrooms LDO6pm

M CTV 12P ⌂

GH Rosedale Hotel 11 Talbot St ☎(0704) 30604 Plan **14** *B2*

Small family-run guesthouse in a quiet side road.

11hc (4fb) ✗ B&b£10–£11 Bdi£13–£14 WBdi£70–£84 LDO4pm

Lic CTV 8P

GH Sidbrook Hotel 14 Talbot St ☎(0704) 30608 Plan **15** *B2*

Nice little hotel in quiet side road close to town centre.

10hc (4fb) CTV in all bedrooms ✗ Ⓡ B&b£10–£11 Bdi£14–£15 WBdi£75.50–£95.50 LDO4pm

Lic CTV 10P pool table sauna bath solarium games room

Credit cards 1 3 Ⓥ

See advertisement on page 380

GH Sunningdale Hotel 85 Leyland Rd ☎(0704) 38673 Plan **16** *D3*

Pleasant detached hotel in quiet side road with large garden to rear.

14hc (1⇌ 11fl) (5fb) CTV in all bedrooms Ⓡ B&b£13–£14.50 Bdi£18.50–£20 WBdi£127–£137 LDO4.30pm

Lic M CTV 10P

Credit cards 1 3 Ⓥ

See advertisement on page 380

GH Talbot Hotel Portland St ☎(0704) 33975 Plan **17** *B2*
Closed Xmas & New Year

Attractive large hotel on corner site. →

24hc (7⇌ 11fl) (2fb) CTV in all bedrooms Ⓡ ✱B&b£14–£15 Bdi£18.90–£31.95 LDO8.30pm

Lic 🍽 CTV 30P

Credit cards 1 3

GH White Lodge Private Hotel 12 Talbot St ☎(0704) 36320 Plan **18** *B2*

Homely guesthouse centrally located in a quiet area of the town.

10hc (3fl) (3fb) ✗ Ⓡ B&b£10–£15 Bdi£13–£19 Bdifr£85 LDO6pm

Lic CTV 6P ⌂

Ⓥ

GH *Whitworth Falls Hotel* 16 Lathom Rd ☎(0704) 30074 Plan **19** *D3*

Comfortable, homely, small hotel in quiet area.

14hc

Lic CTV 14P

GH Windsor Lodge Hotel 37 Saunders St ☎(0704) 30070 Plan **20** *D3*

Well-furnished hotel with bar and games room adjacent to promenade and marine lake.

12hc (1⇌) (1fb) ✗ B&b£10.75–£14.75 Bdi£15–£19.50 WBdifr£97.50 LDO4pm

Lic 🍽 CTV 6P pool solarium

Ⓥ

SOUTHSEA
Hampshire
See **Portsmouth & Southsea**

SOUTH SHIELDS
Tyne & Wear
Map **12** NZ36

GH Sir William Fox Private Hotel 5 Westoe Village ☎Tyneside 091–456 4554

An elegant Georgian house situated in a sedate terrace and offering comfortable accommodation and friendly service.

12hc (1⇌ 12fl) (2fb) CTV in all bedrooms B&bfr£25.30 Bdifr£34 LDO7.45pm

Lic CTV 14P

Credit card 3 Ⓥ

SOUTHWOLD
Suffolk
Map **5** TM57

INN *Kings Head Hotel* 23/25 High St ☎(0502) 723829
Etr–Oct rs Nov–Etr

Small, old fashioned inn in the centre of this quiet resort town.

3hc (1fb) CTV in all bedrooms Ⓡ LDO9.30pm

🍽 ₱ nc5yrs

Credit cards 1 3 5

SOUTH ZEAL
Devon
Map **3** SX69

GH Poltimore ☎Okehampton (0837) 840209

7hc (2⇌ 2fl) Ⓡ B&b£13–£16.50 Bdi£19–£22.50 WBdi£125–£142.50 LDO10.30am

Lic 🍽 CTV 20P nc12yrs

SOWERBY BRIDGE
West Yorkshire
Map **7** SE02

INN The Hobbit Hob Ln, Norland ☎Halifax (0422) 832202

Extended and converted row of stone moorside cottages overlooking the Calder Valley.

16fl (1fb) CTV in all bedrooms ✗ Ⓡ B&b£14.50–£28 Lunch£4.75–£6.75&alc High Teafr£3.25 Dinner11pm£5.25–£8.75&alc

🍽 100P nc4yrs

Credit cards 1 2 3 Ⓥ

SPARROWPIT
Derbyshire
Map **7** SK08

⊢⊣**FH** Mrs E Vernon **Whitelee** *(SK099814)* ☎Chapel-en-le-Frith (0298) 812928
Apr–Oct

Modernised farmhouse, part-built in 1600, in pleasant hillside setting. Good centre for hill walking or touring.

3hc Ⓡ B&b£8–£10 WB&b£56–£63

▥ TV 6P 42acres beef

SPAXTON
Somerset
Map **3** ST23

FH Mrs D M Porter ***Headford*** *(ST208345)* Higher Merridge ☎(027867) 250

3½m SW unclass.

2rm (1fb) ✗ LDO2pm

▥ CTV 10P 3🏠 104acres mixed

Credit cards ① ③

SPEAN BRIDGE
Highland *Inverness-shire*
Map **14** NN28

⊢⊣**GH Coire Glas** ☎(039781) 272
Apr–Oct

Well-appointed modern bungalow with private garden situated 50yds back from A86.

14hc (5⥂) (2fb) Ⓡ B&bfr£9 Bdifr£16.50 WBdifr£108 LDO8.30pm

Lic CTV 20P

Ⓥ

⊢⊣**GH Inverour** ☎(039781) 218
Apr–Oct

An attractive roadside house in a central position with a pleasant lounge featuring an open fire.

7hc (3⥂) TV in all bedrooms Ⓡ B&bfr£9 Bdifr£15 WBdifr£100 LDO6pm

▥ 7P

SPITTAL
Dyfed
Map **2** SM92

⊢⊣**FH** Mrs N M Thomas **Lower Haythog** *(SM996214)* ☎Clarbeston (043782) 279

2m SE off B4329.

4rm (3hc) (2fb) ⚟ in 2 bedrooms ✗ Ⓡ B&b£9–£10.50 Bdi£13–£15 WBdifr£91 (W school holidays only)

▥ CTV P ⚲ 246 acres dairy sheep

Ⓥ

STAFFORD
Staffordshire
Map **7** SJ92

GH Bailey Hotel 63 Lichfield Rd (Guestaccom) ☎(0785) 214133

Small friendly establishment on the A34 1m S of town centre.

12hc (2⥂) (2fb) CTV in all bedrooms Ⓡ B&b£15.95–£16.50 Bdi£18.45–£19 WBdifr£120 LDO8pm

Lic ▥ CTV 12P

Credit cards ① ③ Ⓥ

GH Leonards Croft Hotel 80 Lichfield Rd ☎(0785) 223676
Closed Xmas

12hc (2fb) Ⓡ B&b£10

Lic ▥ CTV 10P

STAMFORD
Lincolnshire
Map **4** TF00

INN ***Bull & Swan*** St Martins ☎(0780) 63558

14th-century inn of great charm and character offering simple accommodation. ½m S on B1081.

6rm CTV in all bedrooms ✗ Ⓡ LDO9.30pm

▥ CTV 25P ⛟

Credit card ③

STAMFORD BRIDGE
Humberside
See **High Catton**

STANDLAKE
Oxfordshire
Map **4** SP30

FH Mr & Mrs W J Burton **Church Mill** *(SP396038)* Downs Rd ☎(086731) 524
Mar–Oct

A grade II listed 17th-century Mill House with adjoining water mill, on mixed farm on the River Windrush. Well-situated for fishing and water sports in the area. Off Downs Rd between A415 and B4449, N of Standlake.

2hc ✕

4P nc12yrs 70acres mixed

FH Mrs S R Pickering **Hawthorn** *(SP373048)* ☎(086731) 211
Apr–Oct

Recently modernised ground-floor accommodation on a working farm where you can try spinning, bottle-feeding the lambs and milking the cows.

2hc ⊁ in bedrooms ✕ Ⓡ B&b£9.50–£10

⅏ CTV 3P 25acres mixed

STANFORD-LE-HOPE
Essex
Map **5** TQ68

GH Homesteads 216 Southend Rd ☎(0375) 672372
rs Xmas

Small, homely guesthouse with neat accommodation.

15hc (2fb) B&b£10–£14 LDO2pm

Lic ⅏ CTV 6P 2⌂

STAPLE FITZPAINE
Somerset
Map **3** ST21

⊢⊣**FH** Mrs D M Jee **Ruttersleigh** *(ST261164)* ☎Buckland St Mary (046034) 392

Small, very pleasant farmhouse off A303.

3rm (1fb) ⊁ in all bedrooms ✕ B&b£7–£8.50 Bdi£11.50–£12.50

2P 69acres dairy

Stamford Bridge — Steyning

STAUNTON
Gloucestershire
Map **3** SO51

FH Mrs S Fairhead ***Upper Beaulieu*** *(SO530118)* ☎Monmouth (0600) 5025

Situated on the Gloucester/Gwent border, near the Forest of Dean off A4136 SW of village.

3hc (1fb) LDO3pm

⅏ CTV 8P 1⌂ 60acres mixed

STEEPLE ASTON
Oxfordshire
Map **4** SP42

GH Westfield Farm Motel The Fenway (Guestaccom) ☎(0869) 40591

Clean, well-kept motel style accommodation grouped around a farm yard.

7⇌ ⋔ (1fb) CTV in all bedrooms Ⓡ ✱B&b£12–£16 Bdi£18.50–£22.50 WBdifr£130 LDO5.30pm

Lic ⅏ CTV 12P U

Credit cards 1 3 Ⓥ

Credit Cards

1 Access/Euro/Mastercard
2 American Express
3 Barclaycard/Visa
5 Diners

STEPASIDE
Dyfed
Map **2** SN10

GH Bay View Hotel Pleasant Valley ☎Saundersfoot (0834) 813417
Apr–Oct

Modern proprietor-run hotel catering for family holidays.

12hc (6⋔) (4fb) ✕ B&b£11.50–£14 Bdi£13.60–£16.50 WBdi£95–£115 (W only 23 Jun–3 Sep) LDO5pm

Lic ⅏ CTV 14P ⌂ ⌓(heated)

STEVENAGE
Hertfordshire
Map **4** TL22

GH *Archways* 11 Hitchin Rd ☎(0438) 316640

This spacious Victorian hotel comprises three houses close to the old town. The middle house contains an elegant reception, dining room and bar. The large bedrooms are comfortable and well-equipped.

15⇌ Annexe: 22⇌ (8fb) CTV in all bedrooms ✕ Ⓡ LDO9pm

Lic ⅏ CTV 60P ⌂

Credit cards 1 2 3 5

STEYNING
West Sussex
Map **4** TQ11

GH Nash Hotel Horsham Rd ☎(0903) 814988

Remotely situated and skilfully extended country house, surrounded by a vineyard and a pond.

6hc (1⇌) (2fb) CTV in all bedrooms Ⓡ B&b£19–£21 Bdi£27–£29 WBdifr£189 LDO7pm

Lic ⅏ CTV 18P ♿ ⌓ ℛ(hard)

GH *Springwells* 9 High St ☎(0903) 812446

Comfortable, pretty bedrooms in a charming ivy-clad house with swimming pool.

10hc (6⇌) (1fb) CTV in all bedrooms Ⓡ

Lic ⅏ CTV 6P ⌓(heated)

Credit cards 1 2 3 5

STIPERSTONES
Shropshire
Map **7** SJ30

GH Tankerville Lodge ☎ Shrewsbury (0743) 791401

4hc Ⓡ ✱B&b£10–£12 Bdi£16–£18 WBdifr£106 LDO4pm

Lic 🍽 CTV 4P nc2yrs

Ⓥ

STIRLING
Central *Stirlingshire*
See **Denny**

STOCKBRIDGE
Hampshire
Map **4** SU33

GH Carbery Salisbury Hill ☎Andover (0264) 810771
Closed 2 wks Xmas

Comfortable house with many facilities including pool, badminton, and swimming pool.

11hc (1⇌ 2fl) (1fb) ✖ ✱B&bfr£14.37 Bdifr£21.84 WBdi£150 LDO6pm

Lic 🍽 CTV 14P ⇌(heated)

GH Old Three Cups Private Hotel
☎Andover (0264) 810527
Closed Xmas & Jan rs Sun night & Mon

15th-century coaching inn with comfortable bedrooms and popular well-managed restaurant.

8hc (3⇌) (2fb) CTV in 7 bedrooms TV in 1 bedroom ✖ B&b£16–£30 Bdi£23.50–£37.50 LDO9.30pm

Lic 🍽 12P

Credit cards 1 3 Ⓥ

STOCKPORT
Greater Manchester
Map **7** SJ98

GH Ascot House Hotel 195 Wellington Rd North, Heaton Norris ☎061-432 2380
Closed 2 wks Xmas

A large family-run house situated on the A6 north of Stockport.

18hc (10⇌) (1fb) CTV in all bedrooms ✖ Ⓡ B&b£16–£30 LDO7.15pm

Lic 🍽 CTV 20P 1🚗 sauna bath

Credit cards 1 2 3 Ⓥ

STOCKTON-ON-TEES
Cleveland
Map **9** NZ41

GH Court Private Hotel 49 Yarm Rd ☎(0642) 604483

Three-storey, mid-terrace property near the town centre with small dining room and comfortable sitting room.

7hc (2fb) CTV in all bedrooms ✖ Ⓡ B&b£10.50–£13 Bdi£13–£17 LDO6pm

Lic 🍽 🅿 nc2yrs

STOKE FLEMING
Devon
Map **3** SX84

GH Endsleigh Hotel ☎(0803) 770381

Personally-run small but pretty hotel located in village centre. A friendly atmosphere prevails. It enjoys an elevated position with spectacular sea views.

8hc (2fl) (2fb) Ⓡ ✱B&b£12–£16 Bdi£18–£22 WBdi£119–£147 LDO9pm

Lic CTV 20P

See advertisement under Dartmouth

STOKE HOLY CROSS
Norfolk
Map **5** TG20

FH Mr & Mrs Harrold **Salamanca** *(TG235022)* ☎Framingham Earl (05086) 2322
Closed 15 Dec–15 Jan & Etr

Comfortable Victorian farmhouse, with comfortable rooms and large garden, 4 miles south of Norwich.

3hc Annexe: 1⇌ ✖ B&b£9.50–£12.50 Bdi£14.50–£17.50 LDO24hrs prior

🍽 CTV 7P nc6yrs 168acres dairy mixed

Ⓥ

Stokeinteignhead — Stornoway

STOKEINTEIGNHEAD
Devon
Map **3** SX97

⊢**GH Bailey's Farm** ☎Shaldon (062687) 3361
May–Oct

10hc (3fb) B&b£9–£11 Bdi£12–£15 WBdi£84–£100 LDO7pm

CTV 10P

STOKE-ON-TRENT
Staffordshire
Map **7** SJ84

GH The White House Stone Rd, Trent Vale (Guestaccom) ☎(0782) 642460
Closed Xmas period

Comfortable, modern accommodation is offered at this guesthouse, 2 miles SW of city.

8hc (2fb) CTV in 4 bedrooms ✗ Ⓡ B&b£14–£28 Bdi£20.90–£34.90 WBdifr£170.80 LDO6pm

Lic 🍽 CTV 10P

Credit cards 1 3 Ⓥ

STOKE ST GREGORY
Somerset
Map **3** ST32

GH Jays Nest ☎North Curry (0823) 490250

7hc (2fb) ⊬ in 4 bedrooms ✗ Ⓡ B&b£12–£15 Bdi£17.50–£20 WBdifr£115 LDO9pm

Lic 🍽 CTV 15P 2🚗

STONE (nr Berkeley)
Gloucestershire
Map **3** ST69

GH The Elms ☎Falfield (0454) 260279

A well-appointed small hotel set in garden, alongside the A38.

10hc (3fb) ✱B&b£12–£14

Lic 🍽 CTV 14P

STONE (in Oxney)
Kent
Map **5** TQ92

FH Mrs E I Hodson **Tighe** *(TQ937268)* Tighe ☎Appledore (023383) 251
Mar–Nov

Late 16th-century farmhouse with panoramic views of Romney Marsh, situated in spacious gardens with a pond. The rooms have antique furniture, with residents lounge having an inglenook fireplace and historic dining room with exposed beams.

3hc (1fb) ✗ B&b£10.50–£11.50 WB&bfr£66.50

🍽 CTV 3P nc8yrs ♩ 100acres sheep

STON EASTON
Somerset
Map **3** ST65

⊢**FH** Mrs J Doman **Manor** *(ST626533)* ☎Chewton Mendip (076121) 266
Closed Dec

Large stonebuilt listed Somerset farmhouse with nice atmosphere and home-grown produce served at meals.

2rm (1hc) (1fb) ✗ Ⓡ in 1 bedroom B&bfr£9 Bdifr£15 WBdifr£100

🍽 CTV P 350acres dairy mixed

Ⓥ

STONEHOUSE
Gloucestershire
Map **3** SO80

FH Mrs D A Hodge **Welches** *(SO813065)* Standish ☎(045382) 2018
Closed Xmas

3rm (1hc) (2fb) ✗ ✱B&b£9 WB&b£63

🍽 CTV 10P 101acres dairy

STORNOWAY
Isle of Lewis, Western Isles *Ross & Cromarty*
See **Lewis, Isle of**

STOURBRIDGE
West Midlands
Map **7** SO98

GH Limes 260 Hagley Rd, Pedmore ☎Hagley (0562) 882689

10hc (1fb) Ⓡ B&bfr£15 Bdifr£22 LDO7pm

CTV 12P ♿

STOW-ON-THE-WOLD
Gloucestershire
Map **4** SP12

GH Limes Evesham Rd ☎Cotswold (0451) 30034

Large gabled house within walking distance from town centre offering friendly family service.

5hc Annexe: 1hc (1fb) CTV in 3 bedrooms TV in 1 bedroom ✱B&b£9.50–£10.50 WB&bfr£67

Lic CTV 6P 1

FH Mrs D S Smith **Corsham Field** *(SP217249)* Bledington Rd ☎Cotswold (0451) 31750
Closed Xmas Day & Boxing Day

Newly constructed, Cotswold-stone farmhouse incorporating many traditional features.

3hc (1) (1fb) CTV in 1 bedroom TV in 2 bedrooms Ⓡ B&b£10–£13.50 Bdi£13.50–£17 WBdi£94.50–£119 LDO6pm

CTV 10P 100acres arable beef sheep

STRAITON
Lothian *Midlothian*
Map **11** NT26

FH Mrs A M Milne **Straiton** *(NJ273667)* Straiton Rd ☎031-440 0298
Mar–Oct

Georgian farmhouse on southern outskirts of Edinburgh off A701. Pets, play area for the children. Dogs welcome.

4hc (3fb) Ⓡ ✱B&b£11.50–£12

CTV 10P 200acres arable beef dairy mixed

STRATFORD-UPON-AVON
Warwickshire
Map **4** SP25
See plan on page 387

GH Ambleside 41 Grove Rd ☎(0789) 297239 Plan **1** *A2*
Closed Xmas

7hc (3fb) CTV in all bedrooms Ⓡ B&b£10–£12 WB&b£70

CTV 15P 1

Credit cards 1 3 5 Ⓥ

GH Avon View Hotel 121 Shipston Rd ☎(0789) 297542 Plan **2** *C1*
Apr–5 Jan

9hc (1 5) (2fb) CTV in all bedrooms Ⓡ B&b£15–£17 Bdi£23–£25 WBdi£160 LDO4pm

Lic 10P nc5yrs

Credit cards 1 2 3

GH Brook Lodge 192 Alcester Rd ☎(0789) 295988 Plan **3** *A3*
Closed Xmas

8hc (2) (3fb) CTV in all bedrooms Ⓡ B&b£8–£15 Bdi£30–£40 WB&b£50–£95

CTV 10P

Credit cards 1 3 Ⓥ

See advertisement on page 388

GH Coach House 17 Warwick Rd (Guestaccom) ☎(0789) 204109 Plan **4** *C3*
rs 23–25 Dec

12hc (3 4) (2fb) CTV in all bedrooms Ⓡ B&b£13.50–£18 Bdi£20.90–£25.40 WBdi£135.40–£156.40 LDO4pm

Lic 8P

Credit cards 1 3 Ⓥ

GH Eastnor House Hotel Shipston Rd ☎(0789) 68115 Plan **5** *C1*
Closed Xmas

Attentive, friendly service at this comfortable Victorian house close to centre.

9hc (5⇌) (2fb) CTV in all bedrooms Ⓡ
✱B&b£14–£20 WB&b£88.20–£126

Lic ▥ CTV 8P

Credit cards 1 2 3 Ⓥ

See advertisement on page 388

GH Hardwick House 1 Avenue Rd ☎(0789) 204307 Plan **7** *C4*
Closed Xmas

Stratford-upon-Avon

14hc (2⇌ 2fl) (3fb) CTV in all bedrooms
✖ B&b£13–£18

▥ 12P

Credit cards 1 2 3

See advertisement on page 388

GH *Hollies* 16 Evesham Pl ☎(0789) 66857 Plan **8** *A2*

Friendly guesthouse on corner-site with own car park. Handy for town centre and theatre.

6hc (1fl) (3fb) ✖ Ⓡ

CTV P ⌂

GH Hunters Moon 150 Alcester Rd ☎(0789) 292888 Plan **9** *A3*

7hc (5fl) (5fb) CTV in all bedrooms Ⓡ

▥ CTV 6P

Credit cards 1 3 Ⓥ

See advertisement on page 389

Stratford-upon-Avon

1 Ambleside
2 Avon View Hotel
3 Brook Lodge
4 Coach House
5 Eastnor House Hotel
7 Hardwick House
8 Hollies
9 Hunters Moon
10 Kawartha House
11 Marlyn
12 Melita Private Hotel
13 Moonraker House
14 Nando's
15 Parkfield
16 Penryn House
17 Penshurst
18 Ravenhurst
19 Salamander
20 Sequoia House Hotel
21 Stretton House
22 Virginia Lodge
23 Woodburn House Hotel

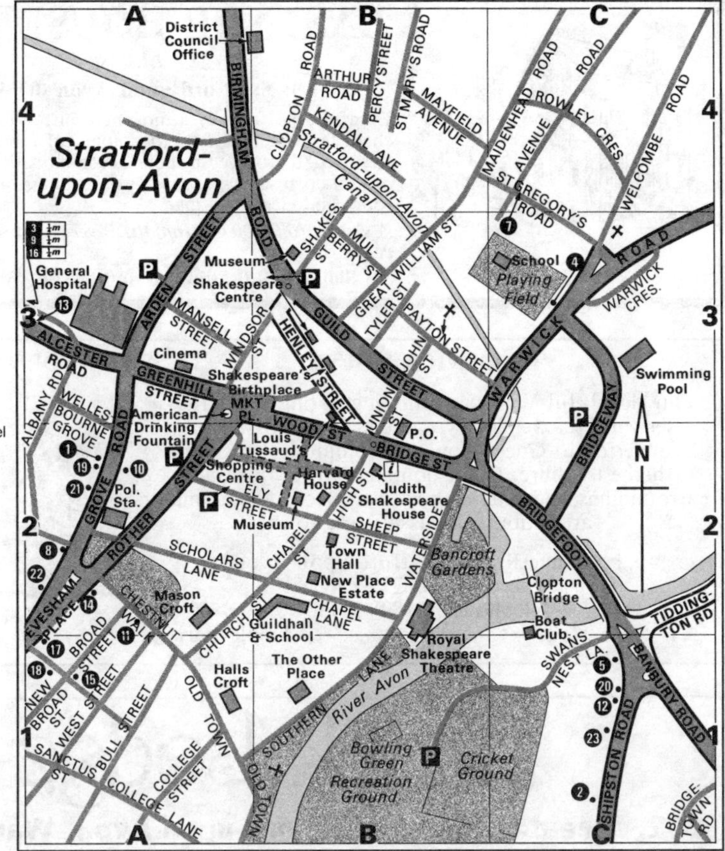

GH Kawartha House 39 Grove Rd ☎(0789) 204469 Plan **10** *A2*
Closed Mar & 20 Dec–1 Jan
Semi-detached house on busy road just out of town centre in area of hotels, opposite a small park. Family atmosphere.
6hc (2fb) Ⓡ ✱B&b£10–£12 WB&b£70–£84
CTV 2 (charge)
See advertisement on page 389

GH Marlyn 3 Chestnut Walk ☎(0789) 293752 Plan **11** *A1*
Closed Xmas
8hc Ⓡ ✱B&b£12.95–£13.95
CTV

GH Melita Private Hotel 37 Shipston Rd ☎(0789) 292432 Plan **12** *C1*
Closed 24 & 25 Dec
12 (3fb) CTV in all bedrooms Ⓡ B&b£17–£22 WB&b£107–£138
Lic CTV 12P 2
Ⓥ

GH Moonraker House 40 Alcester Rd ☎(0789) 67115 Plan **13** *A3*
6 Annexe: 9hc (2 7) (4fb) in 4 bedrooms CTV in all bedrooms Ⓡ B&b£9.50–£14 WB&b£66.50–£95
12P 3
See advertisement on page 390

GH Nando's 18–19 Evesham Pl ☎(0789) 204907 Plan **14** *A2*
21hc (1 5) (10fb) TV in 6 bedrooms CTV in 1 bedroom B&b£10–£14 Bdi£14–£18 WBdi£98
CTV 8P
Ⓥ

GH Parkfield 3 Broad Wlk ☎(0789) 293313 Plan **15** *A1*
Closed Xmas
Attractive Victorian house in quiet setting. Superb breakfasts provided by friendly proprietor.
7hc (3) (2fb) CTV in all bedrooms Ⓡ B&b£11–£14 WB&b£75–£95
CTV 5P nc5yrs
Credit cards 1 3 Ⓥ
See advertisement on page 390

GH Penryn House 126 Alcester Rd ☎(0789) 293718 Plan **16** *A3*
Detached corner house where most rooms have en-suite facilities.
7hc (1 4) (2fb) CTV in all bedrooms Ⓡ B&b£11–£15
9P
Credit cards 1 2 3 5

GH Penshurst 34 Evesham Pl ☎(0789) 205259 Plan **17** *A1*
Comfortable, friendly guesthouse close to the town's attractions.
8hc (4) (3fb) in 4 bedrooms CTV in all bedrooms B&b£10.50–£15 WB&b£65–£85
Lic 3P nc3yrs
See advertisement on page 390

GH Ravenhurst 2 Broad Walk ☎(0789) 292515 Plan **18** *A1*
Closed Xmas

A small hotel located near to the town centre and theatre with a bar and neat bedrooms all equipped with CTV.

7hc (1⇌ 2fl) (2fb) CTV in all bedrooms ✈ Ⓡ ✱B&b£9.50–£25

Credit cards 1 2 3

GH Salamander 40 Grove Rd ☎(0789) 205728 Plan **19** *A2*

7hc (3fb) B&b£10–£12.50 Bdi£14.50–£17 LDO6.30pm

CTV 2 (charge)

Ⓥ

See advertisement on page 391

GH Sequoia House Hotel 51 Shipston Rd ☎(0789) 68852 Plan **20** *C1*
Closed 25 & 25 Dec

16hc (3⇌ 5fl) (4fb) CTV in all bedrooms ✈ Ⓡ B&b£12.50–£25

Lic CTV 20P nc5yrs

Credit cards 1 3 Ⓥ

See advertisement on page 386

GH Stretton House 38 Grove Rd ☎(0789) 68647 Plan **21** *A2*

Victorian town house close to town centre.

7hc (2fb) CTV in all bedrooms Ⓡ B&b£10–£13 Bdi£15–£18 WBdi£105–£126 LDO4pm

P(200yds)

⊢⊣**GH Virginia Lodge** 12 Evesham Pl ☎(0789) 292157 Plan **22** *A2*

7hc (3⬚) (3fb) CTV in all bedrooms Ⓡ B&b£9–£13 WB&b£60–£72

Lic ⬚ 7P

GH Woodburn House Hotel 89 Shipston Rd ☎(0789) 204453 Plan **23** *C1*
Closed Xmas–New Year

7hc (3⬚) (3fb) CTV in all bedrooms ✱ Ⓡ B&b£14–£20

⬚ 12P nc5yrs

⊢⊣**FH** Mrs M K Meadows **Monk's Barn** *(SP206516)* Shipston Rd ☎(0789) 293714
Closed Xmas Day & Boxing Day

Warm and welcoming small farm, just two miles from centre of Stratford-upon-Avon.

4hc (1⬚) (1fb) ✱ B&b£8–£8.50

⬚ CTV 5P 75acres arable beef sheep mixed

STRATHAVEN
Strathclyde *Lanarkshire*
Map **11** NS74

GH *Springvale Hotel* 18 Letham Rd ☎(0357) 21131
Closed 25, 26 Dec & 1 & 2 Jan

Grey-stone detached house with painted annexe on opposite side of road. A friendly and comfortable family-run establishment in a residential area not far from the central shopping area.

13hc (1⇌ 8⬚) (3fb) CTV in 11 bedrooms LDO6.45pm

Lic ⬚ CTV 8P

STRATHPEFFER
Highland *Ross & Cromarty*
Map **14** NH45

GH *Kilvannie Manor* Fodderty ☎(0997) 21389

Country manor house situated 1 mile east of A834. Dinners served to non-residents.

7hc (2fb) LDO6.30pm

Lic CTV 20P ⬚

⊢⊣**FH** Mrs M Tait **Beechwood House** *(NH497594)* Fodderty ☎(0997) 21387
May–Oct

Spacious and comfortable two-storey house, approx 1m NE of the village on A834.

3hc (1fb) ✱ Ⓡ B&b£8.50–£9 Bdi£12.50–£13 WBdi£91 LDO4pm

⬚ CTV 10P 18acres mixed

Ⓥ

STRETE
Devon
Map **3** SX84

GH *Tallis Rock Private Hotel* ☎Stoke Fleming (0803) 770370
Apr–Oct

9hc (4fb)

CTV 10P

STRETTON
Leicestershire
Map **8** SK91

INN *Shires Hotel* ☎Castle Bytham (078081) 332

200-year-old Georgian inn situated next to the A1 (southbound) offering spacious facilities and fresh home-cooked food.

5hc (2fb) CTV in all bedrooms Ⓡ LDO10.30pm

⬚ 100P ⬚

Credit cards 1 3

STROUD
Gloucestershire
Map **3** SO80

GH Downfield Hotel Cainscross Rd ☎(04536) 4496
Closed 1 wk Xmas

Pleasant, personally-run hotel situated on the A419 on the western edge of town.→

20hc (4⇌ 6fl) (3fb) TV available in bedrooms B&b£13–£16.50 WBdi£115–£133 LDO7.45pm

Lic ♨ CTV 20P 2🚗

STUDLAND
Dorset
Map **4** SZ08

GH Studholme Hotel Ferry Rd
☎(092944) 271
mid Mar–Oct

A pleasant detached hotel situated close to Studland Beach in its own gardens, offering good home cooking and an informal atmosphere.

6hc (3⇌ 1fl) (3fb) ✘ Ⓡ ✱B&b£13–£32 Bdi£20–£39 LDO6pm

Lic CTV 6P nc3yrs

STURMINSTER NEWTON
Dorset
Map **3** ST71

FH Mrs S Wingate-Saul **Holbrook** *(ST743117)* Lydlinch ☎Hazelbury Bryan (02586) 348
Closed Xmas Day & New Years Day

Attractive 'stable' bedroom-suites at this farm which also offers simply fly fishing, clay-pigeon shoot and a small outdoor pool. 3m W off A357 Stalbridge Rd.

2rm (1hc) Annexe: 4rm (3fl) (3fb) CTV in 3 bedrooms TV in 1 bedroom ✘ Ⓡ in 4 bedrooms B&b£10–£12 Bdi£16–£18 WBdifr£112 LDO4pm

♨ CTV 12P ⛱ ♩ 126acres mixed

Ⓥ

STURTON BY STOW
Lincolnshire
Map **8** SK88

Selected

FH Mrs S Bradshaw **Village Farm** *(SK889807)* ☎Gainsborough (0427) 788309
Apr–Oct

This attractive 19th-century farmhouse enjoys a central position in the village. Bedrooms have been tastefully furnished by proprietor, Mrs Bradshaw, whose embroidery is featured throughout on samplers and cushions. The rooms also benefit from her other hobby of collecting and selling antiques.

4hc ⊬ in all bedrooms ✘ Ⓡ B&b£10–£13 Bdi£16.50–£20 WBdi£105–£110 LDO1 day prior

Lic ♨ CTV 6P nc10yrs ℛ(hard) ♩

400acres arable beef sheep mixed

Ⓥ

SUDBURY
Suffolk
Map **5** TL84

GH *Hill Lodge Private Hotel* 8 Newton Rd ☎(0787) 77568
Closed Xmas wk

16hc (5fl) CTV in all bedrooms ✘ LDOnoon

♨ CTV 20P 2🚗

INN Black Boy Hotel Market Hill
☎(0787) 79046

5hc (1fb) ✘ B&b£12.50 Lunch£7alc Dinner9pm£7alc

♨ CTV 10P

Credit cards 1 2

SUMMERCOURT
Cornwall
Map **2** SW85

FH Mrs R J B Richard ***Goonhoskyn*** *(SW871573)* ☎Mitchell (087251) 226
Mar–Oct

Friendly proprietors run this farmhouse of character with well-decorated bedrooms and public areas.

3hc (1fb) CTV in all bedrooms ✘

♨ CTV 3P nc6yrs

50acres arable sheep

FH Mrs W E Lutey **Trenithon** *(SW895553)* ☎St Austell (0726) 860253

Closed Dec

Modern farmhouse situated in quiet location in open countryside a few miles from the coast.

4hc (2fb) ✘ ✱B&b£7–£8 Bdi£10–£12 WBdi£68–£80 LDO3.30pm

♨ CTV 6P 130acres arable beef sheep

Credit cards 1 2 3 5

SURBITON
Gt London
London plan **4** B1
(pages 258–259)

GH Holmdene 23 Cranes Dr ☎01-399 9992
Closed Xmas

Attractive two-storey house in residential area, peaceful and comfortable, near to town centre.

6hc (1fb) CTV in 1 bedroom TV in 1 bedroom ✘ Ⓡ ✱B&b£12–£15 WB&bfr£91

CTV 🅿 nc5yrs

GH Warwick 321 Ewell Rd ☎01-399 5837

Small centrally-located guesthouse run by cheerful and friendly proprietors. Comfortable bedrooms but limited public areas.

9hc (1⇌) (2fb) CTV in all bedrooms ✘ Ⓡ B&b£15.65–£20.80 Bdi£20.65–£25.80 WBdifr£140 LDO2pm

♨ CTV 8P

Ⓥ

SUTTON
Gt London
London plan **4** C1
(pages 258–259)

GH Dene Hotel 39 Cheam Rd ☎01-642 3170

Enjoying a central position, this personally-run hotel has an informal and relaxed atmosphere. Although the bedrooms are comfortable and well-kept, some have narrow beds.

27hc (8⇌ 4fl) (4fb) CTV in 23 bedrooms TV in 4 bedrooms ✘ Ⓡ B&b£16.10–£36.80

♨ 18P nc5yrs

Ⓥ

See advertisement on page 393

GH Eaton Court Hotel 49 Eaton Rd ☎01-643 6766
Closed Xmas

Charming Victorian house, well-positioned in quiet residential area.

14hc (2fl) (3fb) CTV in 9 bedrooms ✱B&b£20–£26 WB&bfr£140

Lic ♨ CTV 6P

Credit cards 1 2 Ⓥ

GH Tara House 50 Rosehill ☎01-641 6142

Converted private house with warm homely atmosphere in residential area.

8hc (2⇌) (2fb) CTV in all bedrooms ✘ Ⓡ B&b£17–£19.50 Bdi£25–£27.50 WBdifr£175 LDO7.30pm

♨ CTV 9P nc6yrs

SUTTON COLDFIELD
West Midlands
Map **7** SP19

GH Standbridge Hotel 138 Birmingham Rd ☎021-354 3007 Birmingham plan **13**

8hc CTV in 1 bedroom TV in 1 bedroom Ⓡ B&b£13.88–£17.50 Bdi£19.57–£23.19 LDO6pm

Lic ♨ CTV 11P nc5yrs jacuzzi

See advertisement under Birmingham

SWANAGE
Dorset
Map **4** SZ07

GH Bella Vista Hotel 14 Burlington Rd ☎(0929) 422873
Jun–Aug rs Apr–May & Sept–Oct

Neat, pleasant accommodation in a cottage-style property within easy reach of beach and town centre.

6hc (4fl) (4fb) ✘ Ⓡ available in bedrorooms ✱B&b£10–£12 Bdi£14.50–£16 WBdifr£84 (W only Jul & Aug) LDO4pm

Lic CTV 6P nc4yrs

GH Burlington House Hotel 7 Highcliffe Rd ☎(0929) 422422
27 Feb–Oct

Views of Swanage Bay and located in quiet cul de sac.

9hc (2⇌ 3fl) (5fb) CTV in 3 bedrooms TV in 5 bedrooms B&b£9.90–£14.25 Bdi£14.90–£19.25 WBdi£99.10–£128.58 LDO5pm

Lic 🍴 CTV 9P

Ⓥ

⊢⊣ **GH Byways** 5 Ulwell Rd ☎(0929) 422322
Mar–Sep

Well-appointed and comfortable guesthouse a short distance from the beach.

11hc (4fb) B&b£8.50–£11 Bdi£13–£16 WBdi£85–£100 LDO2pm

CTV 6P

GH Chines Hotel 9 Burlington Rd ☎(0929) 422457
Apr–24 Oct

Neat two-storey house in quiet road near beach and town.

12hc (5fl) (5fb) ✖ B&b£11.65–£14.95 Bdi£17.95–£21.30 WBdifr£128.80 (W only Jul & Aug) LDO4pm

Lic 🍴 CTV 9P ⌂

GH *Eversden Private Hotel* Victoria Rd ☎(0929) 423276

Private hotel with good views, a few minutes walk from the beach.

Swanage

12hc (2⇌ 3fl) (3fb) ⚡ in 2 bedrooms ✖ LDO6pm

Lic 🍴 CTV 12P

GH Firswood Hotel 29 Kings Rd ☎(0929) 422306
rs Nov & Jan–Mar (Closed Dec)

7hc (4fb) ✖ Ⓡ B&bfr£10 Bdifr£14 WBdifr£86 LDO3pm

🍴 CTV 7P nc5yrs

Credit cards 1 3

Credit Cards

1 Access/Euro/Mastercard

2 American Express

3 Barclaycard/Visa

5 Diners

GH Havenhurst Hotel 3 Cranbourne Rd ☎(0929) 424224
Apr–Oct

Pleasant guesthouse in quiet area with neat bedrooms.

17hc (6⇌ 11fl) (4fb) ✖ Ⓡ B&b£16–£18 Bdi£21.50–£23.50 WBdi£130–£140 (W only Jun–Aug) LDO7pm

Lic 🍴 CTV 17P

Ⓥ

See advertisement on page 394

GH Ingleston Private Hotel 2 Victoria Rd ☎(0929) 422391
Feb–Nov

Corner sited villa in quiet position minutes from the beach.

9hc (3fb) ✖ B&b£10–£13 Bdi£13–£16 WBdi£95–£115 LDO5pm

Lic 🍴 CTV 9P nc6mths

GH *Kingsley Hall Hotel* 8 Ulwell Rd ☎(0929) 422872
rs Dec–Feb

Situated a short distance from the beach with uninterrupted views across bay.

13hc (3⇌ 4fl) (4fb) CTV in all bedrooms Ⓡ LDO6.15pm

Lic 🍴 CTV 20P

GH *Nethway Hotel* Gilberts Rd ☎(0929) 423909
Whit–21 Oct
Near to shops and sea front.
12hc (4fl) (4fb) ✖ Ⓡ LDO6.30pm
Lic 𝍡 CTV 10P nc5yrs

GH Oxford Hotel 3/5 Park Rd ☎(0929) 422247
Located on the rise of hill leading from town centre and sea front.
14hc (1⇨ 5fl) (4fb) CTV in 12 bedrooms ✖ Ⓡ available B&b£10–£12.50 Bdi£16–£18.50 WBdi£112–£126 LDO4.30pm
Lic 𝍡 CTV ₱
Ⓥ

GH *St Michael Hotel* 31 Kings Rd ☎(0929) 422064
Mar–Nov
Neat town centre guesthouse with attractive bedrooms and attentive service.
6hc (3fl) (4fb) CTV in all bedrooms Ⓡ LDO2pm
Lic 𝍡 5P nc5yrs

GH Sandringham Hotel 20 Durlston Rd ☎(0929) 423076
Mar–Oct
Detached house in quiet residential area 10 minutes walk from beach.

Swanage — Swansea

10hc (8fl) (4fb) TV available in bedrooms Ⓡ B&b£11–£13 Bdi£17–£19 WBdifr£98 LDO6.30pm
Lic 𝍡 CTV 8P ⌂
Ⓥ

GH Seychelles Private Hotel 7 Burlington Rd ☎(0929) 422794
May–Sep
Attractive, comfortable property with own private beach and beach hut, 1½ minutes walk.
10hc (6fl) (4fb) CTV available in bedrooms ✖ Ⓡ B&b£11.50–£14.95 Bdi£17.25–£20.70 WBdi£97.75–£116.15 LDO6.30pm
Lic 𝍡 CTV 10P

SWANSEA
West Glamorgan
Map **3** SS69
See also **Bishopston, Langland Bay** and **Mumbles**

GH Alexander Hotel 3 Sketty Rd, Sketty ☎(0792) 470045
Closed Xmas wk
Proprietor-run commercial guesthouse in city.
7hc (4⇨ 2fl) (3fb) CTV in all bedrooms ✖ Ⓡ B&b£16–£21 Bdi£23–£27 WBdi£130 LDO2pm
Lic 𝍡 CTV ₱ nc2yrs
Credit cards 1 2 3 5 Ⓥ

GH Cefn Bryn 6 Upland Cres ☎(0792) 466687)
Closed Xmas
Tastefully and comfortably appointed with interesting objects d'art and paintings.
7hc (3fl) (2fb) CTV in 6 bedrooms TV in 1 bedroom ✖ Ⓡ ✱B&b£13–£14.50 Bdi£19.50–£21 WBdi£109–£114 LDOnoon
CTV ₱

GH Channel View 17 Bryn Rd, Brynmill ☎(0792) 466834
Stone-built house overlooking St Helens cricket and rugby ground.
6hc (1fb) ✱B&b£7.50–£8 WB&bfr£56
𝍡 CTV ₱

GH Crescent 132 Eaton Cres, Uplands ☎(0792) 466814
Closed Xmas & New Year
Family-run guesthouse.

7hc (1⋔) (1fb) TV in all bedrooms ® ✱B&b£11–£12 Bdi£16–£17 WBdifr£107 LDO4pm

⅏ CTV 4P

Credit cards 1 3 Ⓥ

⊢⊣ **GH The Guesthouse** 4 Bryn Rd ☎(0792) 466947

Small friendly guesthouse opposite St Helen's County Cricket Ground. Small bar for residents.

7hc (1fb) ✖ B&b£8–£9 Bdi£12–£13 WBdifr£83 LDO1pm

Lic ⅏ CTV ⱣP nc12yrs

Ⓥ

Swansea

GH Parkway Hotel 253 Gower Rd, Sketty ☎(0792) 201632
Closed 24 Dec–3 Jan

A warm welcome awaits at this small private hotel in lovely mature grounds.

17hc (12⋔) (1fb) CTV in all bedrooms ® B&b£14–£26 Bdi£20–£32 LDO8pm

Lic ⅏ CTV 17P pool table

Credit cards 1 2 3 5

GH *St Davids Private Hotel* 15 Sketty Rd, Uplands ☎(0792) 473814

Commercial city guesthouse with cosy bar for residents.

11hc (2⇌ 2⋔) (3fb) CTV in 2 bedrooms TV in 9 bedrooms LDO4pm

Lic ⅏ CTV 2P

Credit cards 1 3

GH Tregare Hotel 9 Sketty Rd, Uplands ☎(0792) 470608

Small hotel. →

10hc (3⇌ 6ℳ) (3fb) CTV in all bedrooms Ⓡ B&b£12–£16 Bdi£18.50–£22.50 WBdifr£135 LDO4pm

Lic 卌 CTV 5P snooker

Credit cards 1 3 Ⓥ

GH Uplands Court 134 Eaton Cres ☎(0792) 473046

Property of character in an elevated position with views over city and coast.

8hc (2fb) TV in all bedrooms Ⓡ B&b£11 Bdi£16.50 WBdi£105 LDO12am

Lic 卌 CTV ✗

SWINESHEAD
Bedfordshire
Map **4** TL06

Selected

FH D Marlow **The Manor Farm** *(TL057659)* ☎Bedford (0234) 708126
Closed Xmas

Beautiful farmhouse, recently renovated and comfortably furnished.

3rm (1fb) ⚟ in all bedrooms ✗ B&b£12–£13 WBdi£84–£91

卌 CTV 6P nc10yrs 3acres mixed small holding

SYMONDS YAT, EAST
Hereford & Worcester
Map **3** SO51

Swansea — Tal-y-Llyn

GH *Garth Cottage Hotel* ☎(0600) 890364
Mar–mid Nov

Small, modernised hotel on the banks of the River Wye, run on informal lines.

7hc (1⇌ 2ℳ) ✗ LDO6pm

Lic 卌 CTV 9P nc7yrs

Credit card 1

INN *Saracens Head* ☎(0600) 890435

Well-restored inn on banks of River Wye with good accommodation.

10hc (4ℳ) ✗ LDO10pm

CTV P ♪ solarium

Credit cards 1 2 3

SYMONDS YAT, WEST (nr Ross-on-Wye)
Hereford & Worcester
Map **3** SO51

GH Woodlea ☎(0600) 890206
Closed Feb

10hc (3ℳ) (2fb) Ⓡ B&b£12.50–£15.50 Bdi£20–£23 WBdi£128–£140 LDO7.30pm

Lic 卌 CTV 8P ⩫

Ⓥ

TADCASTER
North Yorkshire
Map **8** SE44

GH Shann House 47 Kirkgate ☎(0937) 833931

Charming, well-restored Georgian house with spacious, well-fitted bedrooms and attractive lounge.

8⇌ℳ (1fb) CTV in all bedrooms Ⓡ B&b£13–£17.50

卌 CTV 8P

Credit cards 1 3

TALGARTH
Powys
Map **3** SO13

FH Mrs B Prosser **Upper Genffordd** *(SO171304)* ☎(0874) 711360

Cheerful and welcoming family farmhouse of character with good food and mountain views. 3m S by A479.

2hc (1⇌ 1ℳ) (1fb) ✱B&b£9–£10 Bdi£12–£12.50 WBdifr£87.50 LDO5pm

卌 CTV 4P 200acres dairy mixed

TAL-Y-LLYN
Gwynedd
Map **6** SH60

GH Dolffanog Fawr Tywyn ☎Corris (065 473) 247
Mar–Oct

Originally a 17th-century farmhouse, rebuilt in 1907, this charming house stands beside the Tal-y-Llyn lake and has been furnished with great care.

3hc ✈ Ⓡ ✱B&b£10.50 Bdi£16 WBdi£105 LDO7pm

🍽 CTV 8P Babies to 1yr nc6yrs

Ⓥ

TARPORLEY
Cheshire
Map **7** SJ56

GH Perth Hotel High St ☎(08293) 2514
Closed Jan

Attractively furnished, family run hotel in the centre of the village.

8hc (1⇌ 1⋒) TV in all bedrooms Ⓡ ✱B&b£15–£21 Bdi£25–£29 WBdi£157.50–£182.70 LDO9.30pm

Lic 🍽 12P

Credit cards 1 3 5

TAUNTON
Somerset
Map **3** ST22

GH Brookfield 16 Wellington Rd ☎(0823) 272786

5hc (1⋒) (1fb) CTV in all bedrooms ✈ Ⓡ B&b£16–£22 Bdi£21.50–£27.50 LDO2.30pm

Lic 🍽 CTV 6P

Credit cards 1 3

Tal-y-Llyn — Tavistock

GH Hamilton 57 Hamilton Rd ☎(0823) 272537
Closed 25 & 26 Dec

A red brick detached guesthouse situated on the main road (A38). A friendly establishment with simple accommodation.

7hc (3fb) ✈ B&b£11 Bdi£16 WBdi£107 LDO4.30pm

🍽 CTV 7P nc10yrs

Ⓥ

Selected

GH Meryan House Hotel Bishop's Hull Rd ☎(0823) 337445

Attractive, 17th-century house in own grounds situated close to A38 and 1m from town centre. Excellent bedrooms with en suite facilities. Friendly service.

8hc (5⇌ 3⋒) CTV in all bedrooms ✈ Ⓡ B&b£23.95–£27.95 Bdi£31.40–£35.40 WBdi£219.80–£247.80 LDO6.30pm

Lic 🍽 CTV 12P

See advertisement on page 398

GH Ruishton Lodge Ruishton ☎Henlade (0823) 442298

Large detached house in own grounds, personally-run with country house atmosphere and sound cooking. Situated a short distance from M5 junction, on A358.

6hc (2fb) TV in all bedrooms B&b£10–£12 Bdi£15–£17 WBdifr£86 LDO8pm

Lic 🍽 CTV 10P

Ⓥ

GH White Lodge Hotel 81 Bridgwater Rd ☎(0823) 333287

10⋒ (1fb) CTV in all bedrooms ✈ Ⓡ B&b£20 Bdi£29 WBdi£175 LDO8.30pm

Lic 🍽 14P nc5yrs

Credit cards 1 2 3

TAVISTOCK
Devon
Map **2** SX47

GH St Anne's 31 Plymouth Rd ☎(0822) 3280
4 Jan–17 Dec

Small family-run guesthouse in an ideal location for touring Dartmoor. Guests can be sure of warm hospitality and comfortable bedrooms.

6hc (1⋒) (2fb) CTV in 5 bedrooms Ⓡ ✱B&b£9–£12 Bdi£14.25–£17.25 WBdifr£94 LDO4pm

🍽 CTV 6P

THE ROCK INN

WATERROW
TAUNTON, SOMERSET
Tel: Wiveliscombe 23293
(STD code 0984)

Situated on the A361, 14 miles west of Taunton in the Brendon foothills making places like Exmoor, Clatworthy Reservoir and the north and south coasts very accessible. Fully centrally heated, with comfortable residents' lounge. All bedrooms have private bath, wc & colour TV. Breakfast, luncheon & dinner are served in addition to food at the bar, all year round.

Whittles Farm

Superior 16th Century farmhouse set in 200 acres of dairyland, and situated at the end of a 'no through road'. 1 mile from the village of Beercrocombe and 7 miles from Taunton. Lovely well appointed rooms with ensuite bathrooms. Colour television and tea/coffee making facilities. Excellent farmhouse food. Personal service. Licensed.

Brochure: Mrs Claire Mitchem, Whittles Farm, Beercrocombe, Taunton, Somerset.
Tel: Hatch Beauchamp (0823) 480301.

NATIONAL WINNER.
BEST NEWCOMER AWARD 1986.

See gazetteer entry under Beercrocombe.

MERYAN HOUSE HOTEL

BISHOPS HULL, TAUNTON, SOMERSET TA1 5EG

Proprietors: Carol & Robert Penney

★ Comfortable Country House Hotel ★ Full En Suite Facilities
★ Close to Town Centre ★ Peaceful Village Surroundings
TAUNTON (0823) 337445

⊢⊣**FH** Mrs E C Blatchford **Parswell Farm Bungalow** *(SX464731)* Parswell ☎(0822) 2789
Etr–Oct

Well-situated bungalow on the Callington road, commanding good views of surrounding countryside.

3rm (1hc) (1fb) 🚫 B&b£8–£8.50 WB&bfr£52

CTV P 106acres mixed

TEIGNMOUTH
Devon
Map **3** SX97

⊢⊣**GH Baveno Hotel** 40 Higher Brimley Rd ☎(06267) 3102

14hc (3⧉) (8fb) CTV in all bedrooms Ⓡ B&b£8–£11 Bdi£10–£15 WBdifr£94 LDO6.30pm

Lic ⧉ CTV 20P ⌂ snooker

⊢⊣**GH Glen Devon** 3 Carlton Pl ☎(06267) 2895

7hc (2⇌ 2⧉) (4fb) 🚫 Ⓡ B&b£8.50–£11 Bdi£12.50–£15 WBdifr£72 LDO5pm

Lic ⧉ CTV 6P

Ⓥ

GH Hill Rise Winterbourne Rd ☎(06267) 3108

Comfortable house with good-sized, bright bedrooms, a separate lounge and bar.

9hc (1⧉) (3fb) Ⓡ ✱B&b£9.50–£10.50 Bdi£12.50–£14.50 WBdi£86–£98 LDO5.30pm

Lic ⧉ CTV 4P 1🚗

Ⓥ

GH *Hillsley* Upper Hermosa Rd ☎(06267) 3878

Semi-detached house with new extension in quiet residential area.

8rm (7hc) (4fb) LDOnoon

Lic CTV 10P nc3yrs

Credit cards 2 3

⊢⊣**GH Knoll Hotel** 5 Winterbourne Rd ☎(06267) 4241

19hc (9⧉) (4fb) CTV in 9 bedrooms Ⓡ B&b£9–£16 Bdi£12–£19 WBdifr£71.50 LDO6.30pm

Lic ⧉ CTV 13P ⌂ games room

GH Lyme Bay House Hotel Den Promenade ☎(06267) 2953
rs Nov–Apr

12hc (3⧉) (1fb) CTV available in bedrooms Ⓡ B&b£12–£15.25 Bdi£17.50–£20.75

Lic lift ⧉ CTV

Ⓥ

⊢⊣**GH Rathlin House Hotel** Upper Hermosa Rd ☎(06267) 4473
Closed Xmas rs Nov–Feb

10hc (5fb) 🚫 Ⓡ B&b£9–£11 Bdi£12–£14 WBdi£70–£90

Lic CTV 10P

Ⓥ

GH Teign Holiday Inn Hotel Teign St ☎(06267) 2976
Apr–Oct

11hc (2⧉) (4fb) LDO5pm

Lic ⧉ CTV 11P

TELFORD
Shropshire
Map **7** SJ60

INN Cock Hotel 148 Holyhead Rd, Wellington ☎(0952) 44954

Former coaching inn with comfortable, well-equipped bedrooms. Located at junction of A442 with B5061

6hc (1fb) CTV in all bedrooms 🚫 Ⓡ B&b£12.50–£15 Lunch£2.50alc Dinner9pm£4alc

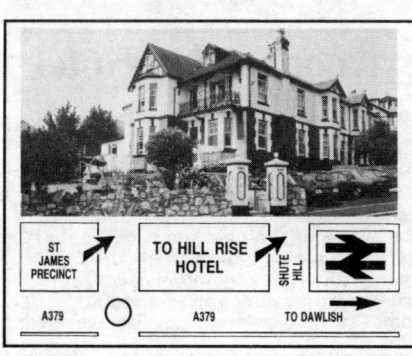

⧉ 30P 4🚗(charge) 🍴

INN Swan Hotel Watling St, Wellington ☎(0952) 3781

12hc (5fb) CTV in all bedrooms B&b£10.66–£17 Bdi£16.41–£22.75 WBdifr£159.25 Lunch£1.50–£2.75 Dinner10pmfr£5.75

𝍖 CTV 150P

Credit cards ① ② ③ ⑤

TEMPLE CLOUD
Avon
Map **3** ST65

FH Mr & Mrs Wyatt **Temple Bridge** *(ST627575)* ☎(0761) 52377
Mar–Oct

Comfortable small listed farm offering good accommodation and friendly atmosphere.

2hc (2fb) ✖ Ⓡ B&b£9.50–£10.50

𝍖 CTV 2P nc2yrs 250acres arable beef

Ⓥ

TENBY
Dyfed
Map **2** SN10

GH Clareston House Warren St ☎(0834) 4148

Family-run guesthouse a few minutes from sea and town centre.

6hc (5fb) ✖ ✻B&b£7.50–£9 Bdi£11–£12.50 WBdi£77–£87.50 LDO11am

Lic 𝍖 CTV 4P

Ⓥ

GH *Hotel Doneva* The Norton ☎(0834) 2460
Mar–Oct

Attractive house situated a few minutes walk from town and harbour.

14hc (3⇌) (7fb) Ⓡ LDO6.30pm

Lic 𝍖 CTV 14P

Credit card ③

GH *Gumfreston Private Hotel* Culver Park ☎(0834) 2871
Closed Nov

A few minutes from town centre and the South Beach with comfortable bedrooms and friendly owners.

11hc (1⇌ 10⋔) (5fb) ✖ Ⓡ LDO4pm

Lic 𝍖 CTV ₱

Credit card ③

GH Heywood Lodge Heywood Ln ☎(0834) 2684
Apr–Oct

Attractive house in own grounds, proprietor-run and well-appointed throughout.

13hc (4⇌ 2⋔) (4fb) Ⓡ B&b£12.50–£15 Bdi£18–£21.50 WBdi£125.75–£143.25 LDO8pm

Lic 𝍖 20P 🏠

Credit cards ① ③

GH Hildebrand Hotel Victoria St ☎(0834) 2403
Closed Dec & Jan rs Feb–Mar & Nov

Cosy modern bedrooms and popular refreshments bar in attractive Victorian property.

11hc (2⇌ 4⋔) (6fb) CTV in all bedrooms Ⓡ B&b£9.50–£16.50 Bdi£13.25–£21.75 WBdi£96–£142 (W only mid Jul–mid Aug)

Lic 𝍖 ₱

Credit cards ① ② ③ ⑤ Ⓥ

GH Myrtle House Hotel St Mary's Street ☎(0834) 2508
Mar–Oct

A well-maintained and enthusiastically run small hotel with bright, airy bedrooms and restaurant of character.

9hc (1⇌ 2⋔) (4fb) ✖ Ⓡ ✻B&b£10.50–£12.50 Bdi£14–£15.50 WBdi£90–£98 LDO4pm

Lic 𝍖 CTV ₱

Credit cards ① ③ Ⓥ

GH Penally Manor Hotel Pennally ☎(0834) 2668
Apr–Oct

16hc (2⇌ 9⋔) (8fb) CTV in all bedrooms Ⓡ ✻B&b£12–£19 Bdi£18–£25 WBdifr£110–£160 LDO8pm

Lic 𝍖 20P 🏠 ⛆(heated) billiards solarium

Credit card ③

GH Red House Hotel Heywood Ln ☎(0834) 2770
Etr–mid Oct

Well-maintained house in own grounds.

29hc (19⇌ 3⋔) (4fb) CTV in all bedrooms ✖ B&b£12.10–£14.10 Bdi£16.70–£18.70 WBdifr£129.95

Lic 𝍖 26P nc3yrs ⛆(heated) 🎾(hard)

Ⓥ

GH Redlands 2 St Florence Pde ☎(0834) 2097
Mar–Oct

Conveniently positioned for sea front and town centre, a recently renovated comfortable Victorian property.

9hc (2⋔) (4fb) Ⓡ ✻B&b£8–£10 Bdi£11.50–£13.50 WBdi£77–£91 LDO5.30pm

Lic 𝍖 CTV ₱

Ⓥ

GH Ripley St Marys Hotel St Mary's Street ☎(0834) 2837
Apr–Oct

14hc (6⇌ ⋔) (6fb) CTV in all bedrooms Ⓡ ✻B&b£11.50–£12.50 Bdi£16.50–£18 WBdi£114–£120LDO6pm

Lic CTV ₱

Credit cards ① ③ Ⓥ

GH Sea Breezes Hotel 18 The Norton ☎(0834) 2753
Mar–Nov rs Nov–Mar

Guesthouse with popular residents' bar, near harbour town and North Beach. Friendly, hospitable, family service.

24hc (10⇌ 2⋔) (6fb) CTV in 12 bedrooms TV in 12 bedrooms ✖ Ⓡ B&b£10–£15 Bdi£13.50–£20 WBdi£85–£112 LDO4.30pm

Lic 𝍖 CTV ₱ snooker

Ⓥ

GH Tall Ships Hotel 34 Victoria St
☎(0834) 2055
Mar–Oct

10hc (4fl) (5fb) CTV in 3 bedrooms ✗ Ⓡ
✱B&b£9.50–£15 Bdi£14–£19 WBdi£95–£130 LDO5pm

Lic CTV 𝐏

Credit cards 1 3 Ⓥ

TETBURY
Gloucestershire
Map **3** ST89

INN Priory London Rd ☎(0666) 52251

Tenby — Tewkesbury

Pat and Paul Gregory offer a warm welcome to their attractive Cotswold stone inn which offers modern bedroom accommodation, a split level lounge bar and separate dining room in a friendly atmosphere.

4hc (1fb) CTV in all bedrooms Ⓡ
✱B&bfr£16.50 Bdifr£21.50 Lunch£6alc Dinner£5alc

100P

TEWKESBURY
Gloucestershire
Map **3** SO83

GH Abbey Hotel 67 Church St ☎(0684) 294247

Comfortable town house with walled garden to the rear.

16hc (7⇌4fl) (3fb) CTV in all bedrooms Ⓡ B&b£20–£28 Bdi£26–£34 WBdi£186 LDO8.30pm

Lic 🏨 11P

Credit cards 1 2 3 Ⓥ

See advertisement on page 402

PENALLY MANOR HOTEL

Penally, Tenby, Dyfed
Telephone: (0834) 2668

The Red House Hotel

Heywood Lane, Tenby, South Pembrokeshire, Dyfed SA70 8BN. Telephone: Tenby (0834) 2770

- ★ No parking problems with our large free car park
- ★ Heated outdoor swimming pool
- ★ Tennis court
- ★ Comfortable licensed lounge bar
- ★ All rooms centrally heated, most with private bathrooms
- ★ The hotel stands in spacious grounds situated in a quiet secluded part of the town yet only 10 minutes walk from the town centre and beaches. From our grounds there are superb views of Caldey Island across the sea.
- ★ Mini Breaks for Spring & Autumn
- ★ Colour TVs in all bedrooms

Sea Breezes Hotel

18 THE NORTON, TENBY, SOUTH PEMBROKESHIRE
Telephone Tenby 2753 (STD 0834)

Cosy comfortable "Sea Breezes" with well furnished bedrooms all with television and residential licence.

Situated opposite Information Bureau within easy walking distance of North Beach (100 yds); shops; coach and rail stations. Central Heating and Tea-makers in all rooms, some rooms with private bathrooms.

Hearty breakfast and four course dinners—and all at a modest price.

THAME
Oxfordshire
Map **4** SP70

GH Essex House Chinnor Rd ☎(084421) 7567

Originally the Thame Railway Station Hotel, this imposing converted Victorian residence offers well equipped accommodation run by the hospitable friendly owners.

10hc (1⇌ 6fl) (2fb) ✗in 5 bedrooms CTV in all bedrooms ✖ ® B&b£18–£25 Bdi£27.45–£34.45 LDO9pm

Lic 🍽 CTV 10P

Credit cards 1 3 Ⓥ

See advertisement under Oxford

FH Mrs M Aitken **Upper Green** *(SU736053)* Manor Rd, Towersey (1½m E unclass rd) ☎(084421) 2496
Closed Xmas & New Year

Homely, friendly atmosphere at this 15th-century thatched farmhouse in lovely countryside. Non-smokers only.

3rm (1hc 1fl) ✗ in all bedrooms TV in all bedrooms ✖ B&b£12–£15

🍽 CTV 8P nc

7 acres poultry sheep

THIRKLEBY
North Yorkshire
Map **8** SE47

FH Mr & Mrs J Knowles **Manor** *(SE478787)* Little Thirkleby ☎(0845) 401216
Closed Xmas

Comfortable Georgian farmhouse in peaceful setting facing the Hambleton Hills.

3rm (3fb) ✗ in 2 bedrooms TV in 1 bedroom ✖ ® ✱B&b£8–£9 WB&b£54

🍽 CTV 5P 🚜 176acres mixed

Ⓥ

THIRLMERE
Cumbria
Map **11** NY31

FH Mr & Mrs J Hodgson **Stybeck** *(NY319188)* ☎Keswick (07687) 73232
Closed Xmas day

Quiet farmhouse at northern end of the lake, within attractive fell country.

3hc (1fb) ✖ ® B&bfr£11 Bdifr£17 WBdifr£119 LDO6pm

🍽 CTV 4P nc5yrs 200acres dairy sheep mixed

THORGANBY
North Yorkshire
Map **8** SE64

INN Jefferson Arms Main St ☎Wheldrake (090489) 316

300-year-old inn fitted and furnished in 'cottage'-style with beamed bars and comfortable bedrooms. Local fresh produce used in restaurant.

3⇌ Annexe: 3rm 2⇌ (2fb) ✗ in 3 bedrooms CTV in 5 bedrooms ® B&b£17.50–£20 Bdi£27.25–£29.75 WBdi£255 Lunch £5.95&alc High tea £4.95 Dinner 9.30pm £9.75&alc

🍽 60P solarium

Credit cards 1 2 3 5

See advertisement under York

THORNHILL
Dumfries & Galloway *Dumfriesshire*
Map **11** NX89

⊢⊣**FH** Mrs J Mackie **Waterside Mains** *(NS870971)* ☎(0848) 30405
Apr–Nov

Farmhouse with nice bedrooms, set on banks of River Nith, catering for fishing parties. 1m N off A76.

3hc (1fb) ® B&b£9 Bdi£13 LDO4pm

Lic 🍽 CTV 4P 🚜 170acres arable beef dairy

THORNTHWAITE (nr Keswick)
Cumbria
Map **11** NY22

GH Thornthwaite Grange ☎Braithwaite (059682) 205

18th-century Manor house.

6hc (3fl) (3fb) CTV in 2 bedrooms ® B&b£11.50–£15 Bdi£19–£22.50 WBdi£120–£142 LDO4.30

Lic 🍽 CTV 10P solarium

Ⓥ

THORNTON HEATH
Gt London London plan **4** D1 *(pages 258–259)*

GH *Dunheved Hotel* 639–641 London Rd ☎01-684 2009
Closed Xmas

Family-run hotel situated on A233, close to Croydon town centre. Central London easily accessible.

17hc (2fl) (4fb) CTV in 1 bedroom TV in 1 bedroom ✖

Lic 🍽 CTV 8P

Credit cards 1 3

THORPE (Dovedale)
Derbyshire
Map **7** SK15

GH Hillcrest House ☎Thorpe Cloud (033529) 436
Mar–Oct

Large house in picturesque situation close to Dovedale.

7hc (2fb) ® B&b£13–£15 Bdi£21–£23 WBdifr£147 LDO3pm

Lic 🍽 CTV 12P

THORPE BAY
Essex
See **Southend-on-Sea**

THRAPSTON
Northamptonshire
Map **4** SP97

INN Court House Hotel ☎(08012) 3618

7hc (2⇌ 1fl) TV in all bedrooms ✖ ® B&b£15–£20 Bdi£20–£30 WBdifr£140 Lunch £6&alc Dinner9.30pm £6–£9&alc

🍽 5P

Credit cards 1 3 Ⓥ

THREE COCKS
Powys
Map **3** SO13

GH *Old Gwernyfed Country Manor*
Felindre (2m SE) ☎Glasbury (04974) 376
mid Mar–mid Dec

A unique Elizabethan manor house in peaceful surroundings offering modern comforts and good home-cooking.

8hc (6⇌) (2fb)LDO8pm

Lic 20P croquet

THRESHFIELD
North Yorkshire
Map **7** SD96

GH Greenways Wharfeside Av (Guestaccom) ☎Skipton (0756) 752598
Apr–Oct

Delightfully furnished house in own grounds with superb views across the River Wharfe.

5hc (1fb) Ⓡ ✱B&b£15 Bdi£23 WBdi£145 LDO5pm

Lic ᵯ CTV 8P nc7yrs ♪

THRINGSTONE
Leicestershire
Map **8** SK41

FH Mr F E White **Talbot House** *(SK423173)* ☎Coalville (0530) 222233

Large old farmhouse and former coaching inn on B587 between Whitwick and Swanington, 2½ miles from Coalville and 4½ miles W M1 junction 23.

4rm (2fb) ✖ B&bfr£9.50 Bdifr£14.50 WBdifr£161 LDO11am

ᵯ CTV 6P 150acres dairy

THROWLEIGH
Devon
Map **3** SX69

FH Mr & Mrs C R Mosse ***East Ash Manor*** *(SX680911)* ☎Whiddon Down (064723) 244

17th-century thatched farmhouse with oak beams. Situated in Dartmoor National Park. 1m E on Whiddon Down road.

3rm (2hc) (1fb) ✖ Ⓡ

ᵯ CTV 4P ⌂ 160acres dairy

REMEMBER

Prices quoted in the gazetteer are minimum double room occupancy to maximum single room occupancy per person.

THURNING
Norfolk
Map **9** TG02

⊢⊣**FH** Mrs A M Fisher **Rookery** *(TG078307)* ☎Melton Constable (0263) 860357
Apr–Oct

Off B1235 onto unclassified road at Briston.

3rm (1⇌) (1fb) ✖ B&bfr£8.50 Bdifr£12.50

400acres arable

THURSBY
Cumbria
Map **11** NY35

⊢⊣**FH** Mrs M G Swainson **How End** *(NY316497)* ☎Wigton (0965) 42487
Apr–Oct

A neat and charming farmhouse with an attractive oak-beamed lounge. Conveniently situated on the A595 between Carlisle and Wigton.

3rm (2fb) TV in 1 bedroom ✖ B&bfr£8 Bdifr£12.50 WBdi£82 LDOnoon

ᵯ CTV 4P 200acres dairy mixed

THWAITE
North Yorkshire
Map **7** SD89

GH Kearton ☎Richmond (North Yorks) (0748) 86277
Closed Jan & Feb

→

Pleasant Swaledale cottage, extended to provide particularly spacious dining facilities.

13hc (2fb) ✗ Ⓡ ✱B&b£11.50 Bdi£17.50 WBdi£115.50 LDO6.30pm

Lic 🍽 14P

Ⓥ

TIDEFORD
Cornwall
Map **2** SX35

FH Mrs B A Turner **Kilna House** *(SX353600)* ☎Landrake (075538) 236
Mar–Oct rs Nov–Feb (Closed Xmas & New Year)

Stone-built house set in a large pleasant garden on A38, ¼ mile outside village. Overlooking the River Tiddy Valley.

5hc (2fb) CTV available Ⓡ B&b£9.80–£10.50 WB&bfr£63

CTV 6P 12acres arable

Ⓥ

TIMSBURY
Avon
Map **3** ST65

GH Old Malt House Hotel & Licensed Restaurant Radford ☎(0761) 70106
Closed Xmas

Quietly situated family-run hotel offering a welcoming atmosphere with personal service.

10hc (4⇌ 4fl) (2fb) CTV in all bedrooms ✗ B&bfr£17 Bdifr£26 WBdifr£182 LDO8pm

Lic 🍽 26P nc3yrs

Credit cards 1 2 3 5

See advertisement under Bath

TINTAGEL
Cornwall
Map **2** SX08

GH *Belvoir House* Tregatta ☎Camelford (0840) 770265
Closed Xmas

7hc (2fl) (1fb) TV in 1 bedroom Ⓡ LDO6pm

Lic CTV 12P nc1yr

⊢⊣**GH Castle Villa** Molesworth St ☎Camelford (0840) 770373

Small, family-run guesthouse, offering fresh home produced food.

5hc (1fb) ⊁ in 2 bedrooms CTV in 1 bedroom Ⓡ B&b£8.50–£11 Bdi£16–£19 WBdi£112–£133 LDO9pm

🍽 CTV 6P 1⌂

Ⓥ

Selected

GH Trebrea Lodge Trenale
☎Camelford (0840) 770410
Etr–Oct

A fine 14th-century, stone-built country house in rural surroundings overlooking village and coastline. The interior is tastefully furnished and includes a comfortable 1st-floor drawing room with excellent views and a Victorian-style smoking room. Good home-cooked dinners are served.

7hc (3⇌ 4fl) (1fb) CTV in all bedrooms ✱B&b£16.50 Bdi£23 WBdifr£150 LDO8pm

Lic 🍽 8P

Credit cards 1 3

⊢⊣**GH Trevervan Hotel** Trewarmett
☎Camelford (0840) 770486

Fine sea views at personally-run guesthouse in village of Trewarmett, 2m S B3263.

6hc (4fb) ⊁ in 4 bedrooms B&b£9–£11 Bdi£14–£16WBdifr£100 LDO9.30pm

Lic 🍽 CTV 10P

Credit cards 1 3 Ⓥ

GH Trewarmett Lodge ☎Camelford (0840) 770460
Closed Nov

Small stone-built hotel with good restaurant.

6hc (1⫼) (2fb) 🚭 in 2 bedrooms Ⓡ B&b£13.50–£15.50 Bdi£21–£23 WBdifr£124 LDO9pm

Lic 𝍥 CTV 10P ⌂

Credit cards 1 3 5 Ⓥ

GH Willapark Manor Hotel Bossiney ☎Camelford (0840) 770782

8hc (6⇌ 1⫼) (2fb) CTV in 6 bedrooms Ⓡ B&bfr£15 Bdifr£22 WBdifr£140 LDO7pm

Lic CTV 20P ⌂

Ⓥ

See advertisement on page 406

TINTERN
Gwent
Map **3** SO50

GH The Parva Farmhouse & Restaurant ☎(02918) 411

A comfortable 17-century house just 50yds from the banks of the River Wye with beamed sitting room and pretty bedrooms.

9hc (2⇌ 6⫼) (3fb) CTV in all bedrooms Ⓡ B&b£13–£28 Bdi£20–£36 WBdi£115–£220 LDO8.30pm

Lic 𝍥 12P 2🚗 ⌂

Ⓥ

See advertisement on page 406

Hotel and Licensed Restaurant
Trewarmett • Tintagel • Cornwall
Tel. Camelford 0840 770460

Trewarmett Lodge

Small family run hotel with magnificent sea and country views. Offering modest comfort coupled with friendly personal service. In quiet surroundings yet close to all amenities, it makes an ideal base for touring or a completely relaxing holiday. Known locally for our excellent restaurant offering Table D'hôte and A La Carte Menus. Small well behaved pets and children catered for, Varied Tariff consessions for children sharing. 2/3/5 day breaks.
Open all the year for bookings. Access/Visa welcome.

Trebrea Lodge
Trenale, Nr. Tintagel, North Cornwall.

This grand old Cornish house dates from 1300 AD and is now a small family-run hotel in its own rural setting on the magnificent north coast. Our bedrooms, all with colour TV and all with private bathrooms, look out across fields to the sea as does the first floor drawing room. The bar and Victorian smoking room are for those comfortable cosy evenings. Our reputation, for really good home-made food and a friendly atmosphere, is borne out by previous guests' written comments which we'll send you with our brochure. We offer reductions for children, there's a games room in the grounds, and dogs are welcome too.

Phone or write for brochure pack to Ann & Guy Murray. Tel. 0840 (STD) 770410.

INN *Fountain* Trellech Grange ☎(02918) 303
rs Mon Closed Dec–Feb
Attractive rural inn with restaurant providing à la carte menu.
5hc CTV in 1 bedroom TV in 4 bedrooms Ⓡ LDO9.30pm
🍽 60P

TISSINGTON
Derbyshire
Map **7** SK15

⊢→**FH** Mrs B Herridge **Bent** *(SK187523)* ☎Parwich (033525) 214
Etr–Oct
Traditional stone-built farmhouse situated in the Peak District National Park.
4hc (1fb) ✖ Ⓡ B&b£9–£10 Bdi£14–£15.50 WBdifr£95 LDO5pm
🍽 CTV 6P nc5yrs 280acres beef dairy mixed sheep

TIVERTON
Devon
Map **3** SS91

⊢→**GH Bridge** 23 Angel Hill ☎(0884) 252804
10hc (2🛁) (2fb) TV in all bedrooms Ⓡ

B&b£9–£14 Bdi£14–£19 WBdifr£100 LDO6.30pm
Lic 🍽 CTV 6P 1🚗 ⌂ ✓
Ⓥ

⊢→**FH** Mr L Fullilove **Lodge Hill** *(ST945112)* Ashley ☎(0884) 252907
Large rendered farmhouse on hillside in the Exe Valley, situated 1 mile S of town, Off A396.
7hc (2⇌) (1fb) Ⓡ B&b£9–£11 Bdi£13–£15WBdifr£86 LDO4pm
Lic 🍽 CTV 8P 10acres beef poultry sheep
Ⓥ

FH Mrs I R Olive **Lower Collipriest** *(SS953117)* ☎(0884) 252321
Etr–Oct
Lovely thatched farmhouse with attractive courtyard offering speciality traditional cooking.
2⇌ ⚟ in 1 bedroom ✖ Ⓡ B&b£14–£15 Bdi£18–£20 WBdi£110–£116 LDOnoon
🍽 CTV 2P 2🚗 nc12yrs ✓ 220acres beef dairy

TOBERMORY
Isle of Mull, Strathclyde *Argyllshire*
See **Mull, Isle of**

TODMORDEN
West Yorkshire
Map **7** SD92

GH Stansfield Cottage Holebottom Rd (Guestaccom) ☎(070681) 2979
Closed Xmas & New Year
This guesthouse occupies part of a Victorian building which was once a mill-owners house. Situated in an elevated position it offers excellent views. Bedrooms are comfortable and well-equipped and public rooms are nicely decorated. Particularly hospitable proprietor.
3🛁 CTV in all bedrooms ✖ Ⓡ B&b£12.30–£18.50 Bdi£19.80–£26 WBdi£138.50–£168 LDO10am
🍽 CTV 5P
Ⓥ

FH Mrs R Bayley **Todmorden Edge South** *(SD924246)* Parkin Ln, Sourhall Rd ☎(070681) 3459
Mar–Dec
Converted 17th-century farmhouse on hillside. Clean, comfortable rooms and a cosy residents lounge 1m from town centre.

3hc (1fb) ✕ ® B&b£10.75–£13.75 Bdi£17.75–£22.50 WBdifr£120 LDOprior arrangement

▥ CTV 10P nc8yrs U 1acre non-working

Ⓥ

TOMDOUN
Highland *Inverness-shire*
Map **14** NH10

FH Mrs H Fraser **No 3 Greenfield** *(NH201006)* ☎(08092) 221
mid May–Sep

Small modern bungalow set in isolated position in rugged, hilly countryside. 2m E on S side of Loch Garry.

3rm (1fb) ✱B&b£8 Bdi£12.50 WBdifr£81 LDO7pm

CTV 6P 172acres mixed

TORBAY
Devon
See **Brixham, Paignton** and **Torquay**

TORCROSS
Devon
Map **3** SX84

GH Cove House ☎Kingsbridge (0548) 580448
Mar–Nov

11hc (1⇌ 2⋒) (2fb) CTV in all bedrooms ✕ B&b£13.80–£14.38 Bdi£21.85–£23.58 WBdifr£148.35 LDO5pm

Lic 11P nc8yrs

Ⓥ

TORQUAY
Devon
Map **3** SX96
See Central & District plans on pages 408–409 & 412

GH Abbey Court Hotel Falkland Rd ☎(0803) 27316 Central plan **1** *B3*
Etr–Sep & Xmas

26hc (11⇌ 1⋒) (9fb) B&b13.50–£19.50 Bdi£16.50–£23 WBdi£103–£147.50 LDO7pm

Lic ▥ CTV 20P ⛱(heated) solarium

Ⓥ

GH *Allandene Seapoint Hotel*
5 Clifton Gv, Old Torwood Rd ☎(0803) 211808 Central plan **33** *F3*
Etr–Nov

10hc (3fb) ✕ LDO4pm

Lic ▥ CTV 4P 1🚗 ⌂

⟼**GH Ambergate Hotel** Solsbro Rd, Chelston ☎(0803) 605146 Central plan **2** *A2*
Apr–Oct

Bright friendly residence overlooking town.

13hc (3⇌) (3fb) ✕ ® ✱B&b£8–£12 Bdi£11–£15 WBdi£77–£105 (W only 15 Jul–Aug) LDO4pm

Lic ▥ CTV 8P

Ⓥ

⟼**GH Ashwood Hotel** 2 St Margarets Rd, St Marychurch ☎(0803) 38173 District plan **45**
Etr–Oct

8hc (2fb) CTV in all bedrooms ✕ ® B&b£9–£12 Bdi£13–£16 WBdifr£85 LDO4pm

Lic ▥ CTV 8P

Credit cards 1 3

⟼**GH Avon Hotel** Torbay Rd, Livermead ☎(0803) 23946 District plan **46**

Bright, modern hotel with lawned frontage, near Livermead beach.

20hc (1⋒ 5⇌) (2fb) CTV in all bedrooms ✕ ® B&b£7.50–£14.50 Bdi£11–£19 WBdifr£92 LDO4.30pm

Lic ▥ CTV 20P ⌂

Credit cards 1 3 Ⓥ

GH Avron Hotel 70 Windsor Rd ☎(0803) 24182 District plan **47**
Apr–Sep

14hc (6⋒) (1fb) TV in all bedrooms ® WBdi£78–£94 LDO6.30pm

CTV 8P

GH *Aylwood House Hotel* 24 Newton Rd ☎(0803) 23501 Central Plan **3** *A4*
Etr–Oct

10hc (2⇌ 1⋒) (2fb) CTV in all bedrooms LDO5pm

▥ CTV 10P ⌂

GH Braddon Hall Hotel Braddons Hill Road East ☎(0803) 23908 Central plan **5** *F3*

This small friendly establishment of some charm and character enjoys an elevated position. Good views across the harbour which is just a short walk away. Vegetarian and wholefood cookery a speciality.

11hc (2⇌ 4⋒) (3fb) ® B&b£9.50–£12.50 Bdi£12.50–£15.50 WBdifr£85 LDO5pm

Lic CTV 8P

GH Burley Court Hotel Wheatridge Ln, Livermead ☎(0803) 607879 District plan **48**
Apr–Oct

21hc (1⇌ 20⋒) (7fb) CTV in all bedrooms ✕ ® B&b£12.50–£15 Bdi£18.21–£21 WBdi£98–£135 (W only Jul & Aug) LDO6.30pm

Lic ▥ 25P ⛱ ⛱(heated) solarium gymnasium

Ⓥ

GH Carn Brea 21 Avenue Rd ☎(0803) 22002 Central plan **6** *B3*
Closed Xmas

20hc (12⋒) (5fb) CTV in 15 bedrooms ✕ ® B&b£11–£13 Bdi£16–£18 WBdifr£130 LDO6pm

Lic ▥ CTV 20P ⛱(heated)

Ⓥ

⟼**GH Chesterfield Private Hotel** 62 Belgrave Rd ☎(0803) 22318 Central plan **8** *B3*

12hc (4⋒) (4fb) CTV in all bedrooms ® B&b£8.50–£11.50 Bdi£13–£16.50 WBdi£77–£99 LDO4pm

Lic ▥ CTV 3P

Credit card 3 Ⓥ

GH *Hotel Concorde* 26 Newton Rd ☎(0803) 22330 Central plan **9** *A4*
Etr–Oct
22hc (6⇌ 5fl) CTV in all bedrooms ✗ ®
Lic 𝕸 CTV 12P ⛱(heated)

⊢⊣**GH Craig Court Hotel** 10 Ash Hill Rd, Castle Circus ☎(0803) 24400 Central plan **10** *D4*
Etr–Oct
10hc (4fl) (2fb) ✗ B&b£8–£11.50 Bdi£13.50–£17 WBdi£94.50–£119 LDOnoon
Lic CTV 8P
Ⓥ

GH Cranborne Hotel 58 Belgrave Rd ☎(0803) 28046 Central plan **11** *B3*
Closed Dec
13hc (6⇌ 2fl) (6fb) CTV in all bedrooms ✗ ® B&b£9.50–£11.50 Bdi£13.50–£15.50 WBdi£80–£100 LDO3pm
CTV 3P
Credit cards [1] [3] Ⓥ

GH *Cranmore* 89 Avenue Rd ☎(0803) 28488 Central plan **12** *A4*
Modest semi-detached guesthouse on main road into town.
8hc (2fb) ✗ LDO5pm
𝕸 CTV 4P

GH *Crewe Lodge* 83 Avenue Rd ☎(0803) 28772 Central plan **13** *A4*
Semi-detached villa on main road into Torquay with bright, modern fittings.
7hc (1fl) (3fb) ✗ ® LDO4pm
𝕸 CTV P

GH Daphne Court Hotel Lower Warberry Rd ☎(0803) 212011 Central plan **14** *F4*
15hc (1⇌ 9fl) (8fb) CTV in all bedrooms ✗ ® ✱B&b£14–£21.50 Bdi£17.50–£25 WBdi£100–£145 LDO7.30pm
Lic 𝕸 15P ⛳ ⛱(heated) games room
Credit card [3] Ⓥ

⊢⊣**GH Devon Court Hotel** Croft Rd ☎(0803) 23603 Central plan **15** *C3*
Friendly hotel with well-maintained gardens, bright bedrooms and comfortable public rooms

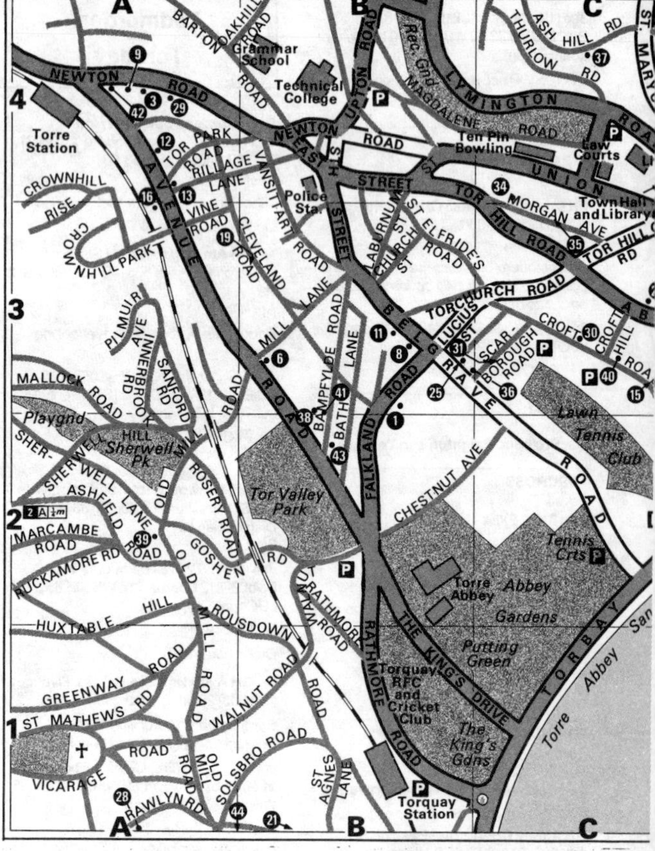

14hc (7fl) (2fb) ✗ ® B&b£8–£14 Bdi£11–£17 WBdi£77–£119 LDO6.30pm
Lic 𝕸 CTV 14P ⛱(heated)
Credit cards [1] [3] Ⓥ

⊢⊣**GH Durlstone** 156 Avenue Rd ☎(0803) 212307 Central Plan **16** *A3*
Small friendly guesthouse with neat and cosy modern bedrooms. Convenient to town and beaches.
6hc (1fb) ✗ ® B&b£7–£9 Bdi£11–£13 WBdi£73–£82 LDO5.30pm
𝕸 CTV 7P

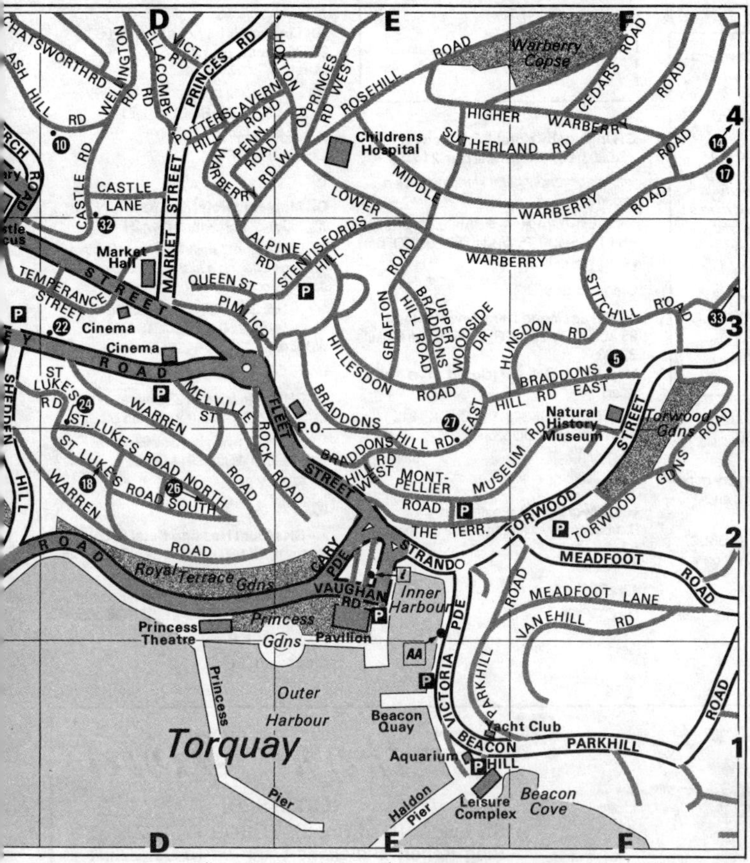

Torquay Central

1 Abbey Court Hotel
2 Ambergate Hotel
3 Aylwood House Hotel
5 Braddon Hall Hotel
6 Carn Brea
8 Chesterfield Private Hotel
9 Hotel Concorde
10 Craig Court Hotel
11 Cranborne Hotel
12 Cranmore
13 Crewe Lodge
14 Daphne Court Hotel
15 Devon Court Hotel
16 Durlstone
17 El Marino Hotel
18 Fretherne Hotel
19 Glenorleigh Hotel
20 Glenwood
21 Ingoldsby Hotel
22 Jesmond Dene Private Hotel
23 Lindum Hotel
24 Mapleton Hotel
25 Marlow Hotel
26 Mount Nessing Hotel
27 Olivia Court
28 Rawlyn House Hotel
29 Richwood Hotel
30 Riva Lodge
31 Rothesay Hotel
32 St Bernards Private Hotel
33 Allandene Seapoint Hotel
34 Sevens Hotel
35 Skerries Private Hotel
36 Southbank Hotel
37 Stephen House Hotel
38 Sun Court Hotel
39 Torbay Rise
40 Torcroft Hotel
41 Tor Dean Hotel
42 Tormohun Hotel
43 Tregantle Hotel
44 Westowe Hotel

GH *El Marino Hotel* Lower Warberry Rd ☎(0803) 26882 Central plan **17** *F4*

Etr–Oct

21hc (3⇌ 15fl) (6fb) ✈ Ⓡ

Lic 🍽 CTV 21P ⌂ ⇌(heated)

⊢⊣**GH Exmouth View Hotel** St Albans Rd, Babbacombe Downs ☎(0803) 37307 District plan **49**

Etr–Oct & Xmas

35hc (7fl) (7fb) CTV in all bedrooms Ⓡ B&b£8–£13.60 Bdi£11.50–£17.10 WBdi£81–£120 LDO5.30pm

Lic 🍽 CTV 25P

GH *Fretherne Hotel* St Lukes Road South ☎(0803) 22594 Central plan **18** *D2*

Etr–Oct

24hc LDO5pm

Lic CTV 20P

See advertisement on page 410

Selected

GH *Glenorleigh Hotel* 26 Cleveland Rd ☎(0803) 22135 Central plan **19** *B3*

This attractive hotel was a worthy winner of the AA 'Best in Britain' Family Hotel in 1984. Situated in its own delightful grounds, Glenorleigh offers very comfortable, modern bedrooms and elegant, public rooms. You can also count on a personal welcome and warm hospitality.

16hc (7fl) (5fb) ✗ Ⓡ LDO6pm

Lic ♛ CTV 10P ⌂(heated) sauna bath solarium gymnasium games room

See advertisement in colour feature

⊢⊣**GH Hart-Lea** 81 St Marychurch Rd ☎(0803) 312527 District plan **50**
Closed Xmas

A comfortable house offering a very good standard of accommodation and an interesting menu.

6hc (2fb) ⚔ in all bedrooms ✗ Ⓡ B&b£7–£9 Bdi£9.50–£12 WBdi£63–£80 (W only Jul & Aug) LDO6.30pm

♛ CTV ₱

Ⓥ

Torquay

GH Ingoldsby Hotel 1 Chelston Rd ☎(0803) 607497 Central plan **21** *B1*

Informal, friendly hotel standing in own grounds.

16hc (6fl) (5fb) ✗ Ⓡ ✱B&b£9.90–£12.90 Bdi£12.65–£18.15 WBdifr£82.50 LDO7pm

Lic ♛ CTV 15P

Credit cards 1 3

⊢⊣**GH Jesmond Dene Private Hotel** 85 Abbey Rd ☎(0803) 23062 Central plan **22** *D3*
May–Sep rs Oct–Apr (closed Xmas & New Year)

11hc (3fb) Ⓡ B&b£8–£11 Bdi£12–£15 WBdi£72–£84 LDOnoon

♛ CTV 3P

Ⓥ

GH *Kilworthy* 157 Westhill Rd, Babbacombe ☎(0803) 36452 District plan **51**
4 Apr–Oct

13hc (2⇌) (6fb)

Lic CTV 12P

GH Lindum Hotel Abbey Rd ☎(0803) 22795 Central plan **23** *C3*
Mar–Nov

20hc (1⇌ 10fl) (3fb) CTV in 8 bedrooms Ⓡ B&b£9.50–£13 Bdi£11.50–£17 WBdi£80–£125 LDO7.15pm

Lic ♛ CTV 14P

Ⓥ

GH Mapleton Hotel St Lukes Rd North ☎(0803) 22389 Central plan **24** *D3*

Select, elegant family hotel in attractive grounds offering a high standard of accommodation and good food.

10hc (1⇌ 6fl) (3fb) CTV in all bedrooms ✗ Ⓡ B&b£12.50–£21 Bdi£15–£23 WBdifr£82

Lic ♛ CTV 9P

⊢⊣**GH Marlow Hotel** 23 Belgrave Rd ☎(0803) 22833 Central plan **25** *B3*

12hc (4fb) Ⓡ available B&b£9–£11 Bdi£13–£15 WBdifr£91 LDO4pm

Lic ♛ CTV 2P

Ⓥ

⊢⊣**GH Mount Nessing Hotel** St Lukes Rd North ☎(0803) 22970 Central plan **26** *D2*

15hc (2⇌ 5fl) (6fb) ✗ B&b£8–£12 Bdi£12–£18 WBdi£69–£105 LDO8.30pm

Lic ♛ CTV 10P

Credit card 3 Ⓥ

GH Olivia Court Braddons Hill Rd ☎(0803) 22595 Central plan **27** *E3*
Apr–Oct (also Xmas)

Very attractive, personally-run property in own secluded gardens overlooking Torbay.

16hc (2fl) (2fb) CTV available in bedrooms Ⓡ B&b£10–£12.50 Bdi£14–£17 WBdifr£85 LDO5pm

Lic 🍽 CTV 3P

GH Pencarrow Hotel 64 Windsor Rd ☎(0803) 23080 District plan **52**
Apr–Oct

13hc (8fl) (2fb) CTV in all bedrooms Ⓡ B&b£12–£14 Bdi£16–£18 WBdi£85–£110 (W only Jul–Aug)

Lic CTV 8P

Ⓥ

GH *Porthcressa Hotel* 28 Perinville Rd, Babbacombe ☎(0803) 37268 District plan **54**

12hc (3fb)

Lic 🍽 CTV 6P

GH Rawlyn House Hotel Rawlyn Rd, Chelston ☎(0803) 605208 Central plan **28** *A1*
Mar–Oct & Xmas

17hc (8fl) (4fb) ✗ Ⓡ Bdi£13–£17 WBdi£88–£122 LDO7.15pm

Lic 🍽 CTV 15P 🏊(heated)

GH Richwood Hotel 20 Newton Rd ☎(0803) 23729 Central plan **29** *A4*
end May–mid Oct (rs Apr–mid May)

22hc (3⇌ 11fl) (10fb) CTV in all bedrooms Ⓡ available B&b£9.50–£14 Bdi£14–£18.50 WBdi£80–£115 (W only mid Summer)

Lic 🍽 CTV 12P 🏊(heated) solarium

GH Riva Lodge Croft Rd ☎(0803) 22614 Central plan **30** *C3*
Apr–Oct

21hc (3⇌ 8fl) (8fb) CTV in 20 bedrooms Ⓡ in 20 bedrooms ✱B&b£11–£16.30 Bdi£16.50–£21.80 WBdi£89.25–£124.95 LDO7pm

Lic CTV 21P 🏊(heated) snooker

Credit cards ① ③

Torquay

GH Rothesay Hotel Scarborough Rd ☎(0803) 23161 Central plan **31** *C3*

30hc (22fl) (7fb) CTV in 25 bedrooms ✗ Ⓡ ✱B&b£14–£17 Bdi£16–£21 WBdi£98–£144 LDO7pm

Lic 🍽 CTV 30P ⌂

Credit cards ① ② ③

GH *St Bernards Private Hotel* Castle Rd ☎(0803) 22508 Central plan **32** *B3*
Closed Xmas

14rm (11hc 3fl) (4fb) ✗ LDO10am

Lic 🍽 CTV 8P

GH Sevens Hotel 27 Morgan Av ☎(0803) 23523 Central plan **34** *C4*

13hc (2fl) (4fb) ✱B&b£8–£11 Bdi£12–£15 WBdi£77–£103.50 LDO4.30pm

Lic 🍽 CTV 10P pool table

Ⓥ

GH Skerries Private Hotel
25 Morgan Av ☎(0803) 23618 Central plan **35** *C3*

12hc (3fb) Ⓡ ✱B&b£7.50–£10.50 Bdi£11–£14 WBdi£73–£87 LDO10am

🍽 CTV 7P

Ⓥ

GH *Southbank Hotel* 15/17 Belgrave Rd ☎(0803) 26701 Central plan **36** *B3*
Closed Jan & Feb

20hc (7fb) ✗ Ⓡ LDO5pm

Lic CTV 14P

GH *Stephen House Hotel* 50 Ash Hill Rd ☎(0803) 25796 Central plan **37** *C4*
Mar–Nov & Xmas

Friendly, detached house with comfortable lounges and modest bedrooms.

15hc (1⇌ 4fl) (4fb) Ⓡ LDO5.30pm

Lic CTV 12P ⌂ 🏊(heated)

⊢⊣**GH Sun Court Hotel** Rowdens Rd ☎(0803) 27242 Central plan **38** *B3*

12hc (2fl) (2fb) CTV in all bedrooms ✗ Ⓡ B&b£7.50–£11.50 Bdi£11–£15 WBdi£75–£105 LDO6.30pm

Lic 🍽 CTV 15P ⌂

Credit cards ① ③ Ⓥ

⊢⊣**GH Torbay Rise** Old Mill Rd ☎(0803) 605541 Central plan **39** *A2*
Apr–Oct

15hc (8⇌) (2fb) B&b£8.50–£15.50 Bdi£13.50–£20.50 WBdi£96–£141 LDO11am

Lic CTV 8P 🏊(heated)

Credit cards ① ③ Ⓥ

See advertisement on page 413

⊢⊣**GH Torcroft Hotel** Croft Rd ☎(0803) 28292 Central plan **40** *C3*
Apr–Oct

Friendly private hotel conveniently positioned for sea and town centre. Compact modern accommodation.

21hc (6fl) (6fb) ✗ B&b£9–£12 Bdi£11–£15.50 WBdi£75–£105 LDO5pm

Lic CTV 15P

GH Tor Dean Hotel 27 Bampfylde Rd ☎(0803) 24669 Central plan **41** *B2/3*
mid Apr–mid Oct

Bright, compact bedrooms in friendly private hotel close to beach and Abbey gardens.

14hc (2fb) ⚔ in 4 bedrooms ✗ ✱B&b£9–£12 Bdi£12–£16 WBdi£75–£109 (W only Jul & Aug) LDO4pm

Lic CTV 10P nc2yrs

GH *Tormohun Hotel* 28 Newton Rd ☎(0803) 23681 Central plan **42** *A4*

23rm (18hc 4⇌ 4fl) (2fb) CTV in all bedrooms LDO7.30pm

Lic 🍽 23P 🏊(heated)

Credit cards ① ②

GH Tregantle Hotel 64 Bampfylde Rd ☎(0803) 27494 Central plan **43** *B2*

Spotlessly clean hotel with friendly service.

11hc (3fb) CTV in all bedrooms ✗ Ⓡ ✱B&b£10.50–£12.50 Bdi£15–£16.50 WBdifr£102 LDO6pm

Lic 🍽 CTV 10P nc5yrs

Credit cards ① ③ Ⓥ

GH *Ventnor* 85 St Marychurch Rd
☎(0803) 39132 District plan **55**
Mar–Oct

Small, friendly guesthouse offering comfortable accommodation in a residential area.

6hc (2fb) CTV in all bedrooms ✈ Ⓡ LDO11am

⦀ nc5yrs

GH Villa Marina Hotel Cockington Ln, Livermead ☎(0803) 605440 District plan **56**
Apr–Oct

Torquay

26hc (20⇌ 4⋒) (6fb) CTV in all bedrooms Ⓡ B&b£11–£15 Bdi£15–£19 WBdi£98–£126 LDO6.45pm

Lic ⦀ CTV 20P

Credit cards 1 3

GH Westowe Hotel Chelston Rd
☎(0803) 605207 Central plan **44** B1
Mar–Oct

Attractively positioned hotel with comfortable, modern bedrooms. For non-smokers only.

12hc (3⇌) ⅟ in all bedrooms CTV in 4 bedrooms ✈ Bdi£13–£18 WBdi£91–£126

Lic ⦀ CTV 8P nc5yrs

Ⓥ

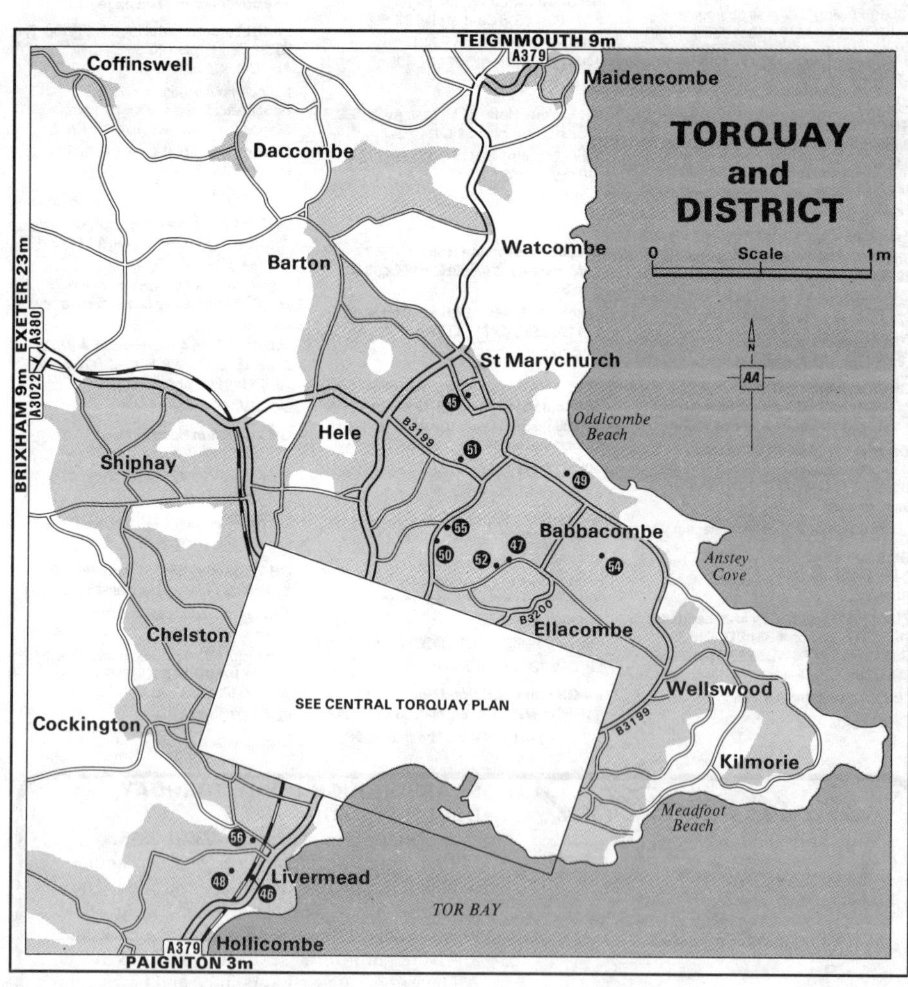

Torquay District

45 Ashwood
46 Avon Hotel
47 Avron Hotel
48 Burley Court Hotel
49 Exmouth View Hotel
50 Hart-Lea
51 Kilworthy
52 Pencarrow Hotel
54 Porthcressa Hotel
55 Ventnor
56 Villa Marina Hotel

TORRINGTON, GREAT

Devon
Map **2** SS42

GH Smytham Manor (Little Torrington 2m S A386) ☏(0805) 22110

6hc (4⇌) Ⓡ ✻B&b£9–£13.50 WB&bfr£64 LDO9.30pm

Lic 𝍪 CTV 14P ⛱(heated)

Credit cards 1 3 Ⓥ

⊢⊣**FH** E J Watkins **Lower Hollam** *(SS501161)* (1m beyond Little Torrington on unclass rd 3m S of Torrington off A386) ☏(0805) 23253
Mar–Oct

Historic house situated in a peaceful, picturesque position. Good play facilities for children.

3hc (2fb) ⚟ in all bedrooms ✖ Ⓡ B&b£8–£8.50 Bdi£12.50–£13 WBdifr£80 LDO 5pm

CTV 3P ⌂ 220acres arable beef sheep

Ⓥ

TORVER

Cumbria
Map **7** SD29

Selected

GH Sunny Bank Mill ☏Coniston (05394) 41300
mid Feb–Dec

Situated on the banks of Torver Beck this former mill cottage was extended in Victorian times, and now offers excellent accommodation including luxury bedrooms with en-suite facilities, a sumptuous lounge and an attractive riverside dining room. The hotel has a private beach on Lake Coniston from which small craft can be launched, with fishing nearby.

5hc (3⇌ 2⋔) (1fb) CTV in all bedrooms ✖ Ⓡ B&b£18–£27 Bdi£28–£37 WBdi£170–£195 LDO10am

Lic 𝍪 8P nc10yrs ⌁

Ⓥ

See advertisement on page 414

TOTLAND BAY

Isle of Wight
See **Wight, Isle of**

TOTNES

Devon
Map **3** SX86

Selected

GH Old Forge Seymour Pl, Bridgetown ☏(0803) 862174
Closed Xmas wk

Jeannie and Peter Allnut provide a warm welcome and friendly service at their charming small guesthouse. The 600 year old building was converted from a smithy, wheelwrights shop and coach houses. The blacksmith's tradition is kept alive today by Peter who has an operational forge. The property has a large walled garden.

8hc (2⇌ 4⋔) (2fb) ⚟in 8 bedrooms CTV in all bedrooms ✖ Ⓡ B&b£12.50–£22.50 WB&b£80.50–£115.50

𝍪 CTV 8P ⌂

Ⓥ

FH Mrs G J Veale **Broomborough House** *(SX793601)* Broomborough Dr ☏(0803) 863134
Mar–Nov

Spacious, country-manor style house in hilly parkland with views of Dartmoor and the surrounding countryside. Games room and local game fishing. →

3hc (1fb) ✕ Ⓡ ✻B&b£13 Bdi£20.50 WBdi£136 LDOam

Lic 🍽 CTV P ⁄ 600acres arable, beef dairy

TOTTENHILL
Norfolk
Map **9** TF61

GH Oakwood House Private Hotel ☎Kings Lynn (0553) 810256
Closed 24–28 Dec

4hc (1⇨ 1fl) Annexe: 3⇨ CTV in all bedrooms ✕ Ⓡ B&b£12.75–£21 Bdi£21–£29.25 WBdi£150–£185 LDO7pm

Lic 🍽 20P

Credit cards 1 2 3 5

See advertisement under Kings Lynn

TOWCESTER
Northamptonshire
Map **4** SP64

INN *Brave Old Oak* Watling St ☎(0327) 50533

12hc (1⇨) (2fb) CTV in all bedrooms Ⓡ LDO9.30pm

🍽 15P ⇏

Credit cards 1 2 3 5

TRALLONG
Powys
Map **3** SN93

FH Mrs M Adams **Brynfedwen** *(SO963297)* ☎Sennybridge (087482) 505
Apr–Oct

This 300-year-old farmhouse is situated just off the A40 and enjoys spectacular views. Fully-modernised to provide very comfortable accommodation.

3rm (1fl) (2fb) ✕ Ⓡ B&bfr£10 Bdifr£15 WBdifr£105

🍽 CTV P 118acres dairy sheep horses

Ⓥ

TREARDDUR BAY
Gwynedd
Map **6** SH27

GH Highground Hotel off Ravenspoint Rd ☎(0407) 860078
Closed 19 Dec–4 Jan

Small personally-run hotel, with sun terrace and panoramic coastal views. Close to beaches and sporting amenities.

7hc (2fb) CTV in all bedrooms ✕ Ⓡ B&b£12 Bdi£19 WBdi£126 LDO3pm

Lic 🍽 7P

Credit cards 1 3 Ⓥ

GH Moranedd ☎(0407) 860324

6hc (1fb) Ⓡ B&b£10 Bdi£15 WBdifr£100 LDO5pm

Lic 🍽 CTV 10P

Ⓥ

TREBARWITH
Cornwall
Map **2** SX08

INN Mill House ☎Camelford (0840) 770200
Closed 24–28 Dec

Imaginatively converted corn mill offering a high standard of accommodation.

9hc (1⇨ 5fl) (1fb) CTV in all bedrooms Ⓡ B&b£16–£19.50 Lunch£4.72–£9.75 Dinner9pm£4.72–£9.75&alc LDO10pm

🍽 60P ⇏ nc10yrs

Credit cards 1 3

TRECASTLE
Powys
Map **3** SN82

INN *Castle Hotel* ☎Sennybridge (087482) 354
Closed Jan

Charming and thoughtfully furnished Georgian building offering good food and excellent modern bedrooms.

8hc (3⚑) (1fb) CTV in all bedrooms ® LDO9.45pm

🅿 40P ⛟

Credit cards 1 3 Ⓥ

TREFRIW
Gwynedd
Map **6** SH76

FH Mr & Mrs D E Roberts **Cae-Coch** *(SH779646)* ☎Llanrwst (0492) 640380

Pleasant farmhouse in elevated position on side of Conwy Valley.

3rm ® in 1 bedroom B&b£9–£9.50 WB&b£60–£63.50

🅿 CTV 4P 1🚗 nc3yrs 50acres mixed

TREGARON
Dyfed
Map **3** SN65

FH M E Davies ***Aberdwr*** *(SN687597)* Abergwesyn Rd ☎(09744) 255
Apr–Oct

Situated 1 mile from the village.

3hc 🐕 LDO5pm

CTV 6P 🎣 14acres smallholding

FH Mrs M J Cutter ***Neuadd Las*** *(SN663620)* ☎(09744) 380

5hc (1⚑) (2fb) 🐕

🅿 CTV 10P 🏠 🎣 25acres mixed

TRENEAR (nr Helston)
Cornwall
Map **2** SW63

FH Mrs G Lawrence **Longstone** *(SW662319)* ☎Helston (0326) 572483
Mar–Oct

Well-appointed farmhouse set in beautiful countryside. Facilities include a playroom and sun lounge. From the Helston–Redruth road, B3297, take unclass road to Coverack Bridges–Helston 1½m; Trenear 1m, turn right & follow road for 2m.

5hc (2fb) B&bfr£8.50 Bdifr£12 WBdifr£80 LDO4pm

🅿 CTV 6P 62acres dairy Ⓥ

TRETOWER
Powys
Map **3** SO12

INN *Tretower Court* ☎Bwlch (0874) 730204

Family-run character inn with good bars and modestly appointed bedrooms.

4hc (1fb) LDO10pm

🅿 CTV 100P

Credit card 3

TREVEIGHAN
Cornwall
Map **2** SX07

FH Mrs M Jory **Treveighan** *(SX075795)* ☎Bodmin (0208) 850286
Closed Dec

Two-storey, stone-built farmhouse with farm buildings attached. Situated in isolated village with views over valley.

2hc (1fb) ⊘in bedrooms CTV in 1 bedroom TV in 1 bedroom 🐕 ® B&b£8–£10 Bdi£13–£15 WBdi£91–£105 (W only Jan–Jun) LDO4pm

🅿 CTV 3P 🏠 175acres beef dairy

TREVONE
Cornwall
Map **2** SW87

GH Coimbatore Hotel West View ☎Padstow (0841) 520390
Apr–Sep

Detached house in quiet situation with some sea views. Comfortable accommodation and friendly proprietors.

11hc (3fb) 🐕 ✱B&bfr£9 Bdifr£13WBdifr£88 (W only Jul & Aug) LDOnoon

Lic CTV 4P 4🚗 (charged)

Selected

GH Green Waves Private Hotel ☎Padstow (0841) 520114
Mar–Oct

Large detached house with some superb sea views.

15hc (8⚑) (4fb) CTV in all bedrooms ® ✱B&b£11.50–£13.25 Bdi£16.50–£18.25 WBdi£92–£111.50 LDO7pm

Lic 🅿 12P 5🚗 nc4yrs

See advertisement under Padstow

TRINITY
Jersey
See **Channel Islands**

TROON
Cornwall
Map **2** SW63

FH Mrs H Tyack **Sea View** *(SW671370)* ☎Praze (0209) 831260

Farmhouse has been modernised, yet still retains atmosphere of family-run farm. Tastefully furnished with extensive pinewood décor.

8rm (7hc) (3fb) ✱B&b£7.50 Bdi£11 WBdi£73.50 LDO9.30am

🅿 CTV 10P 🏠 ⛱(heated) 10acres mixed horticultural

Ⓥ

TROUTBECK (nr Penrith)
Cumbria
Map **11** NY32

FH Mrs R Bird **Askew Rigg** *(NY371280)* ☎Threlkeld (059683) 638
Mar–Nov

17th-century stone-built farmhouse, attractively modernised to retain original character. Entrance to drive is situated only a few yards from the A66.

3rm (2hc) (1fb) ® B&bfr£8 Bdi£12.50–£13 LDO4pm

Lic 🅿 CTV 4P 🏠 200acres mixed

Ⓥ

Selected

FH Mr P Fellows **Lane Head** *(NY375271)* ☎Threlkeld (059683) 220
Mar–Oct

A charming old farmhouse situated just off the A66 in its own attractive gardens. Very good home cooked meals are served in the dining room which features oak beams, polished brasses and a black marble fireplace. The two lounges are very comfortable and have CTV, one also has a pretty collection of china to match the blue decor and furnishings. All the rooms vary in size from a cosy double to one with a grand four-poster bed.

9hc (1⇌ 2⚑) (3fb) ⊘ in 9 bedrooms 🐕 B&b£11–£16 Bdi£19–£24 WBdifr£128 LDO6pm

Lic 🅿 CTV 10P 110acres mixed

Ⓥ

See advertisement on page 416

TRURO
Cornwall
Map **2** SW84

GH Manor Cottage Tresillian (3m NW at Tresillian) ☎Tresillian (087252) 212
Mar–20 Dec

17th century cottage on main road.

6hc (1fb) CTV available in bedrooms ® B&b£10–£10.50 WB&bfr£65LDO8pm

Lic 🅿 CTV 12P

See advertisement on page 416

GH Marcorrie Hotel 20 Falmouth Rd ☎(0872) 77374

Privately owned hotel with modern bedrooms all equipped with colour TVs.

11hc (2⇌ 5⚑) (3fb) CTV in all bedrooms ® B&b£13.50–£23 Bdi£19.50–£27 WBdifr£140.50 LDO5pm

Lic 🅿 CTV 15P

Credit cards 1 3

TUNBRIDGE WELLS (ROYAL)
Kent
Map **5** TQ53

GH *Firwood* 89 Frant Rd ☎(0892) 25596
Closed 20 Dec–5 Jan

10hc (6⇌ 4⚑) (2fb) CTV in all bedrooms 🐕 LDO5.30pm

🅿 CTV 12P

Credit cards 1 2 3 5

See advertisement on page 416

TWEEDSMUIR
Borders *Peebleshire*
Map **11** NT02

Selected

GH Menzion Farmhouse
(Guestaccom) ☎(08997) 247
Guests can expect a peaceful and relaxing stay at this tastefully decorated and furnished country house situated close to the River Tweed. Mr Brett is a dedicated and informative host whilst Mrs Brett is a superb cordon-bleu cook serving her 5 course set-dinners in a house party style. Important to note is that the bathroom has NO BATH only a shower.
5rm (4hc) ✗ Ⓡ B&b£12–£14 Bdi£20–£22 WBdi£126–£138.60 LDOprevious day
CTV 12P nc12yrs

TWO BRIDGES
Devon
Map **2** SX67
GH Cherrybrook Hotel ☎Tavistock (0822) 88260
Closed 20 Dec–4 Jan
Large detached house in pleasant grounds in the middle of Dartmoor.
7hc (6fl) (2fb) CTV in all bedrooms Ⓡ B&b£17.50 Bdi£25.50 WBdi£160 LDO7.15pm
Lic 12P

TYWARDREATH
Cornwall
Map **2** SX05
GH Elmswood Tehidy Rd, Tywardreath Park ☎Par (072681) 4221
Detached Victorian residence in elevated position with country views. Resident proprietors offer friendly services and good home cooking.
6hc (1fl) (2fb) *B&b£9–£10 Bdi£13–£14 WBdifr£91 LDOnoon
Lic CTV 8P

TYWYN
Gwynedd
Map **6** SH50
GH Monfa Pier Rd ☎(0654) 710858
Feb–Nov
Family-run guesthouse adjacent to the beach, a short walk from the shops.
7hc (3fl) (3fb) ✗ B&b£10–£11 Bdi£14.50–£15.50 WBdi£95–£105
Lic CTV 6P
Ⓥ

UCKFIELD
East Sussex
Map **5** TQ41
GH Hooke Hall 250 High St ☎(0825) 61578 Closed Xmas
5hc (2⇌) CTV in all bedrooms ✗ Ⓡ B&b£26.50–£37
Lic 6P nc12yrs
Credit cards 1 2 3 5

UFFCULME
Devon
Map **3** ST01
FH Mrs M D Farley **Houndaller** *(ST058138)* ☎Craddock (0884) 40246
Very old attractive farmhouse standing in beautiful garden. Quiet, though only 800 yards from A38 at Waterloo Cross, close to M5 junction 27.
3hc (2fb) Ⓡ B&b£8.50–£10.50 Bdi£12.50–£14 WBdifr£84
176acres mixed
Credit cards 1 2 3 5 Ⓥ

See gazetteer entry under Llanfihanel-Y-Pennant.

FH Mr & Mrs A F Baker ***Woodrow*** *(ST054107)* ☎Craddock (0884) 40362
Closed Xmas

Farmhouse set in pleasant lawns and gardens with meadowland stretching to River Culm. Trout fishing available.

2hc (2fb) ✱ LDO7pm

CTV 6P 200acres mixed

ULLINGSWICK
Hereford & Worcester
Map **3** SO54

Selected

GH The Steppes ☎Hereford (0432) 820424
Closed 2 wks before Xmas

17th-century listed building, being noted for its many points of historical and architectural interest and although it retains its original features, including a wealth of exposed beams throughout, it has been sympathetically modernised.

3fl (1fb) CTV in all bedrooms Ⓡ
✱B&b£15–£17.50 Bdi£26–£32 WBdi£182–£205 LDO7pm

Lic 6P nc10yrs

Ⓥ

UPLYME
Devon
Map **3** SY39

INN *Black Dog Hotel* Lyme Rd ☎Lyme Regis (02974) 2634
Mar–Oct

Roadside inn with garden offering simply appointed comfortable accommodation.

5hc Ⓡ LDO9.30pm CTV P 2

UPOTTERY
Devon
Map **3** ST20

FH Mrs M M Reed **Yarde** *(ST193045)* ☎(040486) 318

17th-century farmhouse with interesting oak panelling and beams, overlooking the Otter Valley. Near Monkton on the A30.

(3hc) (1fb) ✱ B&b£8.50–£9 Bdi£12.50–£13.50 WBdifr£85 LDO5.50pm

CTV 3P 1 94acres mixed sheep

UPPER HULME
Staffordshire
Map **7** SK06

FH Mrs J Lomas **Keekorok Lodge** *(SK005616)* ☎Blackshaw (053834) 218
Etr–Oct

Modernised stone-built house with views over Tittesworth Reservoir, well known locally for fishing, situated 1m NW of village towards The Roaches (Landmark).

3rm (2hc) ✱ B&b£8.50–£10 Bdifr£17 WBdifr£119 LDO10am

CTV 8P nc2yrs 15acres non-working

UPTON PYNE
Devon
Map **3** SX99

FH Mrs Y M Taverner **Pierce's** *(SX910977)* ☎Stoke Canon (039284) 252
Etr–Sep

Large farmhouse about 1 mile north of A377 Exeter–Barnstaple road.

1hc (1fb) ✱ B&b£8 WB&b£54

CTV 2P 300acres mixed

UPTON UPON SEVERN
Hereford & Worcester
Map **3** SO84

GH Pool House ☎(06846) 2151
Closed Dec

Homely country house on banks of River Severn with charming garden.

9hc (3 3fl) (2fb) in all bedrooms ✱
✱B&b£12.50–£24 Bdi£19.50–£32 WBdi£111–£153 LDO6.30pm

Lic CTV 20P

Credit cards 1 2 3

USK
Gwent
Map **3** SO30

FH J Arnett **Ty Gwyn** (Guestaccom) *(SO391045)* ☎(02913) 2878
Closed Xmas day

Large modernised farmhouse situated between Raglan and Usk at Gwehelog, 2½m NE of Usk.

2hc in all bedrooms ✱ Ⓡ B&b£9–£10.50 Bdi£16–£17 LDO2pm

CTV 3P nc10yrs mixed 26acres mixed

Ⓥ

Credit Cards

1 Access/Euro/ Mastercard

2 American Express

3 Barclaycard/Visa

5 Diners

UTTOXETER
Staffordshire
Map **7** SK03

GH Hillcrest 3 Leighton Rd ☎(08893) 4627 due to change to (0889) 564627
Closed Xmas Day

Large Victorian house in a residential area close to town centre.

7hc (1 2fl) (4fb) CTV available in bedrooms Ⓡ B&b£10.50–£11.50 Bdi£15–£16 LDO4pm

CTV 9P 2

Ⓥ

FH R J & K P Stockton **Popinjay** *(SK074322)* Stafford Rd ☎(08893) 66082 due to change to (0889) 566082

1m SW off A518.

2hc in all bedrooms ✱ Ⓡ available in bedrooms B&b£8.50–£10 Bdi£12–£14 WBdi£95

CTV P 10acres beef

Ⓥ

VENN OTTERY
Devon
Map **3** SY09

GH Venn Ottery Barton Country Hotel ☎Ottery St Mary (040481) 2733

Guesthouse in rural position, having good facilities and a high standard of cuisine.

16hc (5 6fl) (3fb) Ⓡ ✱B&b£14–£22 Bdi£18–£31 WBdi£126–£182 LDO7.30pm

Lic CTV 20P

Credit cards 1 3 Ⓥ

VENTNOR
Isle of Wight
See **Wight, Isle of**

VOWCHURCH
Hereford & Worcester
Map **3** SO33

Selected

GH The Croft ☎Peterchurch (09816) 226
Rs Xmas

A warm welcome and appealing accommodation are offered in a restful situation.

3 in all bedrooms CTV in all bedrooms ✱ (ex guide dogs) Ⓡ B&b£14.50–£17 Bdi£22–£25 WBdi£149–£156 LDO6pm

Lic CTV 8P nc10yrs 7acres livestock

Ⓥ

See advertisement under Hereford

WADHURST
East Sussex
Map **5** TQ63

INN *Fourkeys* Station Rd ☎(089288) 2252

Small, old house with friendly proprietor and comfortable bedrooms, most with modern facilities.

8hc (2fb) CTV in 2 bedrooms TV in 6 bedrooms Ⓡ LDO10.30pm

25P

Credit cards 1 3

WALLASEY
Merseyside
Map **7** SJ29

GH Divonne Hotel 71 Wellington Rd, New Brighton ☎051-639 4727

A popular commercial hotel set on rising ground overlooking the Mersey Estuary.

15hc (6) (1fb) TV in all bedrooms Ⓡ B&b£10–£12 Bdi£15–£17 WBdi£95 LDO8.25pm

Lic CTV 6P

GH Sandpiper Private Hotel 22 Dudley Rd, New Brighton ☎051-639 7870

Edwardian guesthouse in a quiet side road.

7hc (2fb) in 2 bedrooms CTV in all bedrooms Ⓡ B&b£10–£11 Bdi£14–£16 WBdifr£79.90 LDO4.30pm

5P

Ⓥ

WANSFORD
Cambridgeshire
Map **4** TL09

INN Cross Keys ☎Stamford (0780) 782266
Closed 23–31 Dec

2hc Annexe: 5hc (2fb) TV in all bedrooms Ⓡ ✱B&b£10–£12 Bar lunch £1.50–£2.50 Dinner 9.30pm£6.50alc

snooker

Credit card 1

WAREHAM
Dorset
Map **3** SY98

FH L S Barnes **Luckford Wood** *(SY873865)* East Stoke ☎Bindon Abbey (0929) 463098

5rm (3hc 1) (3fb) in 1 bedroom CTV in 1 bedroom TV in 1 bedroom Ⓡ ✱B&b£12–£14 Bdi£18.50–£20.50 WBdifr£115.50

CTV 5P 167acres dairy

Ⓥ

Selected

FH Mrs J Barnes **Redcliffe** *(SY932866)* ☎(09295) 2225

Modern farmhouse in quiet, rural surroundings. Pleasant location adjacent to River Frome and overlooking hills and fields. ½ mile from Wareham.

5rm (3hc 1)

CTV 4P 250acres dairy mixed

WARK
Northumberland
Map **12** NY87

GH Warksburn House ☎Bellingham (0660) 30246
Mar–Nov rs Dec

6hc (1fb) CTV in all bedrooms Ⓡ B&b£11–£11.50 Bdi£18–£18.50 WBdi£91–£105 LDO6.30pm

Lic 12P

Ⓥ

WARREN STREET (nr Lenham)
Kent
Map **5** TQ95

Selected

INN Harrow ☎Maidstone (0622) 858727
Closed Xmas & New Year

Difficult to find but worth the search. In the heart of the North Downs, in a small hamlet, close to the Pilgrims Way, nestles this charming inn of great character. Bedrooms have modern furnishing and facilities but retain an old world atmosphere. The lounge is cosy and comfortable – a haven of peace and relaxation. In contrast, the bar is quite lively, being as popular with locals as it is with residents of the inn.

7hc (1 3) (1fb) Ⓡ available in bedrooms ✱B&b£16–£32 Bdi£24.50–£40.50 WBdifr£162 Bar lunch £2–£10 Dinner9.45pm fr£8.50&alc

CTV 30P

Credit cards 1 3 Ⓥ

WARSASH
Hampshire
Map **4** SU40

GH Solent View Private Hotel 33–35 Newton Road ☎Locks Heath (04895) 2300

Well-furnished good quality accommodation with very well-equipped bedrooms. There is a cosy quiet lounge with separate bar and dining room. All food is freshly prepared and cooked by the proprietor.

6hc (1 5) CTV in all bedrooms Ⓡ B&b£14–£17 Bdi£20–£23

Lic CTV 8P

Ⓥ

WARWICK
Warwickshire
Map **4** SP26

GH Austin House 96 Emscote Rd ☎(0926) 493583

Large, personally-run Victorian house on the busy Warwick–Leamington Rd. Rear garden. →

7hc (6⫏) (3fb) CTV in all bedrooms ®
*B&b£11–£13 Bdi£16–£18 WBdifr£119
LDOnoon

CTV 6P 2🚗

GH Avon 7 Emscote Rd ☎(0926) 491367
Small, well-run private hotel on Warwick–Leamington Rd. Close to tourist amenities.
7hc (4fb) ✗ ® B&b£10 Bdi£15
WBdifr£105 LDO4.30pm
CTV 6P 1🚗
Ⓥ

GH Cambridge Villa Private Hotel
20A Emscote Rd ☎(0926) 491169
Closed Xmas Day & Boxing Day
16hc (4⫏ (2fb) CTV in all bedrooms ✗ ®
B&b£12.65–£24 LDO7pm
Lic CTV 16P
Credit cards 1 3 5

GH Old Rectory Sherbourne (off A46 2m SW) ☎Barford (Warwicks) (0926) 624562
Closed 23 Dec–1 Jan
Tastefully restored house offering very comfortable accommodation and home-cooked food.
7hc (1⇌ 6⫏) (1fb) CTV in all bedrooms ®
B&b£11–£20 Bdi£16–£24 WBdifr£140
LDO3pm
Lic CTV 8P ♿
Ⓥ

Warwick — Waterhouses

GH Penderrick 36 Coten End ☎(0926) 499399
Closed Xmas Day
An attractive family run hotel with views of St Nicholas' Park and the Castle, affording well equipped bedrooms, an elegant lounge and very hospitable hosts.
7hc (4⫏) (2fb) CTV in all bedrooms ®
B&b£14–£28 Bdi£22.50–£36.50
LDO8.30pm
Lic P
Credit cards 1 2 3 5

WASHFORD
Somerset
Map **3** ST04

GH Langtry Country House Hotel
☎(0984) 40484
Secluded Victorian house in 3 acres, set well back on A39. Fine views of Quantock Hills and only 6 miles from Minehead.
6hc (5⇌ 1⫏) (1fb) ⊁ in 5 bedrooms CTV in all bedrooms ® B&b£14–£17.50
Bdi£20–£24.50 WBdi£135–£160 LDO9pm
Lic CTV 20P nc5yrs
Credit cards 1 3 Ⓥ

WATERGATE
Cornwall
Map **2** SX25

⊢⊣ **GH Harescombe Lodge** ☎Looe (05036) 3158
This former shooting lodge dates back over 200 years and is situated in a peaceful wooded valley beside a brook which runs into the River Looe. Good facilities and friendly service can be found here.
3hc (2⇌ 1⫏) ® B&b£8.75–£15.50
Bdi£16.25–£23 LDO5pm
CTV 4P nc12yrs

WATERHOUSES
Staffordshire
Map **7** SK05

⊢⊣ **GH Croft House Farm** Waterfall (1m NW unclass) ☎(05386) 553
Former farmhouse dating back to the 17th century, recently extended to provide good well-equipped accommodation.
6hc (2fb) CTV in all bedrooms ✗ ®
B&b£9–£10.50 Bdi£15–£16.50
WBdi£97.50–£108.50 LDO8.30pm
Lic CTV 14P
Ⓥ

⊢FH Mrs K Watson **Weaver** *(SK102467)* ☎Oakamore (0538) 702271

Solid stone-built 19-century farm in a hollow of the Weaver hills.

5hc (3fb) ✗ Ⓡ B&b£8–£10 Bdi£12–£14 WBdifr£80 LDO9pm

Ⓜ CTV P 320acres mixed

Ⓥ

INN *Ye Olde Crown* ☎(05386) 204

A warm and friendly atmosphere awaits you at this 17th-century village inn on the A523.

8hc (3⚿) (2fb) CTV in all bedrooms ✗ Ⓡ LDO10pm

Ⓜ 50P

WATERLOO
Isle of Skye, Highland *Inverness-shire*
See **Skye, Isle of**

WATERPERRY
Oxfordshire
Map **4** SP60

FH Mrs S Fonge **Manor** *(SP628064)* ☎Ickford (08447) 263

Stone farmhouse standing in large garden, in centre of village. Coarse fishing available.

3hc B&b£10–£13 Bdi£18–£21 WBdi£126–£140 LDO10am

Ⓜ TV 4P 160acres arable beef poultry sheep mixed

Ⓥ

WATERROW
Somerset
Map **3** ST02

FH Mr J Bone **Hurstone Farmhouse Hotel** *(ST056252)* ☎Wiveliscombe (0984) 23441

17th-century farmhouse, furnished in keeping, in 65 acres. Much of food served is produced on the farm.

5⇌ (1fb) ⚟ in 3 bedrooms CTV in all bedrooms Ⓡ B&b£17.50–£20.50 Bdi£29–£32 LDO7.30pm

Lic Ⓜ CTV 8P ⌂ ✓ 65acres dairy

Credit cards 1 2 3 Ⓥ

INN Rock ☎Wiveliscombe (0984) 23293

A 400-year-old Inn offering a character bar and modern bedrooms. Situated on the A361 approximately 2 miles from Wiveliscombe.

7rm (6hc 4⇌) (1fb) CTV in all bedrooms ✱B&b£12.50–£16 Lunch fr£2.50alc High Tea £3alc Dinner fr£6.50alc

Ⓜ CTV 20P

Credit cards 1 3 Ⓥ

See advertisement under Taunton

WATFORD
Hertfordshire
Map **4** TQ19

GH White House Hotel 26–29 Upton Rd ☎(0923) 37316 Telex no 895543

Close to town centre, offers well-equipped bedrooms. Ideal for business people.

37hc (15⇌ 22⚿) Annexe: 27hc (17⇌ 10⚿) (6fb) CTV in all bedrooms Ⓡ B&b£40–£51 Bdi£50.50–£61.50 WBdi£357 LDO9.45pm

Lic Ⓜ 50P

Credit cards 1 2 3

WEEDONLOIS
Northamptonshire
Map **4** SP64

FH Mrs C Raven **Croft** *(SP600465)* Milthorpe ☎Blakesley (0327) 860475
Feb–Nov

New detached house, built of Cotswold stone, in rural surroundings on edge of delightful Northamptonshire village.

2rm ✗ B&bfr£12

Ⓜ CTV P 25acres pigs turkeys

WEETON
Lancashire
Map **7** SD33

⊢FH Mrs E Colligan **High Moor** *(SD388365)* ☎(039136) 273
Closed Xmas & New Year

Compact, homely farmhouse, clean and tidy. Much farm produce used in cooking.

2rm (1fb) TV in 1 bedroom CTV in 1 bedroom ✗ Ⓡ B&bfr£8 WB&bfr£48

Ⓜ CTV 10P 2🚗 7acres non-working

WELLINGBOROUGH
Northamptonshire
Map **4** SP86

GH Oak House Private Hotel 9 Broad Green ☎(0933) 71133
Closed Xmas

10hc (9⚿) (1fb) CTV in all bedrooms Ⓡ B&b£15–£21 Bdi£21.50–£27.50 WBdifr£150.50 LDOnoon

Lic Ⓜ CTV 8P

Credit cards 1 3 Ⓥ

WELLINGTON
Shropshire
See **Telford**

WELLINGTON
Somerset
Map **3** ST12

FH Mrs N K Ash **Pinksmoor Mill House** *(ST109198)* (3m W off A38 at Beam Bridge Hotel) ☎Greenham (0823) 672361

Part 13th-century property, 3m W of Wellington, with neat comfortable accommodation. Original mill house on site.

3hc (1⇌ 2⚿) (1fb) ⚟ in all bedrooms Ⓡ B&b£11–£12.50 Bdi£17–£18.50 WBdifr£115.50 LDO4pm

Ⓜ CTV 6P 98acres dairy sheep

Ⓥ

WELLS
Somerset
Map **3** ST54

GH Bekynton House 7 St Thomas Street ☎(0749) 72222
Closed Xmas & New Year

9hc (3⚿) (1fb) CTV in all bedrooms ✗ Ⓡ ✱B&b£12–£19 WBdifr£125 LDO11am

Ⓜ 8P

Selected

GH Coach House Stoberry Pk ☎(0749) 76535
Closed 24–31 Dec

A delightful converted coach house, standing in 6 acres of attractive parkland, with excellent furnishings and décor. Unique views of the city of Wells with the majestic Cathedral taking prominence.

3⇌ ⚟ in all bedrooms B&b£13–£14 Bdi£20.50–£24 WBdi£136.50–£157.50 LDO8.30am

Lic Ⓜ CTV 6P

Ⓥ

GH Torr 20 Tor St ☎(0749) 72322

9hc (1⚿) (4fb) Ⓡ B&b£10.50–£13 Bdi£17–£19.50 WBdifr£110 LDO3pm

Ⓜ CTV 11P 1🚗

Ⓥ

See advertisement on page 422

⊢FH Mrs P Higgs **Home** *(ST538442)* Stoppers Ln, Upper Coxley ☎(0749) 72434
Closed 2 wks Xmas

2m SW off A39.

7hc (3fb) B&b£9–£10 WB&b£63–£77

Lic Ⓜ CTV 10P 10acres pig

See advertisement on page 422

FH Mrs J Gould **Manor** *(ST546474)* Old Bristol Rd, Upper Milton (1m W A39 towards Bristol, 200 yds beyond roundabout) ☎(0749) 73394
Closed Xmas

Attractive stone-built farmhouse on the edge of the City. Simple, clean standard of furnishings and appointments.

3hc (1fb) ✗ Ⓡ B&b£10–£11 WB&b£60

Ⓜ CTV 6P ⌂ 130acres beef

FH Mr & Mrs Frost **Southway** *(ST516423)* Polsham (3m SW off A39) ☎(0749) 73396

This ivy-clad Georgian farmhouse is located on the A39. Guests are made welcome by friendly proprietors.

3hc ✗ ✱B&b£10–£15 WB&b£63–£95

Ⓜ CTV 5P 170acres dairy

WELLS-NEXT-THE-SEA
Norfolk
Map **9** TF94

GH Scarborough House Clubbs Ln
☎Fakenham (0328) 710309
Closed Dec & Jan

Spacious Victorian manse set in a quiet residential road. Comfortable accommodation with friendly proprietors.

6hc (2⇌) CTV in all bedrooms B&b£15–£18 Bdi£24–£27 WBdifr£154

Lic 🍽 8P nc5yrs

Ⓥ

WELSHPOOL
Powys
Map **7** SJ20

FH Mrs K Owens **Coed-y-Brenin** *(SJ248025)* Kingswood Ln (3m S off A490 at Kingswood) ☎Forden (093876) 510

Modern farmhouse in lovely Border countryside, signposted Kingswood from B4388. ½m E off B4388 on unclass rd.

2hc ✖ Ⓡ B&b£9.50–£10 WB&bfr£66.50

🍽 CTV 6P 320acres beef dairy sheep mixed

Ⓥ

FH Mrs E Jones **Gungrog House** *(SJ235089)* Rhallt ☎(0938) 3381
Apr–Oct

300-year-old farmhouse in quiet situation high on hillside, commanding superb views of the Severn Valley 1m NE off A458.

3hc (2⫷) ✖ B&b£10.50–£11 Bdi£16–£16.50 WBdi£110 LDO5pm

🍽 CTV 6P 21acres mixed

⊢FH Mr & Mrs M C Payne **Heath Cottage** *(SJ239023)* Kingswood (3m S off A490)
☎ Forden (093876) 453
Closed Xmas & New Year

Former country pub within yards of Offa's Dyke. Clean, modest accommodation.

3rm (1⇨ ⫪) ✖ Ⓡ B&b£9–£11 Bdi£14–£16 WBdi£93–£107

⫪ CTV 4P 6acres poultry sheep

Ⓥ

FH Mr & Mrs W Jones **Moat** *(SJ214042)*
☎(0938) 3179
Apr–Oct

16th-century farmhouse with timbered dining room and canopied stone fireplace. The gardens have a tennis lawn, and lead down to the river. Situated in the Severn Valley.

3hc (1fb) TV in 1 bedroom ✖ Ⓡ B&b£10–£11 Bdi£15–£16 WBdi£99–£108 LDO2pm

⫪ CTV 3P ⌂ ℛ(grass) 260acres dairy

Ⓥ

FH Mr & Mrs J Emberton **Tynllwyn** *(SJ215085)* ☎(0938) 3175

Peaceful 19th-century farmhouse offering good, modern accommodation. On A490 N of Welshpool.

6hc (3fb) CTV in all bedrooms ✖ Ⓡ ✱B&b£10.50 Bdi£16 WBdi£94 LDO6.30pm

Lic ⫪ CTV P 150acres mixed

Ⓥ

WEST BAGBOROUGH
Somerset
Map **3** ST13

GH Higher House ☎Bishops Lydeard (0823) 432996
Closed Xmas wk rs Dec–Mar

A country guesthouse set amid pleasant gardens and courtyards. Comfortable good-sized bedrooms and attractive lounge area. Fine views.

7hc (1⇨ 2⫪) Ⓡ B&b£14–£17 Bdi£22–£25 LDO4.30pm

Lic ⫪ CTV 13P ⩲(heated)

Ⓥ

WEST CHILTINGTON
West Sussex
Map **4** TQ01

FH Mrs A M Steele **New House** *(TQ091186)* ☎(07983) 2215
Closed Dec

Listed 15th-century farmhouse with oak-beamed rooms and inglenook fireplace, in pleasant surroundings.

3hc (1⇨ 1⫪) (2fb) CTV in all bedrooms ✖ Ⓡ B&b£12.50–£16 WB&b£80.50–£105

CTV 4P 2⌂ nc10yrs 50acres mixed

Ⓥ

WESTCLIFF-ON-SEA
Essex
See **Southend-on-Sea**

WEST COKER
Somerset
Map **3** ST51

GH Old Rectory Church St ☎(093586) 2048

A detached, stone-built Victorian rectory off the A30 offering sound accommodation.

4hc (4fb) CTV in 2 bedrooms TV in 1 bedroom ✖ Ⓡ ✱B&bfr£10 WB&bfr£56

CTV 6P

See advertisement under Yeovil

WEST DOWN
Devon
Map **2** SS54

⊢**GH Sunnymeade Country House Hotel** Dean Cross (1m W on A361)
☎Ilfracombe (0271) 63668 Plan **25** *B1*

10hc (5⫪) (2fb) ✖ Ⓡ B&b£9–£12.50 Bdi£14–£18.50 WBdi£84–£118.50 LDO6pm

Lic ⫪ CTV 14P ⌂

Credit cards 1 2 3 5

WEST KIRBY
Merseyside
Map **7** SJ28

GH Park Hotel Westbourne Rd ☎051-625 9319

Large detached guesthouse situated very close to the sea front and within easy reach of Liverpool and Chester.

20hc (5⫪) (3fb) CTV available in bedrooms ✖ B&b£15–£20 Bdi£20–£25 WBdifr£125 LDO9pm

Lic ⫪ CTV 15P

Credit cards 1 3 Ⓥ

See advertisement on page 424

WEST LAYTON
Just off A68
North Yorkshire
Map **12** NZ10

Selected

GH West Layton Manor Hotel
☎Darlington (0325) 718633

An outstanding country house set in 30 acres of grounds on the southern outskirts of town. Spacious and thoughtfully-equipped bedrooms and delightfully appointed public rooms. Including a wood panelled baronial hall and an elegant drawing room. The hospitality extended by Mrs Waterson, cannot be bettered, and includes a complementary sherry before the beautifully-cooked set dinner.

6⇨ (1fb) CTV in all bedrooms Ⓡ B&b£22–£29 Bdi£30–£37 WBdi£175–£199 LDO7.30pm

Lic ⫪ CTV 20P snooker

Credit cards 1 3 Ⓥ

WEST LINTON
Borders *Peeblesshire*
Map **11** NT15

Selected

GH Medwyn House Medwyn Rd ☎(0968) 60542

Nice, spacious bedrooms in country mansion close to village golf course.

3⇌ ⅄ in all bedrooms Ⓡ B&b£18–£27 Bdi£29–£38 WBdifr£196

𝍖 CTV 12P 2🚗 nc12yrs sauna bath

Ⓥ

WEST LULWORTH
Dorset
See **Lulworth**

WESTON-SUPER-MARE
Avon
Map **3** ST36
See plan

GH Baymead Hotel Longton Grove Rd ☎(0934) 22951 Plan **1** *C4*

32hc (7⇌) (9fb) Ⓡ B&b£12–£16 Bdi£15–£19 WBdi£85–£120 LDO6.30pm

Lic lift 𝍖 CTV 𝐏̸

Ⓥ

⊢⊣ **GH Edelweiss** 24 Clevedon Rd ☎(0934) 24705 Plan **2** *B1*
Closed Xmas

6hc (3fb) ✗ B&b£8.50–£9.50 Bdi£13.50–£14.50 WB&b£54–£58 LDO4pm

Lic 𝍖 CTV 𝐏̸

GH Fourways 2 Ashcombe Rd ☎(0934) 23827 Plan **3** *C3*
Apr–Oct rs Nov & Feb–Mar

6hc Annexe: 3hc ✗ (ex in Annexe) ✱B&b£7.50–£10.50

𝍖 CTV 6P nc10yrs

GH Milton Lodge 15 Milton Rd ☎(0934) 23161 Plan **4** *C4*
Apr–Oct

Recent guesthouse created with painstaking care to provide a good standard of accommodation.

6hc (3⇌ 3fl) CTV in all bedrooms ✗ Ⓡ B&b£12 Bdi£17 WBdi£93–£105 (W only 28 May–16 Sep LDO4pm

𝍖 CTV 5P nc16yrs

GH Moorlands Hutton (3m E unclass between A368 and A370) ☎Bleadon (0934) 812283 Not on plan

9hc (2⇌ 2fl) (6fb) ✗ B&b£11.50–£13.80 Bdi£17.25–£19.55 WBdi£92–£97.75 LDO5pm

Lic 𝍖 CTV 8P

Ⓥ

GH Newton House 79 Locking Rd ☎(0934) 29331 Plan **5** *C3*

Small, comfortable and friendly guesthouse.

8hc (2fl) (4fb) Ⓡ B&b£10.50–£12.50 Bdi£15–£17 WBdifr£88.50 LDO2pm

Lic 𝍖 CTV 9P

Ⓥ

GH *Shire Elms* 71 Locking Rd ☎(0934) 28605 Plan **6** *C3*
Closed 23 Dec–2 Jan

11hc (1⇌) Annexe: 2hc (3fb) CTV in all bedrooms ✗ LDO3pm

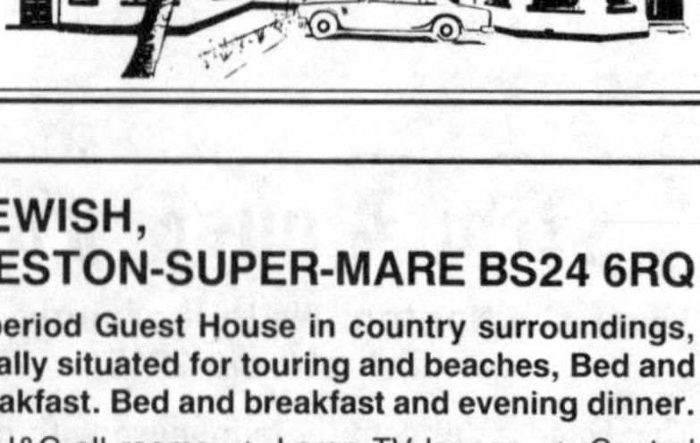

Lic 𝍖 CTV 10P

See advertisement on page 426

⊢⊣ **GH Southmead** 435 Locking Rd ☎(0934) 29351 due to change to 629351 Plan **7** *C3*

Tudor styled house on approach road to town. Modest bedrooms.

6hc (2fb) CTV available in bedrooms Ⓡ available in bedrooms B&b£9–£10.50 Bdi£13.50–£15 WBdifr£75 LDO4pm

𝍖 CTV 6P

Ⓥ

GH *Willow* 3 Clarence Road East
☎(0934) 413736 Plan **8** *B1*
Etr–Oct
8hc (2⇌ 1fl) (4fb) ✗ Ⓡ LDO9pm
CTV 8P (heated)

GH Wychwood Hotel 148 Milton Rd
☎(0934) 27793 Plan **9** *C4*
10hc (4fl) (3fb) CTV in all bedrooms ✗
B&b£12–£15 Bdi£18–£21 WBdi fr£117
LDO5.45pm
Lic 14P (heated)
Ⓥ

WEST PENNARD

Somerset
Not on map

INN Red Lion Newtown ☎Glastonbury
(0458) 32941 →

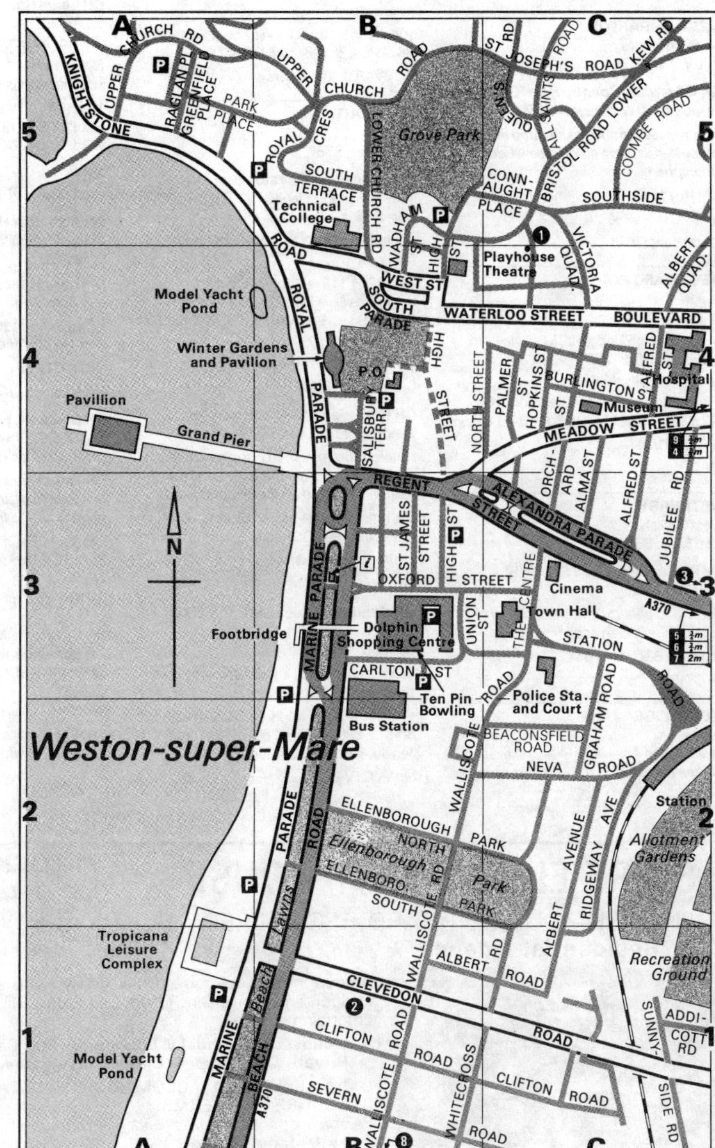

Weston-super-Mare

1 Baymead Hotel
2 Edelweiss
3 Fourways
4 Milton Lodge
5 Newton House
6 Shire Elms
7 Southmead
8 Willow
9 Wychwood Hotel

Attractive 17th-century inn and tastefully converted barn offering comfortable, well-appointed bedrooms with en suite facilities. Friendly staff and extensive menu.

Annexe: 7⋔ CTV in all bedrooms ✕ Ⓡ B&b£18.50–25 Bdi£21.50–£31 WBdi£132–£192 Lunch£3–£7 Dinner 9.30pm£3–£7

꧁ 60P 4🚘

Credit cards 1 3 Ⓥ

WEST SCRAFTON
North Yorkshire
Map **7** SE08

GH *Coverdale Country Hotel* Great Swineside ☎Wensleydale (0969) 40601

A converted farmhouse situated in an unspoilt, rural area of the dales. Friendly atmosphere.

7⋔ (1fb) ✕ Ⓡ

Lic ꧁ CTV 15P ⌂

Credit cards 1 3

WESTWARD HO!
Devon
Map **2** SS42

GH Buckleigh Lodge 135 Bayview Rd ☎Bideford (02372) 75988
Apr–Oct rs Nov–Mar

6hc (1⇨) (2fb) CTV in 1 bedroom ✕ B&b£10.50 Bdi£15.50 WBdi£102 LDO8pm

Lic ꧁ CTV 8P

Ⓥ

WETHERBY
West Yorkshire
Map **8** SE44

GH Prospect House 8 Caxton St ☎(0937) 62428

Bright and cheerful guesthouse with comfortable, clean accommodation.

6hc (1fb) B&b£11 WB&b£77

꧁ CTV 6P

WEYBRIDGE
Surrey
London plan **4** A1
(pages 258–259)

West Pennard — Weymouth

GH Warbeck House Hotel 46 Queens Rd ☎(0932) 48764
Closed 22 Dec–3 Jan

Fine Edwardian house with comfortable, modernised bedrooms and relaxing atmosphere.

10hc (1⇨) (1fb) CTV in all bedrooms ✕ Ⓡ B&b£23–£28 WB&bfr£170

Lic ꧁ CTV 20P nc3yrs

WEYMOUTH
Dorset
Map **3** SY67

GH Beechcroft Private Hotel 128–129 The Esplanade ☎(0305) 786608
Apr–Sep

Located on sea front with continental awnings.

29hc (2⇨ 11⋔) (10fb) CTV in all bedrooms Ⓡ ✱B&b£11.96–£14.95 Bdi£16.96–£19.95 WBdi£109.25–£126.50 LDO4.30pm

Lic 3P(charge) 12🚘(charge)

Credit cards 1 3

GH Hazeldene 16 Abbotsbury Rd, Westham ☎(0305) 782579

Comfortably furnished guesthouse, a short distance from the town centre and harbour, situated on the Bridport road.

7hc (4fb) ✕ Ⓡ B&b£8–£9 Bdi£10–£11 WBdi£65–£80 LDOnoon

Lic ꧁ CTV 7P 1🚘 nc5yrs

Ⓥ

GH Kenora 5 Stavordale Rd ☎(0305) 771215
Etr–Sep

In quiet cul-de-sac a short distance from the harbour.

17hc (1⇨ 8⋔) (5fb) ✕ Ⓡ B&b£10–£15.50 Bdi£15–£20.50 WBdi£86–£112 (W only Jun Jul & Aug) LDO4.30pm

Lic ꧁ CTV 20P

GH Kings Acre Hotel 140 The Esplanade ☎(0305) 782534
Feb–Sep & Xmas (rs Oct)

Terraced Georgian hotel on sea front.

14hc (4fb) CTV in all bedrooms ✕ Ⓡ B&b£12–£16 Bdi£16–£20 WBdi£87.50–£105 LDO4.30pm

Lic ꧁ 9P

Credit cards 1 3

GH Leam Hotel 103 The Esplanade ☎(0305) 784127
Closed Dec (rs Oct–May)

Sea front hotel with wrought iron balcony situated opposite the Jubilee clock.

19hc (7fb) CTV in all bedrooms ✕ Ⓡ B&b£12.50–£13 Bdi£17.50–£18 WBdifr£104 LDO4pm

Lic ꧁̸

Credit cards 1 3

GH Richmoor Hotel 146 The Esplanade ☎(0305) 785087
rs Jan–Etr

Georgian terraced hotel opposite the pier and bandstand.

22hc (1⇨ 1⋔) ✕ Ⓡ ✱B&b£10–£14 Bdi£14–£18 (W only Jul–Aug) LDO4pm

Lic lift CTV 8P

Credit cards 1 3

GH Sou'west Lodge Hotel Rodwell Rd ☎(0305) 783749
Closed 21 Dec–1 Jan

Family-run guesthouse, a short distance from sea front and town centre. Good bedrooms and friendly service.

9hc (2⇨ 2⋔) (2fb) CTV in all bedrooms Ⓡ B&b£13–£15 Bdi£17.50–£19.50 WBdifr£115

Lic ꧁ CTV 14P

Ⓥ

GH Sunningdale Private Hotel 52 Preston Rd, Overcombe ☎(0305) 832179
Mar–Oct

Hotel set back off main Preston road enjoying elevated position.

21hc (5⇌ 2fl) (8fb) CTV in 5 bedrooms TV in 2 bedrooms Ⓡ B&b£12.65–£16.65 Bdi£17.25–£20.80 WBdi£106–£133 LDO7pm

Lic Lift CTV 20P ⌂ ≋(heated) putting

GH Tamarisk Hotel 12 Stavordale Rd, Westham ☎(0305) 786514
Mar–Oct

Situated in a quiet cul-de-sac a short walk from the town centre and harbour.

16hc (4⇌ 8fl) (7fb) CTV available in bedrooms ✗ Ⓡ B&b£12–£15 Bdi£15–£18 WBdifr£101 (W only Jul & Aug) LDO2pm

Lic ꟷ CTV 19P

GH Westway House 62 Abbotsbury Rd ☎(0305) 784564
Closed Xmas

Family run guesthouse 10 minutes walk from town centre and sea front.

11hc (1⇌ 8fl) (2fb) CTV in all bedrooms ✗ Ⓡ B&b£11.50–£14 Bdi£17–£19.50 WBdi£98 (W only Jul & Aug) LDO6.30pm

Lic ꟷ CTV 10P nc3yrs

Ⓥ

INN Turks Head Hotel & Restaurant 6–8 East St (3m NW B3157) ☎(0305) 783093
(For full entry see **Chickerell**)

WHADDON
Buckinghamshire
Map **4** SP83

INN *Lowndes Arms & Motel* 4 High St ☎Milton Keynes (0908) 501706

11fl Annexe: 11fl CTV in all bedrooms ✗ Ⓡ LDO9.30pm

ꟷ 30P ⌗ nc16yrs

Credit cards 1 3 5

See advertisement under Milton Keynes

WHAPLODE
Lincolnshire
Map **8** TF32

FH Mrs A Thompson **Guy Wells** *(TF337241)* ☎Holbeach (0406) 22239
Mar–Oct

Beautifully preserved Queen Anne farmhouse with a wealth of charm and character.

3hc (1fb) ⊬in all bedrooms ✗ Ⓡ B&b£10–£12 Bdi£16.50–£18.50 WBdi£105 LDO4pm

ꟷ CTV 3P 85acres arable flowers

Ⓥ

WHEDDON CROSS
Somerset
Map **3** SS93

GH Higherley ☎Timberscombe (064384) 582

Higherley is an attractive modern detached building standing in pleasant gardens alongside six acres of smallholding. Well-appointed rooms enjoying fine country views.

6hc (1fb) CTV in 2 bedrooms ✱B&b£9–£10.75 Bdi£16.75–£17.75 WBdifr£123 LDO9pm

Lic ꟷ CTV 30P 6⌂

Credit cards 1 3 Ⓥ

⊢FH Mrs J C Norman **Gupworthy** *(SS969353)* ☎Brompton Regis (03987) 267
May–Dec

Comfortable, clean farmhouse in the Exmoor National Park. Good-sized bedrooms.

4hc (1fb) ✗ B&b£9–£11 Bdi£14–£17 WBdi£98–£119 LDO8.30pm

ꟷ CTV 12P 1⌂

676acres arable beef mixed sheep

Ⓥ

WHIDDON DOWN
Devon
Map **3** SX69

FH Mrs J S Robinson **South Nethercott** *(SX688947)* ☎(064723) 276
Mar–Nov

A warm welcome awaits you at this 16th-century farmhouse with its oak beams and open fireplaces.

2hc (1⇌) ✗ B&b£12.50–£14 Bdi£20.50–£22

CTV P nc12yrs 170acres arable dairy

Ⓥ

WHIMPLE
Devon
Map **3** SY09

⊢**GH Down House** ☎(0404) 822860
Feb–Nov

Attentive, friendly owners provide sound accommodation at this attractive, gabled house. Fine views of surrounding countryside.

6hc (2fb) CTV in 2 bedrooms TV in 2 bedrooms ✗ Ⓡ B&b£9–£10 Bdi£14–£15 WBdi£85 LDO5pm

ꟷ CTV 8P ⌂

5acres mixed small holding

Ⓥ

WHITBY
North Yorkshire
Map **8** NZ81

GH *Esklet* 22 Crescent Av ☎(0947) 605663
Closed Nov & Jan

Small, friendly guesthouse in residential area.

7hc (3fb) ⊬ in 1 bedroom Ⓡ LDO5.30pm

ꟷ CTV 1P

⊢**GH Europa Private Hotel** 20 Hudson St ☎(0947) 602251
Closed Xmas & New Year

Pleasant small guesthouse near harbour, well-furnished and with good, comfortable accommodation.

9hc (1fl) (1fb) CTV in 1 bedroom ✗ B&b£8–£8.50 Bdi£12–£12.50 WBdifr£77 LDO4.30pm

ꟷ CTV ⊅ nc2yrs

Ⓥ

GH Glendale 16 Crescent Ave ☎(0947) 604242
Apr–Oct

Cosy and cheerful establishment offering neat, well-maintained rooms.

6hc (3fb) CTV in 2 bedrooms TV in 4 bedrooms Ⓡ B&b£10–£10.50 Bdi£13.50–£14 WBdifr£90

Lic CTV 6P

Ⓥ

GH Haven 4 East Cres ☎(0947) 603842

An attractive guesthouse nicely furnished. Front-facing rooms overlook the sea.

8hc (1🛁 2🚿) (3fb) CTV in all bedrooms ✕ Ⓡ B&b£9.50–£11 Bdi£14–£15.50 WBdifr£95 LDO4pm

Lic ⊞ CTV ₱ nc2yrs

Ⓥ

GH Old Hall Hotel Ruswarp ☎(0947) 602801
Mar–Oct

A rambling 17th-century hotel full of character and standing in its own grounds. 1½m SW B1416.

20hc (4🛁 3🚿) (2fb) ✕ ✱B&b£13–£15 Bdifr£20 WB&bfr£84 LDO6pm

Lic CTV 18P ⌂

Ⓥ

Whitby

GH Prospect Villa 13 Prospect Hill ☎(0947) 603118
Feb–Nov

Guesthouse offering a good selection of home-cooked meals.

6hc (1🚿) (2fb) CTV in 1 bedroom TV in 1 bedroom ✕ Ⓡ B&b£10–£12.50 WB&bfr£65 LDO4pm

Lic ⊞ CTV 4P sauna bath

Ⓥ

Credit Cards

1 Access/Euro/Mastercard
2 American Express
3 Barclaycard/Visa
5 Diners

GH Sandbeck Hotel Crescent Ter, West Cliff ☎(0947) 604012
Apr–Sep

A high standard of accommodation and a warm welcome are assured at this charming hotel.

19hc (4🚿) (3fb) Ⓡ B&bfr£11 Bdifr£16 WBdifr£105 LDO5pm

Lic CTV ₱

GH Seacliffe Hotel North Prom, West Cliff ☎(0947) 603139

A detached house overlooking the sea, with spacious public areas.

19hc (2🛁 13🚿) (4fb) CTV in all rooms ✱B&b£13.23–£31.05 WB&bfr£87 LDO8.30pm

Lic CTV 8P ⌂ solarium

Credit cards 1 2 3 5 Ⓥ

⊢⊣ **GH Waverley Private Hotel** 17 Crescent Av ☎(0947) 604389
Mar–Oct

A very comfortable mid/terrace house situated in a quiet residential area close to the promenade and town centre.

6hc 2🚿 (5fb) ✕ Ⓡ B&b£9–11 Bdi£12.50–£14.50 WBdifr£85 LDO5.45pm

Lic ⊞ CTV ₱

Ⓥ

FH Mrs E Morley **Cross Butts** *(NZ881101)* (1½m W A171) ☎(0947) 602519
Apr–Oct

Near to the beaches and the moors, a 17th-century farmhouse W of the town off the A171.

3rm (1hc) ⅍ in all bedrooms ✗ B&b£10–£12 WB&b£66.50–£80

CTV P nc5yrs

240acres dairy mixed

WHITCHURCH
Hereford & Worcester
Map **3** SO51

GH Portland ☎Symonds Yat (0600) 890757
Closed Jan

Genial village centre guesthouse.

8hc (2fb) CTV in 7 bedrooms TV in 1 bedroom Ⓡ B&b£12–£12.50 Bdi£16–£18 WBdifr£108.

Lic 🕮 CTV 7P

Credit card ③

INN Crown Hotel ☎Symonds Yat (0600) 890234
Closed Xmas Day & Boxing Day

5hc (1⇌ 4⥂) (3fb) Ⓡ B&b£15–£18 Bdi£17.50–£23 WBdi£115–£135 Lunch £4.50–£6&alc Dinner10pm £4.50–£6&alc

🕮 CTV 40P pool table

Credit cards ① ② ③ ⑤

Ⓥ

WHITCHURCH
Shropshire
Map **7** SJ54

FH Mrs M H Mulliner **Bradeley Green** *(SJ537449)* (Waterfowl Sanctuary) Tarporley Rd ☎(0948) 3442
Closed Xmas

Nature trails, water gardens and wild fowl number among the attractions of this comfortable Georgian farmhouse on the A49.

3hc (1⇌ 2⥂) (2fb) ⅍ in 2 bedrooms Ⓡ in 2 bedrooms B&b£10.50–£12.50 Bdi£15.50–£17.50 WBdifr£100

🕮 CTV 6P ↙

Whitby — Whitley Bay

180acres dairy waterfowl sanctuary fish farming

WHITESTONE
Devon
Map **3** SX89

⊢⊣**FH** Mrs S K Lee **Rowhorne House** *(SX880948)* ☎Exeter (0392) 74675

Farmhouse set in attractive gardens and lawns.

3hc (2fb) TV in 1 bedroom ✗ B&b£8.50 Bdi£13 WBdi£91

6P 103acres dairy

Credit cards ① ② ③ ④ ⑤ Ⓥ

WHITEWELL
Lancashire
Map **7** SD64

INN The Inn at Whitewell ☎Dunsop Bridge (02008) 222

Old stone-inn in the lovely Bowland Forest. Good range of food.

11hc (6⇌) (4fb) CTV in 6 bedrooms B&b£21.50–£32 Bdi£26.50–£47 WBdifr£181 LDO9.30pm

🕮 CTV 50P ↙

Credit cards ① ② ③ ⑤

WHITHORN
Dumfries & Galloway *Wigtownshire*
Map **10** NX44

FH Mrs E C Forsyth **Baltier** *(NX466429)* ☎Garlieston (09886) 241
Mar–Nov

Modernised, stone-built farmhouse situated 2m NW on B7004.

2hc (1fb) ✗ Ⓡ ✱B&bfr£8.50 Bdifr£14 WBdifr£98

🕮 CTV 4P 220acres dairy sheep

WHITLAND
Dyfed
Map **2** SN21

FH C M & I A Lewis ***Cilpost*** *(SN191184)* ☎(0994) 240280
Apr–Sep

Well-appointed 300 year old farmhouse offering good meals and a warm welcome. 1½ miles south of the village.

7hc (3⇌ 3⥂) (3fb) ✗

Lic 🕮 12P ↙ snooker 160acres dairy

WHITLEY BAY
Tyne & Wear
Map **12** NZ37

GH Lindisfarne Hotel 11 Holly Av ☎091-251 3954

Friendly, family-run house situated in a quiet residential area. Good value dinners are a speciality.

9hc (1fb) CTV in all bedrooms ✗ Ⓡ ✱B&b£9–£10 Bdi£13–£14 WBdifr£91 LDO4pm

Lic 🕮 CTV ⱣP

Ⓥ

GH Marlborough 20–21 East Pde, Central Prom ☎091-251 3628

Sea front hotel managed by resident proprietors. Very comfortable sitting rooms overlooking the sea.

18rm (14hc 3⇌) (2fb) CTV in all bedrooms Ⓡ ✱B&bfr£13.50 Bdifr£18 LDO7pm

Lic CTV 7P

Credit cards ① ③

GH White Surf 8 South Pde ☎091-253 0103

Situated close to the sea and town centre this charming house is decorated throughout in a Scandinavian theme to create a light and spacious effect. Also, dinners are especially recommended for quality and value.

8hc (3fb) ⅍ in all bedrooms CTV in all bedrooms ✗ Ⓡ B&b£9.50–£10.50 Bdi£13–£14 WBdifr£88 LDO7.30pm

🕮 CTV 7P 2🚗 nc2yrs

Ⓥ

GH York House Hotel 30 Park Pde ☎091–252 8313

A family-run guesthouse offering comfort, good home-cooking and a friendly atmosphere.

8hc (1⇌ 6⋒) (1fb) CTV in all bedrooms ® B&bfr£14 Bdifr£18.50 WBdi£122.50 LDO7pm

Lic 𝍐 CTV 2P

Credit cards 1 3 Ⓥ

WHITNEY-ON-WYE
Hereford & Worcester
Map **3** SO24

INN Rhydspence (2m W A438) ☎Clifford (04973) 262

Lovely old timber-framed inn offering high quality accommodation and food.

5hc (4⇌ 1⋒) CTV in all bedrooms ✗ ® B&b£18 Bdifr£25 WBdifr£175 Lunch £8alc Dinner9.30pm £8alc

𝍐 60P ⇏

Credit cards 1 2 3

WHITTINGTON
Shropshire
Map **7** SJ33

FH Mrs H M Ward **Perry** *(SJ348303)* ☎Oswestry (0691) 662330
Mar–Dec

Comfortable accommodation in a large, early 19th century farmhouse 1m E of A5, approx 2m from village.

2hc (1fb) ✗ B&b£10–£13 Bdi£15–£18 WBdifr£105 LDO7.30pm

𝍐 CTV P ⌡ 750acres arable dairy

Ⓥ

WHITTLESFORD
Cambridgeshire
Map **5** TL44

INN *Red Lion Hotel* Station Rd ☎Cambridge (0223) 832047
Closed Xmas

A rambling, flint-faced and timber inn, 750 years old. Modern, fitted-bedrooms.

18hc (4⇌ 14⋒) (3fb) CTV in all bedrooms ✗ ® LDO9.30pm

175P

Credit cards 2 3 5

WICKFORD
Essex
Map **5** TQ79

GH Wickford Lodge 26 Ethelred Gdns ☎ (0268) 762663

Tudor-style detached house in quiet residential area, offering modern, comfortable accommodation.

6hc (2fb) B&b£16.50–£17

𝍐 CTV 6P

WICKHAM
Berkshire
Map **4** SU47

INN Five Bells ☎Boxford (048838) 242

4hc CTV in all bedrooms ® B&b£17–£25 Bdi£22–£30 Lunch £5–£10&alc Dinner10pm £5–£10&alc

𝍐 50P ⇒ U solarium

Credit card 3

WIDDINGTON
Essex
Map **5** TL53

FH Mrs L Vernon **Thistley Hall** *(TL556311)* ☎Saffron Walden (0799) 40388
mid Jan–Nov rs Sept

The historic farmhouse is pleasantly surrounded by gardens and pastureland with beautiful views of the countryside.

3rm (2hc) (1fb) ✗ B&b£10–£15 WB&bfr£65 (W only Jan–May)

𝍐 CTV 4P nc5yrs 30acres mixed

WIDEGATES
Cornwall
Map **2** SX25

GH Coombe Farm ☎(05034) 223
Mar–Oct

Attractive 1920's detached house affording superb views.

8hc (4fb) ✗ B&b£10–£16 Bdi£18–£24 WBdi£120–£160 LDO7pm

Lic 𝍐 CTV 12P nc5yrs ⇒(heated)

Ⓥ

See advertisement under Looe

WIDEMOUTH BAY
Cornwall
Map **2** SS20

GH Beach House Hotel ☎(028885) 256
Etr–Sep

13hc (5⋒) (5fb) ✗ ® B&b£11.50–£12.50 Bdi£15.50–£16.50 WBdifr£99 LDO7pm

Lic CTV 20P

Ⓥ

See advertisement under Bude

WIGAN
Gt Manchester
Map **7** SD50

GH Aalton Court 23 Upper Dicconson St (Guestaccom) ☎(0942) 322220

Small, family-run guesthouse close to the town centre, museums and Wigan pier.

6hc (2⇌ 4⋒) (1fb) CTV in all bedrooms ✗ B&b£17.50 Bdi£25 WBdifr£175 LDO2pm

Lic 𝍐 CTV 8P

INN *Th'old Hall* 240A Warrington Rd, Lower Ince, Ince in Makerfield ☎(0942) 866330

A typical Lancashire pub with modern bedrooms.

4hc (2⇌) CTV in all bedrooms ✗ ®

𝍐 30P snooker

Credit card 2

WIGHT, ISLE OF
Map **4**

ARRETON
Map **4** SZ58

GH *Stickworth Hall* ☎(098377) 233
May–Sep

Lovely 18th-century home in extensive grounds with lake for fishing.

25hc (2⇌ 14⋒) (6fb) ✗ ® LDO7pm

Lic 𝍐 CTV 50P nc5yrs

See advertisement under Sandown

CHALE
Map **4** SZ47

INN Clarendon Hotel & Wight Mouse (Guestaccom) ☎(0983) 730431

Delightful antique furnished bedrooms.

13hc (2⇌ 6⋒) (8fb) CTV in all bedrooms ® ✱ B&b£17.25–£19.55 Bdi£25.30–£27.60 WBdifr£143.75 Lunch£3.50–£7&alc Dinner10pm £3.50–£11&alc

𝍐 CTV 100P ⌂

Ⓥ

FRESHWATER
Map **4** SZ38

GH *Blenheim House* Gate Ln ☎(0983) 752858
May–Sep

Small guesthouse with relaxing atmosphere. Outdoor swimming pool.

8hc (6⋒) (5fb) CTV in all bedrooms ✗ LDOam

Lic 𝍐 CTV 6P 1⌂ nc3yrs ⇒(heated)

NEWPORT
Map **4** SZ48

INN *Shute* Clatterford Shute, Carisbrooke ☎(0983) 523393
Feb–Nov

Georgian country residence on hillside nesting below the famous Carisbrooke Castle, with a lovely restaurant/bar. 1m W B3323.

3hc (1⋒) CTV in all bedrooms ✗ ® LDO9.30pm

𝍐 25P nc10yrs

Credit cards 1 3

NITON
Map **4** SZ57

GH Pine Ridge Niton Undercliff ☎(0983) 730802

A comfortable house with a homely atmosphere and good views.

7hc (1⇌ 2⋒) (3fb) CTV in all bedrooms Ⓡ B&b£15–£18 Bdi£18–£25 WBdi£155

Lic 🍽 CTV 10P

Ⓥ

See advertisement under Ventnor

RYDE
Map **4** SZ59

GH Teneriffe 36 The Strand ☎(0983) 63841

Large house close to the sea, with large bar and dance floor, two lounges and basement restaurant.

34hc (21⇌ 4⋒) (7fb) CTV in all bedrooms ✗ Ⓡ ✱B&b£12.65–£13.80 Bdi£16.17–£17.25 WBdifr£113.19 LDO7pm

Lic 🍽 9P

Ⓥ

FH Mrs S Swan ***Aldermoor*** *(SZ582906)* Upton Rd ☎(0983) 64743
Apr–Oct

Modernised old stone and brick farmhouse.

3hc ✗

🍽 CTV 20P 2🚗 nc7yrs 27acres beef

ST LAWRENCE
Map **4** SZ57

Wight, Isle of

GH Woody Bank Hotel Undercliff Dr ☎Ventnor (0983) 852610
Mar–Oct

Personally supervised by the owners, this small hotel has a warm, informal atmosphere and comfortable lounges.

8hc (4⇌ 4⋒) B&b£16–£18 Bdi£22.50–£24.50 WBdi£155–£165 LDO7.30pm

Lic 🍽 CTV 10P nc5yrs

Ⓥ

SANDOWN
Map **4** SZ58

GH Braemar Hotel 5 Broadway ☎(0983) 403358
Apr–Sept

Small family-run hotel with relaxing atmosphere.

16hc (1⇌ 7⋒) (6fb) CTV in all bedrooms ✗ Ⓡ B&b£14–£16 Bdi£18–£20 WBdi£120 LDO6.30pm

Lic 🍽 CTV 12P

Credit cards 1 2 3 5 Ⓥ

GH Chester Lodge Hotel Beachfield Rd ☎(0983) 402773
Closed mid Dec–mid Jan rs Oct

Small, comfortable, family-run guesthouse near to beach, five minutes walk to town centre.

19hc (2⇌ 8⋒) (4fb) CTV in all bedrooms Ⓡ B&b£11.50–£12.65 Bdi£14.95–£16.10 WBdifr£105.80 (W only Jul–Aug)

Lic 🍽 CTV 19P

Ⓥ

GH *Culver Lodge* Albert Rd ☎(0983) 403819
Apr–Oct

Small and friendly private hotel with good public rooms and relaxing atmosphere.

24hc (2⇌ 11⋒) (3fb) ✗ Ⓡ B&b£10–£15.25 Bdi£13.50–£17 W£89–£118 ⱡ LDO7.30pm

Lic 🍽 CTV 20P nc3yrs

GH Meadway House Hotel 12 Beachfield Rd ☎(0983) 402137

A personally supervised hotel offering simple and comfortable accommodation.

13hc (11⋒) (8fb) CTV in all bedrooms ✗ Ⓡ ✱B&b£12–£15 Bdi£15–£18 WBdi£89–£110 LDO6.30pm

Lic 🍽 CTV 13P ⌂

Ⓥ

Selected

GH St Catherine's Hotel 1 Winchester Park Rd ☎(0983) 402392
Closed Xmas & New Year

Excellent accommodation, with all bedrooms en-suite, at this smart private hotel.

18hc (11⇌ 7ⓜ) (3fb) CTV in all bedrooms ✗ ® B&b£14.25–£16.50 Bdi£19.25–£23 WBdi£115.50–£138 LDO6pm

Lic ᛗ CTV 8P

Credit cards [1] [3] ⓥ

Wight, Isle of

SEAVIEW
Map **4** SZ69

GH Northbank Hotel Circular Rd ☎(098371) 2227
Etr–Sep

Large traditional family house with excellent sea views.

18hc (6fb) CTV in 3 bedrooms ® ✱B&b£15–£20 Bdi£23.50–£30 W£118–£150 Ⱡ LDO8pm

Lic ᛗ CTV 8P 4🚗 ⌂ snooker

SHANKLIN
Map **4** SZ58
See plan

GH Afton Hotel & Restaurant Clarence Gdns ☎(0983) 863075 Plan **1** *B4*

Luxurious guesthouse with period furniture and comfortable accommodation.

6fl ⅟ in 2 bedrooms CTV in all bedrooms ✈ Ⓡ B&b£17–£20 Bdi£24–£27 WBdi£144–£162 LDO9pm

Lic 🍽 5P 1🚗 nc5yrs

Credit cards 1 3

GH *Aqua Hotel* The Esplanade ☎(0983) 863024 Plan **2** *C2*
Etr–Oct

Modern hotel in an elevated position overlooking the beach and seafront.

24hc (3⇌) (8fb) ✈ LDO6pm

Lic CTV 2P

Credit card 3

GH Apse Manor Country House Apse Manor Rd ☎(0983) 866651 Plan **3** *A1*

Good bedrooms and a warm and friendly atmosphere at this charming 16th-century manor house.

Wight, Isle of

6hc (5⇌) (2fb) CTV in all bedrooms Ⓡ ✱B&b£15–£16 Bdi£20–£23 WBdi£140–£160 LDO7.30pm

Lic 🍽 10P nc5yrs

Ⓥ

GH *Bay House Hotel* 8 Chine Av, off Keats Green ☎(0983) 863180
Plan **4** *C2*
Closed Xmas

Overlooks the chine with lovely sea views.

20hc (13⇌ 3fl) (3fb) CTV in 5 bedrooms LDO6.30pm

Lic 🍽 CTV 25P 2🚗 ♿

Credit card 3

See advertisement on page 434

Selected

GH Chine Lodge East Cliff Rd ☎(0983) 862358 Plan 5 *B2*

Reputed to be the birthplace of the Duke of Hamilton this charming and homely Victorian hotel has tastefully appointed bedrooms and two interesting smuggling tunnels.

7⇌ CTV in all bedrooms ✈ Ⓡ ✱B&b£15–£17.50 Bdi£20–£22.50 LDO7.15pm

Lic 6P

GH Culham Private Hotel 31 Landguard Manor Rd ☎(0983) 862880 Plan **6** *A3*
Apr–Oct

Attractive small hotel in tree-lined road with heated swimming pool in secluded garden.

10hc (1⇌ 6fl) ✈ Ⓡ ✱B&b£10.50–£11.50 Bdi£15–£16 WBdi£93–£102 LDO4pm

🍽 CTV 8P nc12yrs ⛱(heated) solarium

Shanklin

1 Afton Hotel
2 Aqua Hotel
3 Aspe Manor Country House
4 Bay House Hotel
5 Chine Lodge
6 Culham Private Hotel
7 Curraghmore Hotel
8 Edgecliffe Hotel
9 Fawley Hotel
10 Kenbury Private Hotel
12 Luccombe Chine House Country Hotel
13 Monteagle Hotel
14 Norfolk House Hotel
15 Ocean View Hotel
16 Osborne House
17 Overstrand Private Hotel
18 Perran Lodge Private Hotel
19 Soraba

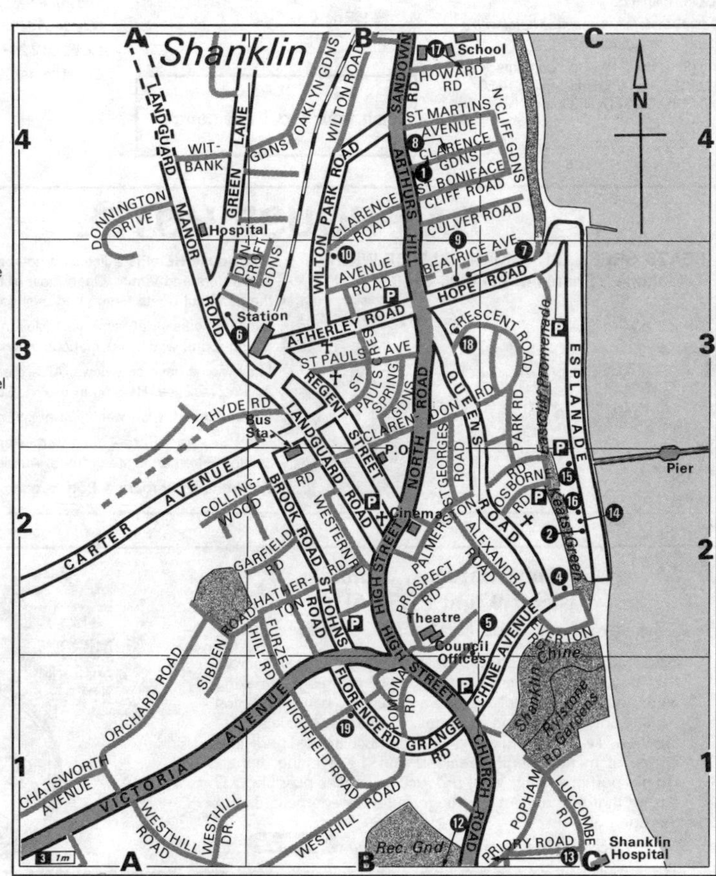

GH *Curraghmore Hotel* 22 Hope Rd ☎(0983) 862605 Plan **7** *B3*
Mar–Oct

Small private hotel close to sea front. Nicely appointed with the emphasis on entertainment.

24hc (10⇌ 6⋒) (9fb) ® LDO6pm

Lic CTV 20P putting

Credit cards 1 3

GH Edgecliffe Hotel Clarence Gdns ☎(0983) 866199 Plan **8** *B4* Telex no 89441
Closed Dec

A warm friendly atmosphere exists in this converted private house situated in quiet residential area.

10hc (2⇌ 4⋒) (2fb) CTV in all bedrooms ✗ ® available in bedrooms *B&b£11–£13 Bdi£15–£19 WBdi£96–£114 LDO6.30pm

Lic 3P nc5yrs

Credit cards 1 2 3 Ⓥ

GH Fawley Hotel 12 Hope Rd ☎(0983) 862190 Plan **9** *B3*

A small tastefully appointed hotel with a friendly atmosphere.

9hc (3⋒) (4fb) CTV in all bedrooms ✗ ® B&b£12.50–£14.50 Bdi£14.50–£16.50 WBdi£85–£115 LDO4.30pm

Lic CTV 10P

Wight, Isle of

GH Kenbury Private Hotel Clarence Rd ☎(0983) 862085 Plan **10** *B3*
Etr–Oct

Comfortable accommodation in a small family hotel.

17hc (4⇌ 9⋒) (3fb) ⅟ in 2 bedrooms CTV in all bedrooms ✗ ® B&b£11–£14 Bdi£15–£18.50 WBdi£95–£125 LDO6.30pm

Lic CTV 6P nc3yrs snooker

Credit card 3 Ⓥ

GH *Luccombe Chine House Country Hotel* ☎(0983) 862037
Plan **12** *B1*
Closed Xmas

An old manor house in a secluded setting. All bedrooms are en-suite and have four-poster beds.

6⋒ CTV in all bedrooms ✗ ® LDO8pm

Lic 16P nc16yrs

Credit cards 1 3

GH Monteagle Hotel Priory Rd ☎(0983) 862854 Plan **13** *C1*

Large hotel with many facilities including snooker table and outdoor swimming pool.

40hc (20⇌ 10⋒) (8fb) CTV in all bedrooms ✗ ® B&b£14–£20 Bdi£18–£24 WBdi£95–£140 LDO7.30pm

Lic CTV 25P ⩠(heated) snooker

Ⓥ

GH Norfolk House Hotel 19 The Esplanade ☎(0983) 863023 Plan **14** *C2*
Feb–Nov

A seafront hotel with well-appointed lounges and an informal atmosphere.

19hc (2fb) ✗ ® B&b£10.50–£12.50 Bdi£12.50–£16 WBdi£80–£110 LDO9.30pm

Lic CTV 6P

GH *Ocean View Hotel* 38 The Esplanade ☎(0983) 862602 Plan **15** *C2*
Mar–Nov

Seafront hotel with excellent sun lounge and attractive wood-panelled dining room.

36hc (4⇌ 17⋒) (12fb) ® LDO7.30pm

Lic CTV 25P

Credit cards 1 2 3

GH Osborne House Esplanade ☎(0983) 862501 Plan **16** *C2*
1 Jan–5 Nov

A personally run seafront hotel in a prime position opposite the pier.

12hc (3⇌ 9⋔) CTV in all bedrooms ✈ Ⓡ ✱B&b£18.50 Bdi£27 LDO8pm

Lic 𝍦 ⍴ nc13yrs

Ⓥ

GH Overstrand Private Hotel Howard Rd ☎(0983) 862100 Plan **17** *B4*
Etr–Sep

Stone-built house in attractive gardens. Rooms have character and comfort.

15hc (4⇌ 7⋔) (8fb) CTV in all bedrooms ✈ Ⓡ B&b£14–£19 Bdi£18–£23 WBdi£120–£155 LDO6pm

Lic 𝍦 CTV 25P 𝒫(grass)

Credit cards ①③

GH Perran Lodge Private Hotel
2 Crescent Rd ☎(0983) 862816
Plan **18** *B3*
Apr–Oct

Red-brick two-storey south-facing house with lawn and verandah.

20hc (5⇌ 5⋔) (8fb) B&b£11–£15.50 Bdi£13.50–£17.50 WBdi£81.50–£107.50 LDO6pm

Lic CTV 8P nc3yrs

Ⓥ

Wight, Isle of

⊢⊣**GH Soraba Private Hotel** 2 Paddock Rd ☎(0983) 862367 Plan **19** *B1*
rs Xmas

Quiet location near the chine within a few minutes walk of sea and shops. Personal attention and home-cooking.

6hc (1⋔) (2fb) TV in 2 bedrooms B&b£8.95–£10.95 Bdi£12.95–£14.95 WBdi£75–£92 LDO3pm

Lic 𝍦 CTV 4P

Ⓥ

TOTLAND BAY
Map **4** SZ38

GH *Hermitage Hotel* Cliff Rd ☎(0983) 752518
Mar–Nov

Small, family-run hotel with comfortable lounges and nicely appointed bedrooms.

12hc (2⇌ 2⋔) (4fb) LDO7pm

Lic 𝍦 CTV 12P 1⌂(charge) ⌂ ≙

Credit cards ①③

GH Hilton House Private Hotel Granville Rd ☎(0983) 754768
Mar–Sep rs Oct–Feb

A small, well-appointed guesthouse with a warm, informal atmosphere. Good, honest cooking.

6hc (1⋔) (1fb) CTV in all bedrooms ✈ Ⓡ ✱B&b£12 Bdi£17.50 WBdifr£108

Lic 𝍦 CTV ⍴

Credit cards ①③ Ⓥ

GH Lismore Private Hotel 23 The Avenue ☎(0983) 752025

Small, friendly, well-kept accommodation.

7hc (5⋔) (3fb) CTV in all bedrooms ✈ Ⓡ B&b£13.25–£14.25 Bdi£15.50–£18 WBdi£108.50–£115.50 LDO3pm

Lic 𝍦 8P nc5yrs

Ⓥ

See advertisement on page 436

GH Littledene Lodge Granville Rd ☎(0983) 752411
Closed Dec–Feb

7hc (3⋔) (3fb) Ⓡ B&b£11–£13 Bdi£17–£18.25 WBdifr£99

Lic 𝍦 CTV 5P

Ⓥ

GH Nodes Country Hotel Alum Bay Old Rd ☎(0983) 752859

A country house set in 2½ acres of downland countryside, with modern compact well-appointed bedrooms. →

11hc (2⇌ 6ffl) (5fb) Ⓡ B&b£12.50–£17 Bdi£18.50–£23.50 WBdifr£112 LDO1pm

Lic 𝍖 CTV 15P

Ⓥ

GH Sandford Lodge Private Hotel
61 The Avenue ☎(0983) 753478
Mar–Oct

A well-appointed house with comfortable bedrooms and a relaxing atmosphere.

6hc (1⇌ 1ffl) (1fb) TV in 2 bedrooms Ⓡ B&b£11–£12.50 Bdi£16.50–£17.50 WBdifr£102 LDOnoon

Lic 𝍖 CTV 7P

Ⓥ

Wight, Isle of

GH Westgrange Country Hotel Alum Bay Old Rd ☎(0983) 752227
Mar–Oct & New Year

Small, friendly country hotel with comfortable bedrooms and good cooking.

13hc (2⇌ 7ffl) (8fb) CTV available in bedrooms Ⓡ ✱B&b£13.50–£18.50 Bdi£20.50–£26 WBdi£113.50–£150 LDO7pm

Lic 𝍖 CTV 12P

Ⓥ

VENTNOR
Map **4** SZ57

GH Channel View Hotel Hambrough Rd
☎(0983) 852230
20 Mar–19 Oct rs 1–20 Mar

Set on a cliff between the sea and town.

14hc (2ffl) (6fb) ✗ Ⓡ B&b£12–£14 Bdi£15–£18 WBdifr£105

Lic CTV 𝒫

Credit cards 1 3 Ⓥ

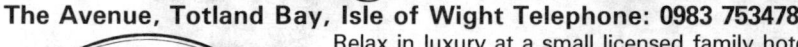

GH Glen Islay Hotel St Boniface Rd ☎(0983) 854095

This small, homely hotel is under the personal supervision of owners. Exceptionally well-appointed bedrooms and first class menu.

9rm (8fl) (8fb) CTV in all bedrooms ® B&b£13.50–£15 Bdi£16.50–£18.50 WBdi£115–£125

Lic 🍽 CTV 5P

Ⓥ

GH *Hillside Private Hotel* Mitchell Av ☎(0983) 852271
Mar–Oct

Wight, Isle of

11hc (3⇌ 3fl) (6fb) CTV in all bedrooms ®

Lic 🍽 CTV 16P

GH Horseshoe Bay Hotel Shore Rd, Bonchurch ☎(0983) 852487
Etr–Sep

Small private hotel where a warm welcome is assured. Overlooks Bonchurch Bay.

7hc (4⇌ 1fl) CTV in all bedrooms ® B&b£11–£14 Bdi£15.50–£18.25 WBdi£108.50–£127.75 LDO6pm

Lic 🍽 7P nc8yrs

Ⓥ

GH Lake Hotel Shore Rd, Bonchurch ☎(0983) 852613
Mar–Oct

Set in 2½ acres of gardens close to beach and countryside. →

11hc (1⇨ 8fl) Annexe: 10hc (8fl) (7fb) Ⓡ B&b£11–£15 Bdi£16–£20 WBdi£101.50–£129.50 LDO6.30pm

Lic 🍽 CTV 20P nc2yrs

Ⓥ

GH Llynfi Hotel 23 Spring Hill ☎(0983) 852202

Mr & Mrs Fisher supervise this small well appointed hotel with comfortable rooms.

10rm (7fl) (2fb) Ⓡ ✱B&bfr£12

Lic 7P

Credit cards 1 3

GH Macrocarpa Mitchell Av ☎(0983) 852428
Mar–Oct

A large country style house in a secluded setting offering modestly furnished accommodation and sound cooking personally supervised by Mr and Mrs Precheger.

20hc (7⇨ 13fl) (7fb) CTV in all bedrooms ✗ Ⓡ B&b£16.50–£26.50 Bdi£22–£32 WBdifr£155 LDO7.30pm

Lic 🍽 CTV 25P snooker

Credit cards 1 3 Ⓥ

GH Picardie Hotel Esplanade ☎(0983) 852647
Closed late Nov–Dec rs Jan & Feb

Small house on the sea front that has been modernised to provide comfortable accommodation.

10hc (4fl) (3fb) ⊬ in all bedrooms Ⓡ B&b£11.50–£13 Bdi£17.25–£19 WBdifr£115

Lic CTV 🅿̸

Credit card 3 Ⓥ

GH Richmond Private Hotel The Esplanade ☎(0983) 852496

A family-run seafront hotel with attractive lounges and an informal atmosphere.

12hc (7fl) (3fb) Ⓡ B&b£10.50–£12.50 Bdi£14.95–£16.50 WBdi£103.50–£114 LDO4pm

Lic CTV 🅿̸

Credit cards 1 3 Ⓥ

Wight, Isle of — Willersey

GH St Maur Hotel Castle Rd ☎(0983) 852570
Mar–Oct

Well-kept house run by friendly family, in quiet residential area.

15hc (10⇨ 3fl) (4fb) ✗ Ⓡ B&b£11.50–£14 Bdi£16.50–£19.50 WBdi£122–£136 LDO7pm

Lic 🍽 CTV 12P nc5yrs

Credit cards 1 3 Ⓥ

Selected

GH Under Rock Hotel Shore Rd, Bonchurch (1m E) ☎(0983) 852714
Mar–Oct

A secluded comfortable small hotel, personally supervised by the proprietors who offer a warm welcome together with good, honest home-cooking. Delightful gardens.

7hc CTV in all bedrooms ✗ ✱B&b£15 Bdi£21 WBdi£147 LDO4.30pm

Lic 🍽 12P nc10yrs

Ⓥ

WIGMORE
Hereford & Worcester
Map **7** SO46

INN *Compasses Hotel* ☎(056886) 203

A stone-built inn in rural village close to the Welsh Marches, offering pleasant accommodation and good food.

3hc (1fb) CTV in all bedrooms Ⓡ LDO10pm

🍽 70P

Credit cards 1 2 3 5

Visit your local AA centre

WILBERFOSS
Humberside
Map **8** SE75

FH Mrs J M Liversidge **Cuckoo Nest** *(SE717510)* ☎(07595) 365
Closed Xmas

Traditional Yorkshire farmhouse with bright and homely rooms. 1m W of village on south side of A1079.

2hc (1fb) ⊬ in 2 bedrooms ✗ B&b£9–£10

🍽 TV P nc2yrs 150acres arable beef dairy sheep mixed

WILLAND
Devon
Map **3** ST01

FH Mrs J M Granger **Doctors** *(ST015117)* Halberton Rd ☎Tiverton (0884) 820525
Closed Nov–Feb

Farmhouse situated in garden and farmland. Tiverton and Cullompton 4 miles.

2rm (1fb) ⊬ in bedrooms ✗ Ⓡ in 1 bedroom B&b£8 WB&b£60

CTV 6P ↲ 95acres

Ⓥ

WILLERSEY
Gloucestershire
Map **4** SP13

Selected

GH Old Rectory Church St ☎Broadway (0386) 853729
Closed Xmas wk

Outstanding 17th-century house with relaxing bedrooms and a secluded walled garden.

6hc (4⇨ 2fl) CTV in all bedrooms ✗ Ⓡ B&b£24.50–£33 WB&b£154.35–£207.90

🍽 CTV 10P 2🚗 nc10yrs

Credit cards 1 3

See advertisement under Broadway

WILLITON
Somerset
Map **3** ST14

Selected

GH Curdon Mill Country Hotel
Lower Vellow (2m SE off A358)
☎Stogumber (0984) 56522
Recently converted Curdon Mill stands in pleasant gardens amid 200 acres of arable and beef farmland 3 miles from the town. Tastefully furnished accommodation with friendly staff.
6hc (1⇌ 5fl) CTV in all bedrooms ✗ Ⓡ B&b£11.50–£17.50 Bdi£19.50–£21.50 WBdi£116–£150 LDO8.30pm
Lic 🝖 P ⛱ ⚲(grass) ✓ U

WIMBORNE MINSTER
Dorset
Map **4** SZ09

GH Riversdale 33 Poole Rd ☎(0202) 884528
Mar–Oct closed Xmas wk rs Nov Dec Jan & Feb
Detached guesthouse with sound, neat accommodation on the edge of town centre.
8hc (3fb) CTV in 5 bedrooms TV in 3 bedrooms Ⓡ B&b£11.50–£16 Bdi£17–£22.50 WBdifr£112 LDO10am
🝖 5P nc3yrs
Ⓥ

GH Stour Lodge 21 Julian's Rd ☎(0202) 888003
Closed 20 Dec–5 Jan
Small, comfortable well-appointed house with sufficient parking, a pleasant garden and friendly hosts. On A31 Dorchester Rd.
3hc (1⇌) (2fb) CTV in all bedrooms Ⓡ ✱B&b£17.50–£20 Bdi£25–£27.50 WBdifr£175
Lic 🝖 CTV 4P

WIMPSTONE
Warwickshire
Map **4** SP24

⊢⊣**FH** Mrs J E James **Whitchurch Farm** *(SP222485)* ☎Alderminster (078987) 275
Lovely Georgian farmhouse built 1750, set in park-like surroundings on edge of Cotswolds, 4½ miles from Stratford-upon-Avon.
3hc (2fb) ✗ B&b£9–£10 Bdi£15–£16
🝖 CTV 6P 208acres arable beef sheep
Ⓥ

WINCANTON
Somerset
Map **3** ST72

⊢⊣**FH** Mrs J Brunt **Hatherleigh** *(ST707276)* ☎(0963) 32142
Apr–Oct
Small cottage farm with simple bedrooms, charming living room and friendly welcome.
2hc (1fb) ⚟ in bedrooms B&b£9–£10 WB&bfr£60
CTV 5P 1🚘 nc3yrs 40acres beef mixed
Ⓥ

WINCHESTER
Hampshire
Map **4** SU52

GH Harestock Lodge Hotel Harestock Rd ☎(0962) 881870 Closed 24 Dec–4 Jan
A commercial hotel with functional modern accommodation. Public rooms are spacious and popular. Situated 2m N of the city centre off the B3420 Andover Road.
20rm (9fl) (5fb) CTV in 18 bedrooms ✗ B&b£15–£22 LDO9.15pm
Lic 🝖 CTV 20P ⛱
Credit card ③ Ⓥ
See advertisement on page 440

WINCLE
Cheshire
Map **7** SJ96

GH Four Ways Diner Motel Cleulow Cross (1m N of A54) ☎(02607) 228 due to change to (0260) 227228

Small, family-run motel in Peak District National Park.

6hc (1⇌ 5fl) (2fb) CTV in all bedrooms Ⓡ B&b£15–£22 Bdi£22–£30 LDO8pm

Lic 50P

Credit cards 1 3 Ⓥ

Wincle — Windermere

WINDERMERE
Cumbria
Map **7** SD49
See plan on page 442

GH Archway College Rd ☎(09662) 5613
Plan **1** *B5*

Neat and cosy guesthouse on quiet side street near town centre. In the delightful dining room, furnished in antique pine, the friendly proprietors serve imaginative and well-cooked dinners. There is a comfortable lounge.

6hc (2fb) Ⓡ B&b£10–£11 Bdi£16–£18 WBdi£110–£121 LDO4pm

CTV 3P nc12yrs

Ⓥ

GH Biskey Howe Villa Hotel Craig Walk, Bowness ☎(09662) 3988
Plan **2** *B2*

An extensive private hotel in an elevated position overlooking the lake.

11hc (7 fl) (5fb) CTV in all bedrooms ✗ Ⓡ ✱B&b£16–£25 Bdi£23–£32 WBdi£145–£205 LDO6pm

Lic lift 10P ⛳ ⩦(heated)

Credit cards 1 3

GH Brendan Chase 1 & 3 College Rd ☎(09662) 5638 Plan **3** *C5*

8hc (1 fl) (4fb) ⍻in 1 bedroom CTV in all bedrooms Ⓡ ✱B&bfr£10.50 Bdifr£16 WB&bfr£126 LDO4pm

lift CTV 8P ⛳

Selected

GH Brooklands Ferry View, Bowness ☎(09662) 2344 Plan **4** *B1* Feb–Nov

An extremely friendly atmosphere and excellent cooking can be found at this cosy little hotel set in its own gardens. Len Stanley is always around chatting to guests while his wife Ivy is busy preparing very special meals. Decor and furnishings are also of the highest standards.

6hc (3 fl) (1fb) Ⓡ Bdi£22–£25 WBdi£150–£165 LDO5.30pm

Lic lift CTV 6P

Ⓥ

GH Crag Brow Cottage Private Hotel Helm Rd, Bowness ☎(09662) 4080 Plan **5** *B2*

Attractive Georgian house in its own grounds. Comfortable and well-decorated throughout.

5⇌ fl (2fb) CTV in all bedrooms Ⓡ B&b£17.50–£19 WB&b£110.25–£119.70 LDO9pm

Lic lift 20P

Credit cards 1 2 3

GH Cranleigh Hotel Kendal Rd, Bowness ☎(09662) 3293 Plan **6** *B2* Mar–Nov

Attractive Victorian house. Well-equipped bedrooms include remote control colour TVs and hairdryers.

Windermere

9⇌ (1fb) CTV in all bedrooms ✗ Ⓡ B&b£17–£19 Bdi£27–£29 WBdi£170 LDO8pm

Lic lift CTV 9P nc5yrs

Credit cards 1 2 3 5 Ⓥ

See advertisement on page 443

GH Eastbourne Hotel Biskey Howe Rd ☎(09662) 3525 Plan **7** *B3*

Cheery, friendly proprietors run this large end-terrace house.

9hc (2fb) Ⓡ ✱B&b£11.50–£12.50 Bdi£18.50–£19.50 WBdi£128–£135 LDOam

Lic lift CTV 3P

Credit cards 1 3 5 Ⓥ

See advertisement on page 443

GH *Elim Bank Hotel* Lake Rd, Bowness ☎(09662) 4810 Plan **8** *B3* Mar–Dec

This large, detached house is built of traditional Lakeland slate. The à la carte restaurant is also open to non-residents.

7hc (3fb) CTV in 2 bedrooms ✗ LDO9pm

Lic lift CTV 6P

Credit cards 1 2 3

See advertisement on page 444

GH Fairfield Country House Hotel Brantfell Rd, Bowness ☎(09662) 6565 Plan **9** *B2*

Peaceful hotel in secluded gardens above the lake.

10hc (3⇌ 7 fl) (3fb) CTV in all bedrooms Ⓡ B&b£16.50–£28 Bdi£25.50–£36 WBdi£162.50–£172.50 LDO9.30pm

Lic lift 10P

Credit cards 1 2 3 5 Ⓥ

See advertisement on page 444

GH Fir Trees Lake Rd ☎(09662) 2272 Plan **10** *B4*

A very comfortable and spacious house with a friendly atmosphere. All bedrooms are en-suite.

7hc (1⇌ 6 fl) (2fb) CTV in all bedrooms ✗ Ⓡ available B&b£13.50–£16.50 WB&b£90–£110

lift 8P

Credit cards 1 3 Ⓥ

See advertisement on page 444

GH Glenburn New Rd ☎(09662) 2649 Plan **11** *C4*

A delightful house with very friendly proprietors and good home-cooking. Most of the charming bedrooms have en-suite facilities and all are decorated with co-ordinated colour schemes.

10hc (3⇌ 5 fl) (3fb) ⍻in 2 bedrooms CTV in all bedrooms ✗ Ⓡ ✱B&b£14–£18 Bdi£22–£27 WBdifr£169 LDO4.30pm

Lic lift CTV 12P

See advertisement in colour feature

GH Glen Cree Private Hotel Lake Rd ☎(09662) 5822 Plan **12** *B4* Closed Dec & Jan Weekends only Feb

An appealing house overlooking the beach with spacious well fitted bedrooms and an elegant lounge.

5hc (3⇌ 2 fl) ✗ Ⓡ ✱B&b£17.50–£21 Bdi£28–£31.50 WBdi£188–£210

Lic lift 8P nc14yrs

Ⓥ

See advertisement on page 444

GH Glenville Hotel Lake Rd ☎(09662) 3371 Plan **13** *B3* Feb–Nov

Elegant house with comfortable lounges, attractive dining room and neat bedrooms.

9hc (5 fl) (1fb) ⍻in 2 bedrooms CTV in all bedrooms ✗ Ⓡ B&b£11.50–£15 Bdi£19.50–£23 WBdi£136–£156 LDO2pm

Lic lift 12P

Ⓥ

See advertisement on page 445

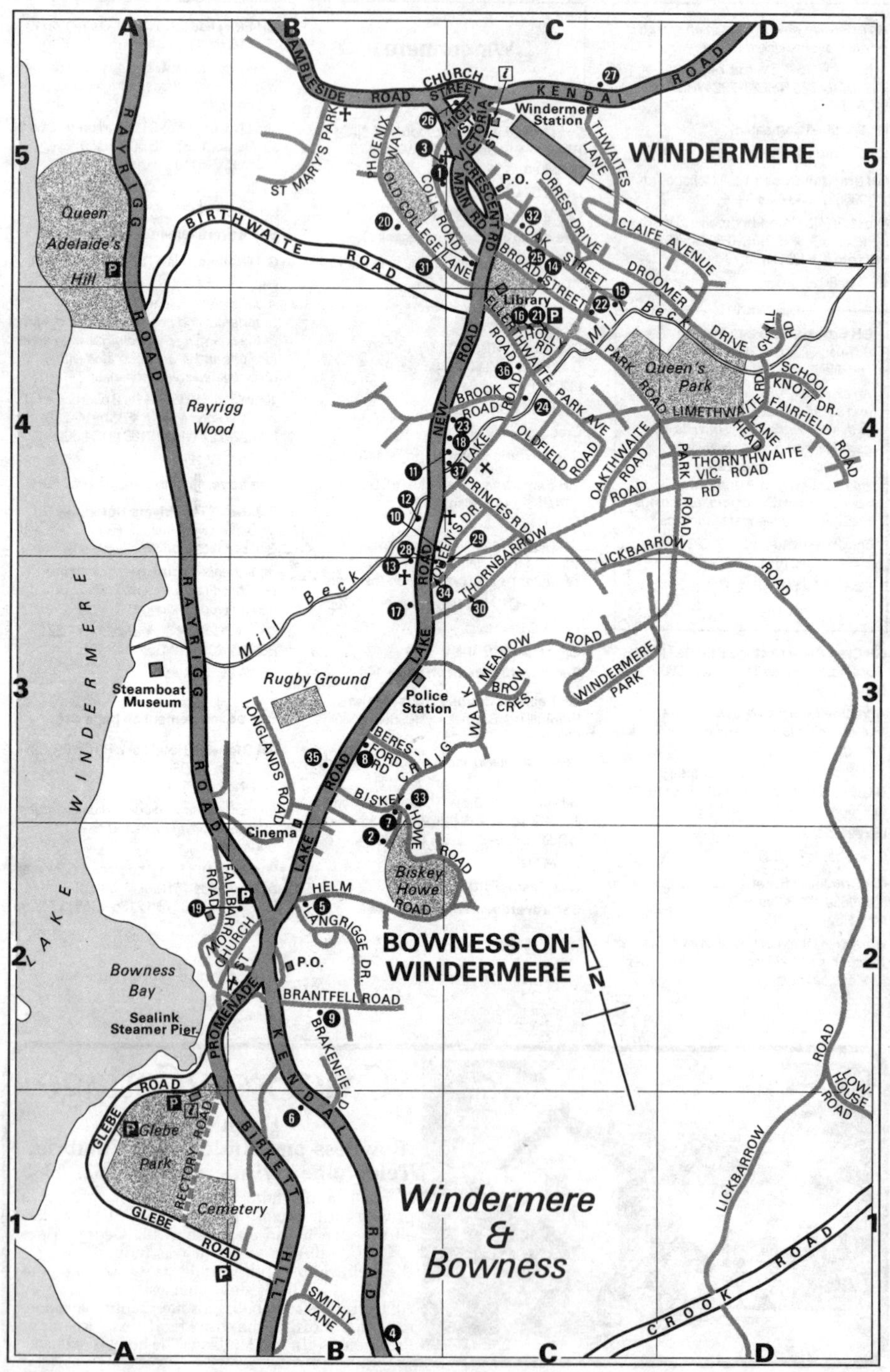

WINDERMERE
BOWNESS-ON-WINDERMERE
Windermere & Bowness
Queen Adelaide's Hill
Rayrigg Wood
LAKE WINDERMERE
Steamboat Museum
Rugby Ground
Police Station
Cinema
Biskey Howe
Bowness Bay
Sealink Steamer Pier
Glebe Park
Cemetery
Queen's Park
Windermere Station
Library
P.O.
RAYRIGG ROAD
BIRTHWAITE ROAD
AMBLESIDE ROAD
CHURCH STREET
KENDAL ROAD
NEW ROAD
LAKE ROAD
Mill Beck

Windermere

1 Archway
2 Biskey Howe Villa Hotel
3 Brendon Chase
4 Brooklands
5 Crag Brow Cottage Private Hotel
6 Cranleigh Hotel
7 Eastbourne Hotel
8 Elim Bank Hotel
9 Fairfield Country House Hotel
10 Fir Trees
11 Glenburn
12 Glen Cree Private Hotel
13 Glenville Hotel

Windermere

14 Green Gables
15 Greenriggs
16 Halsthorpe
17 Hawksmoor
18 Hilton House Hotel
19 Holly Cottages
20 Holly Lodge
21 Kenilworth
22 Lynwood
23 Meadfoot
24 Mylne Bridge Private Hotel
25 Oakfield
26 Oakthorpe Hotel
27 Orrest Head House
28 Rosemount
29 St Johns Lodge
30 Thornleigh
31 Tudor
32 Westbeck House
33 Westbourne Hotel
34 Westlake
35 White Lodge Hotel
36 Winbrook
37 Woodlands

ELIM BANK HOTEL

Lake Road,

Bowness-on-Windermere, Cumbria

Telephone: 09662 4810

Bowness-on-Windermere

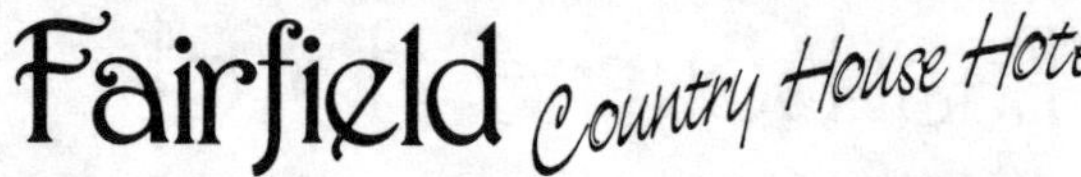

Welcome to Fairfield Country House Hotel, where a warm and friendly atmosphere awaits you in the heart of the most beautiful corner of Britain. An original country house family owned and run where you are assured of a high standard of personal family service. Situated in peaceful, secluded surroundings, screened by fine mature beech and pine trees, yet only two minutes from the village and lake shore.

The Fairfield enables you to enjoy the best that Lakeland has to offer. Once you have found us, you won't want to leave. . .

Brantfell Rd., Bowness-on-Windermere, Cumbria. LA23 3AE
Telephone: (09662) 6565

Fir Trees

Lake Road, Windermere,
Cumbria LA23 2EQ
Telephone:
Windermere (09662) 2272

A luxurious guest house within easy walking distance to Windermere, Bowness, or the lake. Spacious and lovely bedrooms, all with private bath/ shower rooms and colour televisions. Look forward to a hearty, full English breakfast to start each day. Attractive lounge, full central heating, and excellent parking facilities. Most of all, old-fashioned hospitality.

GLENCREE

PRIVATE HOTEL

Lake Road, Windermere, Cumbria LA23 2EQ
Telephone: Windermere (09662) 5822

Glencree is situated mid-way between the villages of Windermere and Bowness-on-Windermere and within easy walking distance of the Lake. The Hotel is of the Victorian period, stone-built in traditional lakeland style and overlooks a private wooded valley. Glencree combines period charm with twentieth century comforts and the facilities demanded by the discerning traveller.

Please telephone us or write for our Brochure.

GH Green Gables 37 Broad St ☎(09662) 3886 Plan **14** *C5*
Closed Xmas & New Year

Small friendly guesthouse with very pretty bedrooms.

6hc (2fb) ⊘ in 3 bedrooms ✗ *B&b£8–£9.50 Bdi£14–£15.50 WBdi£94–£98 LDO4pm

ⅢⅢ CTV ₱

⊢⊣ **GH Greenriggs** 8 Upper Oak St ☎(09662) 2265 Plan **15** *C4*
Mar–Nov

Quiet, conveniently situated hotel offering friendly comfortable accommodation.

6hc (2fb) Ⓡ B&b£9 WB&b£60

ⅢⅢ CTV 3P

Windermere

GH *Haisthorpe* Holly Rd ☎(09662) 3445 Plan **16** *C4*
Mar–Oct

Cosy and welcoming guesthouse in a quiet part of the town.

6hc (3fb) ✗ LDO4.30pm

ⅢⅢ CTV

GH Hawksmoor Lake Rd ☎(09662) 2110 Plan **17** *B3*
Feb–Nov

An attractive house offering a cosy atmosphere. It stands in its own grounds, backed by woodland, half-way between Bowness and Windermere.

10hc (6⇌ 4ⅢⅢ) (3fb) ⊘ in 3 bedrooms CTV in all bedrooms ✗ Ⓡ B&b£13.50–£19.50 Bdi£21–£27 WBdifr£135 LDO5pm

Lic ⅢⅢ 12P

Ⓥ

GH Hilton House Hotel New Rd ☎(09662) 3934 Plan **18** *C4*

This detached Edwardian house of charm and character enjoys an elevated position. Decor and furnishings are of a high standard throughout. Shops and lake are within easy reach.

7hc (3fl) (2fb) CTV in 6 bedrooms Ⓡ B&b£10.95–£14.95 Bdi£19.45–£23.45 WBdi£129.35–£155.95 LDO5.30pm

Lic fff CTV 14P

ⓥ

GH Holly Cottages Rayrigg Rd ☎(09662) 4250 Plan **19** *B2*
Feb–mid Nov

Small, attractive bedrooms in a family-run establishment close to town centre.

7hc (2fl) (1fb) B&b£11–£17 WB&b£65–£119

fff CTV 5P

Credit cards 1 3

|—|**GH Holly Lodge** College Rd ☎(09662) 3873 Plan **20** *B5*

10hc (3fb) CTV in alll bedrooms Ⓡ B&b£8–£10 Bdi£13.50–£16 WB&b£94.50–£112 LDO10.30am

Lic fff CTV 6P

ⓥ

GH Kenilworth Holly Rd ☎(09662) 4004 Plan **21** *C4*
Mar–Oct

Windermere

A comfortable guesthouse with a spacious lounge and a friendly atmosphere.

7hc (1fb) ✈ Ⓡ B&bfr£10 Bdifr£15.50 WBdifr£102 LDO2pm

fff CTV

ⓥ

|—|**GH Lynwood** Broad St ☎(09662) 2550 Plan **22** *C4*
Closed Dec & Jan

Six-bedroomed Lakeland stone house, built in 1865, situated in a quiet residential area.

6hc (2fb) Ⓡ B&b£9–£10 WB&bfr£140

fff CTV 2P 1⛟ nc2yrs

ⓥ

GH Meadfoot New Rd ☎(09662) 2610 Plan **23** *C4*
Feb–Nov

A very nice detached house with attractive gardens and comfortable bedrooms.

8hc (4fl) (1fb) CTV in all bedrooms Ⓡ B&b£10–£13.50 WB&b£63–£84

fff 9P nc3yrs

ⓥ

GH Mylne Bridge House Brookside, Lake Rd ☎(09662) 3314 Plan **24** *C4*
Mar–Oct

Very comfortable, friendly house with good choice of dishes at dinner.

13hc (4fl) (1fb) CTV in all bedrooms Ⓡ B&b£11–£14 WB&bfr£70

Lic fff 12P

ⓥ

|—|**GH Oakfield** 46 Oak St ☎(09662) 5692 Plan **25** *C5*

Comfortable little guesthouse in good central position.

5hc (3fb) CTV in all bedrooms Ⓡ B&b£9–£11.50 Bdi£12–£16 WB&bfr£63 LDOnoon

Lic fff CTV ♦

GH Oakthorpe Hotel High St ☎(09662) 3547 Plan **26** *C5*
Closed 25 Dec–24 Jan

Personally supervised, comfortable hotel with Continental and English dishes served at dinner.

20hc (2⇌ 2fl) (3fb) CTV available Ⓡ ✱B&b£13–£18 Bdi£22–£29 WBdi£148–£190 LDO8.15pm

Lic CTV 18P

Credit cards 1 3

LYNWOOD

Broad Street, Windermere, Cumbria LA23 2AB
Telephone: Windermere (096 62) 2550

Gateway to the Lake District

The seven bedroomed Lakeland stone house built in 1865 offers bed and full English breakfast. All rooms have central heating, shaver points and tea & coffee making facilities. Situated 150 yards from the village shops and restaurants and only five minutes from the bus and railway stations. Your host is a Lakeland Tour Guide and will assist you at all times planning your holiday. Open February through to end of November.

MEADFOOT GUEST HOUSE

New Road, Windermere. Telephone: (096 62) 2610

Meadfoot is a modern house set in its own grounds and offers a high standard of comfort. All rooms are centrally heated and have tea making facilities. Most double bedrooms have en suite shower/toilet. There is ample off road parking. Colour T.V. all rooms.

Situated on edge of Windermere village and ¾ mile from Bowness Bay and Lake we are ideally situated for restaurants and all local amenities.

Ashley Courtenay recommended
Cumbria Tourist Board

Proprietors: John & Gladys Irving

Mylne Bridge House

Brook Side, Lake Road, Windermere
Cumbria LA23 2BX
Telephone: 09662 3314

Comfortable family-run guesthouse with large car park quietly situated off the main road but within a few minutes' walk of Windermere town and all its shops and amenities.

Some of the bedrooms have en-suite shower room facilities, all have tea and coffee making facilities and colour TV. There is a comfortable residents' lounge and a cosy private bar for your evening relaxation.

Please write to us at
High Street Windermere, Cumbria LA23 1AF
or Phone Windermere (096 62) 3547

The Hotel is ideally situated for walking, boating, fishing and golf.

Tony & Sue Tasker resident proprietors offer a warm welcome and the guarantee of a relaxing family holiday.

We have a licensed bar, an excellent restaurant, 20 bedrooms each with tea and coffee trays, 8 with private facilities.

The advantage of being two minutes walk from Windermere Station, Coach and Bus stops. Car Parking.

GH Orrest Head House Kendal Rd ☎(09662) 4315 Plan **27** *C5*
Mar–Oct

Large detached house in extensive gardens in a peaceful location outside town.

7hc Ⓡ ✱B&b£10–£11.50 WB&b£65–£68

▥ CTV 12P nc8yrs

GH Rosemount Lake Rd ☎(09662) 3739 Plan **28** *B4*
Closed 13 Dec–23 Jan

Bright and cheerful guesthouse with a nice warm atmosphere.

Windermere

8hc (5fl) (1fb) ⅟ in all bedrooms CTV in all bedrooms ✕ Ⓡ ✱B&b£10.50–£13.50 WB&b£70–£91

Lic ▥ 6P 2🚗

Credit cards 1 3 Ⓥ

GH St Johns Lodge Lake Rd ☎(09662) 3078 Plan **29** *B3*

A charming private hotel with comfortable accommodation.

11hc (1⇌ 9fl) (3fb) CTV in all bedrooms Ⓡ B&b£11.50–£13.50 Bdi£18.50–£20 WBdi£128–£132 LDO6pm

Lic ▥ 11P nc2yrs

GH Thornleigh Thornbarrow Rd, Bowness ☎(09662) 4203 Plan **30** *C3*
Mar–Nov

A small family-run house with pretty window boxes, friendly atmosphere and a warm welcome.

6hc (4fb) CTV in 5 bedrooms ✕ Ⓡ B&b£10–£12.50 WB&b£70–£85

Lic ▥ CTV 5P

Credit cards 1 3 Ⓥ

|→→|**GH Tudor** 60 Main St ☎(09662) 2363 Plan **31** *C5*
Mar–Nov
A roadside Tudor-style house in town centre. Restaurant open to non-residents.
6hc (2fl) CTV in all bedrooms ® B&b£8.50–£9.50 LDO9pm
Lic CTV 5P nc

GH *Westbeck House* 11 Oak St ☎(09662) 4763 Plan **32** *C5*
Closed Xmas
Simple, neat, clean bed-and-breakfast accommodation in small guesthouse.
5hc (1fl) (2fb) TV in all bedrooms ®
CTV 2P

GH Westbourne Hotel Biskey Howe Rd ☎(09662) 3625 Plan **33** *B3*
Closed 3–31 Jan
A spacious detached house with an attractive and comfortable lounge bar.
7fl (4fb) ® B&b£16.50–£17.50 Bdi£24–£25 WBdifr£144 LDO7.30pm
Lic CTV 8P
Credit cards 1 3 Ⓥ

GH Westlake Lake Rd ☎(09662) 3020 Plan **34** *B3*
rs Nov–Feb
Comfortable private hotel with attractive bedrooms and good home cooking.

7hc (2⇌ 5fl) (2fb) CTV in all bedrooms ® B&b£10.50–£15 Bdi£16–£22 WBdi£125–£135 LDO5pm
Lic 7P

GH White Lodge Hotel Lake Rd, Bowness ☎(09662) 3624 Plan **35** *B3*
Mar–Oct
Relaxed, high standard of accommodation and an interesting menu.
12hc (4⇌ 8fl) (3fb) CTV in all bedrooms ® B&b£18–£20 Bdi£24–£28 WBdifr£156 LDO7pm
Lic CTV 20P ♿
Credit cards 1 3
See advertisement on page 450

GH Winbrook 30 Ellerthwaite Rd ☎(09662) 4932 Plan **36** *C4*
Mar–Nov & Xmas
Traditional family-run guesthouse with warm welcome and good home-cooking.
6hc (1⇌ 2fl) CTV in all bedrooms ® B&b£9.75–£12.95 Bdi£17.05–£20.25 WBdi£115.85–£138.25 LDO4pm
CTV 7P nc6yrs
Ⓥ

GH *Woodlands* New Rd ☎(09662) 3915 Plan **37** *C4*
Closed Dec
Spacious and really comfortable house with high quality decor and furnishings throughout. The four-course dinners are freshly prepared and most enjoyable.
10hc (8fl) (1fb) CTV in all bedrooms LDO4pm
Lic CTV 10P 2 nc5yrs
See advertisement on page 450

WINDSOR
Berkshire
Map **4** SU97

GH Christopher Hotel High St ☎(07535) 52359
(For full entry see **Eton**)

WINTERBOURNE ABBAS
Dorset
Map **3** SY69

GH Church View ☎Martinstown (030588) 296
Mar–Oct
10hc (1fb) ® B&b£10–£11 Bdi£15–£16 WBdi£100–£110
Lic CTV 6P 1
Ⓥ

WISBECH
Cambridgeshire
Map **5** TF40

GH Glendon Sutton Rd ☎(0945) 584812 Mar–Oct

18hc (2fb) B&b£16.10 Bdi£21.10 WBdi£120

Lic CTV 60P

WITHERIDGE
Devon
Map **3** SS81

FH Mr & Mrs Sankey ***Coombe Barn Cottage*** *(SS791141)* ☎Tiverton (0884) 860646

Detached farmhouse offering comfortable accommodation and good food. Just outside village.

4hc (1⇌ 1fl) (2fb) TV in all bedrooms ✱ Ⓡ LDO8pm

Lic ♨ CTV 6P 4🚗 sauna bath

3acres smallholding

WIVELISCOMBE
Somerset
Map **3** ST02

GH Mount Country Ford ☎(0984) 23992

A detached country cottage of character, offering pleasant accommodation in a rural setting.

5hc (1fl) ✱B&b£11.50–£12.50 Bdi£18–£19WBdifr£105

♨ CTV 6P 1🚗 nc7yrs

Ⓥ

FH Mr & Mrs L Featherstone **Deepleigh Farm Hotel** *(ST079294)* Langley Marsh (1m N unclass) ☎(0984) 23379
Mar–Nov

16th-century farmhouse converted into small hotel having comfortable lounge with original beams, panelling and log fire. 1m N unclass rd.

7hc (4fb) (2⇌ 5fl) ⊬in 4 bedrooms CTV in 5 bedrooms TV in 1 bedroom ✈ B&b£13.50–£17.50 Bdi£22–£26 WBdifr£154 LDOam

Lic ▥ 8P ⚘ U 2½acres

ⓥ

FH Mrs E M Wyatt ***Hillacre*** *(ST104275)* Crowford ☎(0984) 23355

Traditional farmhouse set back about 200 yds to the north of A361.

2rm (1hc) CTV in 1 bedroom

CTV 4P 1🚗 850acres mixed

INN *Bear* 10 North St ☎Langley Marsh (0984) 23537

17th-century coaching inn with pleasant rooms and friendly personal service.

4hc (1fb) Ⓡ LDO9.30pm

CTV 6P 1🚗

WIX
Essex
Map **5** TM12

FH Mrs H P Mitchell **New Farmhouse** *(TM165289)* ☎(025587) 365 due to change to (0255) 870365

A modern farmhouse with open views and self-contained well-equipped kitchen. ½m N on right off Wix/Bradfield rd.

5hc (2fb) ⊬ in all bedrooms CTV in all bedrooms ✈ Ⓡ B&b£11.50–£13.80 Bdi£18–£20.30 WBdi£108–£121.80 LDO6pm

▥ CTV 12P ⚘ 52acres arable

Credit card ③ ⓥ

WOLSINGHAM
Co Durham
Map **12** NZ03

FH Mr & Mrs T Allen **Chatterley** *(NY075359)* ☎Weardale (0388) 527385
May–Oct

A cosy farmhouse on a dairy farm in an attractive setting. 1m out of town on the Homsterly Rd.

2rm (1fb) ✈ Ⓡ ✱B&b£8 WB&bfr£50

▥ CTV 3P

145acres dairy mixed sheep

WOODHALL SPA
Lincolnshire
Map **8** TF16

GH Duns The Broadway ☎(0526) 52969

Large semi-detached house opposite the golf club.

7hc (1fl) (2fb) ✱B&bfr£12.50 Bdifr£16.50 WBdifr£115.50 LDOnoon

▥ CTV 10P

WOODY BAY
Devon
Map **3** SS64

GH The Red House ☎Parracombe (05983) 255
Apr–Oct

Detached house in lovely elevated position, yet in wooded valley, offering friendly, personal services, comfort, and good home cooking.

6hc (3⇌ 1fl) (1fb) CTV in all bedrooms Ⓡ B&b£13–£19Bdi£20–£26 WBdifr£133LDO6pm

Lic ▥ 8P nc4yrs

ⓥ

WOOLACOMBE
Devon
Map **2** SS44
See also **Mortehoe**

GH Barton House Hotel Barton Rd ☎(0271) 870548
Etr–Oct

12hc (6⇌ 2fl) (5fb) Ⓡ B&b£10–£16 Bdi£16–£22 WBdi£112–£154

Lic ▥ CTV 13P

GH Camberley Beach Rd ☎(0271) 870231

A family run guest house enjoying panoramic countryside views. Guests can use an indoor heated swimming pool, sauna, solarium and squash courts at the large hotel next door.

6⇌fl (3fb) CTV in all bedrooms Ⓡ B&b£11.50–£15 Bdi£16–£20 WBdi£100–£130 LDO6.30pm

Lic CTV 6P

Credit card ①

GH Castle The Esplanade ☎(0271) 870788
Apr–Oct

9hc (3fl) (2fb) B&b£10.50–£15.50 Bdi£16–£21 WBdi£98.50–£133

Lic ▥ CTV 7P

GH Combe Ridge Hotel The Esplanade ☎(0271) 870321
Feb–Nov

8hc (4fl) (4fb) Ⓡ B&b£10.50–£14.50Bdi£14.50–£18.50 WBdi£85–£115 (W only Jul & Aug) LDO5pm

Lic ▥ CTV 7P

GH Holmesdale Hotel Bay View Rd ☎(0271) 870335
Closed 3–31 Jan

15hc (7fl) (10fb) CTV in all bedrooms Ⓡ ✱Bdi£14–£17 WBdi£90–£145 (W only 18 Jul–29 Aug) LDO8.30pm

Lic ▥ CTV 14P

Credit cards ① ③

GH *Springside Country Hotel* Mullacott Rd ☎(0271) 870452
Mar–Oct

7hc (2⇌) (4fb) ✈ LDO5pm

Lic ▥ CTV 10P

WOOLFARDISWORTHY
Devon
Map **2** SS32

FH R C & C M Beck ***Stroxworthy*** *(SS341198)* ☎Clovelly (02373) 333
Apr–Oct

Tastefully decorated and set in beautiful countryside offering a variety of farm produce on menu. Herd of Guernsey cows.

10rm (9hc) (3fb) LDO6.30pm

Lic 🍽 CTV 20P ♩ 90acres dairy

FH Mrs P I Westaway **Westvilla** *(SS329215)* ☎Clovelly (02373) 309
Mar–Nov

3hc (1fb) ✗ Ⓡ in 2 bedrooms B&b£8.50–£9 Bdi£13.50–£15 WBdi£80–£85

CTV 5P 22acres beef mixed sheep

WOOLHOPE
Hereford & Worcester
Map **3** SO63

INN Butchers Arms ☎Fownhope (043277) 281

3hc TV in all bedrooms ✗ Ⓡ B&b£15.50–£19.50WB&b£98–£126 Bar lunch £5.35alc Dinner8.30pm £10alc

🍽 80P nc14yrs

Ⓥ

Woolfardisworthy — Workington

WOOTTON BASSETT
Wiltshire
Map **4** SU08

INN Angel Hotel 47 High St ☎Swindon (0793) 852314

Standing in High St this semi-detached inn is built of red brick and has a good bar and restaurant menu.

6hc CTV in all bedrooms ✗ Ⓡ ✱B&b£15–£17.50 Lunch £6alc Dinner10pm £10alc

🍽 CTV 8P nc12yrs

Credit cards 1 2 3 5

REMEMBER

Prices quoted in the gazetteer are minimum double room occupancy to maximum single room occupancy **per person.**

WORCESTER
Hereford & Worcester
Map **3** SO85

GH Barbourne 42 Barbourne Rd ☎(0905) 27507
Closed Xmas

Comfortable Victorian house on busy main road.

7hc (3fb) CTV in all bedrooms B&b£8.50–£12 Bdi£12–£15 WBdifr£100 LDOnoon

Lic 🍽 CTV 🅿

Credit cards 1 2 3 Ⓥ

GH Loch Ryan Hotel 119 Sidbury ☎(0905) 351143

A large hotel situated close to the Cathedral and other tourist attractions with a secluded garden.

13hc (1⇌ 2⋒) Annexe: 4hc (1fb) ✗ ✱B&b£15–£21

Lic 🍽 CTV 🅿 ⌂

Ⓥ

WORKINGTON
Cumbria
Map **11** NY02

INN Morven Hotel Siddick ☎(0900) 2118

Busy little inn with lots of oak beams and polished brasses.

8hc (4fb) TV in 4 bedrooms Ⓡ B&bfr£11 Bdifr£15 LDO4pm

🚿 CTV 20P 🐕

Ⓥ

WORMBRIDGE
Hereford & Worcester
Map **3** SO43

FH J T Davies **Duffryn** *(SO415319)* ☎(098121) 217

Very hospitable farmhouse where guests are welcome to take an interest in the farm. Traditional farmyard, complete with duck pond.

4hc (2fb) Ⓡ B&bfr£9 Bdifr£15 WBdifr£100 LDO5pm

🚿 CTV 8P 🏠 184acres mixed

Ⓥ

WORTHING
West Sussex
Map **4** TQ10

GH Blair House 11 St Georges Rd ☎(0903) 34071

Three-storey Victorian house close to sea front in quiet residential area.

7hc (2⇌ 4🚿) (1fb) CTV in all bedrooms Ⓡ B&b£12.50–£15 Bdi£18.50–£21 WBdifr£129.50 (W only Xmas) LDO6.30pm

Lic 🚿 CTV 3P 1🚗(charge)

Ⓥ

GH Camelot House 20 Gannon Rd ☎(0903) 204334
Closed Xmas & New Year

A small cosy guesthouse with a friendly atmosphere. Nicely appointed bedrooms and good lounge faciities.

7hc (1⇌ 1🚿) (1fb) CTV in 5 bedrooms TV in 2 bedrooms ✗ Ⓡ B&b£10–£11.50Bdi£15.50–£17 WBdifr£105

Lic 🚿 5P

Credit cards 1 3 Ⓥ

GH Heene House 140 Heene Rd ☎(0903) 33213

Workington — Worthing

Personally supervised by Mrs Hatch this large Edwardian house has been thoughtfully furnished and decorated to provide comfortable accommodation in a friendly informal atmosphere.

12hc (2⇌ 6🚿) (3fb) CTV in all bedrooms ✗ Ⓡ ✱B&b£16.50–£25 LDO8pm

Lic 8P

Credit cards 1 2 3 5

GH Meldrum House 8 Windsor Rd ☎(0903) 33808
Closed Dec

Small terraced house with friendly atmosphere offering simple yet comfortable accommodation.

6hc (2fb) TV in all bedrooms ✗ Ⓡ ✱B&b£10–£12 Bdi£15–£17 WBdifr£95 LDO5.30pm

🚿 CTV 🅿 nc3yrs

Ⓥ

GH Moorings Private Hotel 4 Selden Rd ☎(0903) 208882

Comfortably modernised Victorian house close to the sea front.

7hc (2⇌ 1🚿) (2fb) CTV in all bedrooms ✗ Ⓡ ✱B&b£10–£14 Bdi£15.50–£19.50 WBdifr£98

Lic 🚿 3P

Credit cards 1 3 Ⓥ

GH Osborne 175 Brighton Rd ☎(0903) 35771

Two-storey Georgian house facing the sea, run by friendly, helpful proprietors.

7hc (1🚿) (3fb) CTV in all bedrooms Ⓡ ✱B&b£10.50–£13.50 WB&b£72–£82

Lic CTV 🅿 nc10yrs

Credit cards 1 3

GH *St George's Lodge Hotel* 46 Chesswood Rd ☎(0903) 208926

19hc (6⇌ 7🚿) (13fb) CTV in all bedrooms Ⓡ LDO9.30pm

Lic lift 18P sauna bath solarium gymnasium

Credit cards 1 2 3

GH Southdene 41 Warwick Gdns ☎(0903) 32909

Quiet three-storey Victorian house close to the sea.

6hc (1🚿) (1fb) CTV in 3 bedrooms ✗ Ⓡ ✱B&b£10–£13 Bdi£15–£18 WBdi£93–£114LDO3pm

Lic 🚿 CTV 🅿 nc14yrs

Ⓥ

GH *Wansfell Hotel* 49 Chesswood Rd (Guestaccom) ☎(0903) 30612

Town house close to sea front.

12hc (2⇌ 4🚿) (2fb) CTV in all bedrooms ✗ Ⓡ LDO7.15pm

Lic 🚿 10P nc4yrs

Credit card 1

GH *Windsor House Hotel*
14–20 Windsor Rd ☎(0903) 39655

Large house in quiet residential area.

29hc (5⇌ 12🚿) (6fb) CTV in all bedrooms Ⓡ LDO6.30pm

Lic 🚿 CTV 18P

Ⓥ

GH *Windsor Lodge Hotel* 3 Windsor Rd ☎(0903) 200056
Closed Xmas

Family-run house close to sea front with comfortable lounge and pleasant dining room.

6hc Ⓡ LDO2pm

🚿 CTV 🅿 nc2yrs

GH *Wolsey Hotel* 179–181 Brighton Rd ☎(0903) 36149
Closed Xmas

Two terraced houses on the sea front simply but prettily furnished.

14hc (3fb) CTV in all bedrooms Ⓡ LDO6.30pm

Lic 🚿 CTV 🅿

Credit cards 1 3

WREXHAM
Clywd
See **Hanmer**

WYE
Kent
Map **5** TR04

INN New Flying Horse Upper Bridge St ☎(0233) 812297

Comfortable and well-managed inn with well-equipped bedrooms, an à la carte dining room and a rear patio garden.

6hc Annexe: 4⇌ (1fb) CTV in all bedrooms Ⓡ B&b£17.50–£30 Bdi£29.50–£42 WBdifr£175 Bar Lunch£6alc Dinner9.50pm £11.25–£15

🅼 100P

Credit cards 1 2 3 5 Ⓥ

YARMOUTH, GREAT
Norfolk
Map **5** TG50

GH Avalon 4 Avondale Rd, Gorleston-on-Sea (2m S off A12) ☎(0493) 661521

A small guesthouse in a quiet residential road where the proprietors aim to provide a personal service.

7hc (3fb) B&b£8–£10.50 Bdi£11.50–£14 WBdi£69.50–£76.50 LDOnoon

Lic 🅼 CTV

Ⓥ

GH Frandor 120 Lowestoft Rd, Gorleston-on-Sea (2m S A12) ☎(0493) 662112

A small guesthouse situated close to the centre of Gorleston. Children are made especially welcome here.

8hc (3fb) in 4 bedrooms CTV in all bedrooms Ⓡ *B&b£10–£12 Bdi£14–£16 WBdi£75 (W only mid May–Sept) LDO6.30pm

Lic 🅼 CTV 12P

Credit cards 1 3

GH Georgian House Private Hotel 16–17 North Dr ☎(0493) 842623
rs winter (closed Xmas)

25hc (10⇌ 5fl) (1fb) CTV in all bedrooms *B&b£12.50–£20 WB&b£75–£105 (W only Jun–Sep)

Lic 🅼 24P nc5yrs

GH Gladstone House 92 St Peters Rd ☎(0493) 843181
Closed Xmas

A neat, modern guesthouse offering fresh home cooking.

11hc (1fb) CTV in all bedrooms *B&bfr£13.80 Bdifr£18.80 WBdifr£98.90 LDO6pm

Lic CTV 4P

Credit cards 1 3 Ⓥ

GH Hazelwood House 57 Clarence Rd, Gorleston-on-Sea ☎(0493) 662830

7hc (3fb) CTV in 4 bedrooms TV in 3 bedrooms Ⓡ *B&bfr£8 Bdifr£10 WBdifr£70 LDO4pm

Lic 🅼 CTV

Credit cards 1 2 3 Ⓥ

GH Jennis Lodge 63 Avondale Rd, Gorleston-on-Sea (2m S off A12) ☎(0493) 662840

Situated in a quiet residential road 100 yards from Marine Parade and steps to the promenade and beach.

11hc (4fb) Ⓡ B&b£9–£11.50 Bdi£11–£14.50 WBdifr£69.50

Lic 🅼 CTV

GH Palm Court Hotel 10 North Dr ☎(0493) 844568

47hc (14⇌ 18fl) (6fb) CTV in all bedrooms Ⓡ B&b£15–£37.50 Bdi£20–£42.50 WBdi£115–£184.50 LDO8pm

Lic lift 🅼 CTV (heated) sauna bath solarium gymnasium

Credit cards 1 3 Ⓥ

GH Squirrels Nest 71, Avondale Rd, Gorleston ☎(0493) 662746

10hc (1⇌ 7fl) (1fb) CTV in all bedrooms Ⓡ B&b£10–£15 Bdi£18–£28 WBdi£78–£137 LDO8pm

Lic 🍽 CTV 5P

Credit cards 1 2 3

YEALAND CONYERS
Lancashire
Map **7** SD57

GH *Holmere Hall Hotel* ☎Carnforth (0524) 735353
Closed mid Jan–mid Feb

A small, comfortable country hotel in a garden setting. Building dates from the 17th century.

6hc (1⇌) (1fb) CTV in all bedrooms Ⓡ LDO9pm

Lic 🍽 12P

Credit cards 1 3

YEALMPTON
Devon
Map **2** SX55

Selected

FH Mrs A German **Broadmoor** *(SX574498)* ☎Plymouth (0752) 880407

Stone-built farmhouse and outbuildings, situated in open countryside midway between Yealmpton & Newton Ferrers.

3hc ✖ Ⓡ B&bfr£8.50

nc7yrs 200acres mixed

YELVERTON
Devon
Map **2** SX56

GH Harrabeer Country House Hotel Harrowbeer Ln ☎(0822) 853302
Closed Xmas

Country house hotel on the edge of Dartmoor offering friendly services and large garden with swimming pool.

7hc (2⇌ 3fl) (1fb) CTV in all bedrooms ✖ Ⓡ B&b£16.25–£18.25 Bdi£25.25–£27.25 WBdi£162–£174 LDO7.30pm

Lic 🍽 CTV 10P

Credit cards 1 2 3 5 Ⓥ

See advertisement under Plymouth

GH Waverley 5 Greenbank Ter ☎(0822) 854617

Family-run guesthouse situated on the edge of Dartmoor.

5hc (2fb) CTV in all bedrooms B&b£11–£12 Bdi£16–£17 WBdifr£112 LDO10am

🍽 CTV 2P

Ⓥ

YEOVIL
Somerset
Map **3** ST51

FH Mrs M Tucker **Carents** *(ST546188)* Yeovil Marsh ☎(0935) 76622
Feb–Nov

Clean, pleasant traditional additional-style farmhouse on outskirts of Yeovil 2m N of A37.

3rm (1hc) ⊁ in all bedrooms ✖ Ⓡ B&b£9.50–£10 Bdifr£16 LDOnoon

CTV P 350acres arable beef

YORK
North Yorkshire
Map **8** SE65
See also **Acaster Malbis, Copmanthorpe** and **Rufforth**

GH Aberford Hotel 35–36 East Mount Rd ☎(0904) 22694

Three-storey Edwardian town house with basement lounge bar and snug-lounge. Well equipped bedrooms.

13hc (2⑪) (2fb) CTV in all bedrooms ✱ Ⓡ B&b£11.75–£13.75 Bdi£15.70–£16.75 LDO5.30pm

Lic 🀫 7P 2🚗

Credit cards 1 2 3

GH Abingdon 60 Bootham Cres, Bootham ☎(0904) 21761 due to change to 621761

Closed Dec

York

Nicely furnished Victorian terraced house.

9hc (5⑪) (2fb) CTV in 8 bedrooms TV in 1 bedroom ✱ Ⓡ B&b£10–£15

🀫 CTV 4P 2🚗

Ⓥ

GH Acomb Rd 128 Acomb Rd ☎(0904) 792321

Three-storey, end-of-terrace house about a mile from city centre.

12hc (6⑪) (3fb) CTV in all bedrooms Ⓡ B&b£10–£14 Bdi£14–£18 WBdi£98–£126 LDO7.30pm

Lic CTV 20P

GH Adams House Hotel 5 Main St, Fulford ☎(0904) 55413 due to change to 655413

Closed Xmas

Guesthouse of great charm and elegance about a mile from city centre.

7hc (2⇌ 4⑪) (2fb) CTV in all bedrooms Ⓡ B&b£12.50–£17 WB&b£84–£98

Lic 🀫 8P

Ⓥ

GH Alcuin Lodge 15 Sycamore Pl, Bootham ☎(0904) 32222
Feb–Nov
Three-storey, brick-built Edwardian mid-terraced property in quiet residential area a short distance from city centre.
6hc (2fb) CTV in all bedrooms ✈ Ⓡ
✱B&b£8–£11 WB&b£56–£77
🅿 3P nc

GH Alfreda 61 Heslington Ln, Fulford ☎(0904) 31698
Pair of Edwardian houses in Regency style with lawns and trees. Small cosy public rooms have style and character and bedrooms are spacious with modern fittings.
10hc (2fb) CTV in all bedrooms
✱B&b£15–£25
🅿 CTV P
Credit card 3

GH Alhambra Court Hotel 31 St Marys, Bootham ☎(0904) 28474
Two stylishly converted and restored Victorian townhouses with an excellent restaurant.
25⇌ fl (3fb) CTV in all bedrooms ✈ Ⓡ
B&b£14.50–£23 Bdi£22–£30.50
WBdi£154–£213.50 LDO10pm
Lic lift 🅿 CTV 20P solarium
Credit cards 1 3

York

GH Ambleside 62 Bootham Crescent ☎(0904) 37165
Conveniently situated for York Minster this small terraced house offers neat accommodation.
8hc (2fl) CTV in all bedrooms ✈ Ⓡ
B&b£10–£15
🅿 CTV nc10yrs

Credit Cards

1 Access/Euro/Mastercard
2 American Express
3 Barclaycard/Visa
5 Diners

GH Arndale Hotel (formerly the Voltgeur Hotel) 290 Tadcaster Rd ☎(0904) 702424
Closed Xmas & New Year
Spacious, well-fitted bedrooms and an especially beautiful lounge in Victorian building retaining many original features.
10hc (6⇌ 4fl) (1fb) CTV in all bedrooms
Ⓡ B&b£15–£18.50 Bdi£21–£25.50
WBdifr£140 LDOnoon
Lic 🅿 15P

GH Arnot House 17 Grosvenor Ter Bootham ☎(0904) 641966
6hc (2fb) CTV in all bedrooms ✈ Ⓡ
B&b£9.25–£12.50 Bdi£16.75–£20
WBdi£117.25–£140 LDO1pm
Lic 🅿 2P nc5yrs
Ⓥ
See advertisement on page 458

GH Ascot House 80 East Pde ☎(0904) 426826
Attractive Victorian house with unusual oriel staircase window. Bedrooms have modern fittings.
9hc (2⇌ 7fl) (2fb) TV in all bedrooms Ⓡ
B&b£12–£15 Bdi£19.50–£24 WBdifr£130
LDO6pm
🅿 CTV 10P 1🚗 sauna bath solarium
Ⓥ

GH Ashbourne House 139 Fulford Rd
☎(0904) 39912
mid Feb–mid Nov

About a mile from the town centre, this large, well proportioned house has been converted with a degree of simple good taste and offers charming bedroom accommodation and comfortable public rooms.

6hc (2⚜) ✖ Ⓡ B&b£10–£14 WB&b£63–£88.20

Ⓜ CTV 5P 2🚗

Ⓥ

York

⊢•⊣**GH Avenue** 6 The Avenue, Clifton
☎(0904) 20575 due to change to 620575

Three-storey, late Victorian house with attractive small forecourt garden, in quiet tree-lined street, near city centre.

6hc (1⚜) (3fb) CTV in 1 bedroom TV in 5 bedrooms ✖ Ⓡ in 1 bedroom B&b£8–£10 Bdi£14–£16 WBdi£90–£102 LDO10am

Ⓜ CTV

Ⓥ

GH Beckett 58 Bootham Cres ☎(0904) 644728
Closed 14 Dec–14 Jan

Situated on the northern side of town offering clean bright bedrooms with good matching fabrics and furnishings.

7hc (4fl) (2fb) TV in 1 bedroom CTV in 4 bedrooms ✗ Ⓡ ✱B&b£11–£14 WB&b£77–£98

𝔐 CTV P̸

Ⓥ

GH Beech Hotel 6–7 Longfield Ter, Bootham ☎(0904) 34581
Closed Xmas & New Year

A pair of Victorian terraced houses converted into very smart and comfortable accommodation.

7hc (5fl) (1fb) CTV in all bedrooms ✗ Ⓡ B&b£9–£16

𝔐 5P nc5yrs

Ⓥ

GH Bootham Bar Hotel 4 High Petergate ☎(0904) 58516

Delightfully restored 18th-century town house adjacent to the old city walls.

10hc (1⇨ 9fl) (2fb) CTV in all bedrooms ✗ Ⓡ B&b£15–£24 LDO8.30pm

Lic 𝔐 P̸

Ⓥ

See advertisement on page 460

GH *Brönte House* 22 Grosvenor Ter, Bootham ☎(0904) 21066
Closed 5 days Xmas

Bay-windowed Victorian terraced house near the Minster, with good facilities and smart bedrooms.

7hc (4fl) (1fb) ✗ Ⓡ LDO4pm

𝔐 CTV 3P

See advertisement on page 461

GH Byron House Hotel (formerly Albert Hotel) The Mount ☎(0904) 32525

An impressive early 19th-century building situated close to the race course, featuring an interesting staircase which leads to a first floor reception and lounge bar. The dining room is located on the ground floor with meals to suit guests.

10hc (1⇨ 6fl) (3fb) CTV in all bedrooms ✗ Ⓡ B&b£18.50–£21 Bdi£26.50–£29.50 WBdifr£203 LDOnoon

Lic 𝔐 7P

Credit cards 1 2 3 5

See advertisement on page 461

York

GH Cavalier 39 Monkgate ☎(0904) 36615
Closed Xmas & New Year

Stylish town house near the walls of Monks Bar with restful lounge and good restaurant.

10hc (2⇨ 4fl) (4fb) CTV in all bedrooms ✗ Ⓡ B&b£12–£14.50 LDO3.30pm

Lic 𝔐 CTV 3P sauna bath

See advertisement on page 462

GH Coach House Hotel Marygate ☎(0904) 52780 due to change to 652780

Tastefully furnished old building with beams and exposed brickwork situated a short way from city centre.

13hc (5⇨ 6fl) ✗ Ⓡ B&b£14.50–£17 Bdi£19.50–£22 WBdifr£133 LDO9.30pm

Lic 𝔐 CTV 13P

Credit card 3

GH Collingwood Hotel 163 Holgate Rd ☎(0904) 783333

This 200-year-old Georgian house has been sympathetically restored to retain many period features. Comfortable well-equipped bedrooms, lounge bar, separate television room and a small attractive dining room.

7hc (2⇨ 5fl) (2fb) CTV in all bedrooms ✗ Ⓡ B&b£14–£16 Bdi£20–£22 WBdifr£140 LDO10am

Lic 𝔐 CTV 10P

Credit cards 1 2 5 Ⓥ

⊢⊣**GH Coppers Lodge** 15 Alma Ter, Fulford Rd ☎(0904) 39871

Simple, good value accommodation in a former police HQ (and jail house) 1m from town centre.

8hc (5fb) CTV in all bedrooms B&b£9–£10 Bdi£14–£15 LDO2pm

𝔐 CTV P

Credit card 3 Ⓥ

⊢⊣**GH Craig-y-Don** 3 Grosvenor Ter, Bootham ☎(0904) 37186
Feb–Oct

A town house of Victorian vintage, neat, tidy accommodation and hospitable welcome.

6hc (1fl) (1fb) CTV in all bedrooms Ⓡ B&b£9–£15

𝔐 4P

GH Crescent 77 Bootham ☎(0904) 23216

End of terrace property, above shops, with reception and public rooms on the first floor. Bedrooms have much style and character. Close to Minster and town centre.

9hc (4fb) CTV in all bedrooms ✗ Ⓡ B&b£10.50–£13 Bdi£15–£19 WBdifr£100 LDO2pm

𝔐 CTV 2P 1🚗

Credit cards 1 2 3

GH Croft Hotel 103 Mount Rd ☎(0904) 22747

Tall Victorian end-of-terrace house with friendly lounge and caring hosts.

10hc (2fl) (1fb) CTV in all bedrooms Ⓡ B&b£10–£13.50 Bdi£15–£19 LDO4pm

Lic 𝔐 CTV 1🚗

Credit card 3

GH Dairy 3 Scarcroft Rd ☎(0904) 39367
Feb–Nov

Restored Victorian house with stylish décor and many pleasing features.

4hc (1⇨) Annexe: 2hc (1⇨ 1fl) (2fb) CTV in all bedrooms ✗ Ⓡ B&b£10–£12.50

𝔐 CTV P̸

GH Dray Lodge Moor Ln, Murton (3m E off A166) ☎(0904) 489591

This carefully converted 16th-century residence offers purpose-made accommodation yet still retains some of the original features and character of the building.

6hc (2fl) ✗ Ⓡ ✱B&bfr£10.35 Bdifr£16.35 LDO8pm

Lic CTV 15P

Credit cards 1 3

See advertisement on page 462

Selected

GH *Field House Hotel* 2 St George's Pl ☎(0904) 39572

Beautiful gardens surround this carefully refurbished late 19th-century building situated close to the race course. The fine Victorian exterior blankets a superb mix of modern styles and comfort inside including a tasteful spacious ground floor lounge and separate lounge bar. On the lower ground floor there is an elegant and charming dining room.

17hc (1⇌ 10fl) CTV in all bedrooms ✖ Ⓡ LDO7pm

Lic 🏛 20P

Credit cards 1 2 3

See advertisement on page 462

GH *Gables* 50 Bootham Cres ☎(0904) 24381

Clean, compact and friendly accommodation.

6hc (2fb) CTV in all bedrooms ✖ Ⓡ

🏛 CTV

GH Georgian 35 Bootham ☎(0904) 22874
Closed Xmas

A Georgian building with well equipped bedrooms and a first-floor breakfast-room

York

and television lounge. The Minster and medieval walls are close by.

12hc (2⇌ 1fl) (1fb) CTV in 5 bedrooms Ⓡ ✱B&b£11–£14

🏛 CTV 16P

Selected

GH Grasmead House Hotel 1 Scarcroft Hill, The Mount ☎(0904) 29996 due to change to 629996

Within walking distance of the town centre, this very friendly hotel offers a high standard of bedroom accommodation each with its own genuine antique four-poster bed. Style and character can be found throughout the lounge small bar and separate breakfast room, all supervised by the very affable proprietors.

6⇌ (2fb) ⚡ in 2 bedrooms CTV in all bedrooms ✖ Ⓡ B&b£19–£21 WB&bfr£133

Lic 🏛 CTV 1P

Credit cards 1 3 Ⓥ

See advertisement on page 463

GH Greenside 124 Clifton ☎(0904) 23631
Closed Xmas Day

Charming detached house in centre of Clifton Hamlet, about a mile from city centre.

6hc (2fl) (2fb) CTV in 1 bedroom TV in 1 bedroom ✱B&b£10–£12

🏛 CTV 5P 1🚗

Ⓥ

See advertisement on page 463

Selected

GH Hazelwood 24–25 Portland St, Gillygate ☎(0904) 26548
Closed 21–31 Dec

This pair of four storeyed town houses have been tastefully converted into a small hotel of some character. Guests receive a warm and friendly welcome. There is good home cooking. Bedrooms are attractive and well-equipped.

15hc (2⇌ 6fl) (1fb) CTV in all bedrooms ✖ Ⓡ B&b£12–£15.50 Bdi£20–£23 WBdifr£126.50 LDOnoon

Lic 🏛 10P 1🚗

Credit card 3

York

GH *Heworth* 126 East Pde ☎(0904) 426384

Neat and tidy guesthouse convenient for town facilities.

7hc (1fb) LDO2pm

Lic ⅲ CTV 1P 1🚗

Ⓥ

GH Hobbits 9 St Peters Grove, Clifton ☎(0904) 24538

Set amidst a garden of trees and shrubs this large Victorian house offers comfortable accommodation with interesting well-equipped bedrooms.

5hc (1⇌ 4fl) (1fb) CTV in all bedrooms Ⓡ ✱B&bfr£15

Lic CTV 6P

GH Inglewood 7 Clifton Gn ☎(0904) 653523

Commendable hotel with delightful fittings and furnishings in bustling suburb of Clifton.

7hc (3fl) (2fb) CTV in all bedrooms ✈ B&bfr£11

ⅲ CTV 1🚗

⊢⊣**GH Limes** 135 Fulford Rd ☎(0904) 24548 (due to change to 624548) rs Oct–Mar

To the south of the town this imposing detached house offers an annexe of spacious modern bedrooms, whilst within the house itself there is a stylishly decorated lounge with bar and separate dining room. →

9hc (6fl) (4fb) CTV in all bedrooms B&b£9–£35 Bdi£13–£39 WBdi£92–£273 LDO7pm

Lic 🍴 CTV 14P

Credit cards ① ② ③ ⑤ Ⓥ

GH Linden Lodge Nunthorpe Av, Scarcroft Rd ☎(0904) 20107 due to change to 620107
Closed Dec

9hc (3fb) ® B&b£9.50–£12.50 Bdi£15.50–£18.50 LDOnoon

Lic 🍴 CTV P̸

GH Mayfield Hotel 75 Scarcroft Rd ☎(0904) 54834

A cosy end of terrace house near the race course offering pleasant accommodation and a commendable à la carte menu prepared by the lady proprietors.

7hc (2⇌ 4fl) (4fb) CTV in all bedrooms B&b£19–£24 Bdi£25–£32 WBdifr£196

Lic 🍴 CTV 2P 1🚗

Credit cards ① ② ③

GH Midway House 145 Fulford Rd ☎(0904) 59272 (due to change to 659272)
Mar–Nov

Modern suburban house situated a short distance from the town centre. Spacious, well-fitted bedrooms and attractive public rooms.

York

6hc (4fl) (1fb) CTV in all bedrooms ✖ ®
B&bfr£11 WB&bfr£77

🍴 10P

GH *Minster View* 2 Grosvenor Ter ☎(0904) 55034

Tall Victorian terraced house, comfortably converted, situated about ½ mile from the town centre.

8hc (3⇌ 1fl) (4fb) CTV in all bedrooms ® LDO5.30pm

Lic 🍴 CTV 6P

GH Moat Hotel Nunnery Ln ☎(0904) 52926
Closed Xmas & New Year

Interesting Victorian-style house beneath medieval walls, with comfortable, suitably furnished accommodation.

12hc (6fl) (2fb) ✖ ✱B&b£10–£15

Lic 🍴 CTV 10P

Credit cards ② ③ ⑤ Ⓥ

GH Orchard Court Hotel 4 St Peters Gv ☎(0904) 653964

An elegant Victorian house in quiet cul-de-sac, close to city centre. The lofty public rooms are tastefully decorated.

11hc (2⇌ 6fl) (4fb) CTV in all bedrooms ✖ ® B&b£15–£19 Bdi£22–£26 LDO7.30pm

Lic CTV 12P

Credit cards ① ③ Ⓥ

GH Priory Hotel 126 Fulford Rd ☎(0904) 25280
Closed Xmas week

A pair of large double-fronted Victorian town houses with rear gardens, near city centre.

20hc (2⇌ 18fl) (5fb) CTV in all bedrooms ✖ ® B&b£16–£17.50 LDO9.15pm

Lic 🍴 CTV 25P

Credit cards ① ② ③ ⑤ Ⓥ

See advertisement on page 466

GH St Denys Hotel St Denys Rd ☎(0904) 22207
Closed 2 wks Xmas

Former vicarage offers comfortable spacious accommodation and cosy lounge.

11hc (7⇌ 4fl) (4fb) CTV in all bedrooms ® B&b£18–£36 Bdi£25–£32 LDOnoon

Lic 🍴 CTV 9P

Ⓥ

⊢⊣**GH Sycamore Hotel** 19 Sycamore Pl ☎(0904) 24712

Compact terraced property with well-fitted bedrooms.

6hc (2fb) CTV in all bedrooms ✱ ® B&b£8.50–£10.50 WB&b£59.50–£71.50

Lic ꟾꟾꟾ P nc5yrs

Ⓥ

GH *Town House Lodge* 112–114 Holgate Rd ☎(0904) 34577
Closed 24 Dec–1 Jan

Very comfortable bedrooms and a feature top floor lounge with views of the city are the attractions here.

12hc (3⇌ 6ffl) (7fb) CTV in all bedrooms ®

ꟾꟾꟾ 18P

Credit cards 1 2 3 5

YOULGREAVE
Derbyshire
Map **8** SK26

INN Bulls Head Church St ☎(062986) 307

4hc (2fb) CTV in all bedrooms ✱ ®
✱B&b£9–£11 Bdi£11–£18 LDO8.30pm

Lic 8P nc5yrs

Ⓥ

YSBYTY IFAN
Gwynedd
Map **6** SH84

FH Mrs F G Roberts **Ochr Cefn Isa** *(SH845495)* ☎Pentrefoelas (06905) 602
Apr–Sep

Farm set in elevated position with good views high above A5.

1hc (1fb) ✱ ® ✱B&b£8.50

TV P nc5yrs 103acres mixed

Index of Selected Guesthouses, Farmhouses and Inns

ENGLAND

OXFORDSHIRE

Banbury	GH	The Mill House
Kidlington	GH	Bowood House
Kingston Bagpuize	FH	Fallowfields
Lew	FH	University

SHROPSHIRE

Church Stretton	FH	Rectory
Diddlebury	FH	Glebe

SOMERSET

Beercrow-combe	FH	Frogstreet
	FH	Whittles
Glastonbury	FH	Berewell Farm Country Guest House
Kilve	INN	Hood Arms
Taunton	GH	Meryan House
Wells	GH	Coach House
Williton	GH	Curdon Mill Country House

SUFFOLK

Gislingham	GH	Old Guildhall
Higham	GH	Old Vicarage

SURREY

Redhill	GH	Ashleigh House Hotel

SUSSEX (East)

Battle	FH	Little Hemingfold
Brighton	GH	Adelaide
	GH	Twenty One
Eastbourne	FH	Chalk Farm
	GH	Park View Hotel

SUSSEX (West)

Bepton	GH	Park House
Rogate	FH	Mizzards

WARWICKSHIRE

Atherstone	GH	Chapel House
Bidford on Avon	FH	Bidford Grange
Hatton	FH	Northleigh

WIGHT, ISLE OF

Sandown	GH	St Catherines
Shanklin	GH	Chine Lodge
Ventnor	GH	Under Rock

WILTSHIRE

Melksham	FH	Shaw

YORKSHIRE (North)

Aislaby	FH	Intake
Askrigg	GH	Winville
Giggleswick	GH	Woodlands
	FH	Close House
Hutton le Hole	GH	Barn
Kirkbymoor-side	GH	Appletree Court Town Farm
Pateley Bridge	GH	Grassfields Country House Hotel
Raskelf	GH	Old Farmhouse
Richmond	FH	Whashton Springs
Scotch Corner	INN	Vintage Hotel
West Layton	GH	West Layton Manor
York	GH	Field House Hotel
	GH	Grasmead House Hotel
	GH	Hazelwood

ISLES OF SCILLY

St Marys	GH	Carnwethers Country House
	GH	Brantwood

CHANNEL ISLES

GUERNSEY

St Peter Port	GH	Midhurst House

JERSEY

St Aubin	GH	Panorama

WALES

CLWYD

Llanfair D C	GH	Eyarth Station

DYFED

Llanfair Clydogau	FH	Pentre

GLAMORGAN (West)

Bishopston	GH	Winstow

GWENT

Llandogo	INN	Sloop
Monmouth	INN	Queens Head

GWYNEDD

Beaumaris	INN	Liverpool Arms
Harlech	GH	Castle Cottage
Llanddeiniolen	FH	Ty'n Rhos
Llandudno	GH	Buile Hill Private Hotel
	GH	Craiglands

POWYS

Knighton	GH	Milebrook House

SCOTLAND

BORDERS

Tweedsmuir	GH	Menzion Farm
West Linton	GH	Medwyn House

CENTRAL

Bo'ness	FH	Kinglass
Callander	GH	Highland House Hotel

DUMFRIES & GALLOWAY

Boreland	FH	Gall
Clarencefield	GH	Comlongon Castle
Moffat	GH	Well View

GRAMPIAN

Aberdeen	GH	Cedars
Ballater	GH	Moorside

HIGHLAND

Beauly	FH	Tomich House
Boat of Garten	GH	Moorfield House
Gairloch	GH	Horisdale House
Inverness	GH	Craigside House
Nairn	GH	Sunnybrae
Rogart	FH	Rovie

LOTHIAN

Dunbar	GH	St Beys
Edinburgh	GH	Dorstan

STRATHCLYDE

Abington	FH	Netherton
Coll (Isle of) Arinagour	GH	Tigh-na-Mara
Connel	GH	Loch Etive
Machrihanish	GH	Ardell House
Prestwick	GH	Fernbank

TAYSIDE

Aberfeldy	GH	Guinach House
Blairgowrie	GH	Rosebank House
Brechin	FH	Blibberhill
	FH	Wood of Auldbar
Fortingall	GH	Rose Villa
Pitlochry	GH	Balrobin Private Hotel
	GH	Dundarave House

The National Grid

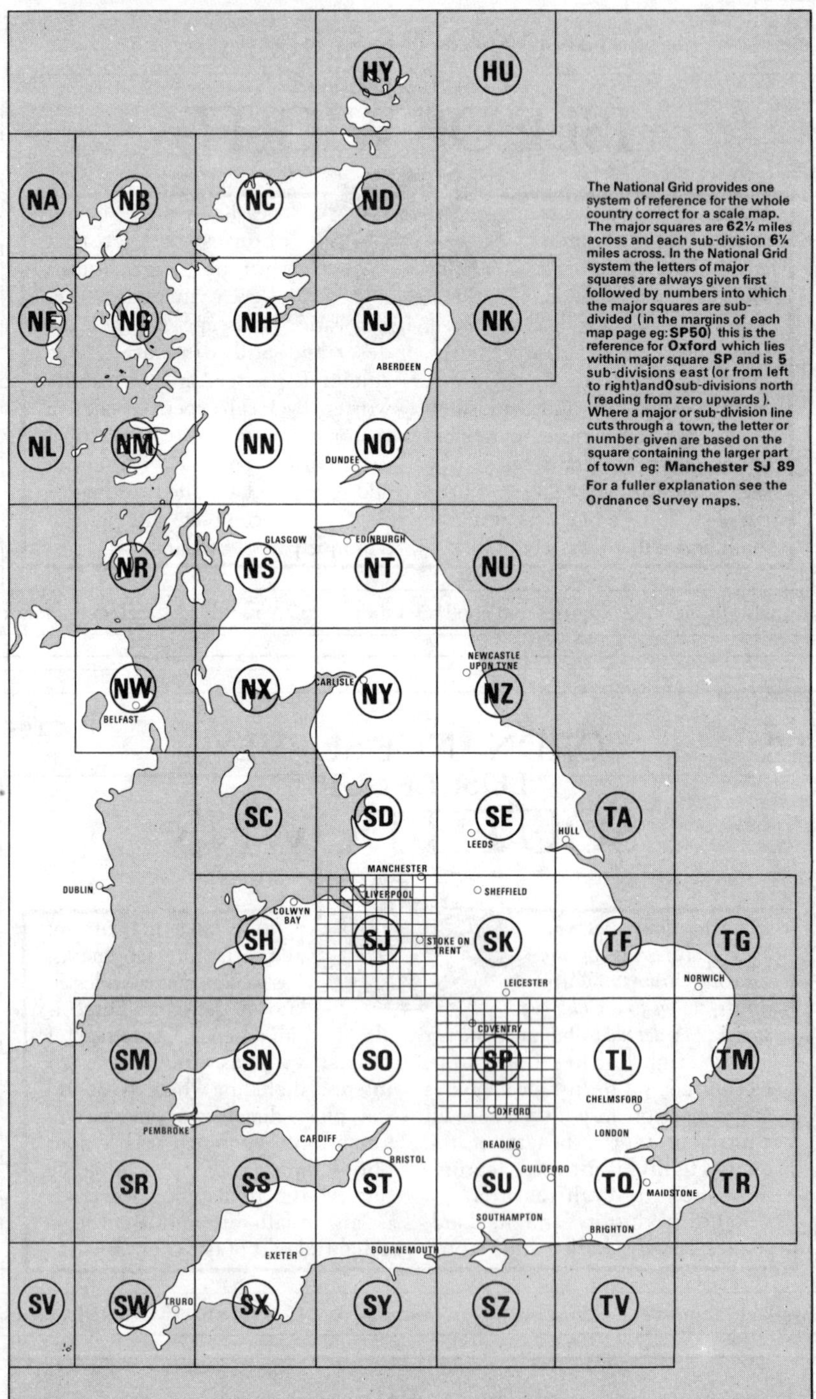

The National Grid provides one system of reference for the whole country correct for a scale map. The major squares are **62½** miles across and each sub-division **6¼** miles across. In the National Grid system the letters of major squares are always given first followed by numbers into which the major squares are sub-divided (in the margins of each map page eg: **SP50**) this is the reference for **Oxford** which lies within major square **SP** and is **5** sub-divisions east (or from left to right) and **0** sub-divisions north (reading from zero upwards). Where a major or sub-division line cuts through a town, the letter or number given are based on the square containing the larger part of town eg: **Manchester SJ 89**

For a fuller explanation see the Ordnance Survey maps.

Key to Atlas

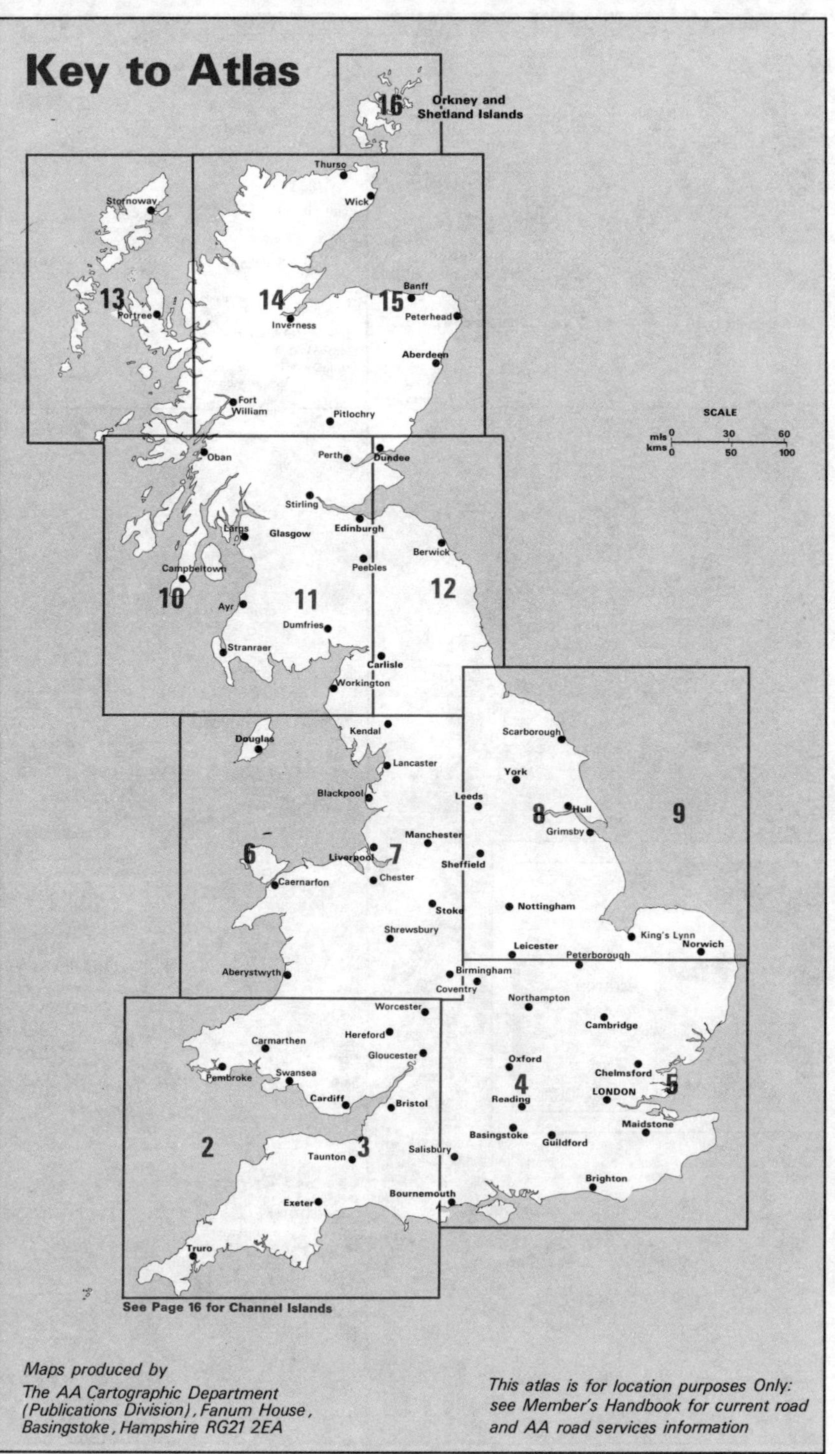

See Page 16 for Channel Islands

Maps produced by The AA Cartographic Department (Publications Division), Fanum House, Basingstoke, Hampshire RG21 2EA

This atlas is for location purposes Only: see Member's Handbook for current road and AA road services information

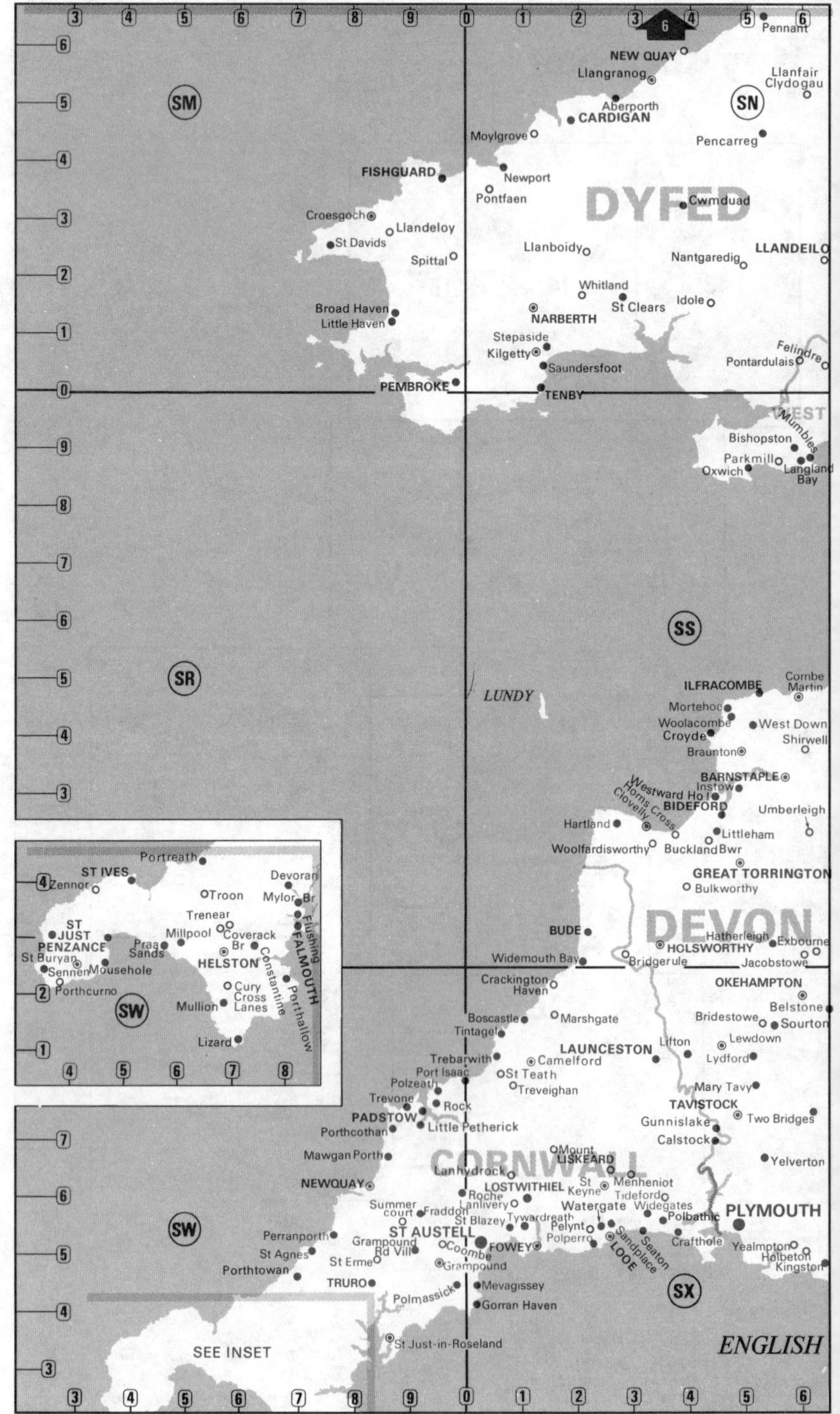

For continuation pages refer to numbered arrows

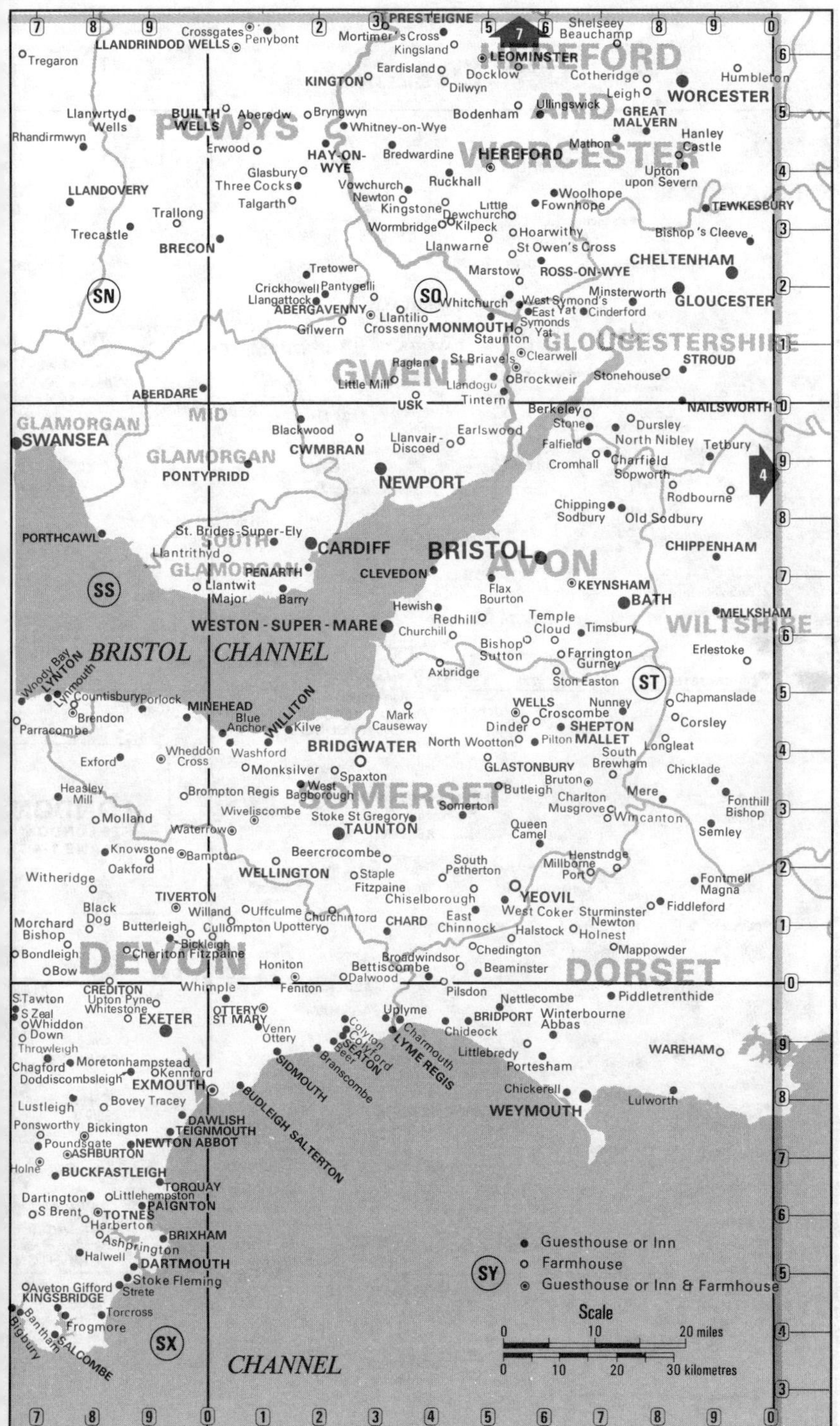
PRESTEIGNE
Crossgates
Penybont
LLANDRINDOD WELLS
Tregaron
Mortimer's Cross
Kingsland
LEOMINSTER
HEREFORD
AND
WORCESTER
Shelsey Beauchamp
Eardisland
Docklow
Dilwyn
KINGTON
Cotheridge
Humbleton
Leigh
WORCESTER
POWYS
Llanwrtyd Wells
BUILTH WELLS
Aberedw
Bryngwyn
Whitney-on-Wye
Bodenham
Ullingswick
GREAT MALVERN
Rhandirmwyn
Erwood
HAY-ON-WYE
Bredwardine
HEREFORD
Mathon
Hanley Castle
Upton upon Severn
Glasbury
Three Cocks
Talgarth
LLANDOVERY
Vowchurch
Newton
Ruckhall
Woolhope
Fownhope
Kingstone
Little Dewchurch
Kilpeck
Wormbridge
TEWKESBURY
Trallong
Trecastle
BRECON
Llanwarne
Hoarwithy
St Owen's Cross
Bishop's Cleeve
Marstow
ROSS-ON-WYE
CHELTENHAM
Tretower
Crickhowell
Pantygelli
Llangattock
ABERGAVENNY
Llantilio Crossenny
Gilwern
Whitchurch
West Symond's Yat
East Symonds Yat
Minsterworth
Cinderford
GLOUCESTER
SN
SO
MONMOUTH
Staunton
GLOUCESTERSHIRE
Clearwell
STROUD
GWENT
Raglan
St Briavels
Brockweir
Stonehouse
Little Mill
Llandogo
Tintern
ABERDARE
USK
NAILSWORTH
GLAMORGAN
MID GLAMORGAN
SWANSEA
Blackwood
CWMBRAN
Llanvair-Discoed
Earlswood
Berkeley
Stone
Dursley
North Nibley
Falfield
Tetbury
Charfield
Cromhall
Sopworth
PONTYPRIDD
NEWPORT
Rodbourne
Chipping Sodbury
Old Sodbury
PORTHCAWL
St. Brides-Super-Ely
CARDIFF
SOUTH GLAMORGAN
Llantrithyd
PENARTH
BRISTOL
AVON
CHIPPENHAM
CLEVEDON
SS
Llantwit Major
Barry
Flax Bourton
KEYNSHAM
BATH
Hewish
Redhill
WESTON-SUPER-MARE
Churchill
Temple Cloud
Timsbury
MELKSHAM
WILTSHIRE
BRISTOL CHANNEL
Bishop Sutton
Farrington Gurney
Erlestoke
Axbridge
Woody Bay
LYNTON
Lynmouth
Countisbury
Porlock
Brendon
Ston Easton
ST
MINEHEAD
WILLITON
Blue Anchor
Kilve
WELLS
Croscombe
Nunney
Chapmanslade
Corsley
Parracombe
Mark Causeway
Dinder
SHEPTON MALLET
Pilton
Washford
BRIDGWATER
North Wootton
South Brewham
Longleat
Exford
Wheddon Cross
Monksilver
Spaxton
GLASTONBURY
Chicklade
Bruton
Heasley Mill
Brompton Regis
West Bagborough
SOMERSET
Butleigh
Charlton Musgrove
Mere
Fonthill Bishop
Wiveliscombe
Somerton
Wincanton
Molland
Waterrow
Stoke St Gregory
TAUNTON
Queen Camel
Semley
Knowstone
Bampton
Oakford
Beercrocombe
Henstridge
Milborne Port
Witheridge
WELLINGTON
Staple Fitzpaine
South Petherton
Fontmell Magna
TIVERTON
Chiselborough
YEOVIL
Black Dog
Willand
Uffculme
West Coker
Sturminster Newton
Fiddleford
Morchard Bishop
Butterleigh
Cullompton
Upottery
Churchinford
CHARD
East Chinnock
Halstock
Holnest
Bickleigh
Bondleigh
Cheriton Fitzpaine
DEVON
Chedington
Mappowder
Bow
Honiton
Broadwindsor
Bettiscombe
Beaminster
DORSET
Dalwood
CREDITON
Whimple
Feniton
Pilsdon
Nettlecombe
Piddletrenthide
S.Tawton
Upton Pyne
Whitestone
S Zeal
EXETER
OTTERY ST MARY
Uplyme
BRIDPORT
Winterbourne Abbas
Whiddon Down
Venn Ottery
Colyton
Colyford
SEATON
Beer
Charmouth
LYME REGIS
Chideock
Throwleigh
Branscombe
Littlebredy
WAREHAM
Chagford
Moretonhampstead
Kennford
SIDMOUTH
Portesham
Doddiscombsleigh
EXMOUTH
Chickerell
Lustleigh
Bovey Tracey
BUDLEIGH SALTERTON
WEYMOUTH
Lulworth
Ponsworthy
Bickington
DAWLISH
TEIGNMOUTH
Poundsgate
NEWTON ABBOT
ASHBURTON
Holne
BUCKFASTLEIGH
TORQUAY
Dartington
Littlehempston
PAIGNTON
S Brent
TOTNES
Harberton
BRIXHAM
Ashprington
Halwell
DARTMOUTH
Guesthouse or Inn
Farmhouse
Guesthouse or Inn & Farmhouse
SY
Aveton Gifford
Stoke Fleming
Strete
KINGSBRIDGE
Torcross
Scale
0
10
20 miles
Frogmore
Bantham
Bigbury
SALCOMBE
SX
CHANNEL
0
10
20
30 kilometres

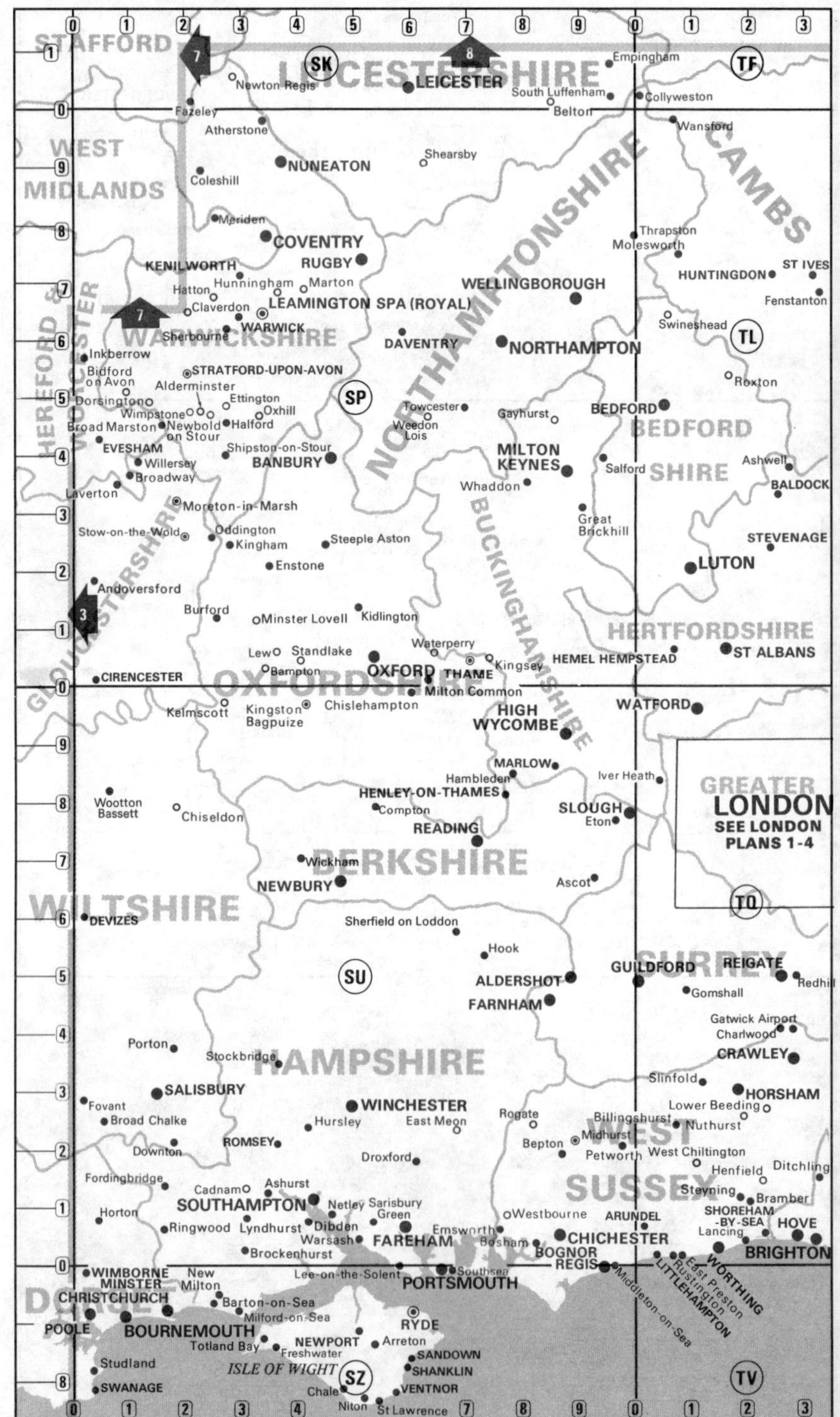

For continuation pages refer to numbered arrows

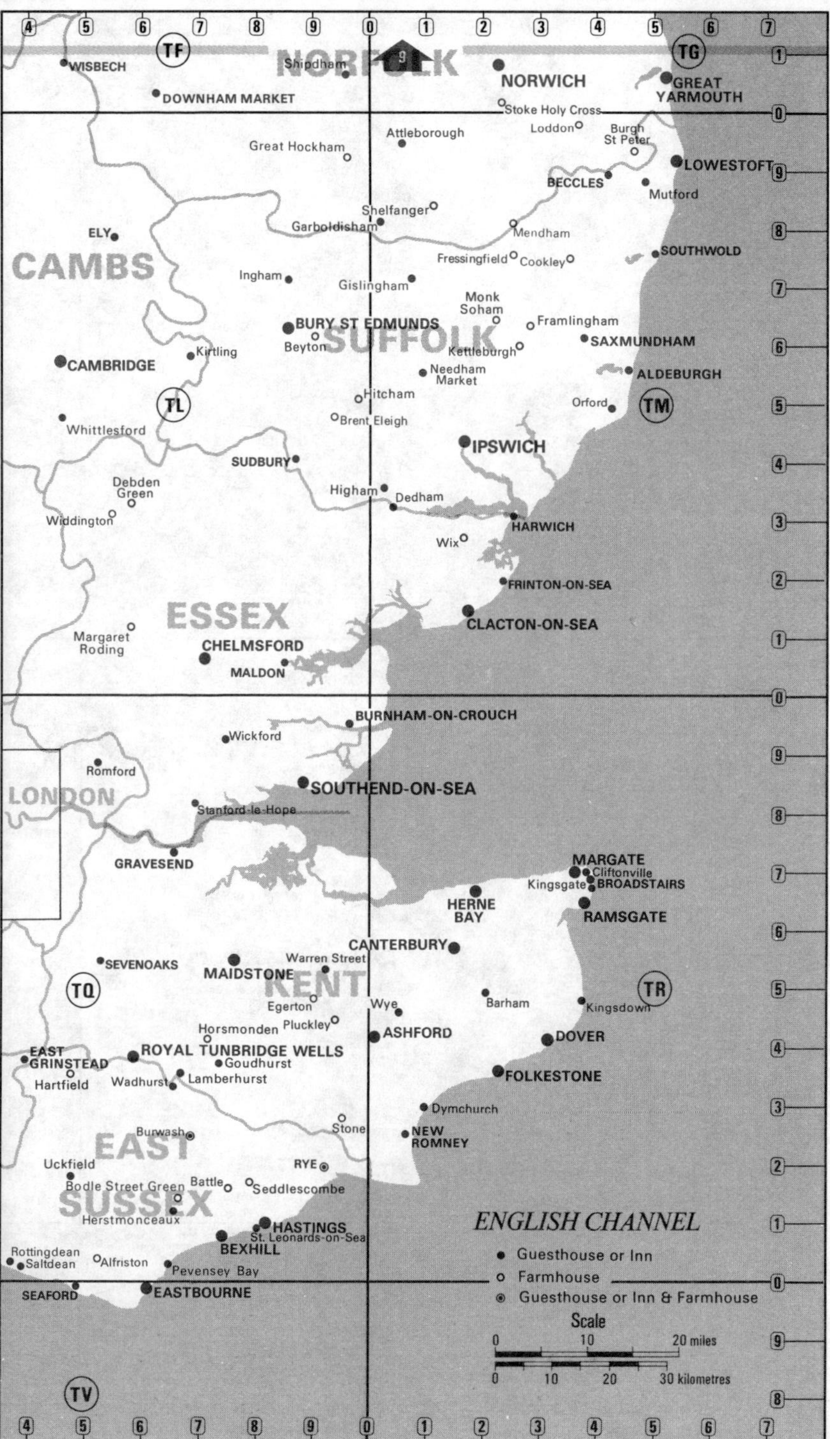
NORFOLK
9
TF
TG
TL
TM
TQ
TR
TV
WISBECH
DOWNHAM MARKET
Shipdham
NORWICH
Stoke Holy Cross
GREAT YARMOUTH
Loddon
Burgh St Peter
Attleborough
Great Hockham
LOWESTOFT
BECCLES
Mutford
Shelfanger
Garboldisham
Mendham
ELY
CAMBS
Fressingfield
Cookley
SOUTHWOLD
Ingham
Gislingham
Monk Soham
Framlingham
BURY ST EDMUNDS
SUFFOLK
Beyton
Kettleburgh
SAXMUNDHAM
Kirtling
CAMBRIDGE
Needham Market
ALDEBURGH
Hitcham
Orford
Whittlesford
Brent Eleigh
IPSWICH
SUDBURY
Debden Green
Higham
Dedham
Widdington
HARWICH
Wix
FRINTON-ON-SEA
ESSEX
CLACTON-ON-SEA
Margaret Roding
CHELMSFORD
MALDON
BURNHAM-ON-CROUCH
Wickford
Romford
LONDON
SOUTHEND-ON-SEA
Stanford-le-Hope
GRAVESEND
MARGATE
Cliftonville
Kingsgate
BROADSTAIRS
HERNE BAY
RAMSGATE
CANTERBURY
SEVENOAKS
Warren Street
MAIDSTONE
KENT
Egerton
Wye
Barham
Kingsdown
Pluckley
Horsmonden
ASHFORD
DOVER
EAST GRINSTEAD
ROYAL TUNBRIDGE WELLS
Goudhurst
Hartfield
Wadhurst
Lamberhurst
FOLKESTONE
Dymchurch
Burwash
Stone
NEW ROMNEY
EAST
Uckfield
RYE
Bodle Street Green
Battle
Seddlescombe
SUSSEX
Herstmonceaux
HASTINGS
St. Leonards-on-Sea
BEXHILL
Rottingdean
Saltdean
Alfriston
Pevensey Bay
SEAFORD
EASTBOURNE
ENGLISH CHANNEL
Guesthouse or Inn
Farmhouse
Guesthouse or Inn & Farmhouse
Scale
0 10 20 miles
0 10 20 30 kilometres

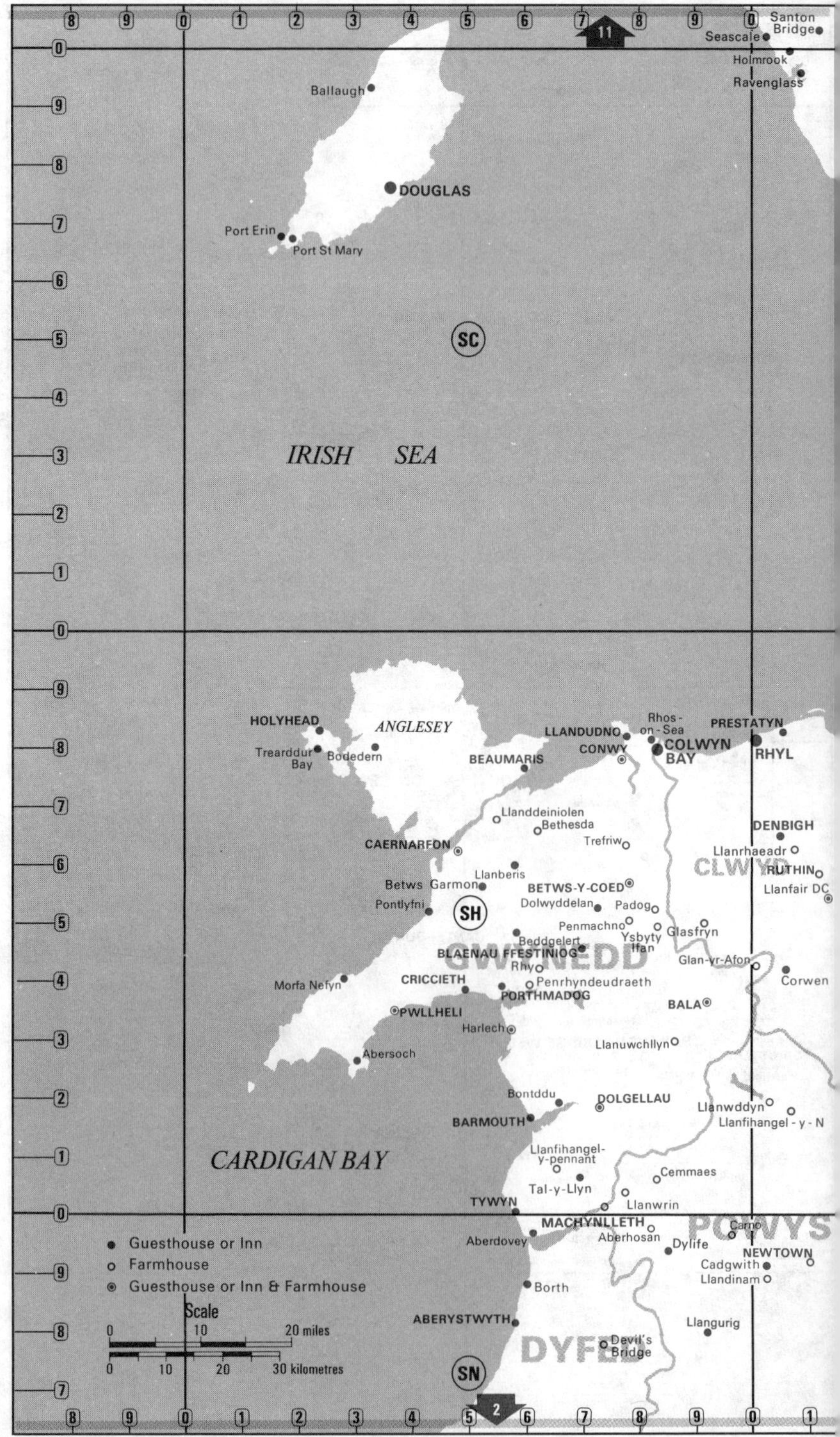

For continuation pages refer to numbered arrows

CUMBRIA
NY
12
NZ
Boot
AMBLESIDE
Hawkshead
Coniston
WINDERMERE
Bowness-on-Windermere
Crook
KENDAL
Torver
Near Sawrey
Far Sawrey
Brigsteer
Blawith
Newby Bridge
Broughton in Furness
Kirkby Lonsdale
Yealand Conyers
GRANGE-OVER-SANDS
MORECAMBE
HEYSHAM
Thwaite
Low Row
Reeth
RICHMOND
Hunton
Askrigg
Leyburn
NORTH
West Scrafton
Hubberholme
Litton
YORKSHIRE
Ingleton
Horton-in-Ribblesdale
Kettlewell
Austwick
Settle
Grassington
Pateley Bridge
Giggleswick
Threshfield
Burnsall
Malham
SD
SE
Bell Busk
Gargrave
Slaidburn
SKIPTON
Harrop Fold
Whitewell
Sawley
ILKLEY
Hambleton
Garstang
Inglewhite
CLITHEROE
COLNE
Haworth
BINGLEY
BLACKPOOL
LANCASHIRE
LONGRIDGE
Weeton
Higham
Oxenhope
WEST
BRADFORD
PRESTON
Luddenden Foot
Northowram
LYTHAM ST ANNE'S
Todmorden
HALIFAX
Sowerby Bridge
YORKSHIRE
SOUTHPORT
GREATER
Holmfirth
WIGAN
MANCHESTER
ASHTON-UNDER-LYNE
SOUTH
SALFORD
MANCHESTER
YORKSHIRE
WALLASEY
MERSEYSIDE
HOYLAKE
LIVERPOOL
STOCKPORT
GLOSSOP
BIRKENHEAD
WEST KIRBY
ALTRINCHAM
Marple
Hayfield
KNUTSFORD
BOLLINGTON
Sparrowpit
8
HOLYWELL
Babell
Helsby
Rhes-y-cae
MACCLESFIELD
BUXTON
Litton
DERBYSHIRE
CHESTER
CHESHIRE
MOLD
Wincle
Upper Hulme
Tarporley
Rushton Spencer
Higher Burwardsley
Astbury
Rudyard
CLWYD
Holt
SJ
NANTWICH
LEEK
Longsdon
Tissington
Waterhouses
Ilam
SK
Ipstones
Thorpe
NOTTS
Audley
Blore
Okeover
Betley
NEWCASTLE-UNDER-LYME
STOKE-ON-TRENT
Mayfield
LLANGOLLEN
Aston
Oakamoor
Hanmer
Roston
WHITCHURCH
STAFFORDSHIRE
Alkmonton
UTTOXETER
Whittington
OSWESTRY
Newborough
STAFFORD
Abbots Bromley
LEICESTERSHIRE
Llansantffraid-ym-Mechain
Shawbury
Rowton
Nesscliff
Four Crosses
Llandrinio
Bomere Heath
Middletown
SHREWSBURY
Wellington
Halfway House
WELSHPOOL
Cruckton
SHROPSHIRE
TELFORD
LICHFIELD
Forden
Codsall
Stiperstones
Hughley
SUTTON COLDFIELD
WEST
Church Stoke
CHURCH STRETTON
BRIDGNORTH
4
Newcastle on Clun
Diddlebury
MIDLANDS
Rowley Regis
BIRMINGHAM
STOURBRIDGE
Clun
Clunton
Craven Arms
Kinver
Llanfair Waterdine
Bucknell
KIDDERMINSTER
KNIGHTON
SO
LUDLOW
Newnham Bridge
Frith Common
SP
Wigmore
BROMSGROVE
REDDITCH
Lapworth
Abberley
Henley-in-Arden
WARWICKSHIRE
HEREFORD AND WORCESTER
3
Little Hereford
Lindridge

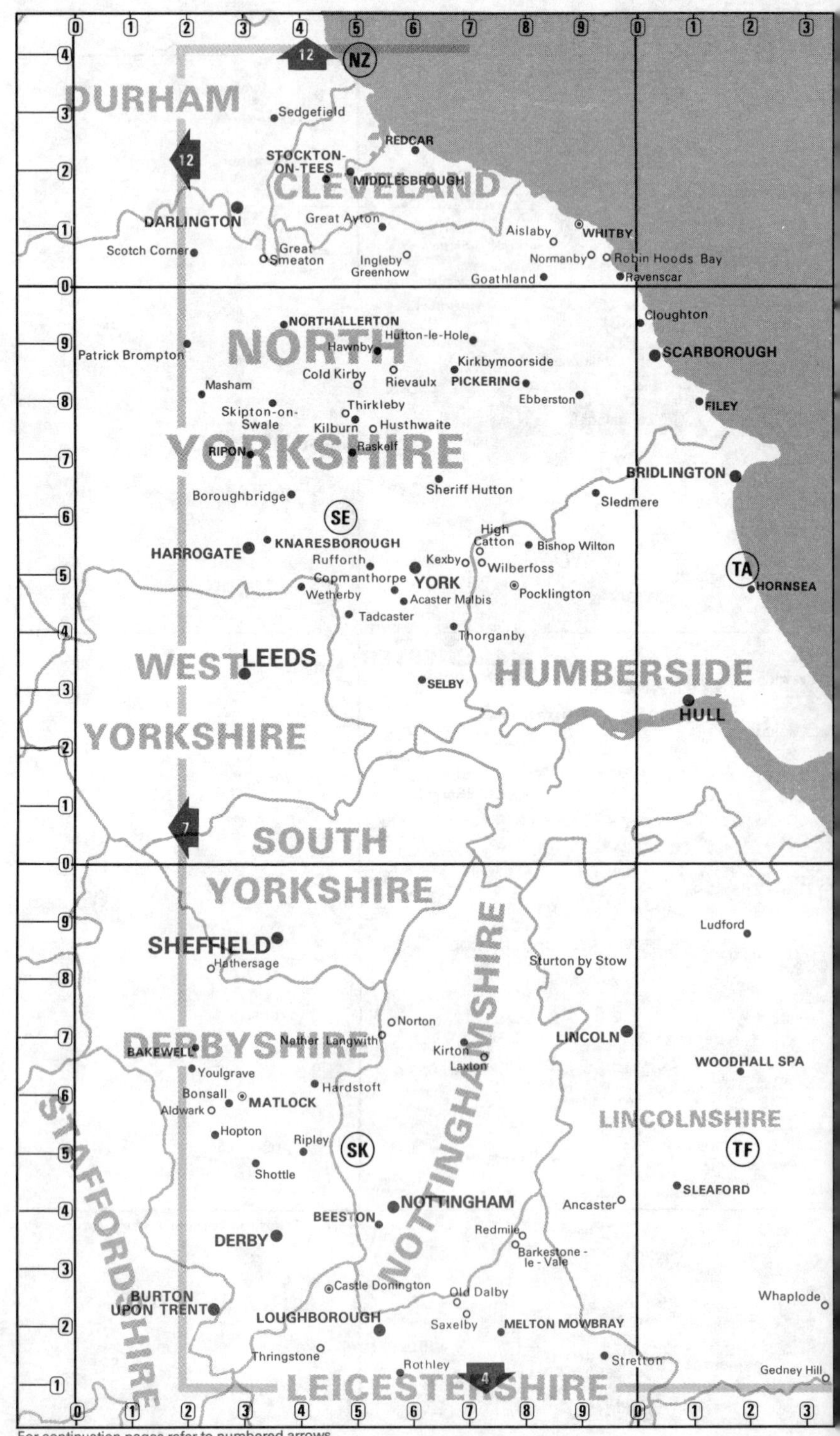

For continuation pages refer to numbered arrows

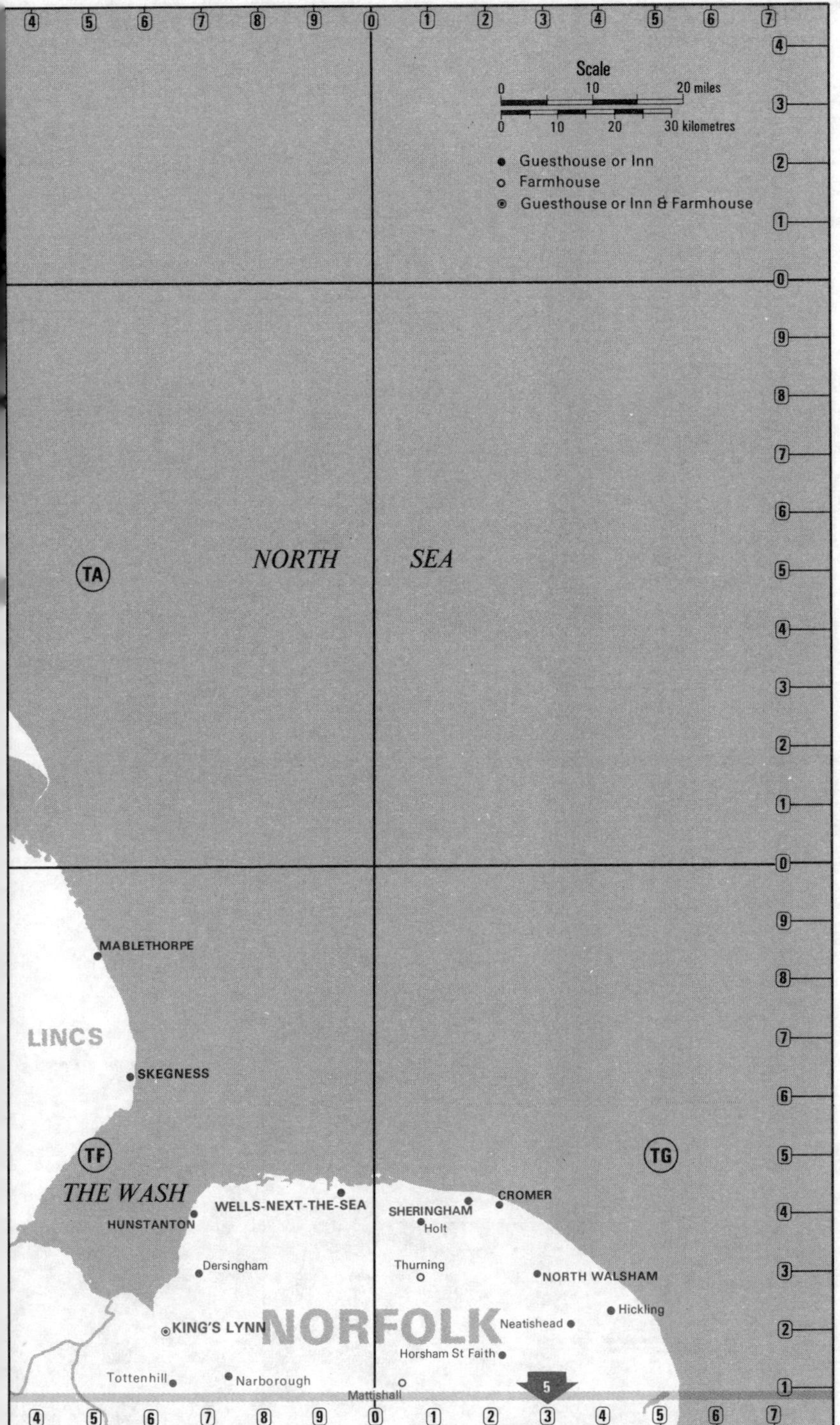

Scale
0
10
20 miles
0
10
20
30 kilometres
Guesthouse or Inn
Farmhouse
Guesthouse or Inn & Farmhouse
TA
NORTH
SEA
MABLETHORPE
LINCS
SKEGNESS
TF
TG
THE WASH
WELLS-NEXT-THE-SEA
HUNSTANTON
SHERINGHAM
Holt
CROMER
Dersingham
Thurning
NORTH WALSHAM
Hickling
Neatishead
KING'S LYNN
NORFOLK
Horsham St Faith
Tottenhill
Narborough
Mattishall
5

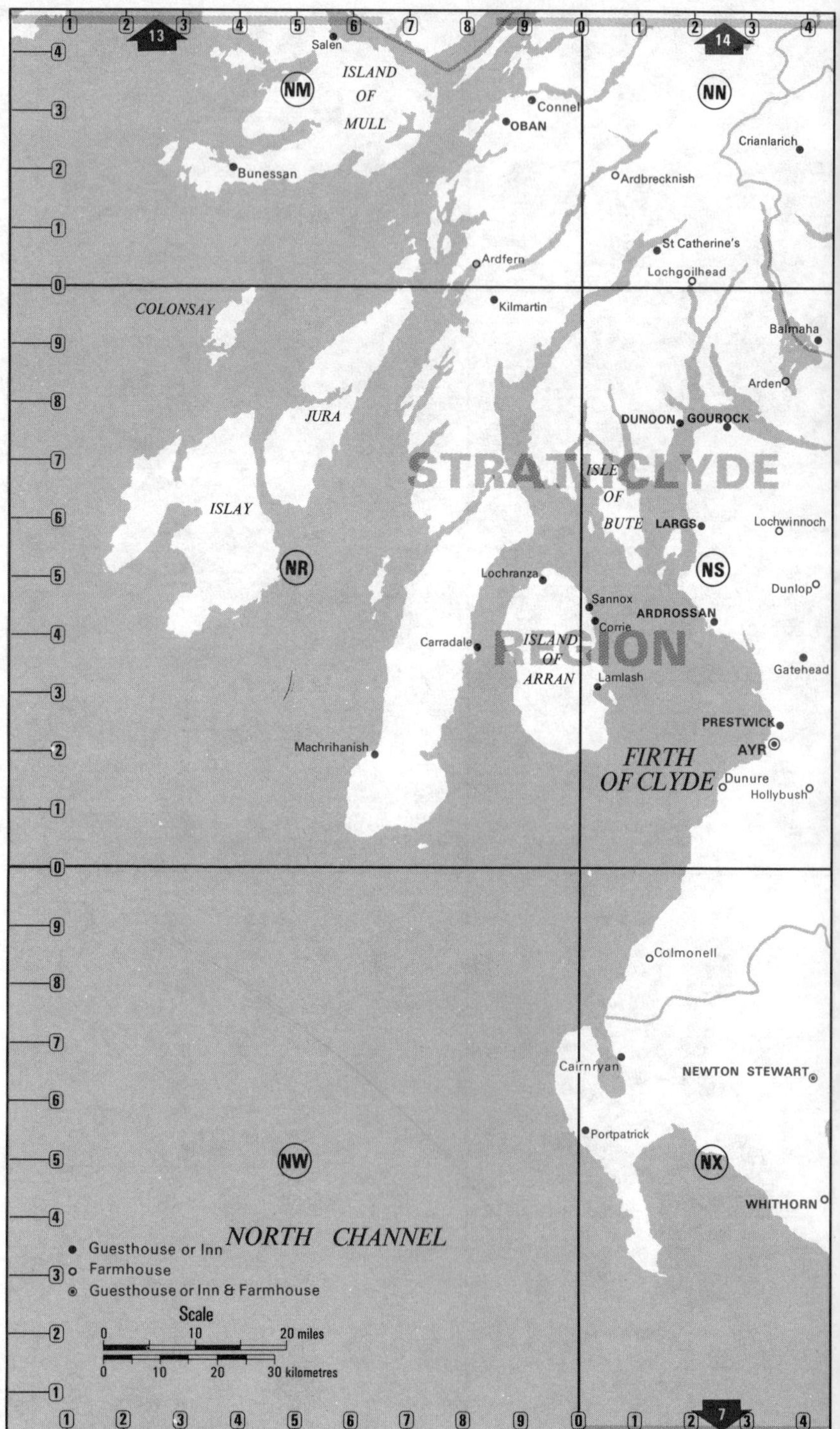

For continuation pages refer to numbered arrows

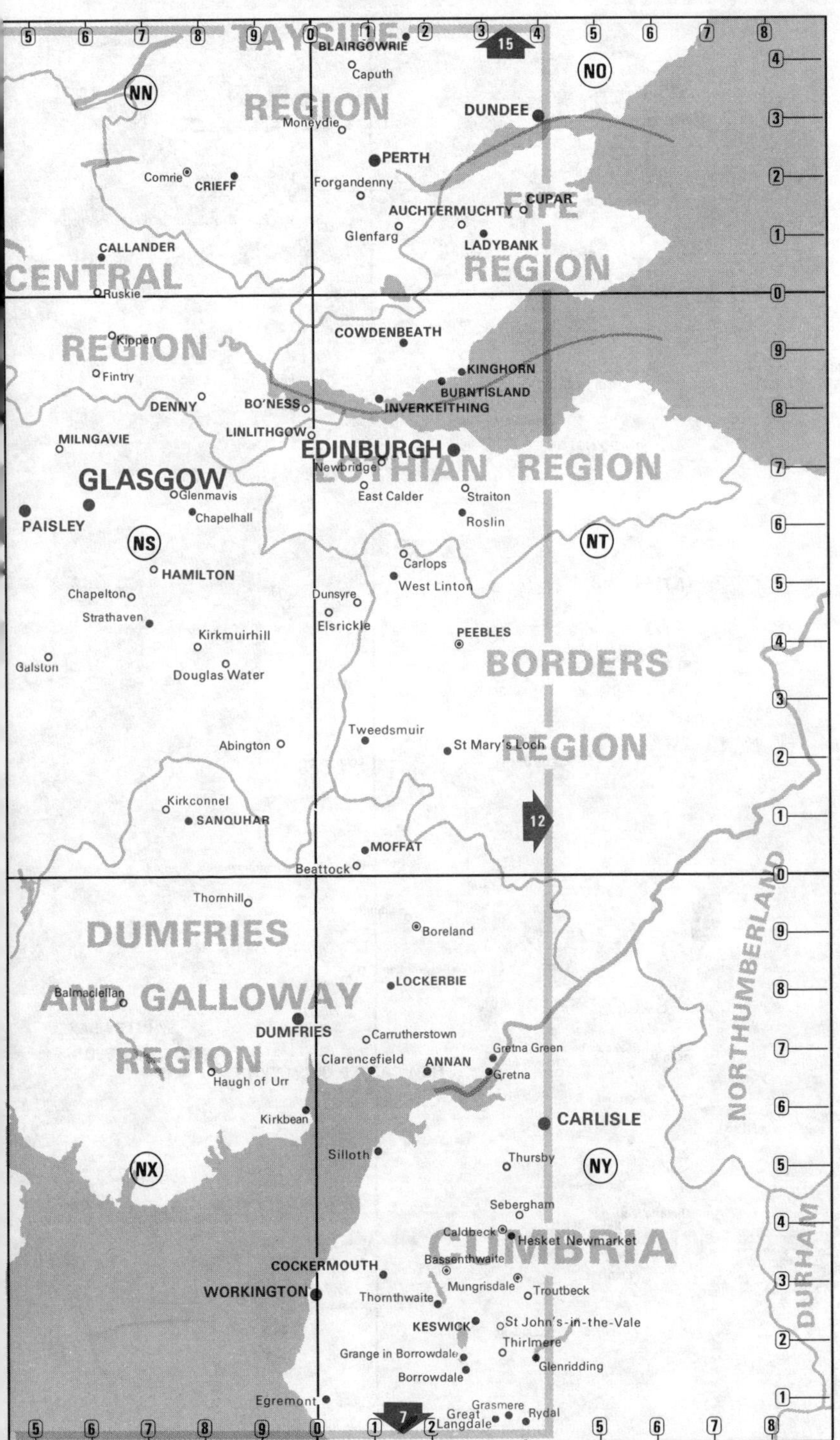
TAYSIDE REGION
BLAIRGOWRIE
Caputh
Moneydie
PERTH
Forgandenny
Glenfarg
AUCHTERMUCHTY
CUPAR
LADYBANK
DUNDEE
FIFE REGION
NN
NO
Comrie
CRIEFF
CALLANDER
CENTRAL REGION
Ruskie
Kippen
Fintry
DENNY
BO'NESS
LINLITHGOW
MILNGAVIE
COWDENBEATH
KINGHORN
BURNTISLAND
INVERKEITHING
EDINBURGH
Newbridge
LOTHIAN REGION
East Calder
Straiton
Roslin
GLASGOW
Glenmavis
Chapelhall
PAISLEY
NS
NT
HAMILTON
Chapelton
Strathaven
Kirkmuirhill
Galston
Douglas Water
Carlops
West Linton
Dunsyre
Elsrickle
PEEBLES
BORDERS REGION
Tweedsmuir
St Mary's Loch
Abington
Kirkconnel
SANQUHAR
MOFFAT
Beattock
Thornhill
DUMFRIES AND GALLOWAY REGION
Boreland
LOCKERBIE
Balmaclellan
DUMFRIES
Carrutherstown
Clarencefield
ANNAN
Gretna Green
Gretna
Haugh of Urr
Kirkbean
CARLISLE
Silloth
Thursby
NX
NY
NORTHUMBERLAND
Sebergham
Caldbeck
Hesket Newmarket
CUMBRIA
Bassenthwaite
COCKERMOUTH
Mungrisdale
Troutbeck
WORKINGTON
Thornthwaite
KESWICK
St John's-in-the-Vale
Thirlmere
Grange in Borrowdale
Glenridding
Borrowdale
DURHAM
Egremont
Grasmere
Great Langdale
Rydal
15
12
7

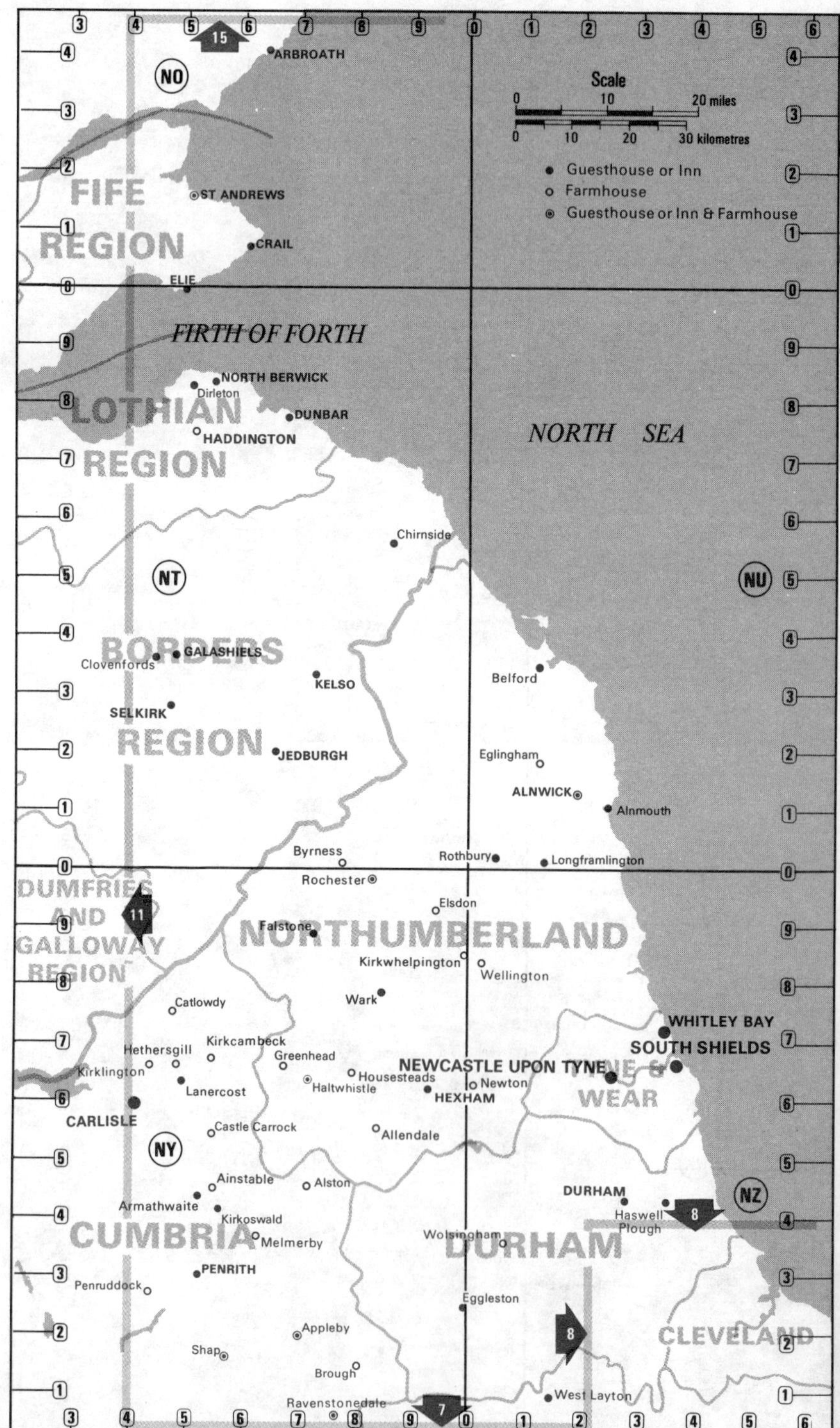

For continuation pages refer to numbered arrows

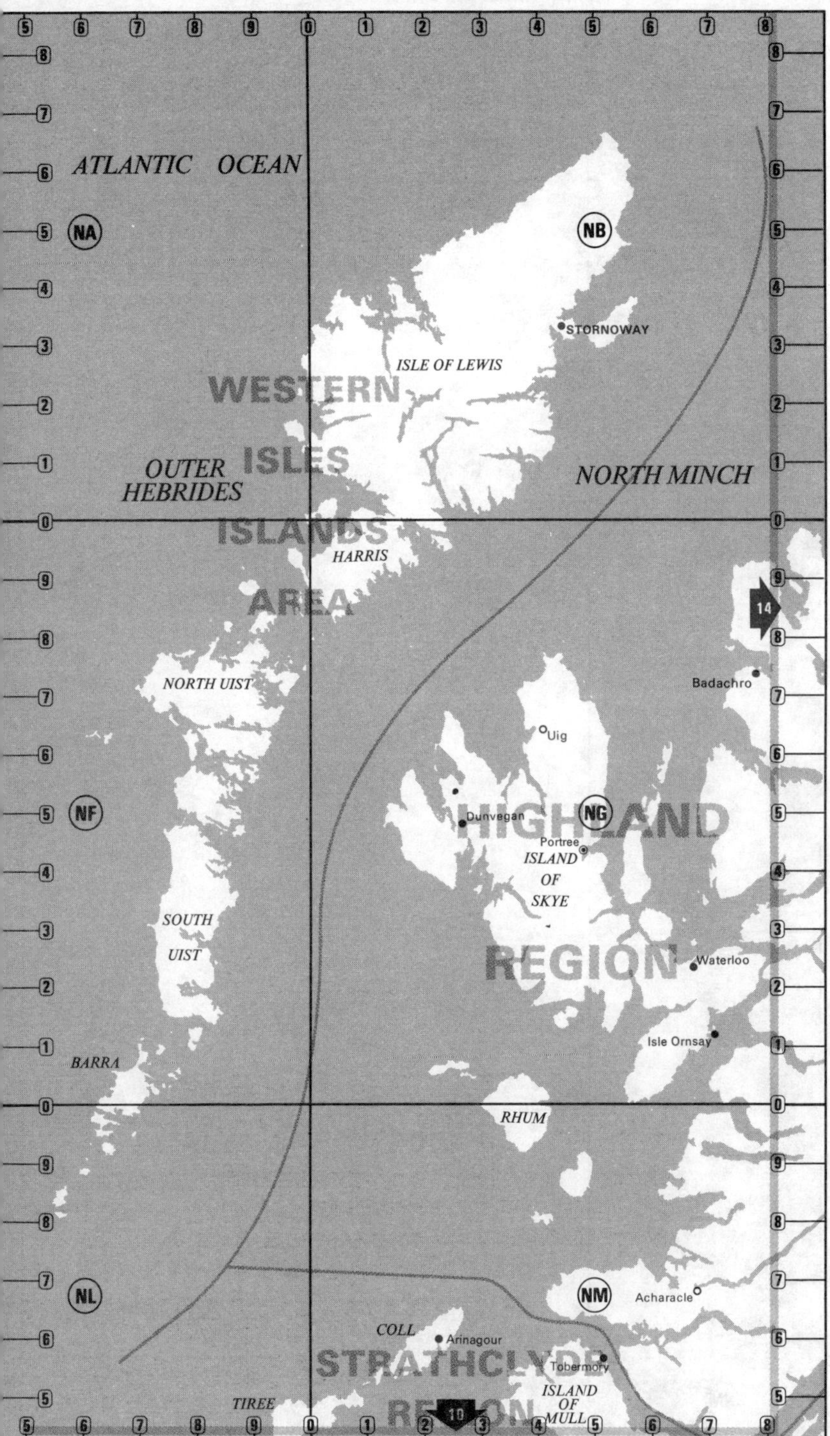

ATLANTIC OCEAN
NA
NB
STORNOWAY
ISLE OF LEWIS
WESTERN
ISLES
ISLANDS
AREA
OUTER
HEBRIDES
NORTH MINCH
HARRIS
14
NORTH UIST
Badachro
Uig
NF
Dunvegan
NG
HIGHLAND
Portree
ISLAND
OF
SKYE
SOUTH
UIST
REGION
Waterloo
Isle Ornsay
BARRA
RHUM
NL
NM
Acharacle
COLL
Arinagour
STRATHCLYDE
Tobermory
ISLAND
OF
MULL
TIREE
REGION
10

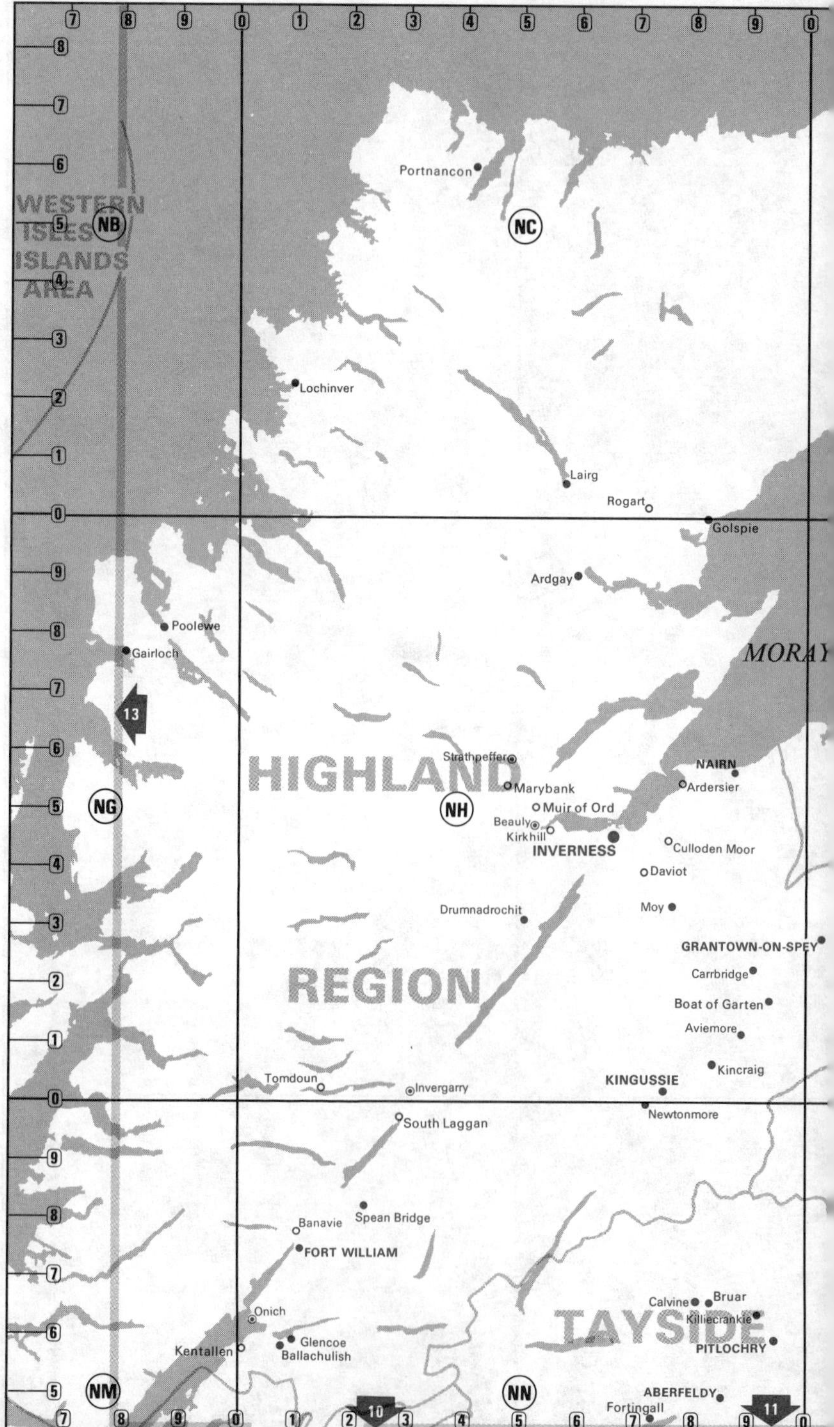

For continuation pages refer to numbered arrows

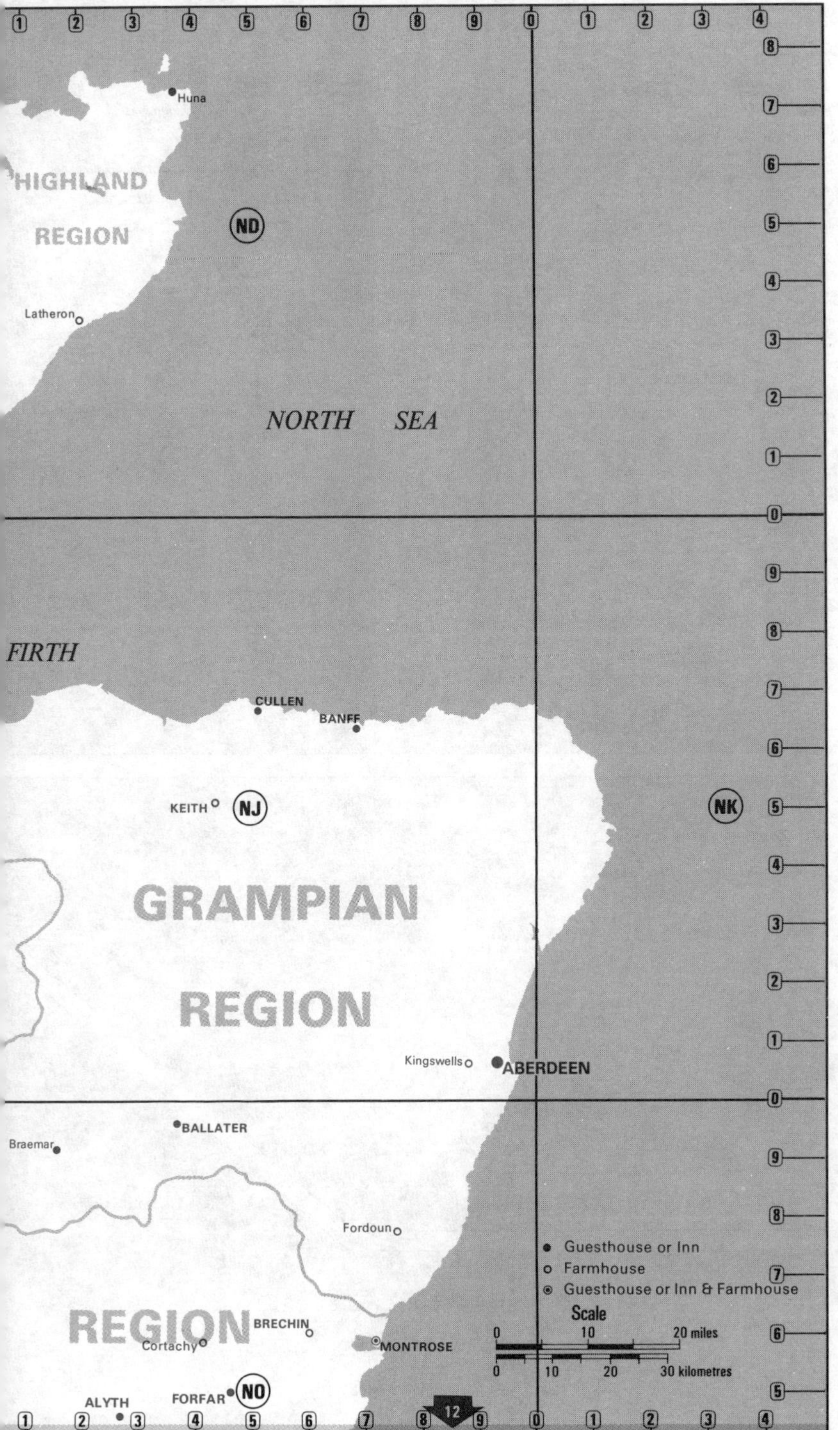

Huna
HIGHLAND
REGION
ND
Latheron
NORTH SEA
FIRTH
CULLEN
BANFF
KEITH
NJ
NK
GRAMPIAN
REGION
Kingswells
ABERDEEN
BALLATER
Braemar
Fordoun
Guesthouse or Inn
Farmhouse
Guesthouse or Inn & Farmhouse
Scale
0 10 20 miles
0 10 20 30 kilometres
REGION
BRECHIN
Cortachy
MONTROSE
ALYTH
FORFAR
NO
12

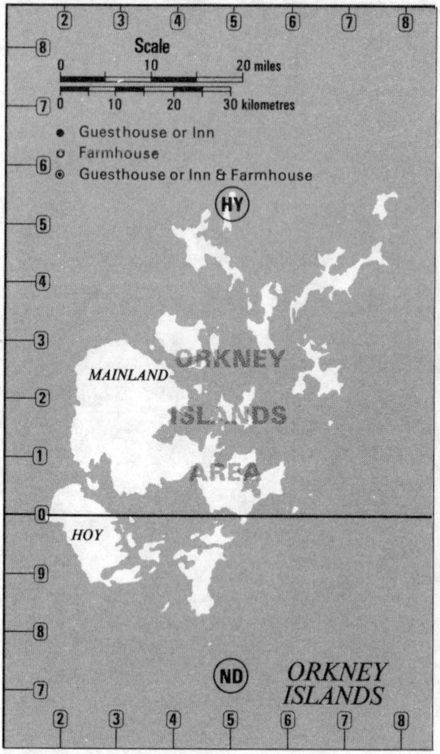

Scale
0 10 20 miles
0 10 20 30 kilometres
● Guesthouse or Inn
○ Farmhouse
◉ Guesthouse or Inn & Farmhouse
HY
MAINLAND
ORKNEY ISLANDS AREA
HOY
ND
ORKNEY ISLANDS

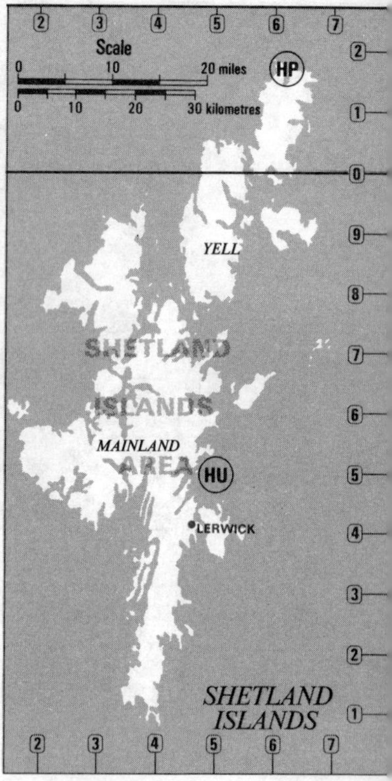

Scale
0 10 20 miles
0 10 20 30 kilometres
HP
YELL
SHETLAND ISLANDS AREA
MAINLAND
HU
LERWICK
SHETLAND ISLANDS

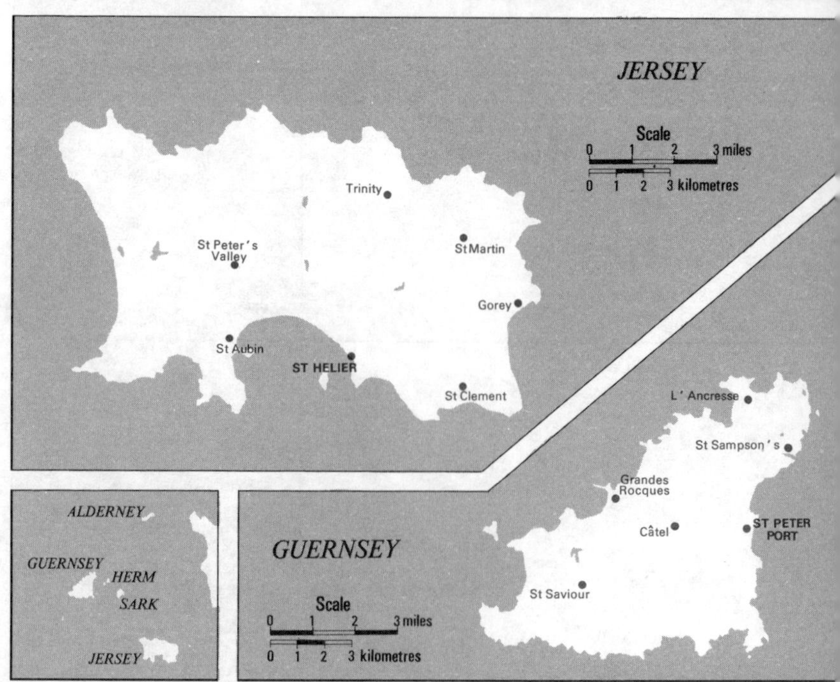